ROTATIONAL SPECTRA
AND
MOLECULAR STRUCTURE

PHYSICAL CHEMISTRY
A Series of Monographs

Edited by

ERNEST M. LOEBL

Department of Chemistry, Polytechnic Institute of Brooklyn
Brooklyn, New York

In preparation

ROTATIONAL SPECTRA
AND
MOLECULAR STRUCTURE

JAMES E. WOLLRAB

RESEARCH DIVISION
MCDONNELL DOUGLAS CORPORATION
LAMBERT-SAINT LOUIS MUNICIPAL AIRPORT
ST. LOUIS, MISSOURI

1967

ACADEMIC PRESS   New York and London

ACADEMIC PRESS INC.
111 Fifth Avenue, New York, New York 10003

United Kingdom Edition published by
ACADEMIC PRESS INC. (LONDON) LTD.
Berkeley Square House, London W.1

LIBRARY OF CONGRESS CATALOG CARD NUMBER: 66-30112

PRINTED IN THE UNITED STATES OF AMERICA

128972

In memory of

Willard C. Ross

PREFACE

Microwave spectroscopy, i.e., the detection and interpretation of rotational and related transitions occurring in the microwave and millimeter wave regions, has progressed rapidly in the past two decades. The advent of new high resolution spectrometers having increased sensitivity and specialized characteristics has forced theoretical treatments to be utilized to new degrees of sophistication. Summarizing most of these recent developments and laying a basic foundation for future work, this volume was assembled as a review of some of the major areas encompassed by microwave spectroscopy with particular emphasis on those subjects which have developed significantly since the publications of Gordy, Smith, and Trambarulo in 1953, Townes and Schawlow in 1954, and Strandberg in 1954.

Chemists, physicists, and electrical engineers working in the many experimental and theoretical areas related to rotational spectroscopy should find this a useful survey of the field. A background in elementary quantum mechanics and a rudimentary knowledge of group theory are required of the reader.

The format is discussed in the latter part of Chapter 1. An attempt has been made to retain the nomenclature used in the literature in order to provide the maximum correlation with new and existing papers. The great diversity which now characterizes gas-phase rotational spectroscopy makes it difficult to treat each topic in the field. For those subjects which are not fully treated or when additional detailed information is required, a bibliography indexed by subject has been included as Appendix 1. Tables of reduced energies and rigid rotor line strengths are not given due to their extensive size and availability elsewhere; however, a useful table of perturbation coefficients for the hindered internal rotation problem has been placed in Appendix 12. The other appendices treat several interesting specialized topics.

St. Louis, Missouri   J. WOLLRAB
March, 1967

ACKNOWLEDGMENTS

The publication of this volume would not have been possible without the help and encouragement provided by many friends, in particular, D. Ames, L. Scharpen, and J. Broerman of the McDonnell Douglas Research Division and J. Muenter, D. Peterson, F. Vilen, S. Wollrab, and J. Burr for criticisms of the manuscript. It is a pleasure to acknowledge the productive atmosphere and encouragement provided at McDonnell Douglas by D. Ames, A. E. Lombard, Jr., and J. Dueker of the Research Division and at Redstone Arsenal by R. Deep, H. Dihm, and W. McCorkle of the Advanced Systems Laboratory, by the staff of the Redstone Scientific Information Center, and by the Commanding Officers of the Army Missile Command. A portion of the bibliography was compiled by Lt. J. Gibbs. A major part of the manuscript was prepared by M. Green.

J.E.W.

CONTENTS

Chapter 3   **Centrifugal Distortion, Coriolis Coupling, and Fermi Resonance**

Chapter 4   **Molecular Structure**

Chapter 5   **Nuclear Quadrupole Coupling**

Chapter 6 **Internal Rotation**

Chapter 7 **Inversion**

Chapter 8   **Stark Effect**

Chapter 9   **Instrumentation**

ROTATIONAL SPECTRA
AND
MOLECULAR STRUCTURE

1-1. Energy Levels and Rotational Transitions

Through advances in experimental techniques, the electromagnetic spectrum has become an abundant source of information concerning molecular structure and intramolecular interactions. This information is obtained by detailed analysis of the transitions which occur in a sample of molecules placed in a radiation field or sufficiently excited by some means to produce its own radiation field. The origin of these spectra is best explained by a consideration of the energy level structure of a molecule. Beginning with the famous work of Planck and Bohr, quantum mechanics predicted that the energies of an atom or a molecule are quantized; i.e., have definite values and are not completely continuous as was previously believed. Thus, in the hydrogen atom, the energies of the "orbiting" electron are restricted to a series of definite values. In molecules, the quantization extends to the vibrational and rotational degrees of freedom as well as to electronic energies. As an illustration, Fig. 1-1 depicts a portion of the energy level structure of a fictitious molecule. Each molecule in a sample of molecules resides in one of the many energy levels available to it. In the absence of a perturbing field, the distribution of molecules among the levels is governed by the laws of statistical mechanics. When a radiation field is present, the molecular population readjusts its distribution as dictated by the time-dependent equations which govern the interaction of radiation and matter.

Every different molecule is characterized by its own unique energy level structure. On an atomic scale, this energy level structure is dependent on the electron distribution, atomic masses, and interparticle forces and distances. When a source of electromagnetic radiation is made available to the molecular sample, certain transitions between energy levels may occur, provided the source emits radiation of an energy corresponding to the difference between pairs of levels. The allowed transitions are determined by a set of selection rules which follow from the symmetry of the molecule and the corresponding properties of its wave functions.

1

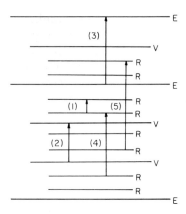

Fig. 1-1. A simplified illustration of transitions between molecular energy levels. Each level has a set of rotational, vibrational, and electronic quantum numbers. All other "degrees of freedom" have been suppressed. E, V, and R refer to electronic, vibrational, and rotational states. In reality these cannot be separated as they are shown here. For instance, the E levels may be considered as electronic states in which the rotational and vibrational quantum numbers are zero. The transitions are identified as: (1) pure rotational transitions, (2) pure vibrational transitions, (3) pure electronic transitions, (4) rotation-vibration transitions, and (5) transitions involving a change in the rotational, vibrational, and electronic quantum numbers.

Electronic, vibrational, and rotational transitions are most easily identified by changes in the quantum numbers which characterize the two interacting levels. Pure rotational transitions occur between two levels in the same vibrational and electronic state, i.e., two levels having identical vibrational and electronic quantum numbers but different rotational quantum numbers. Because the magnitude of the rotational energy of a molecule is usually less than the vibrational energy, rotational energy levels are more closely spaced; rotational transitions are of relatively low energy (on the order of 1 cm^{-1} or $30 \text{ GHz})^{\dagger}$ and generally fall in the microwave region. Selection rules govern which changes in the rotational quantum numbers will produce allowed transitions. Transitions between two vibrational states usually occur in the infrared region because vibrational levels generally are separated by much greater energies. These transitions often show a rotational fine structure which results from simultaneous changes in vibrational and rotational quantum numbers. Much larger energies are normally required to produce the electronic transitions characteristic of the visible and ultraviolet regions.

---

† Gc sec^{-1}, kMc sec^{-1}, and GHz have all been used to represent 10^{9} cycles per second. The Hertz units Hz, MHz, and GHz have been adopted as the appropriate set of units to replace cycles sec^{-1}, megacycles sec^{-1}, and gigacycles sec^{-1}. Most of the literature of microwave spectroscopy has used megacycle (Mc) and kilomegacycle (kMc) notation.

In order to analyze the spectrum of a molecule, particularly the rotational spectrum, it is necessary to formulate an acceptable mathematical model from which solutions characterizing the energy levels may be obtained. To analyze transitions involving only changes in rotational quantum numbers, it seems reasonable to choose a model which exhibits only rotational degrees of freedom, i.e., a rigid rotor. Because a molecule may undergo changes in vibrational, electronic, and nuclear energy as well as rotational energy, it is important to justify the separation of rotation from the other energetic degrees of freedom.

The justification for separating electronic and vibrational energies comes from the well-known Born–Oppenheimer principle [995]. In essence, it states that because the motions of the nuclei are very slow with respect to electron motions in a molecule, the vibrational motions do not significantly affect the electronic energy states. The wave equation can be solved for the electrons in a fixed nuclear frame; when the vibrational motion is treated, the electronic energy is used to formulate the vibrational potential function. This approximation is verified by the relatively large separation of electronic energy states with respect to vibrational energy states. Similarly, vibration and rotation usually can be separated to a good approximation because rotational energies are generally smaller than vibrational energies.

By averaging the relatively rapid vibrational and electronic motions, the molecule may be treated as a rigid rotor with an average vibrational-electronic structure. Energy contributions which are usually much smaller than the rotational energy such as magnetic dipole interactions, nuclear electric quadrupole interactions, and perturbations resulting from relatively small external electric and magnetic fields influence the rotational energy levels only slightly and can be neglected in an approximate treatment, just as rotational and vibrational energies usually can be neglected in an approximate calculation of the electronic energies. These contributions to the total energy can then be evaluated by exact or perturbation methods.

The total energy Hamiltonian can be expressed in the following general form.

$$H = \sum_i H_i^{(0)} + \sum_{ij} H_{ij}^{(1)} + \cdots \tag{1-1}$$

The first set of terms represents the zeroth-order problem composed solely of those contributions from a single energetic degree of freedom such as molecular rotation or molecular vibration. The second summation includes terms resulting from the interaction of two degrees of freedom, e.g., vibration-rotation and rotation-electronic interaction terms. An assumption of complete separation is equivalent to neglecting all terms after the first summation in (1-1). The total wave function is then the product of contributions from each of the zeroth-order terms.

$$\psi^{(0)} \sim \psi_{rot}^{(0)}\psi_{vib}^{(0)}\psi_{ele}^{(0)} \cdots \qquad (1\text{-}2)$$

and the corresponding zeroth-order Hamiltonian is

$$\sum_i H_i^{(0)} = H_{rot}^{(0)} + H_{vib}^{(0)} + H_{ele}^{(0)} + \cdots \qquad (1\text{-}3)$$

Once a solution for the zeroth-order rotational problem $H_{rot}^{(0)}$ has been obtained, it can be used as a basis for treating small interaction terms by applying the appropriate form of perturbation theory. This analysis leads to energy correction terms needed to reproduce the rotational energy levels of the molecule.

In some cases even an approximate separation breaks down. As an example, the vibrational energy level spacing for low-frequency vibrations may approach the rotational energy level spacing, and appropriate near degeneracies can produce strong perturbations of the energy levels and appreciable mixing among the separated wave functions of (1-2). The energy matrix can no longer be diagonalized by perturbation theory; an explicit secular equation involving all of the interacting levels must be solved. Nevertheless, in most cases solutions to the rigid rotor problem form a convenient basis for the analysis of rotational spectra.

Two restrictions are commonly placed on molecules which exhibit pure rotational absorption spectra: (1) they must possess a permanent dipole moment,[†] and (2) they should have sufficient vapor pressure to give an observable microwave spectrum. A large number of molecules which meet these requirements have rotational transitions in the centimeter wavelength region between 3 and 30 GHz as well as in the millimeter and submillimeter regions above 30 GHz. Using microwave techniques, rotational transitions have been observed up to frequencies over 500 GHz [1643]. Some light molecules produce rotational lines above 500 GHz well into the submillimeter-far infrared region. Conversely, heavy molecules with closely spaced rotational levels have allowed transitions which extend into the radio frequencies. Although rotational transitions occur predominantly in the microwave (centimeter) region, there is no sharp demarcation boundary between the radio-frequency, microwave, and infrared domains as far as types of transitions are concerned. Experimental techniques are also found to overlap as illustrated by the successful use of quasi-optical methods in the millimeter region [189].

1-2. Information Contained in Rotational Spectra

Allowing the approximate separation of rotational terms from the total energy, a molecule can be treated as a rigid rotator whose energy is a function

---

[†] Transitions resulting from induced dipole moments in nonpolar molecules are not considered here.

of its moments of inertia. A thorough examination of the rotational transitions usually allows a determination of the moments of inertia which, in turn, are directly related to the molecular structure. In an attempt to calculate a meaningful molecular structure, schemes have been devised to obtain structural data from the spectrum. The structural parameters and their relationships to the equilibrium molecular structure are sensitive functions of the methods used in the structure calculation.

In reality no molecule is a rigid rotor. Centrifugal and Coriolis forces may act on a rotating molecule to alter its energy level structure and its rotational spectrum. Low-frequency motions in the molecule, such as the torsional vibrations associated with a methyl group, can interact with the overall rotation of the molecule. The angular momenta of overall rotation may couple with the internal angular momenta associated with these internal motions to perturb the rotational energy levels. Analysis of the energy level structure then allows information to be gained concerning the nature of these perturbations. Vibrational perturbations are particularly useful for determining the magnitudes and shapes of barriers which hinder internal motions.

The intensities and shapes of rotational lines are indicative of the relative energy level populations and the line-broadening mechanisms producing intermolecular interactions in the gas phase. By assuming a Boltzmann population distribution, relative intensity measurements of rotational transitions in separate vibrational states can give approximate frequency values for vibrational transitions which cannot be easily assigned in the infrared or Raman spectrum.

The rotational spectrum also provides an accurate method for the determination of molecular dipole moments. When an external electric field is applied to a molecule, it perturbs the rotational energy levels through an interaction called the Stark effect. An accurate measurement of the Stark splittings usually gives better dipole moment data than that obtainable from other methods. An external magnetic field can also produce energy level splittings (Zeeman effect), although these are of secondary importance except in paramagnetic molecules.

If a molecule contains a nucleus having a spin greater than $\frac{1}{2}h$, some information concerning the electric field gradient along an axis through this nucleus may be obtained. Each such nuclide possesses a nuclear quadrupole moment which constitutes the local charge asymmetry in the nucleus. This charge asymmetry can couple the nuclear spin axis, which is also the axis of the quadrupole moment, to the molecular axes through the electric field gradient at the nucleus. The resultant coupling causes a splitting of the rotational energy levels and produces hyperfine structure in the spectrum. Analysis of this hyperfine structure can lead to estimates of double-bond character, the extent of hybridization, and the percentages of ionic and covalent character in molecular bonds.

Special experimental systems allow measurements to be extended to free radicals with relatively short lifetimes and to simple molecules which have insufficient vapor pressures under ordinary conditions. The high resolution achieved by combining molecular beam and maser techniques permits small quadrupole, spin-rotation, and spin-spin interactions to be observed in some simple molecules by reducing Doppler broadening effects.

By observing rotational line shapes and intensities in the presence of more than one radiation field, lifetimes of excited vibrational states as well as of rotational levels can be measured. The possibility of preferred collisional transitions between gas–phase molecules may also be investigated.

CHAPTER 2 | RIGID ROTOR

2-1. Introduction

No real molecule is a rigid rotor. The molecules in a waveguide which are subjected to microwave radiation are vibrating as well as colliding with other molecules and the sample cell walls. However, the deviations from rigid rotor behavior are often small enough to be treated by perturbation methods or equivalent techniques. It is therefore mandatory that the solutions to the rigid rotor be worked out in detail, since they will form the basis for calculations of many nonrigid effects. The rigid rotor solutions also provide the general characteristics of the spectrum and allow for its initial interpretation.

The rigid rotor problem has been treated thoroughly by a number of investigators [276, 277, 279] and a review of the most general case of asymmetric rotor was given by Van Winter [291]. For the interpretation of rotational spectra, the group theoretical approach is most advantageous [279]. After the parameters which characterize a rigid rotor have been defined, the principles of classical mechanics and quantum mechanics can be used to evaluate the elements of the energy matrix. The specific form of this matrix is a function of molecular symmetry.

2-2. Molecular Parameters

Every rigid body possesses a unique center of mass (COM). If m_i is the mass of the ith atom and $\mathbf{R}_i^c$ is a vector from the origin of a Cartesian coordinate system whose origin lies at the COM to the ith atom, the center of mass is defined by the conditions (see Eqs. (4-17)–(4-21))

$$\sum_i m_i \mathbf{R}_i^c = 0 \qquad (2\text{-}1)$$

The moment of inertia is a function which relates the positions of the molecular masses with respect to the COM and the Cartesian coordinate system.

7

For a body rotating about a fixed axis, the moment of inertia about that axis is given by

$$I = \sum_i m_i r_i^2 \qquad (2\text{-}2)$$

where r_i represents the distance of the ith mass from the axis and m_i is that mass. If a molecule is viewed as a rigid assembly of point masses, its structure can be described by a tensor whose diagonal elements are the moments of inertia. For a Cartesian coordinate system fixed at the COM, the diagonal elements of the inertia tensor are

$$I_{xx} = \sum_i m_i(y_i^2 + z_i^2) \qquad (2\text{-}3)$$

where I_{yy} and I_{zz} are formed by a permutation of x, y, and z. The off-diagonal elements called products of inertia are given by

$$I_{xy} = -\sum_i m_i x_i y_i \qquad (2\text{-}4)$$

The inertia tensor simplifies because it is symmetric and

$$I_{ij} = I_{ji} \qquad (2\text{-}5)$$

leaving only six independent tensor elements.

The orientation of the coordinate system used to define the inertial system will determine the values of the moments defined above. There is a proper orientation of this coordinate system which forces the off-diagonal elements of the tensor to vanish. The diagonal elements become the principal moments of inertia, and the axis system is termed the principal axis system. As the Cartesian coordinate system is rotated into the principal axis system, the moments of inertia approach either maximum or minimum values. The three principle moments of inertia are designated as I_a, I_b, and I_c.

For any general orientation of the molecule-fixed axes with origin at the COM, the principal moments of inertia can be obtained by diagonalizing the inertial tensor. This is done by solving the determinantal equation (2-6), where the roots λ are the principal moments of inertia.

$$\begin{vmatrix} I_{xx} - \lambda & I_{xy} & I_{xz} \\ I_{yx} & I_{yy} - \lambda & I_{yz} \\ I_{zx} & I_{zy} & I_{zz} - \lambda \end{vmatrix} = 0 \qquad (2\text{-}6)$$

Since the trace, which is the sum of the diagonal elements, is a constant for the diagonalization procedure,

$$I_{xx} + I_{yy} + I_{zz} = I_a + I_b + I_c \qquad (2\text{-}7)$$

If the original coordinate system does not have its origin at the COM of the molecule, it can be translated to the COM using the conditions (2-1).

When the principal axis system of a rigid rotor is employed, the energy can be expressed in a simple form in terms of the angular momenta $\mathbf{P}_i$ about the three principal axes. Solution for the energy levels in a quantum mechanical system follows from

$$\mathbf{H}\Psi = E\Psi \tag{2-8}$$

where $\mathbf{H}$ is the Hamiltonian operator for the system and Ψ is the wave function describing the system. E is the energy. E is a constant which describes the stationary state energy values of the system, since the Hamiltonian operator and wave functions are independent of time. The energy is then

$$\mathbf{H} = \frac{\mathbf{P}_a^2}{2I_a} + \frac{\mathbf{P}_b^2}{2I_b} + \frac{\mathbf{P}_c^2}{2I_c} \tag{2-9}$$

Equation (2-9) can also be expressed in an alternative form,

$$E = \frac{4\pi^2}{h}(A\mathbf{P}_a^2 + B\mathbf{P}_b^2 + C\mathbf{P}_c^2) \tag{2-10}$$

A, B, and C are rotational constants and are defined in frequency units as

$$A = \frac{h}{8\pi^2 I_a}; \qquad B = \frac{h}{8\pi^2 I_b}; \qquad C = \frac{h}{8\pi^2 I_c} \tag{2-11}$$

I_a is the smallest moment while I_c is the largest,

$$I_a \leq I_b \leq I_c, \qquad A \geq B \geq C \tag{2-12}$$

Rotational constants are normally expressed in MHz; the units of I_i are amu A^2.

The operators for momentum about the principal axes may be related to the total angular momentum of the system $\mathbf{P}$

$$\mathbf{P}^2 = \mathbf{P}_x^2 + \mathbf{P}_y^2 + \mathbf{P}_z^2 = \mathbf{P}_a^2 + \mathbf{P}_b^2 + \mathbf{P}_c^2 \tag{2-13}$$

Certain commutation relationships which arise from the Heisenberg uncertainty principle exist between the components of angular momentum:

$$\mathbf{P}_x\mathbf{P}_y - \mathbf{P}_y\mathbf{P}_x = -i\hbar\mathbf{P}_z$$
$$\mathbf{P}_y\mathbf{P}_z - \mathbf{P}_z\mathbf{P}_y = -i\hbar\mathbf{P}_x \tag{2-14}$$
$$\mathbf{P}_z\mathbf{P}_x - \mathbf{P}_x\mathbf{P}_z = -i\hbar\mathbf{P}_y$$

The equations have been expressed in terms of a molecule-fixed axis system. If they were to be reexpressed in terms of a space-fixed system, the sign on the right-hand side of each equation would be positive. These relationships may be derived from the operational definition of angular momentum and the quantum-mechanical equivalents of the operators. Generally,

$$\mathbf{P} = \mathbf{r} \times \mathbf{p} \qquad (2\text{-}15)$$

where $\mathbf{r}$ is the vector location of a particle and $\mathbf{p}$ is the linear momentum of the particle. The components of $\mathbf{P}$ are obtained by expanding (2-15).

$$P_x = yp_z - zp_y$$
$$P_y = zp_x - xp_z \qquad (2\text{-}16)$$
$$P_z = xp_y - yp_x$$

By substituting the quantum-mechanical equivalents for the components of (2-16)

$$p_q \to -ih\frac{\partial}{\partial q}; \qquad q \to q \qquad (2\text{-}17)$$

they become

$$P_x = -ih\left(y\frac{\partial}{\partial z} - z\frac{\partial}{\partial y}\right)$$

$$P_y = -ih\left(z\frac{\partial}{\partial x} - x\frac{\partial}{\partial z}\right) \qquad (2\text{-}18)$$

$$P_z = -ih\left(x\frac{\partial}{\partial y} - y\frac{\partial}{\partial x}\right)$$

The vector relation can be verified from (2-18). Even if the coordinate system is not the principal axis system, equations of the form of (2-14) will still hold for the three components of angular momentum.

From (2-14) it is observed that compatible measurements cannot be performed on any two components of the angular momentum. However, by finding the operator for $\mathbf{P}^2$ in (2-13) it can be shown that the square of the total angular momentum commutes with $\mathbf{P}$ and any of the components of $\mathbf{P}$,

$$[\mathbf{P}^2, \mathbf{P}_i] = \mathbf{P}^2\mathbf{P}_i - \mathbf{P}_i\mathbf{P}^2 = 0 \qquad (2\text{-}19)$$

Therefore, it is possible to simultaneously diagonalize the energy matrix with respect to the square of the total angular momentum and one component of $\mathbf{P}$.

In order to evaluate the Hamiltonian for the different types of molecules which exist, it is necessary to obtain the matrix elements of the total angular momentum of overall rotation and the matrix elements of the individual components of angular momentum. These matrix elements are expressed in units of $h/2\pi$ and in terms of a number of relevant quantum numbers. A good quantum number ζ is identified with the eigenvalues of an operator $\boldsymbol{\zeta}$ which commutes with the Hamiltonian of the system. It also follows that ζ is time-invariant, i.e., a constant of the motion;

$$[\boldsymbol{\zeta}, \mathbf{H}] = 0 \tag{2-20}$$

$$\frac{d}{dt}\langle\zeta\rangle = 0 \tag{2-21}$$

For a rigid rotor, the quantum numbers J, K, and M are of primary importance. J is the quantum number which represents the total rotational angular momentum of the molecule and is often referred to as the rotational quantum number. The quantum number K represents the component (P_z) of $\mathbf{P}$ along the symmetry axis of the limiting symmetric rotor discussed in the next section. If a field defining a space-fixed axis system is applied to the molecule, M gives the component of the total angular momentum on the space-fixed axis:

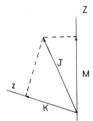

FIG. 2-1. Vector diagram relating the quantum numbers J, K, and M to the space-fixed Z axis and the molecule-fixed z axis.

Figure 2-1 illustrates the relationship between J, K, and M. M and K may take any of $2J + 1$ possible values as determined by the projection of $\mathbf{J}$ on the space-fixed field axis and molecule-fixed figure axis, respectively.

To solve the rotational problem, it is necessary to determine the matrix elements of the angular momentum operators. Using the bra-ket notation where

$$\int \cdots d\tau = \langle \cdots \rangle \tag{2-22}$$

the matrix element of an operator $\mathbf{O}$ between states indexed by the quantum numbers $ijk \cdots$ and $i'j'k' \cdots$ may be written as

$$\int \psi^*_{ijk\cdots} \mathbf{O} \psi_{i'j'k'\cdots} \, d\tau = \langle ijk \cdots |\mathbf{O}|i'j'k' \cdots \rangle \tag{2-23}$$

In a similar manner, the integral of the two wave functions above is

$$\int \psi^*_{ijk\cdots} \psi_{i'j'k'\cdots} \, d\tau = \langle ijk \cdots |i'j'k' \cdots \rangle \tag{2-24}$$

$\mathbf{P}_z$ is conventionally chosen as the component of angular momentum for which there exists simultaneous eigenstates with $\mathbf{P}^2$. The matrix elements are

$$\langle JKM|\mathbf{P}^2|JKM\rangle = J(J + 1)\hbar^2 \qquad (2\text{-}25)$$

$$\langle JKM|\mathbf{P}_z|JKM\rangle = K\hbar \qquad (2\text{-}26)$$

These matrix elements are seen to be diagonal in their quantum numbers, i.e., there are no elements connecting J with J' or K with K'. They have been evaluated in a representation in which $\mathbf{P}^2$ and $\mathbf{P}_z$ are diagonal. If a different representation were chosen, it would be possible to diagonalize $\mathbf{P}_x$ or $\mathbf{P}_y$. Diagonalization of $\mathbf{P}_z$ forces $\mathbf{P}_x$ and $\mathbf{P}_y$ to have off-diagonal elements,

$$\langle JKM|\mathbf{P}_x|JKM\rangle = 0 \qquad (2\text{-}27)$$

$$\langle JKM|\mathbf{P}_y|JKM\rangle = 0 \qquad (2\text{-}28)$$

$$\langle JKM|\mathbf{P}_x|J, K \pm 1, M\rangle = \mp \frac{i\hbar}{2}[(J \mp K)(J \pm K + 1)]^{1/2} \qquad (2\text{-}29)$$

$$\langle JKM|\mathbf{P}_y|J, K \pm 1, M\rangle = \frac{\hbar}{2}[(J \mp K)(J \pm K + 1)]^{1/2} \qquad (2\text{-}30)$$

The matrix elements of $\mathbf{P}_x^2$ and $\mathbf{P}_y^2$ are often of great importance and can be obtained directly from the elements of $\mathbf{P}_x$ and $\mathbf{P}_y$:

$$\langle JKM|\mathbf{P}_x^2|JKM\rangle = \frac{\hbar^2}{2}[J(J + 1) - K^2] \qquad (2\text{-}31)$$

$$\langle JKM|\mathbf{P}_y^2|JKM\rangle = \frac{\hbar^2}{2}[J(J + 1) - K^2] \qquad (2\text{-}32)$$

$$\langle JKM|\mathbf{P}_x^2|J, K \pm 2, M\rangle = -\frac{\hbar^2}{4}[(J \mp K)(J \pm K + 1)(J \mp K - 1)$$

$$\times (J \pm K + 2)]^{1/2} \qquad (2\text{-}33)$$

$$\langle JKM|\mathbf{P}_y^2|J, K \pm 2, M\rangle = \frac{\hbar^2}{4}[(J \mp K)(J \pm K + 1)(J \mp K - 1)$$

$$\times (J \pm K + 2)]^{1/2} \qquad (2\text{-}34)$$

The derivation of these matrix elements is given elsewhere [34]. From these matrix elements it is possible to evaluate the energy as a function of the rotational quantum numbers. By identifying x, y, z with the principal axes of rotation a, b, c, the Hamiltonian operator can be expressed as

$$\mathbf{H} = \frac{\mathbf{P}_x^2}{2I_x} + \frac{\mathbf{P}_y^2}{2I_y} + \frac{\mathbf{P}_z^2}{2I_z} \qquad (2\text{-}35)$$

The energy of a rigid rotor can be obtained by diagonalizing the energy matrix whose nonvanishing elements are

$$\langle JKM|\mathbf{H}|JKM \rangle = \frac{\hbar^2}{4} \left\{ \left(\frac{1}{I_x} + \frac{1}{I_y} \right) [J(J + 1) - K^2] + \frac{2K^2}{I_z} \right\} \quad (2\text{-}36)$$

$$\langle JKM|\mathbf{H}|J, K \pm 2, M \rangle = \frac{\hbar^2}{8} \left\{ \left(\frac{1}{I_y} - \frac{1}{I_x} \right) [J \mp K)(J \mp K - 1) \right.$$
$$\left. \times (J \pm K + 1)(J \pm K + 2)]^{1/2} \right\} \quad (2\text{-}37)$$

2-3. Classes of Molecules

When the overall rotation of a rigid molecule is being studied, the atoms may be considered as point masses. Consequently, molecules fall into four different categories depending upon their symmetry. The first molecular symmetry-type is the linear molecule where all of the atoms lie on a single axis. This type of molecule (e.g., acetylene) has an axis with infinite symmetry since none of the atoms lie off the axis. The symmetric top (e.g., methyl chloride) is characterized by a threefold or higher axis of symmetry. This symmetry axis forces two of the principal moments of inertia to be equal. Threefold symmetry is by far the most common among symmetric tops. It is apparent that the linear molecule is a special form of symmetric top with an axis of infinite-fold symmetry. Molecules with more than one threefold axis of symmetry are called spherical tops (e.g., methane), because all three of their principal moments of inertia are equal. When no two principal moments of inertia in a molecule are equal, the molecule is an asymmetric top (e.g., formaldehyde). This is the most common and most interesting case. An asymmetric rotor can have no threefold or higher symmetry axes; it may possess twofold axes and planes of symmetry. Whenever a molecule does possess a twofold or higher axis of symmetry, that axis is necessarily a principal axis of the molecule and the principal axis which has the highest degree of symmetry is commonly called the figure axis. If a plane of symmetry is present, the figure axis is normally perpendicular to the plane with the other two principal axes being in the plane.

From an experimental point of view, spherical top molecules are of little interest to the microwave spectroscopist, since the high degree of symmetry forces the molecular dipole moment to vanish. Data on these molecules must be obtained by other means, such as infrared and Raman studies.

2-4a. Rigid Linear Molecules

Linear molecules are characterized by a very small moment of inertia about the molecular axis. The other two principal moments lie in a plane perpendicular to the figure axis and are equal in value. The relations between the principal moments are

$$I_b = I_c; \qquad I_a \approx 0 \tag{2-38}$$

Since the rotational energy is a function of $1/I_g$, where I_g is a moment of inertia, excitation of rotation along the symmetry axis would require a large amount of energy. Under normal conditions this mode of rotation is unexcited. The energy matrix then reduces to (for $I_z = I_a$; $I_x = I_y = I_b$)

$$\langle JKM|H|JKM\rangle = \frac{\hbar^2}{2I_b} J(J+1) \tag{2-39}$$

$$\langle JKM|H|J, K \pm 2, M\rangle = 0 \tag{2-40}$$

Note that the term $2K^2/I_z$ in (2-36) vanishes, despite the small value of I_z. This can only occur for $K = 0$. Mathematically, the result is equivalent to disallowing any rotation about the figure axis, since there is no rotational angular momentum along the axis for $K = 0$. For rigid linear molecules with reasonable energies, it is required that K equal zero. Due to the high degree of symmetry which a linear molecule possesses, the energy is diagonal in the rotational quantum numbers J and K and the energy values can be obtained directly from the diagonal elements. In terms of the rotational constant B, the energy becomes

$$E = hBJ(J+1) \tag{2-41}$$

The Schroedinger approach to a rigid linear molecule yields identical values for the energy. The wave equation can be expressed in the polar coordinates θ and ϕ,

$$\frac{1}{\sin\theta}\left(\frac{\partial}{\partial\theta}\right)\sin\theta\,\frac{\partial\psi}{\partial\theta} + \frac{1}{\sin^2\theta}\left(\frac{\partial^2\psi}{\partial\phi^2}\right) + \frac{E}{hB}\psi = 0 \tag{2-42}$$

This wave function for a linear molecule is then

$$\psi_{JM} = N_{JM}e^{iM\phi}P_J^{|M|}(\cos\theta) \tag{2-43}$$

N_{JM} is a normalization factor, $P_J^{|M|}(\cos\theta)$ is the associated Legendre function, and M is the magnetic quantum number. M may have $2J+1$ integral values from J to $-J$ forcing each energy level to be $(2J+1)$-fold degenerate. An external field may be used to lift the degeneracy.

2-4b. Spectrum and Selection Rules

The selection rules for rotational transitions in a linear molecule are

$$\Delta J = \pm 1; \qquad \Delta K = 0; \qquad \Delta M = 0, \pm 1 \tag{2-44}$$

These selection rules result from a consideration of the electric dipole moment and the transformation between the molecule-fixed axis system and a space-fixed system.

Application of the selection rule for J to (2-41) gives the rigid rotational frequencies

$$\nu = 2B(J + 1) \tag{2-45}$$

ν is the transition frequency, and J is the quantum number of the lower state. The rigid rotor spectrum of a linear molecule should consist of a series of equally spaced lines separated by $2B$. The analysis of the spectrum of a linear molecule shows that some perturbations are present which remove the simplicity of the rigid rotor spectrum. These effects include centrifugal distortion, l-type doubling, and Fermi resonance. These interactions are considered in Chapter 3.

2-5a. Rigid Symmetric-Top Molecules

When a nonlinear molecule possesses two equal moments of inertia, it is classified as a symmetric top. There are two possible identifications for the two equal moments. If I_a equals I_b, I_c is the unique moment and is by definition greater than I_a or I_b. The molecule is then designated as an oblate symmetric rotor. If I_b equals I_c, the molecule is a prolate symmetric top. For a prolate rotor the matrix elements of the Hamiltonian are

$$\langle JKM|\mathbf{H}|JKM\rangle = \frac{\hbar^2}{2I_b}J(J + 1) + \frac{\hbar^2}{2}\left(\frac{1}{I_a} - \frac{1}{I_b}\right)K^2 \tag{2-46}$$

$$\langle JKM|\mathbf{H}|J, K \pm 2, M\rangle = 0 \tag{2-47}$$

The energy matrix is diagonal in K, since K is a good quantum number for a true symmetric rotor. In terms of the rotational constants, the energy for a prolate rotor is

$$E = hBJ(J + 1) + h(A - B)K^2 \tag{2-48}$$

For an oblate top the energy is

$$E = hBJ(J + 1) + h(C - B)K^2 \tag{2-49}$$

For a spherical top the coefficient of K^2 vanishes in these two equations.

For a symmetric top $A - B \geq 0$ and $C - B \leq 0$. The effects of these inequalities are shown in Fig. 2-2. Because K is the projection of J on the figure axis, $J \geq K$. For any given value of K, the lowest possible value of J is $J = K$. For an oblate rotor and a given J value, the energy levels are found to decrease with K. This results from the negative coefficient of K^2 in (2-49).

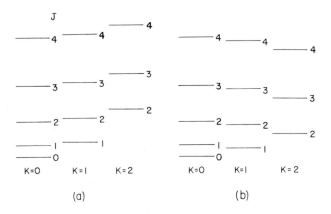

FIG. 2-2.   Energy level structure for (a) prolate symmetric rotor and (b) oblate symmetric rotor. All levels for $K > 0$ are doubly degenerate. Symmetry of the energy levels with respect to inversion is discussed in Chapter 7.

In a prolate top, the energy levels increase with K for a given J.

In terms of the Eulerian angles θ, ϕ, and χ, the Schroedinger equation for a prolate symmetric top is

$$\frac{1}{\sin\theta}\frac{\partial}{\partial\theta}\left(\sin\theta\frac{\partial\psi}{\partial\theta}\right) + \frac{1}{\sin^2\theta}\frac{\partial^2\psi}{\partial\phi^2} + \left(\frac{\cos^2\theta}{\sin^2\theta} + \frac{A}{B}\right)\frac{\partial^2\psi}{\partial\chi^2}$$

$$-\frac{2\cos\theta}{\sin^2\theta}\frac{\partial^2\psi}{\partial\chi\,\partial\phi} + \frac{E}{hB}\psi = 0 \tag{2-50}$$

Through separation of variables, the wave function may be written as

$$\psi_{JKM} = \Theta(\theta)\,e^{iM\phi}\,e^{iK\chi} \tag{2-51}$$

Because ϕ and χ only appear in the differential terms, they are known as cyclic coordinates and always appear in the wave function as exponential terms. M and K must be integers for ψ to be single-valued. The explicit form of the θ dependence is not as simple as that for ϕ and χ. The θ equation has the form

$$\frac{1}{\sin\theta}\frac{d}{d\theta}\left(\sin\theta\frac{d\Theta(\theta)}{d\theta}\right) - \left[\frac{M^2}{\sin^2\theta} + \left(\frac{\cos^2\theta}{\sin^2\theta} + \frac{A}{B}\right)K^2\right.$$

$$\left. -\frac{2\cos\theta}{\sin^2\theta}KM - \frac{E}{hB}\right]\Theta(\theta) = 0 \tag{2-52}$$

A change of variables can be introduced to eliminate the trigonometric functions. Equation (2-52) has singular points at $\theta = 0$ and $\theta = \pi$. Let

$$x = \tfrac{1}{2}(1 - \cos\theta) \tag{2-53}$$

$$\Theta(\theta) = T(x) \tag{2-54}$$

$$\lambda = \frac{E}{hB} - \frac{A}{B}K^2 \tag{2-55}$$

The differential equation for θ now has its singular points at $x = 0$ and $x = 1$ as a result of the transformation.

$$\frac{d}{dx}\left\{x(1-x)\frac{dT}{dx}\right\} + \left[\lambda - \frac{\{M + K(2x-1)\}^2}{4x(1-x)}\right] = 0 \tag{2-56}$$

Letting

$$T(x) = x^{1/2|K-M|}(1-x)^{1/2|K+M|}F(x) \tag{2-57}$$

$$x(1-x)\frac{d^2F}{dx^2} + (\alpha - \beta x)\frac{dF}{dx} + \gamma F = 0 \tag{2-58}$$

where

$$\alpha = |K - M| + 1 \tag{2-59}$$

$$\beta = |K + M| + |K - M| + 2 \tag{2-60}$$

$$\gamma = \lambda + K^2 - [\tfrac{1}{2}|K+M| + \tfrac{1}{2}|K-M|][\tfrac{1}{2}|K+M| + \tfrac{1}{2}|K-M| + 1] \tag{2-61}$$

the equation for F can be solved by using the polynomial

$$F(x) = \sum_{v=0}^{\infty} a_v x^v \tag{2-62}$$

The resulting recursion relation is

$$a_{j+1} = \frac{j(j-1) + \beta j - \gamma}{(j+1)(j+\alpha)}a_j \tag{2-63}$$

Equation (2-58) is the hypergeometric equation with the hypergeometric function being a polynomial in x known as a Jacobi polynomial. The polynomial is terminated after the jth term by the energy expression

$$E = hBJ(J+1) + h(A-B)K^2 \tag{2-64}$$

in which

$$J = j + \tfrac{1}{2}|K+M| + \tfrac{1}{2}|K-M| \tag{2-65}$$

j is the largest value for which a_j does not vanish. The quantum numbers J, K, and M are restricted to their normal range of values with J being zero or any positive integer while K and M go from zero to $\pm J$. The energy expression is identical to that obtained by the Heisenberg method, with the energy being independent of M and the sign of K. This leads to a $(2J + 1)$-fold space degeneracy in M and a $\pm K$ degeneracy for levels with $K \neq 0$.

The explicit form of the hypergeometric series is

$$F(a;b;c;x) = 1 + \frac{a \cdot b}{1 \cdot c}x + \frac{a(a + 1)b(b + 1)}{1 \cdot 2 \cdot c(c + 1)}x^2 + \cdots$$

$$+ \frac{a(a + 1) \cdots (a + r - 1)b(b + 1) \cdots (b + r - 1)}{r!c(c + 1) \cdots (c + r - 1)}x^r \cdots \quad (2\text{-}66)$$

The symmetric top wave functions can be written in terms of the hypergeometric series and a normalization factor N_{JKM}.

$$\psi_{JKM} = N_{JKM}x^{1/2|K-M|}(1 - x)^{1/2|K+M|} e^{iM\phi} e^{iK\chi}F$$

$$\times \left(-J + \frac{\beta}{2} - 1; J + \frac{\beta}{2}; 1 + |K - M|; x\right) \quad (2\text{-}67)$$

$$N_{JKM} = \left[\frac{(2J + 1)(J + \frac{1}{2}|K + M| + \frac{1}{2}|K - M|)!}{8\pi^2(J - \frac{1}{2}|K + M| - \frac{1}{2}|K - M|)!}\right.$$

$$\left.\times \frac{(J - \frac{1}{2}|K + M| + \frac{1}{2}|K - M|)!}{(|K - M|!)^2(J + \frac{1}{2}|K + M| - \frac{1}{2}|K - M|)!}\right]^{1/2} \quad (2\text{-}68)$$

The symmetric rotor functions in (2-67) are often abbreviated as

$$S_{JKM}(\theta, \phi) e^{iK\chi}$$

2-5b. Spectrum and Selection Rules

The selection rules for symmetric top molecules are

$$\Delta J = 0, \pm 1; \qquad \Delta K = 0; \qquad \Delta M = 0, \pm 1 \quad (2\text{-}69)$$

The transitions resulting from $\Delta J = 0$ are of interest in the case where a finite inversion doubling is present. This possibility is discussed in Chapter 7. When inversion is not important, the transition frequencies for a rigid symmetric rotor are

$$v = 2B(J + 1) \quad (2\text{-}70)$$

where J is the quantum number of the lowest state. The spectrum of a rigid symmetric-top molecule is exactly like that of a rigid linear molecule with equally spaced lines appearing $2B$ MHz apart. When nonrigid effects are considered, some K dependence enters the frequency equation, making it possible to discriminate the spectrum of a symmetric top molecule from that of a linear molecule.

2-6a. Rigid Asymmetric-Top Molecules

When a molecule possesses three unequal moments of inertia, it is classified as an asymmetric top. The degree of symmetry present in an asymmetric top is considerably less than that in a linear or symmetric top. This complicates the rotational energy levels of the molecule. The projection of the total rotational angular momentum is no longer constant along any axis or direction fixed in the molecule, with the result that K is no longer a good quantum number. J and M are still good quantum numbers and hold the same meaning as they did for linear and symmetric tops. With K no longer a good quantum number, it becomes impossible (except for very low J values) to express the energy of an asymmetric rotor in a closed form. The asymmetric rotor possesses no quantum number with a simple physical meaning comparable to K; however, the parameter K is kept to label the energy levels. K_1 is the value K would have in the limiting case of an oblate symmetric top, while K_{-1} is the value of K for the limiting prolate symmetric top. Since the K degeneracy of a symmetric top is lifted for an asymmetric top, both of these pseudoquantum numbers are required for the identification of an energy level. Each level may be labelled in the notation $J_{K_{-1}K_1}$.

The $2J + 1$ energy levels of a particular J can be labeled in another way by the single subscript τ. τ takes on $2J + 1$ different values from $+J$ to $-J$. τ has no direct physical meaning and simply serves to order the energy levels of a given J. The relationship between the two sets of labels is $\tau = K_{-1} - K_1$.

In a symmetric rotor representation, the energy matrix for an asymmetric rotor possesses elements which are off-diagonal in K. To obtain the eigenvalues for the asymmetric rotor, it is necessary to diagonalize this energy matrix. The Hamiltonian is conveniently written as the sum of two terms,

$$H = H_s + H_a \qquad (2\text{-}71)$$

where H_s contains the terms representing a symmetric rotor, and H_a contains the remaining asymmetry terms. For a prolate rotor

$$H_s = h\left(\frac{B + C}{2}\right)P^2 + h\left[A - \left(\frac{B + C}{2}\right)\right]P_a^2 \qquad (2\text{-}72)$$

$$H_a = \frac{B - C}{2}(P_b^2 - P_c^2)h \qquad (2\text{-}73)$$

The matrix elements of H_s are given by (2-46) and (2-47). For H_a,

$$\langle JK|H_a|JK\rangle = \left|\frac{B-C}{2}\right|[J(J+1) - K^2]h \qquad (2\text{-}74)$$

$$\langle JK|H_a|J, K+2\rangle = -\left|\frac{B-C}{2}\right|[f(J, K+1)]^{1/2}h \qquad (2\text{-}75)$$

$f(J, K+1)$ is defined in (2-91). The matrix elements of H_a vanish for a prolate symmetric rotor where $B = C$.

The asymmetry of a molecule is conveniently described in terms of an asymmetry parameter κ.

$$\kappa = \frac{2B - A - C}{A - C} \qquad (2\text{-}76)$$

κ varies from -1 for a prolate symmetric top to $+1$ for an oblate top. This parameter comes naturally from the change of variables proposed by Ray [278] to facilitate the calculation of asymmetric rotor energy levels. Let A, B, and C be replaced by $\sigma A + \rho$, $\sigma B + \rho$, and $\sigma C + \rho$ in (2-10). Then

$$E(\sigma A + \rho, \sigma B + \rho, \sigma C + \rho) = \frac{1}{h^2}[(\sigma A + \rho)\mathbf{P}_a^2 + (\sigma B + \rho)\mathbf{P}_b^2 + (\sigma C + \rho)\mathbf{P}_c^2]$$

$$= \frac{4\pi^2}{h^2}[\sigma(A\mathbf{P}_a^2 + B\mathbf{P}_b^2 + C\mathbf{P}_c^2) + \rho(\mathbf{P}_a^2 + \mathbf{P}_b^2 + \mathbf{P}_c^2)]$$

$$(2\text{-}77)$$

Using the matrix elements of $\mathbf{P}^2$, this equation becomes

$$E(\sigma A + \rho, \sigma B + \rho, \sigma C + \rho) = \frac{\sigma E(A, B, C)}{h} + \rho J(J+1) \qquad (2\text{-}78)$$

σ and ρ are scalar quantities which Ray chose as

$$\sigma = \frac{2}{A - C}; \qquad \rho = -\frac{A + C}{A - C} \qquad (2\text{-}79)$$

These values of σ and ρ are then used to determine the scaled rotational constants.

$$\sigma A + \rho = 1 \qquad (2\text{-}80)$$

$$\sigma B + \rho = \frac{2B - A - C}{A - C} = \kappa \qquad (2\text{-}81)$$

$$\sigma C + \rho = -1 \qquad (2\text{-}82)$$

$\sigma B + \rho$ varies between $+1$ and -1 and is the perfect choice for an asymmetry parameter κ. The energy can now be expressed in terms of a reduced energy $E(1, \kappa, -1)$ or just $E(\kappa)$.

$$E(A, B, C) = h\left[\frac{A + C}{2}J(J + 1) + \frac{A - C}{2}E(\kappa)\right] \tag{2-83}$$

The $E(\kappa)$ have been well tabulated and (2-83) is a convenient equation for calculating rotational energy levels. The tabulation of $E(\kappa)$ is simplified by the equality

$$E_\tau^J(\kappa) = -E_{-\tau}^J(-\kappa) \tag{2-84}$$

This allows the reduced energies for positive κ values to be determined from reduced energies of negative κ. Figure 2-3 shows the energy levels of a rigid rotor up to $J = 3$ as a function of the asymmetry parameter κ.

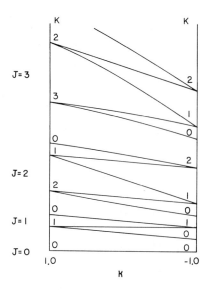

FIG. 2-3. Energy levels of a rigid rotor as a function of the asymmetry parameter κ. The limiting values of K for a symmetric rotor are shown for $\kappa = +1.0$ (oblate) and $\kappa = -1.0$ (prolate).

Other asymmetry parameters have been proposed which are convenient in special situations. The Wang asymmetry parameter [276] is given by a redefinition of σ and ρ.

$$\sigma = \frac{1}{A - \frac{1}{2}(B + C)}; \quad \rho = \frac{B + C}{-2[A - \frac{1}{2}(B + C)]} \tag{2-85}$$

The asymmetry parameter is then

$$b_p = \frac{C - B}{2A - B - C} = \frac{\kappa + 1}{\kappa - 3} \tag{2-86}$$

with b_p varying between zero for a prolate top and -1 for an oblate top. For an oblate top b could be redefined as

$$b_0 = \frac{A - B}{2C - B - A} = \frac{\kappa - 1}{\kappa + 3} \tag{2-87}$$

where b_0 equals zero for an oblate top and equals -1 for a prolate top. It is apparent that the symmetry of κ about zero is one of its advantages over b, although b is convenient for perturbation expansions for near symmetric tops [296, 297]. Another asymmetry parameter δ varies between 0 for a prolate top and $+1$ for an oblate top.

$$\delta = \frac{\kappa + 1}{2} = \frac{B - C}{A - C} \tag{2-88}$$

2-6b. Matrix Elements of $E(\kappa)$

Once the values of $E(\kappa)$ are calculated for all the pertinent $J_{K_{-1}K_1}$, (2-83) allows the energies of an asymmetric rotor to be calculated. King et al. [279] give the matrix elements of the reduced energy as

$$\langle JKM|E(\kappa)|JKM\rangle = F[J(J + 1) - K^2] + GK^2$$
$$= FJ(J + 1) + (G - F)K^2 \tag{2-89}$$

$$\langle J, K + 2, M|E(\kappa)|JKM\rangle = \langle JKM|E(\kappa)|J, K + 2, M\rangle$$
$$= H[f(J, K + 1)]^{1/2} \tag{2-90}$$

The positive square root of f is used.

$$f(J, n) = f(J, -n) = \tfrac{1}{4}[J(J + 1) - n(n + 1)][J(J + 1) - n(n - 1)] \tag{2-91}$$

Tabulated values of $f(J, n)$ are given in Table I of [279] and in Appendix II of [34]. The values of F, G, and H depend upon the representation used to relate the three components of angular momentum P_a, P_b, and P_c with P_x, P_y, and P_z. P_a, P_b, and P_c are the components of rotational angular momentum along the principal axes of the molecule, while the quantities P_x, P_y, and P_z are components of angular momentum in a molecule-fixed coordinate system located at the COM. The representation used to derive the matrix elements of a rigid rotor diagonalizes P_z. There are six possible ways in which the P_a, P_b, P_c may be identified with the P_x, P_y, P_z. Table 2-1 gives the six possible identifications in the notation of King et al. [279].

TABLE 2-1

POSSIBLE IDENTIFICATIONS OF P_x, P_y, AND P_z WITH P_a, P_b, AND P_c [a]

	Representation					
	I^r	I^l	II^r	II^l	III^r	III^l
P_x	P_b	P_c	P_c	P_a	P_a	P_b
P_y	P_c	P_b	P_a	P_c	P_b	P_a
P_z	P_a	P_a	P_b	P_b	P_c	P_c

[a] From King et al. [279].

The r and l superscripts refer to right- and left-handed coordinate systems for the a, b, c components. The x, y, z components are in a right-handed coordinate system. Table 2-2 gives the values of F, G, and H in terms of κ.

TABLE 2-2

EVALUATION OF F, G, AND H[a,b]

	I^r	II^r	III^r
F	$\frac{1}{2}(\kappa - 1)$	0	$\frac{1}{2}(\kappa + 1)$
G	1	κ	-1
H	$-\frac{1}{2}(\kappa + 1)$	1	$\frac{1}{2}(\kappa - 1)$

[a] From King et al. [279].
[b] In the I^l, II^l, and III^l representations the sign of H is reversed.

The K value in (2-89) and (2-90) depends upon the representation which is used. For a limiting prolate top representation I is used, while for a limiting oblate top III is the convenient identification. Type II is best used near $\kappa = 0$ where the asymmetry is most pronounced. The three right-handed representations differ from the three left-handed representations only in the sign of H. The Hermitian property of the energy matrix causes this sign difference to have no effect on the energy values.

In the limiting case of an oblate rotor, the type III energy matrix becomes diagonal and

$$\langle JKM|E(1)|JKM\rangle = J(J + 1) - 2K^2 \qquad (2\text{-}92)$$

where the oblate K is used. In the limiting prolate case,

$$\langle JKM|E(-1)|JKM\rangle = -J(J + 1) + 2K^2 \qquad (2\text{-}93)$$

The prolate K is used. The energy expression for a symmetric top can be obtained by substituting either of the above elements into (2-83).

2-6c. Asymmetric Rotor Functions

The wave functions of an asymmetric top molecule are best described in terms of their symmetry properties. The symmetric rotor wave functions form the basis for the determination of the asymmetric rotor functions; the asymmetric rotor functions may be expanded in terms of a complete set of symmetric functions. For a prolate rotor, the prolate symmetric functions are the most appropriate, while the complete set of oblate symmetric top functions should be used for $\kappa > 0$.

$$\psi_{JK_{-1}K_1M} = \sum_K a_K S_{JKM}(\theta, \phi)e^{iK\chi} \tag{2-94}$$

Summation over J and M is unnecessary, since they are still good quantum numbers for an asymmetric rotor. The symmetric rotor functions belong to the internal rotation group D_∞, which has infinitely many representations characterized by J and K. The character table for D_∞ is given in Table 2-3.

TABLE 2-3

CHARACTER TABLE OF THE CONTINUOUS ROTATION GROUP D_∞

D_∞	E	C_∞^z	∞C_2
Σ_1	1	1	1
Σ_2	1	1	-1
Π	2	$2\cos(2\pi/n)$	0
Δ	2	$2\cos(4\pi/n)$	0
.	.	.	.
.	.	.	.
.	.	.	.

All the representations except those for $K = 0$ are doubly degenerate in $\pm K$. The nondegenerate species Σ_1 and Σ_2 represent odd and even J values, respectively. The Greek symbols give the value of K. The subscripts 1 and 2 give the parity of J.

The wave function for an asymmetric rotor must remain unchanged or only change sign for twofold rotations about the principal axes. As a result, the summation in (2-94) is taken over either even or odd K values. The three twofold rotations and the identity form the four group V to which the asymmetric rotor functions belong. Table 2-4 shows the character table for symmetry group V. In their present form the symmetric rotor wave functions do not belong to the four group V, but the Wang linear combinations of these functions do have the proper symmetry [276].

$$S(JKM\gamma) = \frac{1}{\sqrt{2}}[\psi^x(JKM) + (-1)^\gamma\psi^x(J, -K, M)] \tag{2-95}$$

TABLE 2-4
CHARACTER TABLE OF THE GROUP V

	E	C_2^c	C_2^b	C_2^a
A	1	1	1	1
B_c	1	1	-1	-1
B_b	1	-1	1	-1
B_a	1	-1	-1	1

γ takes on odd or even values such as 0 and 1 and the $\psi^x(JKM)$ are related to the previously defined symmetric rotor functions by a factor which determines the phase.

$$\psi^x(JKM) = (-1)^{(1/2|K+M| + 1/2|K-M|)}\psi_{JKM} \qquad (2\text{-}96)$$

For $K = 0$ only $\gamma = 0$ exists.

$$S(J0M0) = \psi^x(J0M) \qquad (2\text{-}97)$$

The Wang functions are correct zeroth-order wave functions for the degenerate energy levels of a symmetric rotor. These new basis functions $S(JKM\gamma)$ are characterized by the irreducible representations of the four group V(xyz). The representations of the group V(abc) in the principal axis system can be correlated to those of V(xyz). A always corresponds to A, and B_a, B_b, B_c correspond to B_x, B_y, B_z under the same permutation which identifies a, b, c with x, y, z. The Wang functions also belong to D_∞. Table 2-5 [279] shows the correlations between the representations of D_∞, V(xyz) and V(abc). For instance, the correlation between D_∞ and V(xyz) is determined by observing the functions $S(JKM\gamma)$ under the operations C_2^x, C_2^y, C_2^z of V(xyz).

TABLE 2-5
CORRELATIONS BETWEEN THE REPRESENTATIONS OF D_∞, V(xyz), AND V(abc)

D_∞	V(xyz)	I^r	I^l	II^r	II^l	III^r	III^l
Σ_1	A	A	A	A	A	A	A
Σ_2	B_z	B_a	B_a	B_b	B_b	B_c	B_c
Π	B_y	B_c	B_b	B_a	B_c	B_b	B_a
Π	B_x	B_b	B_c	B_c	B_a	B_a	B_b
Δ	A	A	A	A	A	A	A
Δ	B_z	B_a	B_a	B_b	B_b	B_c	B_c
.	.						
.	.						
.	.						

Because matrix elements of the form $\langle JKM|E(\kappa)|J, K \pm 1, M\rangle$ vanish, the reduced energy matrix for a given J can be factored into two submatrices;

one for odd K and one for even K. A further factoring may be effected by applying a transformation to the matrix.

$$\mathbf{X'E}(\kappa)\mathbf{X} = \mathbf{E}^+ + \mathbf{E}^- + \mathbf{O}^+ + \mathbf{O}^- \tag{2-98}$$

E and O refer to the even or odd parity of K while $+$ and $-$ give the parity of $(-1)^y$. The $\mathbf{E}^\pm$ submatrices give the energy levels for even values of the limiting symmetric top quantum number K while the $\mathbf{O}^\pm$ submatrices yield the energies for odd values of the limiting K.

$\mathbf{X}$ is of order $2J + 1$ and is referred to as the Wang transformation.

$$\psi^x = \mathbf{XS} \tag{2-99}$$

$$\mathbf{X} = \mathbf{X'} = \frac{1}{\sqrt{2}}
\begin{bmatrix}
\ddots & & & & & & \reflectbox{$\ddots$} \\
 & -1 & & & & 1 & \\
 & & -1 & 0 & 1 & & \\
 & & 0 & \sqrt{2} & 0 & & \\
 & & 1 & 0 & 1 & & \\
 & 1 & & & & 1 & \\
\reflectbox{$\ddots$} & & & & & & \ddots
\end{bmatrix} \tag{2-100}$$

$\mathbf{X'}$ is the transpose of $\mathbf{X}$. From the top left-hand corner to the lower right ψ^x runs from $\psi^x(J, -J, M)$ to $\psi^x(J, J, M)$; similarly, $\mathbf{S}$ goes from $S(J, J, M, 1) \cdots$ to $S(J, 1, M, 1), S(J, 0, M, 0) \cdots$ to $S(J, J, M, 0)$. In terms of the elements of the original matrix $\mathbf{E}(\kappa)$ the submatrices are

$$\mathbf{E}^+ =
\begin{bmatrix}
E_{00} & \sqrt{2}E_{02} & 0 & \cdots \\
\sqrt{2}E_{02} & E_{22} & E_{24} & \cdots \\
0 & E_{24} & E_{44} & \cdots \\
\vdots & \vdots & \vdots & \ddots
\end{bmatrix} \tag{2-101}$$

$\mathbf{E}^-$ is formed by omitting the first column and row of $\mathbf{E}^+$.

$$\mathbf{O}^\pm =
\begin{bmatrix}
E_{11} \pm E_{-11} & E_{13} & 0 & \cdots \\
E_{13} & E_{33} & E_{35} & \\
0 & E_{35} & E_{55} & \\
\vdots & & & \ddots
\end{bmatrix} \tag{2-102}$$

The matrix elements E_{ij} are obtained from (2-89) and (2-90). Relations simplifying the elements of $E(\kappa)$ are

$$E_{KK} = E_{-K,-K}; \qquad E_{K,K+2} = E_{K+2,K} = E_{-K,-K-2} = E_{-K-2,-K} \qquad (2\text{-}103)$$

Thus the Wang transformation leaves H_s in (2-72) unchanged because it is diagonal in J and K and factors H_a into four submatrices which may be treated separately.

Since the matrix elements of $E(\kappa)$ are now known, calculation of the energy levels of a rigid asymmetric rotor becomes a purely mathematical problem involving the diagonalization of the submatrices E^+, E^-, O^+, and O^-. The matrices can be diagonalized in any of the six representations $I^r \cdots III^l$. Combination of the six representations with the four submatrices leads to twenty-four different submatrices each of which belongs to one of the four irreducible representations of the four group V. The reduced energies $E(\kappa)$ are the characteristic roots of the four submatrices in whichever representation is chosen. The evaluation of the reduced energy is discussed in Appendix 3.

As an alternative approach to the calculation of the energy levels for a near symmetric rotor, a series expansion can be written in terms of an appropriate asymmetry parameter such as δ or b. In the case of a near prolate top, b_p is a logical choice for the expansion parameter, and the energy may be written as

$$\frac{E}{h} = \frac{B+C}{2}J(J+1) + \left(A - \frac{B+C}{2}\right)w \qquad (2\text{-}104)$$

with w expressing the asymmetry dependence.

$$w = K^2_{-1} + C_1 b_p + C_2 b_p^2 + C_3 b_p^3 + C_4 b_p^4 + C_5 b_p^5 \cdots \qquad (2\text{-}105)$$

The coefficients C_n, which may be evaluated by continued fraction or perturbation techniques, have been tabulated for $J \leq 40$ [297]. The tables also directly yield the near-oblate parameters. Errors in the computed value of w increase with J and b but increase with decreasing K.

Energy level evaluations of this type are of considerable value where high J values are encountered because of the limited tabulation of $E(\kappa)$ for $J > 20$. This expansion which is effectively a closed function of the rotational constants leads to a convenient calculation of the derivatives of the energy with respect to the rotational constants. These derivatives enter directly into a number of calculations involving internal rotation, quadrupole coupling, and centrifugal distortion.

2-6d. Selection Rules

Three types of rigid asymmetric rotor spectra occur with respect to the quantum number J. The selection rule for J is $\Delta J = 0, \pm 1$. $\Delta J = 0$ specifies the Q branch with $\Delta J = -1$ and $\Delta J = +1$ representing the $P^\dagger$ and R branches, respectively. The selection rules on the pseudoquantum numbers K_{-1} and K_1 can be derived from a consideration of the four group V.

The character table in Table 2-4 indicates that the wave function for an asymmetric rotor must either remain unchanged or change sign for any of the operations of V(abc). These properties may be identified by the notation even (e) or odd (o), respectively. Performance of any two of the twofold rotations of V is identical to performing the third rotation. This leaves two possible combinations for e and o. Either all three operations are even (A species) or two of them are odd with the third being even (B species). The identity is always even. The B species are identified by a subscript signifying the axis whose character is $+1$, i.e., the axis for which rotation produces no change of sign in the wave function.

The representations A, B_c, B_b, B_a may be identified by the parity of K_{-1}, K_1.

$$A = ee$$
$$B_a = eo$$
$$B_b = oo$$
$$B_c = oe$$

(2-106)

K_{-1} represents the symmetry with respect to rotation about the a axis and K_1 gives the symmetry about the c axis. The symmetry about the b axis is obtained by adding K_{-1} and K_1. An even sum is even and an odd sum is odd with respect to rotation about the b axis. The b axis symmetry may also be obtained by multiplying the characters for rotation about the a and c axes in a particular representation.

A regularity in the symmetry of asymmetric top energy levels is seen when the labeling J_τ is used. The highest level J_J is even with respect to C_2^c which is a 180° rotation about the axis with the largest moment of inertia. The next two levels are odd, with respect to C_2^c, the next two even, and so on in pairs. The lowest level J_{-J} is even with respect to C_2^a, a rotation of 180° about the axis with the smallest moment of inertia. The next two higher levels are odd with respect to C_2^a, the next two even, and so on in pairs. The parity of the level with respect to C_2^b can be deduced from the behavior of C_2^a and C_2^c. Table 2-6 illustrates the parity determination for $J = 4$.

Once the symmetry characteristics of the asymmetric rotor energy levels have been determined, it is possible to formulate the selection rules for pure rotational transitions between these levels. The behavior of the molecular dipole moment under the symmetry operations of the four group V(abc) is

---

$\dagger$ Both $\Delta J = +1$ and $\Delta J = -1$ transitions are often referred to as R branch transitions in pure rotational spectra.

TABLE 2-6
ENERGY LEVEL PARITY OF THE TWOFOLD
ROTATIONS OF THE ASYMMETRIC ROTOR GROUP
V(abc)

C_2^a	C_2^b	C_2^c	J_τ
+	+	+	4_4
+	−	−	4_3
−	+	−	4_2
−	−	+	4_1
+	+	+	4_0
+	−	−	4_{-1}
−	+	−	4_{-2}
−	−	+	4_{-3}
+	+	+	4_{-4}

important. The dipole moment is not restricted to lie along a figure axis as in the symmetric top but may have components in any or all principal axis directions. The symmetry of the dipole moment components μ_a, μ_b, and μ_c will define three different types of asymmetric rotor transitions. μ_a, the component of μ along the a axis, is symmetric (even) with respect to a 180° rotation about the a axis. For operations C_2^b and C_2^c it is antisymmetric (odd). Thus μ_a has the symmetry B_a of V(abc). In a similar manner μ_b belongs to B_b and μ_c to B_c.

The intensities of rotational transitions are proportional to the square of the dipole moment matrix element $\langle JKM|\mu|J'K'M'\rangle^2$.

$$\langle JKM|\mu|J'K'M'\rangle^2 = \langle JKM|\mu_a|J'K'M'\rangle^2 + \langle JKM|\mu_b|J'K'M'\rangle^2$$
$$+ \langle JKM|\mu_c|J'K'M'\rangle^2 \qquad (2\text{-}107)$$

The intensity of a transition will be zero if all the dipole matrix elements in (2-107) vanish. A transition of zero intensity is said to be forbidden by the selection rules which force the matrix elements to vanish. If any one of the three terms on the right hand side of (2-107) does not vanish, the transition is said to be allowed. Consider the dipole moment integral

$$\int \psi_i \mu_j \psi_k \, d\tau = \langle i|\mu_j|k \rangle \qquad (2\text{-}108)$$

where the ψ's are asymmetric rotor wave functions for two levels i and k and μ_j is either μ_a, μ_b, or μ_c. Since the energy of the molecule is invariant under a rotation of π about any of the principal axes, the dipole matrix elements cannot change sign for such a rotation. The symmetry properties of the integral are governed by the symmetry of the product of the individual symmetries of ψ_i, μ_j, and ψ_k. The dipole moment integral is invariant only when its total symmetry is A. In the other cases the integral changes sign for a rotation and must be zero. Table 2-7 gives the symmetries of the wave functions for which the total symmetry is A. These selection rules may also be expressed in terms of changes in the pseudoquantum numbers K_{-1} and K_1 as shown in Table 2-8.

TABLE 2-7

DIPOLE SELECTION RULES FOR AN ASYMMETRIC
ROTOR

Component	Selection rules
μ_a	ee $\leftrightarrow$ eo; $\quad A \leftrightarrow B_a$
	oe $\leftrightarrow$ oo; $\quad B_c \leftrightarrow B_b$
μ_b	ee $\leftrightarrow$ oo; $\quad A \leftrightarrow B_b$
	oe $\leftrightarrow$ eo; $\quad B_c \leftrightarrow B_a$
μ_c	ee $\leftrightarrow$ oe; $\quad A \leftrightarrow B_c$
	eo $\leftrightarrow$ oo; $\quad B_a \leftrightarrow B_b$

TABLE 2-8

ASYMMETRIC ROTOR SELECTION RULES FOR THE LIMITING
OBLATE AND PROLATE K

Component of μ	ΔK_{-1}	ΔK_1
μ_a	$0, \pm 2, \pm 4, \ldots$	$\pm 1, \pm 3, \pm 5, \ldots$
μ_b	$\pm 1, \pm 3, \pm 5, \ldots$	$\pm 1, \pm 3, \pm 5, \ldots$
μ_c	$\pm 1, \pm 3, \pm 5, \ldots$	$0, \pm 2, \pm 4, \ldots$

The spectrum of an asymmetric rotor is complicated by three different types of rotational transitions. These families are called a-type, b-type, and c-type transitions depending upon which component of the dipole moment makes the transition possible. If the molecular dipole moment has significant components along all three principal axes, all three types of lines can be expected. Transitions in which ΔK_{-1} and ΔK_1 are no greater than one will be the dominating lines, while the transitions resulting from greater changes will be correspondingly weaker. For a near prolate top where μ_a is the largest component of μ, the limiting selection rules of a symmetric top show that the transitions with $\Delta K_{-1} = 0$ are most significant. In many cases the Q branch is easiest to identify because these lines fall in a series whose frequencies are obtained by putting the selection rule $\Delta J = 0$ into the energy expression (2-83).

$$v = \frac{A - C}{2} \Delta E(\kappa) \tag{2-109}$$

$\Delta E(\kappa)$ is the difference in $E(\kappa)$ for the lower and upper levels.

One method of determining the J value of a Q-branch transition is through the Stark effect which is discussed in Chapter 8. Once a Q branch in the ground rotational state has been assigned, the values of κ and $(A - C)/2$ are determined. Not enough information is available to uniquely determine the three rotational constants. This can only be done by identifying at least one P- or R-branch transition which allows $(A + C)/2$ to be calculated. Once the rotational constants are known they may be checked by calculating several other Q- and R-branch lines. For molecules which can be treated as nearly rigid rotors only small deviations from the calculated transitions should be observed.

2-6e. *K* Doubling in an Asymmetric Rotor

When the K degeneracy of a symmetric rotor is removed, the separation of the $\pm K$ levels is a function of J, K, and the degree of asymmetry. The K splitting is just the difference between the $\mathbf{E}^+$ and $\mathbf{E}^-$ or $\mathbf{O}^+$ and $\mathbf{O}^-$ energy levels for a given K. For small asymmetries, a perturbation treatment using the symmetric rotor solution as a basis shows that the splitting first appears in the Kth order [276, 290]. For the $\mathbf{E}$ submatrices (even K) in (2-101) the splitting results from the E_{02} term which vanishes for $\mathbf{E}^-$. From (2-102) for odd K the splitting must come from the $\langle 1|1 \rangle$ term which causes $\mathbf{O}^+$ and $\mathbf{O}^-$ to differ. Using the binomial notation

$$\binom{n}{m} = \frac{n!}{[(n - m)!m!]} \tag{2-110}$$

the Kth order splitting formula becomes

$$\Delta E^{(K)} = \frac{(A - C) \binom{J + K}{K} \binom{J}{K} K^2 b^K}{8^{K-1}(1 - b)} \tag{2-111}$$

where b and K are the proper limiting oblate or prolate values. This expression is valid for small asymmetries and small splittings. Coefficients for this formula have been tabulated by Hainer *et al.* [287]. They also discuss the regions where it is valid. To extend the usefulness of Wang's formula and allow an estimation of the error, Kivelson [290] calculated the $(K + 2)$nd-order correction terms,

$$\Delta E^{(K+2)} = \Delta E^{(K)}[1 + (a' + b'J(J + 1) + c'J^2(J + 1)^2)b^2] \quad (2\text{-}112)$$

and tabulated values for the coefficients a', b', c' which depend on K and should not be confused with rotational constants or principal axis labels. For $K = 0$ no doubling is possible, while the $K = 1$ levels produce the largest splitting for a given J value. The doubling rapidly decreases with K and increases with J.

2-6f. Graphical Methods for Determining κ and $(A - C)/2$

Several graphical methods are available for the approximate calculation of $(A - C)/2$ and κ for a particular vibrational state of a molecule. For a rigid rotor, the values of κ and $(A - C)/2$ are independent of the rotational quantum numbers. If κ is plotted against $(A - C)/2$ for a family of Q-branch transitions, the straight lines obtained should intersect in a point at the proper value of κ and $(A - C)/2$. In the actual case of a nonrigid molecule, some spread in the intersection points will occur, although these deviations are usually very small. Lines not intersecting at the point have either been given the wrong J values or belong to different vibrational states. Fig. 2-4 illustrates a typical plot.

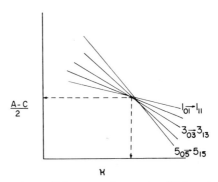

FIG. 2-4.   Plot of $(A - C)/2$ versus κ for a series of Q-branch transitions.

Another approach is to take the logarithm of (2-109).

$$\ln v = \ln \frac{A - C}{2} + \ln \Delta E(\kappa) \qquad (2\text{-}113)$$

The family of Q-branch lines is then plotted as a set of curves on a graph of κ versus $\ln \Delta E(\kappa)$ over the appropriate range of κ. All transitions which appear to belong to the Q branch are then plotted on a strip of graph paper with the same scale as the original graph. They are plotted as ln v. The strip is then displaced horizontally and vertically in search of a correspondence of ln v plots with the family of curves for the Q branch. At the correct κ and ln v marks for the actual Q branch, transitions will fall on the Q-branch curves.

This method was used by Tabor [683] on the spectrum of acetic acid. Figure 2-5 shows an example of this type of plot.

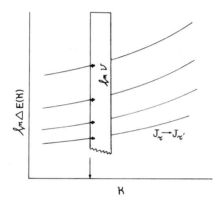

FIG. 2-5.   Sample plot of ln $\Delta E(\kappa)$ versus κ.

These graphical techniques are of value when the Q-branch transitions cannot be identified from their Stark effect or by other means. The latter graphical method is very convenient when trying to fit a Q branch resulting from molecules with a small dipole moment or from isotopic species in natural abundance. An example of the latter is the carbon-13 isotope of a molecule. The one percent natural abundance of carbon-13 ordinarily places the transitions of the carbon-13 isotope near the limit of sensitivity of the microwave spectrometer.

2-7. Rotational Transition Intensities

The intensity of a rotational transition can be derived from a consideration of the Einstein coefficients for induced and spontaneous emission and of induced absorption. For a system in thermal equilibrium at a temperature T, the population ratio between two states is governed by the Boltzmann law.

$$\frac{N_2}{N_1} = \frac{g_2}{g_1}\exp(-hv_{12}/kT) \tag{2-114}$$

N_1 and N_2 are the populations of states 1 and 2 and v_{12} is their frequency separation. The Boltzmann distribution in its most general form contains the statistical weight factors g_i which express the degeneracies of the levels. In the absence of an external field, each rotational level labeled by the quantum number J is $2J + 1$-fold degenerate in the quantum number M. Contributions to the statistical weight factors also arise from the presence of identical nuclear spins in equivalent atomic positions. For low J values, the $2J + 1$ weight factor usually dominates, and the line intensity increases with J. At higher J values, the exponential term takes over and the intensity begins to decrease with J. This variation in intensity is apparent from resolved P and R branches in the vibration-rotation spectrum of molecules like hydrogen bromide and methane. However, this intensity variation is not always apparent in the rotational spectrum and the nuclear statistical weight contribution discussed in Section 2-8 is much more important. Here it is assumed that $g_1 = g_2 = 1$.

Under the influence of the radiation density per unit frequency interval $\rho(v)$, molecules are undergoing induced absorption and emission from $1 \rightarrow 2$ and $2 \rightarrow 1$, respectively, as well as spontaneous emission from $2 \rightarrow 1$. The probability of emission can be expressed as $A + B_{21}\rho(v)$, where A is the coefficient of spontaneous emission and B_{21} is the coefficient of induced emission. The probability of absorption is then $B_{12}\rho(v)$. For dynamic equilibrium to exist

$$N_2[A + B_{21}\rho(v)] = N_1 B_{12}\rho(v) \tag{2-115}$$

It is assumed that the coefficients of induced absorption and induced emission are equal.

$$B_{12} = B_{21} = B \tag{2-116}$$

If $\langle 2|\mathbf{\mu}|1 \rangle$ is the dipole matrix element connecting the levels 1 and 2,

$$A = \frac{64\pi^4 v_{12}^3}{3hc^3}|\langle 2|\mathbf{\mu}|1 \rangle|^2 \tag{2-117}$$

It can be shown that

$$\rho(v) = \frac{8\pi h v_{12}^3}{c^3} \frac{1}{\exp(hv_{12}/kT) - 1} \tag{2-118}$$

and

$$\frac{A}{B} = \frac{8\pi h v_{12}^3}{c^3} \tag{2-119}$$

where c is the velocity of light. Equation (2-118) is the radiation law derived by Planck and represents the thermal radiation associated with a black body.

For a monochromatic radiation field with incident power flow P through an area S [1581]

$$\rho(v) = \frac{P}{cS} \qquad (2-120)$$

The power of induced absorption is $N_1 h v_{12} BP/cS$ and the power of induced emission is $N_2 h v_{12} BP/cS$. The net absorption per unit path length is

$$P' = (N_1 - N_2) h v_{12} B \frac{P}{c} = (N_1 - N_2) \frac{8\pi^3 v_{12}}{3ch} |\langle 2|\boldsymbol{\mu}|1\rangle|^2 P \qquad (2-121)$$

For a gas at temperature T

$$P' \approx \frac{8\pi^3 N_1 v_{12}^2}{3ckT} |\langle 2|\boldsymbol{\mu}|1\rangle|^2 P \qquad (2-122)$$

The relaxation processes of excited molecules which are discussed briefly in Chapter 9 contribute to line broadening. Assuming a Van Vleck–Weisskopf line shape [204] for pressures where the absorption half-width Δv is much less than the transition frequency

$$\frac{P'}{P} = \int_0^\infty \gamma(v)\, dv = \pi \gamma_m \, \Delta v \qquad (2-123)$$

The absorption coefficient $\gamma(v)$ is usually expressed in cm^{-1}.

$$\gamma(v) = \frac{8\pi^2 N_1 |\langle 2|\boldsymbol{\mu}|1\rangle|^2 v_{12}^2 \, \Delta v}{3ckT[(v_{12} - v_0)^2 + \Delta v^2]} \qquad (2-124)$$

v_0 is the frequency of the center of the absorption line and $\Delta v = 1/(2\pi\tau)$. γ_m is the value of $\gamma(v)$ at the frequency of maximum absorption, and τ is the mean collision time between molecules. From (2-122)

$$\gamma_m = \frac{8\pi^2 N_1 v_{12}^2 |\langle 2|\boldsymbol{\mu}|1\rangle|^2}{3ckT \, \Delta v} \qquad (2-125)$$

The intensity is proportional to the square of the dipole matrix element between the two interacting levels. Equation (2-123) is the integrated line intensity; substituting (2-125) into (2-123) yields

$$\int_0^\infty \gamma(v)\, dv = \frac{8\pi^3 N_1 v_{12}^2 |\langle 2|\boldsymbol{\mu}|1\rangle|^2}{3ckT} \qquad (2-126)$$

2-8. Statistical Weights

The approximate total wave function for a molecule, excluding translation, may be written as the product of the individual functions describing the electronic, vibrational, rotational, and nuclear spin coordinates of the molecule.

$$\psi_{\text{total}} \approx \psi_E \psi_V \psi_R \psi_S \tag{2-127}$$

For a nondegenerate quantum-mechanical system, ψ_{total} can only remain unchanged or change sign for the interchange of two equivalent identical particles. This is true because the energy of the system and the probability distribution described by ψ_{total}^2 must remain unchanged for such an operation. For two identical particles to be equivalent, they must be exchanged by a symmetry operation of the molecular point group. The Pauli principle governs which set of wave functions is allowed. For the interchange of nuclei with half-integral spin only the antisymmetric class of functions will exist, while for the exchange of nuclei with integral nuclear spins only the totally symmetric functions are allowed. This holds only for ψ_{total}. The individual functions may have any symmetry which is consistent with the problem as long as their product has the required symmetry.

For a system with nondegenerate levels ψ_E, ψ_V, ψ_R, and ψ_S can be treated separately and then combined to form the appropriate wave functions. For degenerate levels, it may be necessary to treat a combination such as $\psi_R \psi_S$ as illustrated in Section 2-10c for NH_3.

The symmetry properties of the allowed wave functions of a rigid rotor are important in determining the quantum-statistical weights of its rotational energy levels. The weight factor for any given level will be the product of contributions from all the internal quantum numbers. The factor $(N_1 - N_2)$ in (2-121) can be evaluated from statistical mechanics. Relative populations of the two levels will depend on the energy difference and the statistical weight factor g of the partition function. These statistical weights may cause intensity variations in the spectrum which are useful in identifying rotational transitions.

Since rotational spectra in ground electronic and vibrational states are of interest, it is assumed below that ψ_E and ψ_V are totally symmetric. Of particular interest is that class of molecules which possesses one or more sets of identical nuclei that can be exchanged by a symmetry operation of the molecular point group. For n identical nuclei in one set, the total number of spin wave functions ψ_S is given by

$$N(\psi_S) = (2I + 1)^n \tag{2-128}$$

where I is the nuclear spin. These spin functions may be symmetric, antisymmetric, or degenerate. The relative weights of the energy levels are obtained by combining the spin functions with rotational functions of the proper symmetry. In states where ψ_E and ψ_V are not totally symmetric, their contributions to ψ_{total} must also be taken into account.

2-9. Nuclear Spin Statistics for Linear Molecules

A linear molecule can interchange identical equivalent nuclei by a symmetry operation only if it has symmetry $D_{\infty h}$. This class of molecules possesses a center of symmetry through which reflection of the identical particles may occur. The identical nuclei can also be exchanged by a 180° rotation. However, these operations are not possible for $C_{\infty v}$-type molecules such as OCS, where a rotation or reflection will not exchange equivalent nuclei. The presence of a center of symmetry precludes the existence of a nonzero permanent dipole moment and any pure rotational spectrum. Consequently, linear molecules which do have a permanent dipole moment will not show any intensity variation due to nuclear spin; however, nuclear effects in $D_{\infty h}$ molecules like CO_2 can be observed in the vibration-rotation spectrum.

For symmetric electronic and vibrational states, the rotational wave function for a $D_{\infty h}$ molecule is symmetric for even J values and antisymmetric for odd J values. The spin functions will depend on the number and spin of the equivalent nuclei. Nuclei with zero nuclear spin need not be considered, since they generate only one spin function. For two nuclei of spin $\frac{1}{2}$, (2-128) gives four spin functions. If 1 and 2 refer to the two nuclei and α and β to the two possible spin orientations for $I = \frac{1}{2}$, the proper molecular spin functions have the form $\alpha(1)\alpha(2)$, $\beta(1)\beta(2)$, and $(1/\sqrt{2})[\alpha(1)\beta(2) \pm \beta(1)\alpha(2)]$. For the interchange of nuclei 1 and 2 this gives three symmetric spin functions and one antisymmetric spin function. Since the total wave function (2-127) must change sign for the exchange of two half-integral spins, the antisymmetric rotational states combine with the symmetric spin functions, giving these levels a 3:1 weight advantage over the symmetric rotational states. For the exchange of two nuclei with $I = 1$, analogous reasoning gives a ratio of 6:3 favoring the symmetric rotational states.

2-10a. Nuclear Spin Statistics for Symmetric Tops

Symmetric top molecules have threefold or higher symmetry about their figure axes. For an n-fold axis, a rotation of $2\pi/n$ will interchange the n identical off-axis nuclei. In a similar manner identical nuclei can be interchanged by reflection through the n planes of symmetry which accompany the n-fold axis. The rotations which exchange identical nuclei and the identity operation form a subgroup of the molecular point group.

The rotational wave functions ψ_R belong to the irreducible representations of the rotational subgroup. An example is NH_3 which possesses C_{3v} symmetry. The rotational wave functions have the symmetry of the irreducible representations A and E of the rotational subgroup C_3. From (2-128) NH_3 has eight spin functions, and the correct wave functions will be formed by proper combinations of ψ_R and ψ_S.

2-10b. Rotational Wave Functions

For the rotational subgroup C_3 the behavior of ψ_R under a 120° rotation must be investigated. Examination of (2-51) shows that θ and ϕ are unaffected by the rotation while χ changes to $\chi \pm 2\pi/3$. The $2\pi/3$ rotation transforms the original wave functions ψ_{JKM} and ψ_{J-KM} to a new set $\tilde{\psi}_{JKM}$ and $\tilde{\psi}_{J-KM}$.

$$\begin{bmatrix} \tilde{\psi}_{JKM} \\ \tilde{\psi}_{J-KM} \end{bmatrix} = \begin{bmatrix} e^{2\pi i K/3} & 0 \\ 0 & e^{-2\pi i K/3} \end{bmatrix} \begin{bmatrix} \psi_{JKM} \\ \psi_{J-KM} \end{bmatrix} \tag{2-129}$$

ψ_R is totally symmetric when K is a multiple of three; the two sets of wave functions then become identical. The wave functions for $K = 3$ belong to A of the rotational subgroup C_3. The remaining wave functions formed when K is not a multiple of three belong to the irreducible representation E. They are degenerate because the rotation produces a wave function which is neither identical with nor opposite in sign to ψ_R. This degeneracy arises from the identical energy values obtained for $\pm K$. In a rigid symmetric rotor, levels where K is a multiple of three are also degenerate with the exception that this degeneracy may be removed by introducing nonrigid effects. The $K = 0$ levels are nondegenerate and belong to the irreducible representation A.

2-10c. Spin Wave Functions

Appropriate combinations of the eight elementary spin functions for molecules like NH_3 are illustrated in Table 2-9, where ↑ and ↓ represent the relative directions of the nuclear spin vectors. ↑ represents a spin of $\frac{1}{2}$ and ↓ indicates a spin of $-\frac{1}{2}$. (For ND_3 twentyseven spin states exist.) The first two wave functions $\psi(1)$ and $\psi(2)$ are clearly symmetric with respect to the exchange of protons, because all the spins are either $+\frac{1}{2}$ or $-\frac{1}{2}$. In the other six cases, interchange of two sets of spins in one spin function produces a function which is identical to one of the other five functions, i.e., these functions appear degenerate. By properly combining the degenerate rotational functions and the appropriate combinations of spin wave functions, a new set of functions $\psi_R \psi_S$ having the correct symmetry characteristics can be produced. These combinations are symmetric with respect to the two interchanges of identical nuclei which are equivalent to a 120° rotation. When K is not a multiple of three, the appropriate functions are

$$\psi_R \psi_S = \psi_{JKM}[\psi(3) + e^{2\pi Ki/3}\psi(4) + e^{4\pi Ki/3}\psi(5)]$$
$$\pm \psi_{J,-K,M}[\psi(3) + e^{-2\pi Ki/3}\psi(4) + e^{-4\pi Ki/3}\psi(5)] \tag{2-130}$$

$$\psi_R \psi_S = \psi_{JKM}[\psi(6) + e^{2\pi Ki/3}\psi(7) + e^{4\pi Ki/3}\psi(8)]$$

$$\pm \psi_{J,-K,M}[\psi(6) + e^{-2\pi Ki/3}\psi(7) + e^{-4\pi Ki/3}\psi(8)] \qquad (2\text{-}131)$$

From (2-130) and (2-131), functions symmetric to the interchange of two identical nuclei occur when the $+$ sign is used for even J values; antisymmetric functions are formed by using the $-$ sign. For odd values of J the

TABLE 2-9

SYMBOLIC REPRESENTATION OF THE EIGHT SPIN FUNCTIONS OF NH_3

	Symbolic spin orientations	Appropriate linear combinations of spin functions for $\psi_R\psi_S$
$\psi(1)$ $\psi(2)$	↑ ↑ ↑ ↓ ↓ ↓	$\alpha(1)\alpha(2)\alpha(3)$ $\beta(1)\beta(2)\beta(3)$
$\psi(3)$ $\psi(4)$ $\psi(5)$	↓ ↑ ↑ ↑ ↓ ↑ ↑ ↑ ↓	$\frac{1}{\sqrt{3}}[\beta(1)\alpha(2)\alpha(3) + \alpha(1)\beta(2)\alpha(3) + \alpha(1)\alpha(2)\beta(3)]$ $\frac{1}{\sqrt{6}}\Big[\beta(1)\alpha(2)\alpha(3) + \exp\Big(\pm\frac{2\pi Ki}{3}\Big)\alpha(1)\beta(2)\alpha(3)$ $+ \exp\Big(\pm\frac{4\pi Ki}{3}\Big)\alpha(1)\alpha(2)\beta(3)\Big]$
$\psi(6)$ $\psi(7)$ $\psi(8)$	↑ ↓ ↓ ↓ ↑ ↓ ↓ ↓ ↑	$\frac{1}{\sqrt{3}}[\alpha(1)\beta(2)\beta(3) + \beta(1)\alpha(2)\beta(3) + \beta(1)\beta(2)\alpha(3)]$ $\frac{1}{\sqrt{6}}\Big[\alpha(1)\beta(2)\beta(3) + \exp\Big(\pm\frac{2\pi Ki}{3}\Big)\beta(1)\alpha(2)\beta(3)$ $+ \exp\Big(\pm\frac{4\pi Ki}{3}\Big)\beta(1)\beta(2)\alpha(3)\Big]$

symmetries are reversed; the $+$ sign forms antisymmetric functions while the $-$ sign forms symmetric functions.

When K is a multiple of three, the exponentials reduce to unity and the functions are just

$$\psi_R \psi_S = (\psi_{JKM} \pm \psi_{J,-K,M})\psi(1) \qquad (2\text{-}132)$$

$$\psi_R \psi_S = (\psi_{JKM} \pm \psi_{J,-K,M})\psi(2) \qquad (2\text{-}133)$$

$$\psi_R \psi_S = (\psi_{JKM} \pm \psi_{J,-K,M})[\psi(3) + \psi(4) + \psi(5)] \qquad (2\text{-}134)$$

$$\psi_R \psi_S = (\psi_{JKM} \pm \psi_{J,-K,M})[\psi(6) + \psi(7) + \psi(8)] \qquad (2\text{-}135)$$

These combinations of rotational and spin functions indicate that there are twice as many wave functions possible for K as a multiple of three, than when K is not a multiple of three. This condition includes the levels for $K = 0$, where the combinations involving a minus sign vanish. The levels with K a multiple of three will have a weight factor twice that of the other levels. These statistics also hold for molecules like CH_3Cl and BF_3 where three nuclei of spin $\frac{1}{2}$ are interchanged by a 120° rotation. The latter is of less interest because it has no permanent dipole moment. For ND_3 the levels where K is a multiple of three are again favored in the ratio 11:8. In this case none of the $K = 0$ levels vanish, as will be seen in Chapter 7.

Up to this point the possibility of inversion which is discussed in Chapter 7 has not been considered. For molecules where inversion is prominent, ψ_V is symmetric for the lowest inversion level and antisymmetric for the next inversion level, i.e., these states are symmetric and antisymmetric, respectively, for inversion of the molecular configuration. Therefore, in the antisymmetric inversion states the $\pm$ signs in the combinations of $\psi_R \psi_S$ must be reversed to give the correct functions.

2-11a. Nuclear Spin Statistics for Asymmetric Tops

Asymmetric rotor molecules with a twofold symmetry axis can exchange two equivalent nuclei with a 180° rotation. If the two atoms are Bosons, the total wave function must be symmetric to the interchange. For Fermions, it must be antisymmetric. For a rigid asymmetric rotor, the rotational wave functions are all nondegenerate. This must be the case because the point groups to which asymmetric rotors can belong may possess no degenerate irreducible representations, i.e., there are no degenerate vibrations. Since the group which describes the molecular rotations is necessarily a subgroup of the molecular point group, it cannot have any degenerate irreducible representations. Similarly, there may be no more than two equivalent nuclei in one set, although there may be more than one set of equivalent pairs. $CH_2 = CF_2$ is an example of a molecule with two sets of identical nuclei which can be interchanged by a proper symmetry operation.

2-11b. Rotational Wave Functions

The symmetry of the rotational wave functions ψ_R is determined by the axis about which rotation occurs. For a particular rotational level the symmetry of ψ_R is obtained from the character table of the four group given in Table 2-4. As an example, consider the molecule F_2CO whose dipole moment lies along the b axis. The levels 1_{10} and 1_{01} are antisymmetric with respect to C_2^b while the 1_{11} level is symmetric under C_2^b. This occurs because the 1_{11} level belongs to B_b, and the 1_{10} and 1_{01} levels belong to B_c and B_a, respectively.

2-11c. Spin Wave Functions

As an example, consider the water molecule H_2O. There are $(2I + 1)^2$ or four spin functions. The relative spin orientations are shown in Table 2-10.

TABLE 2-10

SYMBOLIC REPRESENTATION OF THE FOUR SPIN FUNCTIONS OF H_2O

	Symbolic spin orientations	Correct form of spin functions
$\psi(1)$	↑ ↑	$\alpha(1)\alpha(2)$
$\psi(2)$	↓ ↓	$\beta(1)\beta(2)$
$\psi(3)$	↑ ↓⎱	$\dfrac{1}{\sqrt{2}}[\alpha(1)\beta(2) \pm \beta(1)\alpha(2)]$
$\psi(4)$	↓ ↑⎰	

$\psi(1)$ and $\psi(2)$ are symmetric with respect to spin interchange; interchange of spins in $\psi(3)$ produces neither $\psi(3)$, nor its negative. The same holds for $\psi(4)$. $\psi(3)$ and $\psi(4)$ are not proper spin functions and must be combined to form functions which are either symmetric or antisymmetric, since the degenerate case has been ruled out. The correct spin functions are then

$$\psi_S = \frac{1}{\sqrt{2}}[\alpha(1)\beta(2) \pm \beta(1)\alpha(2)] \tag{2-136}$$

The plus sign gives a symmetric ψ_S, while the minus sign gives an anti-symmetric ψ_S. The similarity between this case and the exchange of two identical protons in a linear molecule is evident. There are three symmetric and one antisymmetric spin functions. These must combine with the anti-symmetric and symmetric rotational functions, respectively. The anti-symmetric rotational states then have a statistical weight of three, compared to a weight of one for the symmetric rotational states.

For D_2O there exist nine spin functions. Six of these are symmetric, while the remaining three are antisymmetric. In this case the identical nuclei obey Bose–Einstein statistics and the total wave function must be symmetric for the interchange of two equivalent deuterons. The symmetric rotational wave functions are then paired with the symmetric spin functions, and the symmetric rotational levels have a 2:1 weight advantage over the antisymmetric levels.

In the general case of a spin I, there are $(2I + 1)(I + 1)$ symmetric spin functions and $(2I + 1)I$ antisymmetric spin functions. For two half-integral nuclei where Fermi–Dirac statistics apply, the statistical weight ratio for the symmetric:antisymmetric rotational levels is $I:I + 1$. For Bose–Einstein statistics, this ratio is $I + 1:I$.

When more than one pair of equivalent nuclei are exchanged by a $180°$ rotation, the statistics become more complex. If n_{si} and n_{ai} are the numbers of symmetric and antisymmetric functions for the ith pair of nuclei, the product

$$\prod_i^m (n_{si} + n_{ai}) \tag{2-137}$$

contains all the symmetric and antisymmetric spin functions. For m pairs of nuclei, the numbers of symmetric and antisymmetric functions obtained by grouping the terms in (2-137) are

$$n_{\text{sym}} = \frac{1}{2}\left[\prod_{i=1}^m (2I_i + 1)\right]\left[\prod_{i=1}^m (2I_i + 1) + 1\right] \tag{2-138}$$

$$n_{\text{antisym}} = \frac{1}{2}\left[\prod_{i=1}^m (2I_i + 1)\right]\left[\prod_{i=1}^m (2I_i + 1) - 1\right] \tag{2-139}$$

Choice of the correct rotational wave function will depend upon the identity of the nuclei exchanged. If an odd number of pairs of nuclei with half-integral spin are interchanged, the total wave function must change sign. This requires that functions of the opposite parity must combine. For interchange of an even number of half-integral pairs, the combining spin functions and rotational functions have the same parity.

2-12a. Dipole Matrix Elements

The intensity of a rotational transition is proportional to the square of the dipole moment matrix element which connects the two levels involved. The dipole matrix element can be expanded in terms of the dipole moment components along the X, Y, Z space-fixed axes.

$$\langle n|\mu|n'\rangle^2 = \langle n|\mu_X|n'\rangle^2 + \langle n|\mu_Y|n'\rangle^2 + \langle n|\mu_Z|n'\rangle^2 \tag{2-140}$$

Using the direction cosines ϕ_{Fg} relating the space-fixed axes F to the principal axes g, this expansion can be compared to an expansion in terms of dipole components along the principal axes.

$$\langle n|\mu_F|n'\rangle = \sum_g \mu_g \langle n|\phi_{Fg}|n'\rangle \tag{2-141}$$

The direction cosines are coefficients in the orthogonal transformation between the space-fixed axis system and the rotating principal axis system. If $\mathscr{P}_F$ and P_g are the angular momentum components in the two systems,

$$\mathscr{P}_F = \sum_g \phi_{Fg} P_g \tag{2-142}$$

$$P_g = \sum_F \phi_{Fg} \mathscr{P}_F \tag{2-143}$$

The ϕ_{Fg} become important when it is necessary to transfer the properties of a vector quantity between a space-fixed axis system and a molecule-fixed system or when treating an interaction between a space-fixed vector and a molecule-fixed vector such as is encountered in the Stark effect. It is possible to derive commutation rules between the various $\mathscr{P}_F$, P_g, and ϕ_{Fg} by expressing these quantities in terms of the Eulerian angles θ, ϕ, and χ.

$$P_i P_j - P_j P_i = -i\hbar P_k \tag{2-144}$$

$$\mathscr{P}_i \mathscr{P}_j - \mathscr{P}_j \mathscr{P}_i = i\hbar \mathscr{P}_k \tag{2-145}$$

$$\mathscr{P}_i \phi_{jg} - \phi_{jg} \mathscr{P}_i = -\mathscr{P}_j \phi_{ig} + \phi_{ig} \mathscr{P}_j = i\hbar \phi_{kg} \tag{2-146}$$

$$P_i \phi_{Fj} - \phi_{Fj} P_i = -P_j \phi_{Fi} + \phi_{Fi} P_j = -i\hbar \phi_{Fk} \tag{2-147}$$

$$\mathscr{P}_F \phi_{Fg} - \phi_{Fg} \mathscr{P}_F = P_g \phi_{Fg} - \phi_{Fg} P_g = 0 \tag{2-148}$$

$$\phi_{Fg} \phi_{F'g'} - \phi_{F'g'} \phi_{Fg} = 0 \tag{2-149}$$

Also,

$$P^2 = P_a^2 + P_b^2 + P_c^2 = \mathscr{P}_X^2 + \mathscr{P}_Y^2 + \mathscr{P}_Z^2 \tag{2-150}$$

$$P^2 P_g - P_g P^2 = P^2 \mathscr{P}_F - \mathscr{P}_F P^2 = 0 \tag{2-151}$$

$$HP_g - P_g H = H\mathscr{P}_F - \mathscr{P}_F H = 0 \tag{2-152}$$

By choosing a representation in which P^2, P_z, and $\mathscr{P}_Z$ are diagonal, the nonvanishing solutions to these equations are given in (2-26), (2-29), (2-30), and by

$$\langle JKM|\mathscr{P}_Y|JK, M + 1\rangle = -i\langle JKM|\mathscr{P}_X|JK, M + 1\rangle$$

$$= \frac{\hbar}{2}[J(J + 1) - M(M + 1)]^{1/2} \tag{2-153}$$

$$\langle JKM|\mathscr{P}_Z|JKM\rangle = \hbar M \tag{2-154}$$

Phase factors have been chosen to make P_y and $\mathscr{P}_Y$ real and positive, although $\mathscr{P}_X$ and P_x could have been made real and positive just as easily. The arbitrary choice of a phase factor cannot affect any of the physically significant results.

From these solutions and the above equations, it is possible to determine the complete quantum number dependence of the direction cosine elements. The solution of these equations has been presented in detail by Allen and Cross [34]. Each element can be separated in a symmetric rotor basis into three factors each having a different quantum number dependence.

$$\langle JKM|\phi_{Fg}|J'K'M'\rangle = \langle J|\phi_{Fg}|J'\rangle\langle JK|\phi_{Fg}|J'K'\rangle$$

$$\times \langle JM|\phi_{Fg}|J'M\rangle \qquad (2\text{-}155)$$

Values for each factor are tabulated in Table 2-11 [280].

2-12b. Dipole Matrix Elements for a Linear Molecule

In a linear molecule, the permanent dipole moment must lie along the molecular symmetry axis. The components of the total dipole moment μ along the space-fixed axes can be expressed in terms of the spherical polar coordinates θ and ϕ.

$$\mu_X = \mu \sin\theta \cos\phi \qquad (2\text{-}156)$$

$$\mu_Y = \mu \sin\theta \sin\phi \qquad (2\text{-}157)$$

$$\mu_Z = \mu \cos\theta \qquad (2\text{-}158)$$

The nonvanishing matrix components are found from the selection rules of (2-44) and from the wave functions for a linear molecule.

$$\langle JM|\mu_Z|J+1, M\rangle = \mu\left[\frac{(J+1)^2 - M^2}{(2J+1)(2J+3)}\right]^{1/2} \qquad (2\text{-}159)$$

$$\langle JM|\mu_X|J+1, M+1\rangle = -i\langle JM|\mu_Y|J+1, M+1\rangle$$

$$= -\frac{\mu}{2}\left[\frac{(J+M+2)(J+M+1)}{(2J+1)(2J+3)}\right]^{1/2} \qquad (2\text{-}160)$$

$$\langle JM|\mu_X|J+1, M-1\rangle = i\langle JM|\mu_Y|J+1, M-1\rangle$$

$$= \frac{\mu}{2}\left[\frac{(J-M+1)(J-M+2)}{(2J+1)(2J+3)}\right]^{1/2} \qquad (2\text{-}161)$$

The form of the total dipole matrix element depends on the degree of polarization of the radiation. For unpolarized radiation, the square of the dipole matrix element is independent of M, since the absorption of unpolarized radiation is not a function of molecular orientation. For $J \rightarrow J+1$

$$\langle n|\mu|n'\rangle^2 = \mu^2\frac{(J+1)}{(2J+1)} \qquad (2\text{-}162)$$

and for $J + 1 \rightarrow J$

$$\langle n'|\mu|n\rangle^2 = \mu^2 \frac{(J + 1)}{(2J + 3)} \tag{2-163}$$

If the radiation is polarized in the Z direction, the matrix elements for μ_X and μ_Y vanish and the matrix element results from μ_Z only.

$$\langle n|\mu|n'\rangle^2 = \langle JM|\mu_Z|J + 1, M\rangle^2 = \mu^2 \frac{(J + 1)^2 - M^2}{(2J + 1)(2J + 3)} \tag{2-164}$$

With the electric vector in the X or Y directions, the squared matrix elements are formed by squaring the elements in (2-160) and (2-161) for $M \rightarrow M + 1$ and $M \rightarrow M - 1$ transitions, respectively.

2-12c. Dipole Matrix Elements for a Symmetric Rotor

In a rigid symmetric top molecule, the dipole moment is again restrained to the figure axis. The dipole matrix elements can be evaluated from (2-155) and the factors in Table 2-11. The symmetric rotor selection rules force the elements μ_X and μ_Y to vanish (because they are off-diagonal in K), resulting in matrix elements involving μ_Z only.

$$\langle JKM|\mu_Z|J + 1, KM\rangle = \mu \left[\frac{[(J + 1)^2 - M^2][(J + 1)^2 - K^2]}{(J + 1)^2(2J + 1)(2J + 3)} \right] \tag{2-165}$$

$$\langle JKM|\mu_Z|JKM\rangle = \mu \frac{KM}{J(J + 1)} \tag{2-166}$$

$$\langle JKM|\mu_Z|J - 1, KM\rangle = \mu \left[\frac{[(J^2 - K^2)(J^2 - M^2)]}{J^2(4J^2 - 1)} \right]^{1/2} \tag{2-167}$$

Equation (2-166) applies to pure inversion transitions in symmetric tops such as ammonia, which are discussed at length in Chapter 7.

As a matter of interest, the matrix elements for unpolarized radiation are

$$\langle JKM|\mu|J + 1, KM\rangle^2 = \mu^2 \left[\frac{(J + 1)^2 - K^2}{(J + 1)(2J + 1)} \right] \tag{2-168}$$

$$\langle JKM|\mu|JKM\rangle^2 = \mu^2 \left[\frac{K^2}{J(J + 1)} \right] \tag{2-169}$$

$$\langle JKM|\mu|J - 1, KM\rangle^2 = \mu^2 \left[\frac{J^2 - K^2}{J(2J + 1)} \right] \tag{2-170}$$

TABLE 2-11

VALUES OF THE DIRECTION-COSINE MATRIX ELEMENTS IN A SYMMETRIC ROTOR BASIS^{a,b}

Matrix factor	$J' = J + 1$	$J' = J$	$J' = J - 1$
$\langle J \vert \phi_{Fg} \vert J' \rangle$	$[4(J+1)[(2J+1)(2J+3)]^{1/2}]^{-1}$	$[4J(J+1)]^{-1}$	$[4J[4J^2-1]^{1/2}]^{-1}$
$\langle JK \vert \phi_{Fz} \vert J'K \rangle$	$2[(J+K+1)(J-K+1)]^{1/2}$	$2K$	$-2[J^2-K^2]^{1/2}$
$\langle JK \vert \phi_{Fy} \vert J', K \pm 1 \rangle$ $= \mp i \langle JK \vert \phi_{Fx} \vert J', K \pm 1 \rangle$	$\mp [(J \pm K+1)(J \pm K+2)]^{1/2}$	$[(J \mp K)(J \pm K+1)]^{1/2}$	$\mp [(J \mp K)(J \mp K-1)]^{1/2}$
$\langle JM \vert \phi_{Zg} \vert J'M \rangle$	$2[(J+M+1)(J-M+1)]^{1/2}$	$2M$	$-2[J^2-M^2]^{1/2}$
$\langle JM \vert \phi_{Yg} \vert J', M \pm 1 \rangle$ $= \pm i \langle JM \vert \phi_{Xg} \vert J', M \pm 1 \rangle$	$\mp [(J \pm M+1)(J \pm M+2)]^{1/2}$	$[(J \mp M)(J \pm M+1)]^{1/2}$	$\mp [(J \mp M)(J \mp M-1)]$

^{a} From Cross et al. [280].
^{b} These matrix elements include an arbitrary choice of phase. This phase choice is identical to that of Cross et al. [280] and Schwendeman [314].

2-12d. Dipole Matrix Elements for an Asymmetric Rotor

The dipole matrix elements of an asymmetric rotor are not amenable to a closed form, in contrast to those for a linear or symmetric top. This is analogous to the situation concerning the asymmetric rotor energy levels which can not, in general, be expressed as an exact closed function of the quantum numbers and rotational constants. Using the energy problem as a guide, it seems reasonable that the symmetric rotor direction cosine matrix elements can be used to obtain the appropriate elements for an asymmetric rotor [280]. A transformation which produces a set of symmetric rotor basis functions belonging to the four group of the asymmetric rotor must be employed, since the symmetric rotor functions used to evaluate the matrix elements in Table 2-11 belong to the group D_∞. The Wang transformation defined in (2-98) provides the needed transformation properties.

$$\phi^S_{Fg} = X'\phi_{Fg}X \tag{2-171}$$

The direction cosine elements for an asymmetric rotor are now generated by applying the transformation which diagonalizes the energy matrix of an asymmetric rotor. Due to the factoring in (2-98), it is only necessary to find the transformation T which diagonalizes each energy submatrix.

$$T'HT = \Lambda \tag{2-172}$$

The direction cosine elements for an asymmetric rotor are then

$$\phi^A_{Fg} = T'\phi^S_{Fg}T = T'X'\phi_{Fg}XT \tag{2-173}$$

It is assumed that the transformation matrices for the two states which are connected are identical.

It is often important to know the symmetry properties of the direction cosine elements with respect to the four group of the asymmetric rotor. Table 2-12 lists the correlation of the direction cosine products with the asymmetric rotor wave functions under V.

TABLE 2-12

SYMMETRY OF THE DIRECTION-COSINE FACTORS

	K_{-1}	K_1	V
$\phi^2_{Za}, \phi^2_{Zb}, \phi^2_{Zc}$	e	e	A
$\phi_{Zc}\phi_{Zb}, \phi_{Za}$	e	o	B_a
$\phi_{Zc}\phi_{Za}, \phi_{Zb}$	o	o	B_b
$\phi_{Za}\phi_{Zb}, \phi_{Zc}$	o	e	B_c

Since the Wang transformation is diagonal in the quantum numbers J and M, it is of interest to determine the effect this transformation has on the $\langle JK|\phi_{Fg}|JK'\rangle$ factors. Schwendeman [314] has presented the direction cosine matrix for these K dependent terms in the Wang symmetric rotor basis, using a form conveniently adapted to machine calculations. When no external fields are present to perturb the molecule, the diagonalizing transformation T is also diagonal in J and M which allows the ϕ_{Fg}^S to separate into four submatrices analogous to (2-98), with each submatrix representing only one g value. Six $\langle J|J\rangle$ submatrices and twelve $\langle J|J + 1\rangle$ submatrices result with all eighteen reducible to one of five general forms. Blocks of the direction cosine matrix have been listed along with detailed instructions concerning their use [314].

The squares of the direction cosine matrices in the representation which diagonalizes the asymmetric rotor energy matrix have been tabulated for various intervals of κ[20, 280, 302]. The summation over M, M', and F is simplified in the absence of a perturbing field since X, Y, and Z are then equivalent, and the summation over F is accomplished by multiplying the summation for a particular F by three.

$$^gS_{J_\tau J'_{\tau'}} = \sum_{FMM'} |\langle J\tau M|\phi_{Fg}|J'\tau'M'\rangle|^2$$

$$= 3|\langle J|\phi_{Zg}|J'\rangle|^2 \times |\langle J\tau|\phi_{Zg}^A|J'\tau'\rangle|^2 \left[\sum_{MM'}|\langle JM|\phi_{Zg}|J'M'\rangle|^2\right] \quad (2\text{-}174)$$

The tabulated transition strength $^gS_{J_\tau J'_{\tau'}}$ can be defined in terms of the square of the dipole matrix element

$$^gS_{J_\tau J'_{\tau'}} = \frac{(2J + 1)|\langle J\tau|\mu_g|J'\tau'\rangle|^2}{\mu_g^2} \quad (2\text{-}175)$$

$$^gS_{J_\tau J'_{\tau'}}(\kappa) = {}^gS_{J'_{\tau'}J_\tau}(\kappa); \qquad {}^gS_{J_\tau J'_{\tau'}}(\kappa) = {}^{g'}S_{J_{-\tau}J'_{-\tau'}}(-\kappa) \quad (2\text{-}176)$$

Here g' may or may not differ from g. The rules for $g \to g'$ are

$$a \to c; \qquad c \to a; \qquad b \to b \quad (2\text{-}177)$$

It follows from Table 2-11 that the dipole matrix element is given by

$$|\langle J\tau M|\mu_g|J - 1, \tau'M\rangle|^2 = \frac{(J^2 - M^2)\mu_g^2}{J(2J + 1)(2J - 1)}{}^gS_{J_\tau,J-1_{\tau'}} \quad (2\text{-}178)$$

$$|\langle J\tau M|\mu_g|J\tau'M\rangle|^2 = \frac{M^2\mu_g^2}{J(J + 1)(2J + 1)}{}^gS_{J_\tau J_{\tau'}} \quad (2\text{-}179a)$$

$$|\langle J\tau M|\mu_g|J + 1, \tau'M\rangle|^2 = \frac{[(J + 1)^2 - M^2]\mu_g^2}{(J + 1)(2J + 1)(2J + 3)}{}^gS_{J_\tau,J+1_{\tau'}} \quad (2\text{-}179b)$$

2-13. Transition Strengths and Approximate Wave Functions for Near Symmetric Tops

For a near symmetric top, the asymmetry terms (2-73) are relatively small and may be treated as a perturbation to the symmetric rotor problem. This approach can be used [288] to evaluate direction cosine elements for molecules with asymmetries in the range $|\kappa| \geq 0.9$. As the degree of asymmetry increases, the validity of the perturbation approach is weakened. The approximate asymmetric rotor wave functions, which are generated in the process, often find use in other problems such as the determination of off-diagonal quadrupole coupling constants [592, 594]. Using the Wang functions in (2-95), where the $JM\gamma$ notation has been suppressed, the asymmetric rotor wave functions to second order are given as

$$\psi_K^{(2)} = [1 - (\alpha^2 + \beta^2)/2]S_K + \alpha S_{K-2} + \beta S_{K+2} + \mu S_{K-4} + \nu S_{K+4} \quad (2\text{-}180)$$

$$\alpha = \frac{\langle K|H_a|K-2\rangle}{E_K - E_{K-2}} \approx \delta \quad (2\text{-}181)$$

$$\beta = \frac{\langle K|H_a|K+2\rangle}{E_K - E_{K+2}} \approx \delta \quad (2\text{-}182)$$

$$\mu = \frac{\langle K-4|H_a|K-2\rangle\langle K-2|H_a|K\rangle}{(E_K - E_{K-4})(E_K - E_{K-2})} \approx \delta^2 \quad (2\text{-}183)$$

$$\nu = \frac{\langle K+4|H_a|K+2\rangle\langle K+2|H_a|K\rangle}{(E_K - E_{K+4})(E_K - E_{K+2})} \approx \delta^2 \quad (2\text{-}184)$$

The α and β terms constitute the first-order correction, while the μ and ν terms provide the second-order correction. For a near prolate rotor, δ is defined by (2-88) and approaches zero as the molecule approaches a prolate symmetric top. The direction cosine matrix elements which are needed to calculate the transition strengths are obtained by substituting the asymmetric rotor functions of (2-180) into $\int \psi_{J\tau}^* \phi_{Fg} \psi_{J'\tau'} \, d\tau$.

$$\langle J\tau|\phi_{Fg}^{(2)}|J'\tau'\rangle = \int \psi_{J\tau}^{(2)} \phi_{Fg} \psi_{J'\tau'}^{(2)} d\tau \quad (2\text{-}185)$$

The direction cosine matrix elements can now be written in terms of the direction cosine elements for a symmetric rotor. Using a near prolate rotor as an example,

$$\langle JK_{-1}K_1|\phi_{Fg}^{(2)}|J'K_{-1}K_1'\rangle$$

$$= [1 - (\alpha^2 + \beta^2 + \alpha'^2 + \beta'^2)/2]\langle JK_{-1}|\phi_{Fg}^{(0)}|J'K_{-1}'\rangle$$

$$+ \alpha\alpha'\langle J, K_{-1} - 2|\phi_{Fg}^{(0)}|J', K_{-1} - 2\rangle$$

$$+ \beta\beta'\langle J, K_{-1} + 2|\phi_{Fg}^{(0)}|J', K_{-1} + 2\rangle \quad (2\text{-}186)$$

TABLE 2-13

SECOND-ORDER EXPANSION COEFFICIENTS FOR THE PROLATE ASYMMETRIC ROTOR WAVE
FUNCTIONS IN (2-186) AND (2-187)[a]

	α	β
$K = 0$	0	$(\sqrt{2}/8) f^{1/2}(J, 1)\left[\delta + \dfrac{\delta^2}{2}\right]$
$K = 1, \gamma = 0$	0	$\dfrac{1}{16} f^{1/2}(J, 2)\left\{\delta + [16 + J(J + 1)]\dfrac{\delta^2}{32}\right\}$
$K = 1, \gamma = 1$	0	$\dfrac{1}{16} f^{1/2}(J, 2)\left\{\delta + [16 - J(J + 1)]\dfrac{\delta^2}{32}\right\}$
$K = 2, \gamma = 0$	$-(\sqrt{2}/8) f^{1/2}(J, 1)\left[\delta + \dfrac{\delta^2}{2}\right]$	$\dfrac{1}{24} f^{1/2}(J, 3)\left[\delta + \dfrac{\delta^2}{2}\right]$
$K = 2, \gamma = 1$	0	$\dfrac{1}{24} f^{1/2}(J, 3)\left[\delta + \dfrac{\delta^2}{2}\right]$
$K = 3, \gamma = 0$	$-\dfrac{1}{16} f^{1/2}(J, 2)\left\{\delta + [16 + J(J + 1)]\dfrac{\delta^2}{32}\right\}$	$\dfrac{1}{32} f^{1/2}(J, 4)\left[\delta + \dfrac{\delta^2}{2}\right]$
$K = 3, \gamma = 1$	$-\dfrac{1}{16} f^{1/2}(J, 2)\left\{\delta + [16 - J(J + 1)]\dfrac{\delta^2}{32}\right\}$	$\dfrac{1}{32} f^{1/2}(J, 4)\left[\delta + \dfrac{\delta^2}{2}\right]$
$K > 3$	$-\dfrac{1}{8}\dfrac{f^{1/2}(J, K - 1)}{(K - 1)}\left[\delta + \dfrac{\delta^2}{2}\right]$	$\dfrac{1}{8}\dfrac{f^{1/2}(J, K + 1)}{(K + 1)}\left[\delta + \dfrac{\delta^2}{2}\right]$

[a] From Ref. [288].

$$
\langle JK_{-1}K_1|\phi_{Fg}^{(2)}|J', K_{-1} + 1, K_1'\rangle
$$
$$
= [1 - (\alpha^2 + \beta^2 + \alpha'^2 + \beta'^2)/2]
$$
$$
\times \langle JK_{-1}|\phi_{Fg}^{(0)}|J', K_{-1} + 1\rangle + \alpha'\langle JK_{-1}|\phi_{Fg}^{(0)}|J', K_{-1} - 1\rangle
$$
$$
+ \beta\langle J, K_{-1} + 2|\phi_{Fg}^{(0)}|J', K_{-1} + 1\rangle
$$
$$
+ \alpha\alpha'\langle J, K_{-1} - 2|\phi_{Fg}^{(0)}|J', K_{-1} - 1\rangle
$$
$$
+ \beta\beta'\langle J, K_{-1} + 2|\phi_{Fg}^{(0)}|J', K_{-1} + 3\rangle \tag{2-187}
$$

Table 2-13 lists values of α and β for a near-prolate rotor. A similar treatment leads to values for the oblate case although H_s, H_a, and δ must be properly redefined.

CENTRIFUGAL DISTORTION, CORIOLIS COUPLING, AND
CHAPTER 3 | FERMI RESONANCE

3-1. Introduction

When high resolution microwave techniques are used to study the pure rotational spectrum of a molecule, it is realized that the rigid rotor theory developed in Chapter 2 is not sufficient to describe the observed spectrum. The molecular energy levels are not predicted exactly by rigid rotor theory but are influenced by perturbations such as those resulting from rotation-vibration interactions and centrifugal distortion. The deviations from a rigid rotor are usually small, and low J rotational lines are commonly displaced only a few megahertz from their rigid rotor positions or split into closely spaced multiplets. In some situations nonrigid effects can cause significant changes in the spectrum, such as large frequency shifts and complex energy level splittings. Typical examples are the rotational transitions of hydrazine [815] and methylamine [793], which show little immediate resemblance to rigid rotor spectra.

The discussion of the rigid rotor in Chapter 2 forms a convenient basis with which the detailed interactions affecting rotational energy levels may be treated. The present chapter deals with centrifugal distortion, Coriolis coupling, and Fermi resonance. Due to the simplicity of the spectrum and the presence of degenerate vibrational modes, these interactions are most frequently observed and studied in linear and symmetric top molecules. Extension to the asymmetric rotor brings an increase in algebraic complexity.

A large number of theoretical and experimental papers have been published concerning the aspects of vibration-rotation interactions in linear, symmetric, and asymmetric top molecules. From the detailed review of the field given by Nielsen [351] and the studies of Amat and Nielsen [354, 355, 357], it is obvious that a complete nonrigid analysis for a polyatomic molecule is quite involved; the Hamiltonian contains many possible interaction terms. As improved instrumentation leads to better resolution and sensitivity, high-order effects will become observable and important in detailed calculations. Only the perturbations directly affecting the rotational spectrum are mentioned here.

3-2. Classical Appearance of Centrifugal and Coriolis Forces

When a rotating-vibrating molecule is considered with respect to an axis system fixed in the molecule and rotating with it, two forces which perturb the rigid rotor energy levels are present. They are the centrifugal force and the Coriolis force. The Coriolis force is a vibration-rotation interaction, and it vanishes when rotation and vibration are completely separated. If $\mathbf{v}$ is the linear velocity of the molecule relative to the molecule-fixed axis system and ω is the angular velocity of rotation of the molecule-fixed system with respect to a space-fixed axis system, the Coriolis force is defined as

$$\mathbf{F}_\zeta = 2m\mathbf{v} \times \boldsymbol{\omega} \tag{3-1}$$

The centrifugal force differs from the Coriolis force because it does not vanish in the absence of vibrational motion. The centrifugal force on a mass m a distance r from the axis of rotation is

$$\mathbf{F}_c = m\omega^2 \mathbf{r} \tag{3-2}$$

The effects of centrifugal distortion are generally small for low J values but can reach the order of hundreds of megahertz for transitions between levels of high J. In linear and symmetric top molecules, systematic deviations from the calculated rigid rotor levels may usually be observed; in an asymmetric rotor, the deviations due to centrifugal distortion may not follow a simple pattern. To obtain a satisfactory correction for an asymmetric rotor, it is usually necessary to measure the deviation of a large number of transitions from their rigid rotor positions. Although large numbers of rotational transitions may be available for study in an asymmetric rotor, the higher J transitions for a linear or symmetric top may lie in the high frequency millimeter wave region where they are not as easily measured.

Under proper conditions, the Coriolis force can produce large changes in the rigid rotor energy levels. These deviations may occur as energy level splittings resulting from the removal of a degeneracy or as a shift of energy levels due to a near degeneracy. It is advantageous to present a classical representation of Coriolis and centrifugal effects so that better physical concepts of these interactions can be attained. Consider a slowly rotating plane [333] on which a molecular model is placed. The rotation of the plane represents the rotation of the molecule. From (3-1) the Coriolis force is proportional to the velocity of rotation. The normal vibrations of a linear XYZ molecule [2] consist of two nondegenerate stretching vibrations (v_1 and v_3) and a doubly degenerate bending mode (v_2). To a first approximation, the terminal atoms move in opposite directions in the v_1 mode and they move in the same direction in the v_3 mode.

When the plane is not rotating and any one of the vibrational modes is excited, the atoms move along straight lines and pass through their equilibrium positions simultaneously at the frequency of vibration. For purely harmonic modes of vibration, no coupling between normal vibrations can occur. Let the plane rotate slowly. This rotational velocity ω is necessarily much slower than the velocity v of the atoms during a pure vibration. As the molecule rotates, the loci of the atoms change from straight lines to the ellipses shown in Fig. 3-1. Due to the large differences in rotational and vibrational

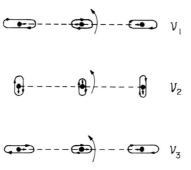

FIG. 3-1. Normal vibrations of a linear XYZ molecule and the effects of Coriolis coupling. v_2 is a degenerate bending vibration and the arrows attached to the atoms represent one component of the vibration. The other component (not shown) results from identical motions perpendicular to the plane of the paper. The ellipses whose eccentricity has been exaggerated for illustrative purposes show the paths of the nuclei in the presence of rotation (represented by the counter-clockwise arrows). In the absence of rotation, the ellipses degenerate to straight lines.

velocities, the eccentricity of the ellipses approaches unity. However, their finite width makes possible a coupling between vibrational modes. This can occur because the Coriolis force produces velocity components perpendicular to the normal velocity vectors. For v_1 and v_3 the new velocity components correspond to the degenerate bending mode v_2. The Coriolis force acting on v_1 tends to excite v_2 but at the frequency v_1; for v_3, the Coriolis force again excites v_2 but at the frequency of v_3. If v_2 and either v_1 or v_3 have approximately the same frequency, a strong Coriolis coupling interaction can occur. No coupling takes place between v_1 and v_3 or between the two components of v_2. This results from the effective absence of rotation about the figure axis in a linear molecule. These two components of the degenerate bending mode can couple in a symmetric top molecule where rotation about the figure axis is allowed. Figure 3-2 illustrates the effects of a Coriolis force on the degenerate bending mode in a symmetric top [2, 34]. When one of the degenerate components is excited, rotation about the figure axis produces vibrational components which excite the other component. Since the two frequencies are identical, the interaction may be very strong. This first-order interaction differs from the second-order effect in linear molecules because it does not vanish in the absence of rotation ($K = 0$).

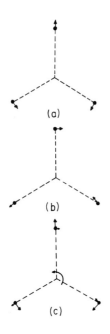

FIG. 3-2. Coriolis coupling of the degenerate bending vibrations in an XYZ_3 symmetric top. (a) and (b) illustrate the two components of the degenerate bending mode. (c) shows the coupling effect of the Coriolis force on the (a) mode as it tends to induce the (b) mode. In all three illustrations, the figure axis is perpendicular to the plane of the paper and only off-axis atoms are shown.

Even when rotation ceases about the figure axis, a vibrational angular momentum coupling the two degenerate components is present. However, the degeneracy is only lifted when rotation is present ($K \neq 0$) because the two modes of vibration still have the same energy when $K = 0$.

In asymmetric top molecules no exact vibrational degeneracies due to symmetry can occur. This precludes the existence of first-order Coriolis interactions, although second-order effects may be observed in the presence of near degeneracies involving energy levels with the proper symmetry.

Centrifugal distortion is pictured in a similar manner. As the molecule rotates, a force is exerted on the atoms in an attempt to produce linear motion. With nonrigid bonds in the molecule, the interatomic distances increase with the velocity of rotation and become functions of the rotational state of the molecule.

3-3. Centrifugal Distortion in a Linear Molecule

The transitions of a rigid linear rotor should occur at intervals of $2B$, where B is the rotational constant defined in (2-11). Observation of the actual spectrum of a linear molecule shows that the series of absorption lines tends to converge with increasing J. This effect is produced by centrifugal forces acting on the rotating molecule and forcing a slight increase in the bond length. The problem may be treated by applying perturbation theory to the distortion effects or by solving the Schroedinger equation for a nonrigid rotor. When only centrifugal effects are considered, the resulting energy expression is

$$E = hBJ(J + 1) - hDJ^2(J + 1)^2 \cdots \tag{3-3}$$

The meaning of B has not been fully defined. This rotational constant is an effective one and is not the equilibrium rotational constant of the molecule. B is a function of the vibrational state and can be written as B_v. v signifies the vibrational quantum number(s) dependence. When centrifugal distortion effects are included in B_v, it can be expressed as

$$B_v^c = B_e - \sum_i \alpha_i \left(v_i + \frac{d_i}{2} \right) - D_v J(J + 1) \tag{3-4}$$

The first two terms on the right side of the equation are equivalent to B in (3-3). D_v identifies the vibrational dependence of the distortion constant. α_i is the vibration-rotation constant for the ith vibrational mode, and the summation in (3-4) is over all vibrational degrees of freedom. v_i represents the vibrational quantum number. B_e is the equilibrium rotational constant and d_i represents the degeneracy of the ith vibration. The effects of zero-point vibrations are apparent from (3-4). For the ground state of the molecule, (3-4) reduces to

$$B_0^c = B_e - \sum_i \frac{\alpha_i d_i}{2} - DJ(J + 1) \tag{3-5}$$

Thus the ground state rotational constant is not equivalent to the equilibrium rotational constant. The distortion constant D (often called D_J) is small compared to the rotational constant. For low values of J the second term in (3-3) may sometimes be neglected. Table 3-1 gives a list of some experimentally determined centrifugal distortion constants for linear molecules.

By applying the selection rules for a linear molecule to (3-3), the frequency expression takes the form

$$v = 2B_v(J + 1) - 4D_v(J + 1)^3 \tag{3-6}$$

D is always positive, and its effect on the rotational energy levels of a linear molecule is illustrated in Fig. 3-3. For a diatomic molecule, the distortion constant has been evaluated in terms of the fundamental frequency of

TABLE 3-1

VALUES OF THE CENTRIFUGAL DISTORTION
CONSTANT D IN THE GROUND STATES OF SOME
LINEAR MODELS

	D(kHz)	Reference
NaBr^{79}	~ 7	[1281]
CsBr^{79}	0.27	[1281]
KI^{127}	1.0	[1281]
Rb^{85}Br^{79}	0.4	[1281]
Rb^{85}I^{127}	0.23	[1281]
N^{15}O^{16}	140	[1316]
N$_2$O	5.7	[1210]
HCN	~ 100	[1141]
FCN	5.3	[1510]
Br^{79}CN	0.9	[379]
Br^{81}CN	0.8	[379]
ICN	0.9	[379]
HCP	~ 30	[1666]
DCP	~ 20	[1666]
OCS	1.31	[92]
OCSe	0.8	[1109]

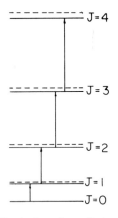

FIG. 3-3. Centrifugal distortion effects on the rotational energy levels of a linear molecule. Rigid rotor levels are shown as dashed lines and the actual energy levels are represented by solid lines.

vibration and the equilibrium rotational constant [331].

$$D = 4B_e^3/\omega^2 \tag{3-7}$$

For a linear XYZ triatomic molecule [340],

$$D = 4B_e^3\left(\frac{\zeta_{21}^2}{\omega_3^2} + \frac{\zeta_{23}^2}{\omega_1^2}\right) \tag{3-8}$$

ζ_{21} and ζ_{23} are the Coriolis coupling constants of the bending mode related to the fundamental frequencies ω_1 and ω_3 and are given in (3-32) and (3-33).

Based on the definitions in Section 3-4 and the general centrifugal distortion treatment in Section 3-12, D for a linear molecule may be expressed as a function of the force constants F_{ij} and the internal symmetry coordinates S_i [395]. From (3-12),

$$I_1 = 2\sum_i m_i z_i^2$$

$$D = \frac{8\pi^4 B_e^4}{h} \sum_{ij} \frac{\partial I_1}{\partial S_i} (F^{-1})_{ij} \frac{\partial I_1}{\partial S_j} \tag{3-9}$$

3-4. Centrifugal Distortion in Symmetric Top Molecules

Just as in a linear molecule, rotation in a symmetric top is accompanied by centrifugal forces which tend to alter the effective moments of inertia. For rotation about any axis in the molecule, this dynamical effect forces the atoms away from the axis of rotation and increases the moment of inertia about that axis. The centrifugal effects enter the energy level expression as higher powers of $J(J + 1)$ and K. For a prolate rotor,

$$E/h = BJ(J + 1) + (A - B)K^2 - D_J J^2(J + 1)^2 - D_K K^4$$
$$- D_{JK}J(J + 1)K^2 - \cdots \tag{3-10}$$

Dependence of the rotational constants on the vibrational state is assumed implicitly. The correction terms for centrifugal distortion are found to depend only on even powers of the angular momentum. This must be the case, because the distortion effects do not depend on the direction of rotation about any axis.

For a rigid symmetric top, (2-70) indicates that the allowed transitions have no K dependence. This K degeneracy can be partially lifted by a non-zero D_{JK} term which allows K^2 to enter the rotational frequency expression. From (3-10) the frequencies of a symmetric top molecule exhibiting detectable centrifugal distortion effects are

$$\nu = 2B(J + 1) - 2D_{JK}(J + 1)K^2 - 4D_J(J + 1)^3 - \cdots \tag{3-11}$$

Although the D values are much smaller than the rotational constant B, the individual $\Delta K = 0$ components for a particular $J \to J + 1$ transition sometimes can be resolved with high resolution microwave techniques. Table 3-2

TABLE 3-2

CENTRIFUGAL DISTORTION CONSTANTS FOR SOME SYMMETRIC TOP MOLECULES

	D_J (kHz)	D_{JK} (kHz)	Reference
CF_3H	11.3	−18.0	[1379]
CH_3F	59	445	[390]
CD_3F	33	228	[1162]
CH_3Cl	18.0	198	[379]
CH_3Cl^{37}	27	184	[379]
CH_3I	6.3	99	[390]
CH_3Br	10	128	[379, 390]
CF_3Cl	0.59	2.06	[404]
CF_3Br	−	1.3	[1204]
CF_3I	−	0.6	[1137]
SiF_3H	7.55	−12.4	[1379]
SiF_3Br	−	0.8	[1176]
CH_3CN	3.81	176.9	[442]
CF_3CN	0.306	5.81	[1379]
$CH_3Hg^{198}Cl$	0.241	21.0	[1312]
H_3CCCH	2.96	162.9	[1379]
D_3CCCD	∼2	90	[1336]
$H_3CCCCCH$	0.07	19.8	[1318]
$D_3CCCCCD$	0.1	13.5	[1318]
AsF_3	−	−9	[1239]
OPF_3	1.02	1.28	[1379]
$(CH_3)_3N$	5	∼0	[690]
$(CH_3)_3P$	3.0	−	[691]
$(CH_3)_3As$	∼3	∼0	[1457]
$(CH_3)_3CH$	∼11	−	[691]
$(CH_3)_3CF$	1.8	−	[691]

lists some experimentally determined distortion constants for symmetric top molecules. Since B tends to decrease due to the centrifugal force, D_J should always be positive. D_{JK} may have either sign. The centrifugal distortion constants can be expressed in terms of the moments of inertia (molecular structure) and molecular force constants of the molecule. However, a theoretical calculation of these constants is very difficult except for the simplest structures.

Assuming the harmonic oscillator approximation for symmetric top molecules with C_{3v} symmetry, Wilson [395] has given explicit formulas for the distortion constants D_J, and D_{JK}, and D_K. This formulation is based on the general development [386] discussed in Section 3-12. Defining the terms

$$I_1 = I_b + I_c = \sum_\alpha m_\alpha(x_\alpha^2 + y_\alpha^2 + 2z_\alpha^2) \tag{3-12}$$

$$I_2 = I_b - I_c = \sum_\alpha m_\alpha(x_\alpha^2 - y_\alpha^2) \tag{3-13}$$

$$I_3 = \sum_\alpha m_\alpha(x_\alpha^2 + y_\alpha^2) \tag{3-14}$$

$$I_4 = 2\sum_\alpha m_\alpha y_\alpha z_\alpha \tag{3-15}$$

where the z axis corresponds with the a axis (figure axis),

$$D_J = \frac{8\pi^4}{h}B_e^4\left[\sum_{i,j}\frac{\partial I_1}{\partial S_i}(F^{-1})_{ij}\frac{\partial I_1}{\partial S_j} + \sum_{i,j}\frac{\partial I_2}{\partial S_i}(F^{-1})_{ij}\frac{\partial I_2}{\partial S_j}\right] \tag{3-16}$$

$$D_{JK} = -2D_J + \frac{32\pi^4 A_e^2 B_e^2}{h}\left[\sum_{i,j}\frac{\partial I_3}{\partial S_i}(F^{-1})_{ij}\frac{\partial I_3}{\partial S_j} + \sum_{i,j}\frac{\partial I_4}{\partial S_i}(F^{-1})_{ij}\frac{\partial I_4}{\partial S_j}\right] \tag{3-17}$$

$$D_K = -D_J - D_{JK} + \frac{32\pi^4 A_e^4}{h}\sum_{ij}\frac{\partial I_3}{\partial S_i}(F^{-1})_{ij}\frac{\partial I_3}{\partial S_j} \tag{3-18}$$

I_b and I_c are regarded as instantaneous moments of inertia. The S_i are internal symmetry coordinates, and F_{ij} is an element of the force constant matrix consistent with the S_i, S_j [21]. The symmetry of the problem must be taken into account in carrying out the indicated summations. The derivatives of I_1 and I_3 are nonzero only for internal symmetry coordinates which have the symmetry A_1 of C_{3v}. Similarly, I_2 and I_4 derivatives vanish unless the S_i have symmetry E.

When centrifugal distortion is treated in rotational spectra of excited vibrational states, an expression analogous to (3-10) is valid only if the excited state rotational constants are used.

For XYZ_3 and YZ_3 molecules, the sign of D_{JK} is apparently determined by the position of the center of mass with respect to the YZ_3 tetrahedron. D_{JK} generally takes positive values when the center of mass lies outside the YZ_3 tetrahedron and it has negative values in those cases where the center of mass lies inside the tetrahedron. The first group includes CH_3F, CF_3I, and F_3CCCH. The second includes NH_3, AsF_3, and CF_3H. Some theoretical calculations of the centrifugal distortion constants for $YZ_3{}^\dagger$ and XYZ_3 molecules have been carried out by Slawsky and Dennison [375]; Dowling et al. [393, 396] have extended the XYZ_3 case.

$\dagger$ For a planar symmetric top the constants D_J, D_{JK}, and D_K are no longer independent [401].

$$D_{JK} = -\tfrac{2}{3}(D_J + 2D_K)$$

In some situations, the first-order constants D_J and D_{JK} are inadequate; D_J shows an apparent J dependence [404] and the distortion correction must be extended to a higher order. When second-order distortion constants are introduced, the frequency expression (3-11) becomes

$$v = 2B(J + 1) - 2D_{JK}(J + 1)K^2 - 4D_J(J + 1)^3 + H_{JJJ}(J + 1)^3$$
$$\times [(J + 2)^3 - J^3] + 4H_{JJK}(J + 1)^3 K^2 + 2H_{JKK}(J + 1)K^4 \quad (3-19)$$

H_{JJJ}, H_{JJK}, and H_{JKK} are the second-order distortion constants. These higher-order terms usually are needed only for high J transitions.

Rotational distortion in symmetric and linear molecules has been treated through the introduction of terms in the total angular momentum $J(J + 1)$ and in K^2, the rotational angular momentum about the figure axis. For an asymmetric top molecule K is no longer a good quantum number and a more detailed approach is necessary. The vibration-rotation Hamiltonian [335] is first derived and then treated for the case of a nonvibrating molecule. This more general approach gives essentially the same results for linear and symmetric rotors as have been obtained here.

3-5. The Coriolis Coupling Constant

The Coriolis coupling constant $\zeta_{ij}^{(\alpha)}$ represents the coupling through rotation of two normal vibrational modes Q_i and Q_j. They are proportionality constants which measure the amount of angular momentum along the α axis produced by vibration-rotation interaction. For a molecule, the vibration-rotation interaction can be described by the matrix $\zeta^{(\alpha)}$ (an array of the elements $\zeta_{ij}^{(\alpha)}$). These matrices are governed by a set of rules which have been presented systematically by Meal and Polo [421, 422]. Once the $\zeta_{ij}^{(\alpha)}$ are determined, they provide information for the normal coordinate analysis and for the determination of molecular potential constants.

The origin of the Coriolis coupling constants can be found in the explicit form of the vibration-rotation constants α_i. α_i has been written as [2]

$$\alpha_i = \alpha_i^{(\text{harmonic})} + \alpha_i^{(\text{anharmonic})} + \alpha_i^{(\text{Coriolis})} \quad (3-20)$$

Resonant terms of the form $N\zeta_{ij}^2/(\omega_i^2 - \omega_j^2)$ appear in the expression for $\alpha_i^{(\text{Coriolis})}$ and couple the modes ω_i and ω_j. If ζ_{ij}^2 is nonvanishing and ω_i and ω_j are nearly degenerate, terms of this form can provide large contributions to α_i and to the rotational constant in (3-4). The zeta matrices may be defined in terms of the transformation between the mass-weighted Cartesian coordinates $\mathbf{q}$ and the normal coordinates $\mathbf{Q}$.

$$\mathbf{Q} = \mathbf{lq} \quad (3-21)$$

In terms of the **l** vectors and the unit vector $\mathbf{e}_\alpha$,

$$\zeta_{ij}^{(\alpha)} = \sum_a (\mathbf{l}_{ia} \times \mathbf{l}_{ja}) \cdot \mathbf{e}_\alpha \qquad (3\text{-}22)$$

The summation is over the atoms of the molecule. The $\zeta_{ij}^{(\alpha)}$ are subject to a series of sum rules [420–422] which are independent of the potential constants and depend only on the atomic masses and molecular geometry.

Coriolis coupling can affect the spectra of linear, symmetric and asymmetric top molecules, although its presence may be more pronounced in symmetric tops where first-order effects are possible. Vibration-rotation bands in the infrared often show pronounced deviations due to Coriolis interactions. Its effect on the pure rotational spectrum is evident in the following sections.

3-6a. *l*-Type Doubling in Linear Molecules

A linear molecule with N atoms exhibits $3N - 5$ normal vibrations. In the ground vibrational state, only the zero-point vibrations are excited. Absorption of radiation of the appropriate wave length can lift a molecule into one of its excited vibrational states. A vibrational mode which has an important effect on the rotational spectrum of a linear molecule is the degenerate bending vibration v_2 illustrated in Fig. 3-1. Although a rigid linear molecule effectively has no rotational angular momentum along its figure axis, excitation of the degenerate bending mode can provide a component of vibrational angular momentum along this axis. It is convenient to describe a linear molecule in one of these states by the two quantum numbers v_i and l_i. l_i represents the component of internal angular momentum excited along the internuclear axis by v_i, the vibrational quantum number for the degenerate bending mode. l_i can never exceed v_i. l_i can assume the possible values $\pm v_i$, $\pm(v_i - 2)$, $\pm(v_i - 4), \ldots, \pm 1$, or 0. To the zeroth order of approximation, the vibrational energy is independent of l_i. However, the rotational energy depends on l_i^2 because l_i has some of the same characteristics as the quantum number K in a symmetric top.

$$E = hB_v[J(J + 1) - l^2] - hD_v[J(J + 1) - l^2]^2 \qquad (3\text{-}23)$$

In addition, the anharmonic terms in the potential function also depend on l_i^2 in the second order [351]. The $(v_i + 1)$-fold degeneracy in l_i is split into $(v_i + 1)/2$ components for odd v_i and $1 + (v_i/2)$ values for even v_i. Thus far each energy level is still two-fold degenerate in l_i, analogous to the K degeneracy in a symmetric top. In the most interesting case, $v_i = 1$ and $l_i = \pm 1$. If K is defined as the total angular momentum along the symmetry axis, $K = l$.

An investigation of the spectrum of a linear molecule indicates that a rotation-vibration interaction exists which tends to remove the $\pm l_i$ degeneracy. Lifting of this degeneracy may be viewed as the effect of different Coriolis interactions between molecular rotation and the two components of the degenerate bending mode. For the triatomic in Fig. 3-1, it was shown that a component of v_2 can couple with v_3 as a result of a Coriolis force. This is true because the excited vibrational mode is perpendicular to the rotational angular momentum. However, for the component of v_2 parallel to the rotational angular momentum, the Coriolis force vanishes. This difference in Coriolis interactions is sufficient to lift the l degeneracy. Because the Coriolis force is proportional to the rotational frequency, the l-type splitting is expected to increase with increasing J. The effect of l-type doubling on the rotational energy levels of OCS in the first excited bending mode is shown in Fig. 3-4 for the $J = 1 \rightarrow 2$ transition. The selection rules governing transitions between levels split by l-type doubling are discussed in Section 3-8.

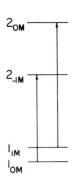

FIG. 3-4. Splitting produced by l-type doubling in the $J = 1 \rightarrow 2$ transition of the first excited bending mode of a linear molecule. Figure 8-10 shows the effects of an external electric field. Each sublevel is identified as $J_{\tau M}$. The identification of K_{-1} and K_1 used to calculate τ is discussed in Section 3-8.

The splitting may also be compared to K doubling in a near-symmetric top molecule. In a degenerate excited state, the molecule has an average structure which is nonlinear. The spectrum is then treated like that of an asymmetric rotor where the K degeneracy has been lifted and the magnitude of the splitting decreases with increasing K. The increase in the splitting with J corresponds to an analogous increase in the K doubling with J.

Nielsen [351] has derived the Hamiltonian to second-order for vibration-rotation interactions in a polyatomic molecule and separated it into three terms.

$$H = H^{(0)} + H^{(1)} + H^{(2)} \tag{3-24}$$

$H^{(0)}$ represents the zeroth-order problem in which the rotational and vibrational coordinates are completely separable. $H^{(1)}$ and $H^{(2)}$ are the first- and second-order perturbation Hamiltonians, respectively. The part of $H^{(2)}$ which causes *l*-type doubling in the second-order approximation has the form [351, 425]

$$H'^{(2)} = \sum_{\alpha} A'_v P_\alpha^2 + {\sum_{\alpha,\beta}}' B'_v P_\alpha P_\beta + \cdots \tag{3-25}$$

A'_v and B'_v are functions of the equilibrium moments of inertia, Coriolis coupling constants, normal coordinates and their transformation coefficients, and the vibrational frequencies. The second summation is for $\alpha \neq \beta$.

Equation (3-25) holds for a general polyatomic molecule which possesses axial symmetry and can be simplified in the case of the degenerate modes mentioned above. The nonvanishing matrix elements for linear and axially symmetric molecules are[†]

$$\langle v_s l_s K | H'^{(2)} | v_s, l_s \pm 2, K \pm 2 \rangle$$

$$= -h(B_e^2/2\omega_s)C'[J(J+1) - K(K \pm 1)]^{1/2}[J(J+1)$$

$$- (K \pm 1)(K \pm 2)]^{1/2}[(v_s \mp l_s)(v_s \pm l_s + 2)]^{1/2} \tag{3-26}$$

C' is a simplified form of A' and B'. The subscript s is retained to remain consistent with the literature. When $|l| = 1$, these matrix elements tend to remove the $\pm l$ degeneracy. For a linear molecule, the matrix elements are greatly simplified.

$$\langle v_s, l_s = \pm 1, K = \pm 1 | H'^{(2)} | v_s, l_s = \mp 1, K = \mp 1 \rangle$$

$$= h(B_e^2/2\omega_s)\{1 + 4 \sum_{s'} (\zeta_{ss'}^{(x)})^2 \omega_s^2/(\omega_{s'}^2 - \omega_s^2)\}(v_s + 1)J(J+1)$$

$$= q_0(v_s + 1)J(J+1)h \tag{3-27}$$

For linear molecules [422]

$$\sum_{s'} (\zeta_{ss'}^{(x)})^2 = 1 \tag{3-28}$$

The actual splitting of the *l*-type doublet can now be calculated. The secular determinant in terms of frequencies is

$$\begin{vmatrix} v_0 - \varepsilon & q_0(v_s + 1)J(J+1) \\ q_0(v_s + 1)J(J+1) & v_0 - \varepsilon \end{vmatrix} = 0 \tag{3-29}$$

[†] These matrix elements lead to what is called rotational *l*-type doubling. Other terms in $H'^{(2)}$ can produce a purely vibrational interaction called vibrational *l*-type doubling. Matrix elements producing this interaction have the form $\langle v_s l_s l_{s'} \cdots | H'^{(2)} | v_s, l_s \pm 2, l_{s'} \mp 2 \cdots \rangle$ [437].

v_0 is the frequency of the unsplit transition and the roots are

$$\varepsilon = v_0 \pm q_0(v_s + 1)J(J + 1) \tag{3-30}$$

The resultant splitting is then

$$\Delta v = 2q_0(v_s + 1)J(J + 1) = 2qJ(J + 1) \tag{3-31}$$

q is called the l-type doubling coefficient. q_0 has been defined as $(B_e^2/2\omega_s)$ $\{1 + 4\Sigma_{s'}(\zeta_{ss'}^{(x)})^2\omega_s^2/(\omega_{s'}^2 - \omega_s^2)\}$. Amat *et al.* [435] have suggested that q_0 should be defined as the negative of this quantity.

For $l_s = 0$, no degeneracy exists. When $l_s > \pm 1$, the l doubling is significantly reduced. For singlet states, it is of the order of $B_e(B_e/\omega_s)^{2l_s - 1}$ which greatly diminishes the splitting for $|l| > 1$. As an illustration for linear XYZ molecules, Nielsen [340] expressed the Coriolis coupling constants as

$$\zeta_{21}^{(x)} = -\zeta_{21}^{(y)} = -\left[\frac{M_x M_z}{\sigma I^e}\right]^{1/2}(z_x^e - z_z^e)\cos\gamma - \left[\frac{M_y \Sigma}{\sigma I^e}\right]^{1/2} z_y^e \sin\gamma \tag{3-32}$$

$$\zeta_{23}^{(x)} = -\zeta_{23}^{(y)} = \left[\frac{M_x M_z}{\sigma I^e}\right]^{1/2}(z_x^e - z_z^e)\sin\gamma - \left[\frac{M_y}{\sigma I^e}\right]^{1/2} z_y^e \cos\gamma \tag{3-33}$$

where

$$\sigma = M_x + M_z \tag{3-34}$$

$$\Sigma = M_x + M_y + M_z \tag{3-35}$$

$$\tan 2\gamma = 2k_4/(k_1 - k_3) \tag{3-36}$$

$$k_1 = [K_1(M_z/\sigma)^2 + K_2(M_x/\sigma)^2]/\mu_1 \tag{3-37}$$

$$k_3 = (K_1 + K_2)/\mu_3 \tag{3-38}$$

$$k_4 = [-K_1(M_z/\sigma) + K_2(M_x/\sigma)]/(\mu_1\mu_3)^{1/2} \tag{3-39}$$

$$\mu_1 = M_x M_y/(M_x + M_z) \tag{3-40}$$

$$\mu_3 = M_y\sigma/\Sigma \tag{3-41}$$

The K_i are valence force constants, the z_i^e are equilibrium coordinates, and the M_i are atomic masses.

Vibrational dependence of the l-type doubling constants for linear XYZ molecules has been considered by Morino and Nakagawa [444]. It is sometimes possible to use the v dependence of q as a check on cubic and quartic potential constants, and in the presence of a strong resonance interaction, it may be possible to use it to estimate dominant anharmonic terms.

3-6b. Direct *l*-Type Transitions

For some linear molecules, the *l*-type doubling constant q is large and transitions between l components of a particular J level may be observed in the microwave region. Because J and v_2 do not change for this type of transition, it is possible to obtain a direct measure of q for each rotational state in which a transition is observed. For HCN [433, 436], q varies with low J by decreasing slightly as J increases.

The energy of a linear molecule is modified by centrifugal distortion effects according to (3-3). Considering these centrifugal distortion effects, q may be written as

$$q = \frac{(B_v^c)^2}{2\omega_2}\left[1 + 4\sum_{s'}\zeta_{2s'}^2\left(\frac{\omega_2^2}{\omega_{s'}^2 - \omega_2^2}\right)\right](v_2 + 1) \qquad (3\text{-}42)$$

The change in q with respect to J is then

$$\frac{\Delta q}{\Delta J} = -\left(\frac{4q}{B_v^c}\right)D_v(2J + 1) \qquad (3\text{-}43)$$

Unfortunately, this expression gives only an order of magnitude estimate of the observed Δq for $\Delta J = 1$. Westerkamp [433] used an expression of the form given by (3-31) with $q' = 2q$,

$$v = q'J(J + 1) = [q'_{J=0} - rJ(J + 1)]J(J + 1) \qquad (3\text{-}44)$$

r is of the order of $q(B/\omega_2)^2 \approx 10^{-5}q$. Some of the observed transitions between *l*-type doublet components of HCN are listed in Table 3-3.

TABLE 3-3
DIRECT *l*-TYPE DOUBLING TRANSITIONS
OBSERVED IN THE SPECTRUM OF HCN[a]

J	Measured frequency (MHz)
1	448.947
2	1346.758
3	2693.349
4	4488.475
5	6731.881
6	9423.3
8	16147.8
9	20181.4
10	24660.4
11	29585.1
12	34953.5

[a] From Refs. [431, 432, 434].

3-7a. Degenerate Coriolis Splitting

In symmetric top molecules both first- and second-order Coriolis splittings may occur [2, 418, 426]. Symmetric tops possess a degenerate bending mode similar to that in linear molecules. This vibration can produce an angular momentum along the figure axis. The internal angular momentum along the symmetry axis is given by L, the rotational momentum of the molecular frame,

$$L = |K - \zeta l| \qquad (3\text{-}45)$$

K is the total angular momentum along the axis and $K \geq l$.

In symmetric top molecules, the degenerate Coriolis interaction for $K \neq 0$ produces energy level splittings. The magnitude of the splitting depends on the Coriolis coupling constant ζ, and the components are identified by the sign of the product Kl. These splittings may be explained by a consideration of the Hamiltonian of the system [419].

The zeroth-order Hamiltonian, which represents complete uncoupling of vibration and rotation, can be written for a prolate top as

$$\mathbf{H}^{(0)} = \frac{1}{2I_b}(\mathbf{P}_b^2 + \mathbf{P}_c^2) + \left(\frac{1}{2I_a}\right)\mathbf{P}_a^2 + \mathbf{H}_v \qquad (3\text{-}46)$$

$\mathbf{H}_v$ is the vibrational energy in a harmonic oscillator representation. The basis functions are formed by products of the symmetric rotor functions and a set of harmonic oscillator functions.

$$\psi^{(0)} = \Theta(\theta)\exp(iK\chi)\exp(iM\phi)\prod_r \psi_{v_r}(Q_r) \qquad (3\text{-}47)$$

Q_r is the rth normal coordinate, and v_r is the vibrational quantum number. The unperturbed energy $E^{(0)}$ is then

$$E^{(0)} = hBJ(J + 1) + h(A - B)K^2 + \sum_r h\left(v_r + \frac{d_r}{2}\right)v_r \qquad (3\text{-}48)$$

v_r is the frequency corresponding to Q_r, and d_r is the degree of degeneracy. The perturbation terms for vibrations of small amplitude are given by

$$\mathbf{H}^{(1)} = -\frac{\mathbf{P}_b\mathbf{p}_b + \mathbf{P}_c\mathbf{p}_c}{I_b} - \frac{\mathbf{P}_a\mathbf{p}_a}{I_a} + \frac{\mathbf{p}_b^2 + \mathbf{p}_c^2}{2I_b} + \frac{\mathbf{p}_a^2}{2I_a} \qquad (3\text{-}49)$$

The p_i are vibrational angular momenta in the molecule-fixed principal axis system. The first-order energy correction from perturbation theory is simply

$$E^{(1)} = \int \psi^{(0)*}H^{(1)}\psi^{(0)}\,d\tau \qquad (3\text{-}50)$$

For the degenerate bending mode, the terms in p_b and p_c vanish because the vibrational angular momentum is parallel to the figure axis. The last term in (3-49) may be omitted because it is not a function of the rotational quantum numbers and produces the same frequency shift for all the rotational transitions in a given vibrational state.

By definition,

$$\mathbf{p}_z = \frac{\hbar}{i} \sum_k \left(\Delta x_k \frac{\partial}{\partial \Delta y_k} - \Delta y_k \frac{\partial}{\partial \Delta x_k} \right) = \mathbf{p}_a \tag{3-51}$$

Δx_k, Δy_k, and Δz_k are Cartesian displacement coordinates from the equilibrium position of the kth atom. From the mass-weighted Cartesian coordinates

$$q_{xk} = \Delta x_k (m_k)^{1/2}; \qquad q_{yk} = \Delta y_k (m_k)^{1/2}; \qquad q_{zk} = \Delta z_k (m_k)^{1/2} \tag{3-52}$$

for which

$$\frac{\partial Q_r}{\partial q_{xk}} = \frac{\partial q_{xk}}{\partial Q_r}; \qquad \frac{\partial Q_r}{\partial q_{yk}} = \frac{\partial q_{yk}}{\partial Q_r}; \qquad \frac{\partial Q_r}{\partial q_{zk}} = \frac{\partial q_{zk}}{\partial Q_r} \tag{3-53}$$

the angular momentum $\mathbf{p}_a$ becomes

$$\mathbf{p}_a = \frac{\hbar}{i} \sum_k^{3N} \left(q_{xk} \frac{\partial}{\partial q_{yk}} - q_{yk} \frac{\partial}{\partial q_{xk}} \right) \tag{3-54}$$

Equation (3-53) represents the real orthogonal property of the transformation between mass-weighted and normal coordinates. From the definition

$$\frac{\partial(Q_r, Q_s)}{\partial(q_{xk}, q_{yk})} \equiv \begin{vmatrix} \dfrac{\partial Q_r}{\partial q_{xk}} & \dfrac{\partial Q_r}{\partial q_{yk}} \\[2ex] \dfrac{\partial Q_s}{\partial q_{xk}} & \dfrac{\partial Q_s}{\partial q_{yk}} \end{vmatrix} \tag{3-55}$$

and the substitutions

$$q_{xk} = \sum_r \frac{\partial Q_r}{\partial q_{xk}} Q_r; \qquad q_{yk} = \sum_r \frac{\partial Q_r}{\partial q_{yk}} Q_r$$

$$\frac{\partial}{\partial q_{xk}} = \sum_s \frac{\partial Q_s}{\partial q_{xk}} \frac{\partial}{\partial Q_s}; \qquad \frac{\partial}{\partial q_{yk}} = \sum_s \frac{\partial Q_s}{\partial q_{yk}} \frac{\partial}{\partial Q_s} \tag{3-56}$$

equation (3-54) becomes

$$\mathbf{p}_a = \frac{\hbar}{i} \sum_{r<s} \left(Q_r \frac{\partial}{\partial Q_s} - Q_s \frac{\partial}{\partial Q_r} \right) \sum_k \frac{\partial(Q_r, Q_s)}{\partial(q_{xk}, q_{yk})} \tag{3-57}$$

For a nonvanishing matrix element to exist, (Q_r, Q_s) must be the normal coordinates of a doubly degenerate vibration. If $(\tilde{X}_r, \ \tilde{Y}_r)$ represent the normal coordinates of a degenerate vibration,

$$\int \psi_v^* \mathbf{p}_a \psi_v \, d\tau = \sum_r^{(\tilde{X}_r, \tilde{Y}_r)} \sum_k \frac{\partial(\tilde{X}_r, \tilde{Y}_r)}{\partial(q_{xk}, q_{yk})} \int \psi_v^* \frac{\hbar}{i} \left(\tilde{X}_r \frac{\partial}{\partial \tilde{Y}_r} - \tilde{Y}_r \frac{\partial}{\partial \tilde{X}_r} \right) \psi_v \, d\tau \tag{3-58}$$

v_r and l_r define the vibrational quantum numbers for the degenerate mode and the component of angular momentum along the figure axis, respectively. For the singly excited degenerate vibrational state, ψ_{v_r, l_r} is

$$\psi_{1, \pm 1} = \exp(-\tfrac{1}{2}\alpha_r(\tilde{X}_r^2 + \tilde{Y}_r^2)(\alpha_r(\tilde{X}_r \pm i\tilde{Y}_r))^{1/2}) \qquad (3\text{-}59)$$

where

$$\alpha_r = 4\pi^2 v_r / h \qquad (3\text{-}60)$$

Evaluating the remaining perturbation term $-P_a p_a / I_a$ gives the energy correction

$$E^{(1)} = -\frac{Kh}{I_a} \sum_k \frac{\partial(\tilde{X}_r, \tilde{Y}_r)}{\partial(q_{xk}, q_{yk})}(\pm h) = \mp 2AK \sum_k \frac{\partial(\tilde{X}_r, \tilde{Y}_r)}{\partial(q_{xk}, q_{yk})} h \qquad (3\text{-}61)$$

Using the Coriolis coupling constant

$$\zeta_r = \sum_k \frac{\partial(\tilde{X}_r, \tilde{Y}_r)}{\partial(q_{xk}, q_{yk})} \qquad (3\text{-}62)$$

the splittings of the transitions in a degenerate vibrational state with $K \neq 0$ are

$$\Delta v = 4K\zeta A \qquad (3\text{-}63)$$

A is the rotational constant for the figure axis. This splitting is illustrated in Figs. 3-5 and 3-6 for C_{3v} and C_{4v} symmetries, respectively, along with the l-type doubling discussed in the next section.

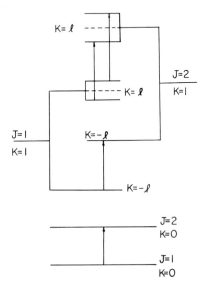

FIG. 3.5. l-type doubling in C_{3v} molecules [429].

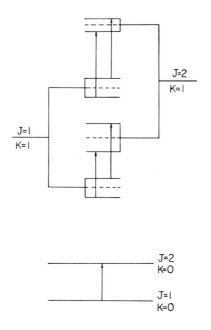

FIG. 3-6. *l*-type doubling in C_{4v} molecules [429].

3-7b. *l*-Type Doubling in Symmetric Top Molecules

Each of the levels where $K \neq 0$ is still doubly degenerate. For one level $K = l$ and for the other $K = -l$. The relative positions of these two levels will depend on the sign of the Coriolis coupling constant. Removal of this degeneracy is made possible by second-order terms in the vibration-rotation Hamiltonian; however, both Coriolis components are not normally split. A group theoretical approach indicates which levels may be split by internal perturbations [429]. For C_{3v} molecules, the degenerate bending vibrations must belong to the degenerate irreducible representation E, and the rotational wave functions belong to the representations of the subgroup C_3. The important case results when $K = \pm 1$, $l = \pm 1$. The rotational wave functions for $K = \pm 1$ belong to E with the resulting symmetry of $\psi_v \psi_r$ coming from the product

$$E \times E = 2A + E \qquad (3\text{-}64)$$

Of the four levels produced by $K = \pm 1$, $l = \pm 1$ permutations, two will be nondegenerate and two form a degenerate pair whose degeneracy cannot be lifted by any internal perturbations of C_3 symmetry.

For $K = \pm 1$ the value of L may be either 0 or 2.[†] From the symmetry considerations of group C_{3v} in Chapter 2, the levels of A symmetry for a given K must have a value of $|K - l|$ which is either zero or a multiple of three. When K is not a multiple of three, the level belongs to the representation E. In this case the levels with $K = l$ have A symmetry and can be split by l-type doubling. Figure 3-5 shows the splittings for the $J = 1, 2$ levels of a C_{3v} molecule where the upper level is taken as $K = l$. For $K = \pm 2, l = \pm 1$, L becomes 1 and 3 and only the lower component is split. Similarly, for $K = \pm 3, l = \pm 1$, no l-type doubling occurs because L can be only 2 or 4.

The question arises whether any case exists where both the levels $K = l$ and $K = -l$ are split by the l-type doubling for $K = \pm 1, l = \pm 1$. The answer is given by the product of the irreducible representations to which ψ_v and ψ_r belong. This splitting should be allowed to take place whenever the product $E \times E$ does not contain a degenerate term. Only in the case of C_{4v} symmetry is this possible. The product gives

$$E \times E = 2A + 2B \tag{3-65}$$

For all other symmetry groups, splitting of both Coriolis levels is impossible. Figure 3-6 shows the energy level splittings for $J = 1, 2$ of a hypothetical C_{4v} molecule. One molecule with C_{4v} symmetry which has been investigated is xenon oxytetrafluoride [1650].

3-7c. Energy Levels and Effects of Centrifugal Distortion

Equation (3-25) may also be used in the calculation of l-type doubling in symmetric top molecules. The actual development and solution of the secular equation has been given by Nielsen [351]. Solution of the $J = 1 \rightarrow 2$ levels shows that the transitions in Fig. 3-7 occur at $4B_v - 32D_J - 6[(B_e^4/\omega_s^2)a^2]/[(1 - \zeta)C_v - B_v - 6D_{JK} - 4D_K]$, $4B_v - 32D_J - 4D_{JK}$, and

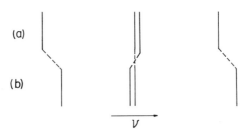

(a)

(b)

ν

FIG. 3-7. Frequency pattern for $J = 1 \rightarrow 2$ transitions with l-type doubling: (a) centrifugal distortion identical for both Coriolis components and (b) centrifugal distortion effects accounted for.

[†] In this case $\zeta = 1$ in (3-45).

$4B_v - 32D_J - 4D_{JK} \pm 4(B_e^2/\omega_s)C'$. The first two lines differ only by terms related to centrifugal distortion and of the order of 1 MHz. The high and low frequency lines are separated by $8(B_e^2/\omega_s)C'$, the difference in the splitting of the $K = l$ levels for $J = 1$ and $J = 2$. This splitting is on the order of 100 MHz in CH_3CN and CH_3NC [426]. For these molecules v refers to v_8.

The actual positions of the transitions are sensitive to centrifugal distortion effects. Figure 3-7 illustrates the relative positions of the four transitions in Fig. 3-5, when the centrifugal distortion of both Coriolis components is assumed to be identical and when the difference in the centrifugal effects on the two components is taken into account. Nielsen has shown that for negative values of ζ_v and D_{JK} and $|D_{JK}| \gg |D_J|$, the two outer transitions are shifted to higher frequency by $8D_{JK}\zeta_v$. Also, the central line is shifted to low frequency by the same amount. The two central transitions are separated by $-4D_{JK} - 8D_{JK}\zeta_v$ and the high frequency member of this pair is $16D_{JK}\zeta_v$ from the center of the two outer transitions.

When centrifugal distortion effects are ignored, the frequency shifts of the components of a $J \to J + 1$, $K \to K$ transition can be expressed to second order as shown in Table 3-4. q_l is the abbreviation for $4q_0$, and r is defined as

$$r = (1 - \zeta_v)C_v - B_v \tag{3-66}$$

K in these tables is always positive, and the last two lines refer to K values greater than one. This table shows that the component $\pm K$, ∓ 1 for $K = J$ is the unshifted component in Fig. 3-7.

TABLE 3-4

FREQUENCY SHIFTS FOR $\Delta J = 1$, $\Delta K = 0$ TRANSITIONS IN SINGLY EXCITED DEGENERATE VIBRATIONAL STATES OF A SYMMETRIC ROTOR[a]

K	l	Δv
0	± 1	$-(q_l^2/4r)J(J + 1)(J + 2)$
± 1	∓ 1	$-(q_l^2/8r)(J - 1)(J + 1)(J + 3)$
1	1	$q_l(J + 1)$
-1	-1	$-q_l(J + 1)$
$\pm K$	∓ 1	$-(q_l^2/4r)(J + 1)\left[\dfrac{(J + 1)^2 - (K + 1)^2}{(K + 1)}\right]$
$\pm K$	± 1	$(q_l^2/4r)(J + 1)\left[\dfrac{(J + 1)^2 - (K - 1)^2}{(K - 1)}\right]$

[a] From Ref. [691].

3-8. Dipole Matrix Elements and Selection Rules for *l*-Doubling

The dipole matrix elements and selection rules for *l*-type doubling in a linear or symmetric top molecule are best obtained by treating the molecule as a slightly asymmetric rotor. For a linear molecule (a special case of a prolate symmetric top), the axial component of angular momentum introduced by the degenerate bending mode is analogous to the limiting prolate K index K_{-1}. Because the sum of the two limiting K values for a given J must be J or $J + 1$, the limiting oblate index K_1 is just $J + 1 - |l|$ and $J - |l|$ for the two components of the l doublet. These labels for the energy levels and the selection rules of an asymmetric rotor lead to the *l*-doubling selection rules,

$$J_{|l|,J+1-|l|} \rightarrow (J + 1)_{|l|,J+2-|l|} \tag{3-67}$$

$$J_{|l|,J-|l|} \rightarrow (J + 1)_{|l|,J+1-|l|} \tag{3-68}$$

$$J_{|l|,J+1-|l|} \rightarrow J_{|l|,J-|l|} \tag{3-69}$$

J refers to the lower rotational state in the $\Delta J = \pm 1$ transitions. The order of the energy levels for a near prolate top causes the $J_{|l|,J-|l|}$ level to lie above the $J_{|l|,J+1-|l|}$ level in the doublet. Because the effective asymmetry is slight, the corresponding dipole matrix elements which determine the line intensity are given by expressions analogous to those for a rigid symmetric top where K is replaced by l.

$$|\langle J,|l|, J + 1 - |l| \, |\boldsymbol{\mu}| J + 1, |l|, J + 2 - |l| \rangle|^2 = \mu^2 \left[\frac{(J + 1)^2 - l^2}{(J + 1)(2J + 1)} \right] \tag{3-70}$$

$$|\langle J,|l|, J - |l| \, |\boldsymbol{\mu}| J + 1, |l|, J + 1 - |l| \rangle|^2 = \mu^2 \left[\frac{(J + 1)^2 - l^2}{(J + 1)(2J + 1)} \right] \tag{3-71}$$

$$|\langle J,|l|, J + 1 - |l| \, |\boldsymbol{\mu}| J, |l|, J - |l| \rangle|^2 = \mu^2 \frac{l^2}{(J + 1)(2J + 1)} \tag{3-72}$$

For a symmetric top the total axial angular momentum component K given by (3-45) is used in these equations.

The electric field dependence of the dipole matrix elements is discussed in Chapter 8. Because the Stark perturbation produces a mixing of wave functions for nearly degenerate levels, transitions which are forbidden in the zero field limit appear in the spectrum when an external electric field is present. Their intensities are dependent on the field strength ε. The close spacing of the *l*-type doublets for the $J = 1$ and $J = 2$ levels of OCS causes the forbidden transitions to be readily observed (Fig. 8-10).

3-9. Fermi Resonance in Linear Molecules

Another perturbation which alters the rotational energy levels of a linear molecule results from an interaction between nearly degenerate vibrational states having the same symmetry. Fermi first observed this form of resonance perturbation in CO_2 [1001]. The basic difference between l-type doubling and Fermi resonance can be recognized by considering the matrix elements for two states identified by the quantum numbers V and V'. If

$$\langle V|H|V \rangle = \langle V'|H|V' \rangle \tag{3-73}$$

the two states V and V' are degenerate. When a perturbing matrix element $\langle V|H'|V' \rangle$ is introduced, the degeneracy is lifted and the process is termed doubling.

If

$$\langle V|H|V \rangle - \langle V'|H|V' \rangle \neq 0 \tag{3-74}$$

the perturbation introduced by the presence of $\langle V|H'|V' \rangle$ is called resonance.

The Fermi interaction is a resonance effect and alters the vibration-rotation constants α_i to produce frequency shifts in the rotational spectrum.

The perturbed energy levels are given by the application of perturbation theory or by the solution of a secular equation:

$$\begin{vmatrix} E_1^{(0)} - \lambda & E_{21} & E_{31} & \cdots & E_{n1} \\ E_{12} & E_2^{(0)} - \lambda & E_{32} & \cdots & \\ \vdots & \vdots & \ddots & & \vdots \\ E_{1n} & \cdots & & & E_n^{(0)} - \lambda \end{vmatrix} = 0 \tag{3-75}$$

where

$$E_{ni} = \int \psi_n^{(0)} H' \psi_i^{(0)} \, d\tau = \langle n|E|i \rangle \tag{3-76}$$

The $E_i^{(0)}$ are the unperturbed energy levels, and $\psi_n^{(0)}$ is the zeroth-order wave function for the nth state. The E_{ni} are nonvanishing only for levels of the same symmetry and therefore for states with the same value of l. The perturbing terms H' are averaged over the unperturbed wave functions in this treatment. These terms are given by the anharmonic terms of the potential function which, in the case of a linear XYZ molecule, are

$$2V' = k_{111}Q_1^3 + k_{113}Q_1^2 Q_3 + k_{122}Q_1 Q_2^2 + k_{133}Q_1 Q_3^2 + k_{223}Q_2^2 Q_3$$
$$+ k_{333}Q_3^3 + \text{quartic terms} \tag{3-77}$$

When levels 1 and 2 perturb each other, the solution of the secular determinant gives an energy separation of

$$\Delta E = (4|E_{12}|^2 + \delta^2)^{1/2} \tag{3-78}$$

δ is the separation of the two unperturbed levels. Low [353] has evaluated the energy separation in the special case of the levels $(v_1, v_2^{|l|}, v_3)$ and $(v_1 - 1, v_2 + 2^{|l|}, v_3)$. Table 3-5 gives examples of this interaction in OCS, OCSe, and

TABLE 3-5

FERMI RESONANCE IN SOME TRANSITIONS OF OCS, OCSe, AND ICN[a]

	v_1	$v_2^{|l|}$	v_3	Frequency (MHz)	Fermi resonance correction (MHz)
OCS					
$J = 1 \to 2$	1	0^0	0	24253.51	-9.52
	0	2^0	0	24401.0	9.52
	2	0^0	0	24179.62	-16.4
$J = 2 \to 3$	0	2^0	0	36600.81	-14.28
OCSe[80]					
$J = 2 \to 3$	1	0^0	0	24026.26	-4.22
	0	2^0	0	24183.97	4.22
ICN					
$J = 3 \to 4$	1	0^0	0	25748.18	-0.35
$(11/2 \to 13/2)$	0	2^0	0	25979.72	0.35

[a] From Refs. [349, 353].

ICN. The off-diagonal element $\langle 1|E|2 \rangle$ of the secular equation (3-75) is

$$\langle 1|E|2 \rangle = \frac{-h^{3/2}}{16\sqrt{2\pi^3 c^{3/2}\omega_1^{1/2}\omega_2}} k_{122} v_1^{1/2}[(v_2 + 2)^2 - l^2]^{1/2} \tag{3-79}$$

The Hermitian character of the problem results in a symmetric perturbation and the centers of the perturbed and unperturbed levels coincide. The perturbation also has the effect of mixing the original set of wave functions to produce a new set of functions for the perturbed levels.

$$\psi_1 = a\psi_1^{(0)} - b\psi_2^{(0)} \tag{3-80}$$

$$\psi_2 = b\psi_1^{(0)} + a\psi_2^{(0)} \tag{3-81}$$

where

$$a^2 = \frac{1}{2} + \frac{\delta}{2(4|E_{12}|^2 + \delta^2)^{1/2}} \tag{3-82}$$

and

$$a^2 + b^2 = 1 \qquad (3-83)$$

The effects of Fermi resonance also appear in the centrifugal distortion constant of a linear molecule. Amat et al. [391] have considered these interactions in CO_2 where the Fermi resonance perturbations are strong. Nielsen et al. [394] have extended the treatment to general resonance effects.

3-10a. Nonrigid Effects in Asymmetric Rotors

Wilson and Howard [335] have derived the quantum-mechanical Hamiltonian for a nonrigid asymmetric rotor. From this Hamiltonian it is possible to evaluate vibration-rotation interactions, centrifugal distortion effects, and the variation of moments of inertia as a function of the vibrational quantum numbers. Darling and Dennison [1034] have constructed an equivalent Hamiltonian. If the corresponding wave functions are correctly normalized, their formalism gives the same energies as the Wilson–Howard treatment. Nielsen [336, 351] also discussed the Hamiltonian extensively and extended the problem to include the contributions of electrons as well as the motions of the nuclei. Goldsmith et al. [354], Amat et al. [355], Amat and Nielsen [357, 359, 362], and Grenier-Besson et al. [364] have extended the Darling-Dennison formulation to higher orders of approximation.

The algebraic complexity inherent in a treatment of the vibration-rotation Hamiltonian prevents a complete discussion of the problem. However, the essential elements of the Wilson–Howard approach are given in Appendix 4. It deals with the most general case of an asymmetric rotor and, with appropriate modifications, leads to simplified results for linear and symmetric molecules.

Using the terms defined in the appendix, the Hamiltonian can be expressed as

$$\mathbf{H} = \tfrac{1}{2}\mu^{1/4} \sum_{\alpha,\beta} (\mathbf{P}_\alpha - \mathbf{p}_\alpha)\mu_{\alpha\beta}\mu^{-1/2}(\mathbf{P}_\beta - \mathbf{p}_\beta)\mu^{1/4} + \tfrac{1}{2}\mu^{1/4} \sum_k \mathbf{p}_k\mu^{-1/2}\mathbf{p}_k\mu^{1/4} + V$$

$$(3-84)$$

The $\mathbf{p}_k$ are operators for the vibrational momenta. $\mathbf{P}_\alpha$ represents the rotational angular momenta along the molecule-fixed axes and $\mathbf{p}_\alpha$ is the operator representing the components of $\mathbf{p}_k$ along the molecule-fixed axes. $\mathbf{p}_k$ and $\mathbf{p}_\alpha$ are related by the Coriolis coupling constant and the vibrational normal coordinate.

$$\mathbf{p}_\alpha = -\sum_{k'}\sum_k \zeta_{k'k}^{(\alpha)}Q_{k'}\mathbf{p}_k \qquad (3-84a)$$

μ is the determinant of $\mu_{\alpha\beta}$. This form of the quantum-mechanical Hamiltonian is exact in the sense that no approximations have been made after the model was formulated. However, it is convenient to simplify this expression through approximations that are valid in the majority of molecules to be studied. Assuming small amplitude vibrations, the dependence of $\mu_{\alpha\beta}$ on the Q_k can be neglected. The Hamiltonian then simplifies to

$$\mathbf{H} = \tfrac{1}{2}\sum_{\alpha\beta} \mu_{\alpha\beta}(\mathbf{P}_\alpha - \mathbf{p}_\alpha)(\mathbf{P}_\beta - \mathbf{p}_\beta) + \tfrac{1}{2}\sum_k \mathbf{p}_k^2 + V \qquad (3\text{-}85)$$

Further, if the molecule-fixed axis system coincides with the principal axis system and the sums $\Sigma_k X_k Y_k$ are negligible

$$\mathbf{H} = \tfrac{1}{2}\sum_\alpha (\mathbf{P}_\alpha - \mathbf{p}_\alpha)^2/I_\alpha + \tfrac{1}{2}\sum_k \mathbf{p}_k^2 + V \qquad (3\text{-}86)$$

Because $\mathbf{P}_\alpha$ commutes with $\mathbf{p}_k$, $\mathbf{H}$ can be expanded as

$$\mathbf{H} = \tfrac{1}{2}\sum_{\alpha\beta} \mu_{\alpha\beta}\mathbf{P}_\alpha\mathbf{P}_\beta - \sum_\alpha \mathbf{h}_\alpha\mathbf{P}_\alpha + \tfrac{1}{2}\mu^{1/4}\sum_{\alpha\beta} \mathbf{p}_\alpha\mu_{\alpha\beta}\mu^{-1/2}\mathbf{p}_\beta\mu^{1/4}$$

$$+ \tfrac{1}{2}\mu^{1/4}\sum_k \mathbf{p}_k\mu^{-1/2}\mathbf{p}_k\mu^{1/4} + V \qquad (3\text{-}87)$$

$$\mathbf{h}_\alpha = \tfrac{1}{2}\sum_\beta [\mu^{-1/4}\mu_{\alpha\beta}\mathbf{p}_\beta\mu^{1/4} + \mu^{1/4}\mathbf{p}_\beta\mu_{\beta\alpha}\mu^{-1/4}] \qquad (3\text{-}88)$$

3-10b. Perturbation Treatment of Vibration-Rotation Hamiltonian

A perturbation treatment is applied to the Hamiltonian to effect its solution for finite vibration-rotation interactions. The Hamiltonian is subdivided in the usual manner neglecting the perturbation parameter λ:

$$\mathbf{H} = \mathbf{H}^{(0)} + \mathbf{H}^{(1)} \qquad (3\text{-}89)$$

$\mathbf{H}^{(1)}$ is the perturbation term which is significantly smaller than the zeroth order terms of $\mathbf{H}^{(0)}$ in the absence of near degeneracies. The basis functions are the product $\psi_R\psi_v$ where ψ_R is the basis function of the rotational part of $\mathbf{H}^{(0)}$ and ψ_v is an orthonormal function of the molecular normal coordinates. $\mathbf{H}^{(0)}$ is diagonal in the vibrational quantum numbers, although it need not be diagonal in all of the rotational quantum numbers. For an asymmetric rotor $\mathbf{H}^{(0)}$ is off-diagonal in K if a symmetric rotor basis is used. $\mathbf{H}^{(1)}$ is generally not diagonal in either the rotational or vibrational quantum numbers. It is possible to perform a transformation[†] on $\mathbf{H}$ to remove the off-diagonal terms to second order in v. By neglecting the remaining off-diagonal terms, the energy can be calculated correctly to fourth order. When off-diagonal terms in the potential energy are neglected, $\mathbf{H}$ factors into

---

[†] Appendix 7 and Chapter 6 discuss the details of the Van Vleck transformation.

submatrices, each characterized by a single vibrational state.

$$\mathbf{H}_v = \langle v|\mathbf{H}|v\rangle = \langle Rv|\mathbf{H}^{(0)}|R'v\rangle + \langle Rv|\mathbf{H}^{(1)}|R'v\rangle$$

$$+ \sum_{R''v''} \frac{\langle Rv|\mathbf{H}^{(1)}|R''v''\rangle\langle R''v''|\mathbf{H}^{(1)}|R'v\rangle}{E_{Rv}^{(0)} - E_{R''v''}^{(0)}} \tag{3-90}$$

It is assumed that the vibrational spacing is much larger than the spacing of the rotational energy levels.

$$E_{Rv}^{(0)} - E_{R''v''}^{(0)} \approx E_v^{(0)} - E_{v''}^{(0)} \tag{3-91}$$

The object of the transformation is to extend the separation of the rotational and vibrational parts of the Hamiltonian. Before the transformation, terms found in $\mathbf{H}^{(1)}$ had to be neglected for complete separation; after the transformation only terms fourth-order in the energy are neglected. It is important to note that the rotational matrices $\langle v|\mathbf{H}|v\rangle$ differ for each vibrational state, because the matrix elements of $\mathbf{H}^{(1)}$ are functions of the vibrational quantum numbers. The eigenvalues of $\mathbf{H}_v$ are the rotational energies for a given vibrational state.

Now consider the properties of the rotational submatrices. An example [335] is the term $\mu_{xy}\mathbf{P}_x\mathbf{P}_y$. The first-order term is

$$\langle vR|\mu_{xy}\mathbf{P}_x\mathbf{P}_y|vR'\rangle = \langle v|\mu_{xy}|v\rangle\langle R|\mathbf{P}_x\mathbf{P}_y|R'\rangle \tag{3-92}$$

The matrix element $\langle v|\mu_{xy}|v\rangle$ is independent of the rotational quantum numbers. To first-order

$$\langle v|\mathbf{H}|v\rangle = \mathbf{E}_v + \tfrac{1}{2}\sum_{\alpha,\beta}\langle v|\mu_{\alpha\beta}|v\rangle\langle R|\mathbf{P}_\alpha\mathbf{P}_\beta|R'\rangle$$

$$- \sum_\alpha \mathbf{h}_\alpha\langle R|\mathbf{P}_\alpha|R'\rangle \tag{3-93}$$

$\mathbf{E}_v$ is a matrix which is diagonal in the rotational quantum numbers and its diagonal elements are all equal to the vibrational energy $E_v^{(0)}$ originating from the purely vibrational terms in $\mathbf{H}$.

For the second-order correction a typical sum of terms is

$$-\frac{1}{2}\sum_{R''v''}{}' \frac{\langle Rv|\mu_{xx}\mathbf{P}_x^2|R''v''\rangle\langle R''v''|\mathbf{h}_y\mathbf{P}_y|R'v\rangle}{E_v^{(0)} - E_{v''}^{(0)}}$$

$$= -\frac{1}{2}\sum_{R''}\langle R|\mathbf{P}_x^2|R''\rangle\langle R''|\mathbf{P}_y|R'\rangle\sum_{v''}{}' \frac{\langle v|\mu_{xx}|v''\rangle\langle v''|\mathbf{h}_y|v\rangle}{E_v^{(0)} - E_{v''}^{(0)}}$$

$$= -\frac{1}{2}\langle R|\mathbf{P}_x^2\mathbf{P}_y|R'\rangle\sum_{v''}{}' \frac{\langle v|\mu_{xx}|v''\rangle\langle v''|\mathbf{h}_y|v\rangle}{E_v^{(0)} - E_{v''}^{(0)}} \tag{3-94}$$

Factoring makes this simplification possible. Each matrix element reduces to a constant times a factor containing $\mathbf{P}_\alpha$, and the matrix $\mathbf{H}_v$ can be written as a polynomial in the $\mathbf{P}_\alpha$ matrices. The coefficients are constants formed from integrals over the vibrational wave functions. Further simplification results because the terms linear in $\mathbf{P}_\alpha$ vanish identically; the cubic terms either vanish or reduce to quadratic terms in $\mathbf{P}_\alpha$. For the linear terms in $\mathbf{P}_\alpha$, the coefficients are $-\mathbf{h}_\alpha$. Because $\mathbf{H}_v$ and $\mathbf{P}_\alpha$ are Hermitian, the matrix $\langle v|\mathbf{h}_\alpha|v'\rangle$ is also Hermitian; however, $\mathbf{h}_\alpha$ is a purely imaginary operator containing the factor $(h/2\pi i)$. All other quantities are purely real. Because ψ_v is real for asymmetric tops which have no vibrational degeneracies, the diagonal term vanishes.

$$\langle v|\mathbf{h}_\alpha^*|v\rangle = -\langle v|\mathbf{h}_\alpha|v\rangle = \langle v|\mathbf{h}_\alpha|v\rangle = 0 \tag{3-95}$$

As an example of the cubic terms, consider the coefficient of $\mathbf{P}_\alpha^3$.

$$\frac{1}{2}\mathbf{P}_x^3 \sum_{v''}{}' \frac{\langle v|\mu_{xx}|v''\rangle\langle v''|\mathbf{h}_x|v\rangle + \langle v|\mathbf{h}_x|v''\rangle\langle v''|\mu_{xx}|v\rangle}{E_v^{(0)} - E_{v''}^{(0)}} \tag{3-96}$$

This term vanishes because $\langle v|\mathbf{h}_x|v''\rangle = -\langle v''|\mathbf{h}_x|v\rangle$ and $\langle v|\mu_{xx}|v''\rangle = \langle v''|\mu_{xx}|v\rangle$. Through use of the commutation relations other nonvanishing cubic terms like $\mathbf{P}_x^2\mathbf{P}_y - \mathbf{P}_y\mathbf{P}_x^2$ can be reduced to quadratic form.

$$\mathbf{P}_x^2\mathbf{P}_y - \mathbf{P}_y\mathbf{P}_x^2 = \mathbf{P}_x(\mathbf{P}_x\mathbf{P}_y - \mathbf{P}_y\mathbf{P}_x) + (\mathbf{P}_x\mathbf{P}_y - \mathbf{P}_y\mathbf{P}_x)\mathbf{P}_x = (h/2\pi i)(\mathbf{P}_x\mathbf{P}_z + \mathbf{P}_z\mathbf{P}_x) \tag{3-97}$$

Thus the rotational matrix for a particular vibrational state v can be written as a polynomial in the even powers of the angular momentum.

$$\mathbf{H}_v = \mathbf{E}_v + \tfrac{1}{2}\sum_{\alpha\beta}\sigma_{\alpha\beta}\langle R|\mathbf{P}_\alpha\mathbf{P}_\beta|R'\rangle + \tfrac{1}{4}\sum_{\alpha\beta\gamma\delta}\tau_{\alpha\beta\gamma\delta}\langle R|\mathbf{P}_\alpha\mathbf{P}_\beta\mathbf{P}_\gamma\mathbf{P}_\delta|R'\rangle \tag{3-98}$$

The coefficients $\sigma_{\alpha\beta}$ and $\tau_{\alpha\beta\gamma\delta}$ depend on the vibrational state to which $\mathbf{H}_v$ belongs. These coefficients can be calculated from the matrix elements of $\mu_{\alpha\beta}$ over the vibrational wave functions.

The Hamiltonian in (3-98) can be reduced to the Wang form only if the quartic terms are neglected. These terms are important in a centrifugal distortion treatment, so the transformation to factored form is not pursued [335].

3-10c. Interactions for Near Degeneracies

The perturbation treatment applied to the vibration-rotation Hamiltonian is valid only for small perturbations. If two vibrational levels happen to be nearly degenerate, the interactions introduced by vibration-rotation coupling can be very large and may invalidate the perturbation calculation. For two nearly degenerate states labeled by v and v', the energy values must be calculated by first separating the matrix block containing the diagonal elements of v and v' and the off-diagonal terms coupling these two states from the rest of the energy matrix and then diagonalizing this vv' submatrix. To separate the v and v' states from the remainder of $\mathbf{H}$, a form of the Van Vleck transformation described in Appendix 7 can be applied to $\mathbf{H}$. Some relatively small correction terms are folded into the vv' block; if all other vibrational energy differences are sufficiently large, these corrections can often be completely neglected. To simplify the problem, v and v' are assumed to be harmonic vibrations.

If $\mu_{\alpha\beta}$ and $\mathbf{h}_\alpha$ are replaced by their approximate average values, the Hamiltonian becomes

$$\mathbf{H} = \frac{1}{2}\left(\frac{\mathbf{P}_x^2}{I_x} + \frac{\mathbf{P}_y^2}{I_y} + \frac{\mathbf{P}_z^2}{I_z}\right) - \left(\frac{\mathbf{p}_x\mathbf{P}_x}{I_x} + \frac{\mathbf{p}_y\mathbf{P}_y}{I_y} + \frac{\mathbf{p}_z\mathbf{P}_z}{I_z}\right) + \mathbf{E} \qquad (3\text{-}99)$$

where $\mathbf{E}$ is the vibrational operator. Because both $\mathbf{p}_\alpha$ and $\mathbf{P}_\alpha$ are diagonal in J, $\mathbf{H}$ is diagonal in J. The Coriolis perturbation terms $\mathbf{p}_\alpha\mathbf{P}_\alpha$ can couple only levels with the same J value.

The presence of a near degeneracy is not sufficient to produce an interaction; it is necessary for the two vibrational modes to have the appropriate symmetry. Using symmetry arguments, Jahn [417] formulated a general rule for predicting which normal modes may be connected by a Coriolis perturbation. Every molecule possesses the symmetry of one of the thirty-two point groups. Each point group contains a certain number of unique irreducible representations. Each of the $3N$ degrees of freedom of a molecule; namely, 3 rotations, 3 translations, and $3N-6$ vibrations (for a nonlinear molecule), has the symmetry of one of the irreducible representations of the molecular point group. The selection rule states that for two normal vibrational modes Q_i and Q_j to be coupled by a Coriolis perturbation, identified with the Coriolis coupling constant ζ_{ij}, the product of the two irreducible representations $\Gamma(Q_i)$ and $\Gamma(Q_j)$ must be an irreducible representation of the point group which contains one of the 3 rotations R_x, R_y, or R_z. This is a necessary but not a sufficient condition to produce a Coriolis interaction. If the two normal modes Q_i and Q_j are widely separated in frequency, the effective interaction is negligible. It is also possible for the l vectors to have a vanishing crossproduct forcing the matrix element connecting the two vibrations to vanish [421].

The vv' block can be factored into $2(2J + 1)$-fold submatrices. Within these submatrices the Coriolis interaction introduces elements which connect K, $K \pm 1$ levels in the separate vibrational states. Using the notation of

Wilson [334], the nonvanishing matrix elements are

$$\langle Kv|\mathbf{H}|Kv\rangle = K^2 + \sigma_v - \sigma \tag{3-100}$$

$$\langle Kv'|\mathbf{H}|Kv'\rangle = K^2 + \sigma_{v'} - \sigma \tag{3-101}$$

$$\langle Kv|\mathbf{H}|K \pm 2, v\rangle = \langle Kv'|\mathbf{H}|K \pm 2, v'\rangle$$
$$= \tfrac{1}{2}b\{[J^2 - (K \pm 1)^2][(J + 1)^2 - (K \pm 1)^2]\}^{1/2} \tag{3-102}$$

$$\langle Kv|\mathbf{H}|Kv'\rangle = -\langle Kv'|\mathbf{H}|Kv\rangle = iG_zK \tag{3-103}$$

$$\langle Kv|\mathbf{H}|K \pm 1, v'\rangle = -\langle Kv'|\mathbf{H}|K \pm 1, v\rangle$$
$$= \tfrac{1}{2}(iG_x \pm G_y)[(J \mp K)(J \pm K + 1)]^{1/2} \tag{3-104}$$

where

$$a = \left(\frac{1}{2c}\right)(1/I_x + 1/I_y) \tag{3-105}$$

$$b = \left(\frac{1}{2c}\right)(1/I_x - 1/I_y) \tag{3-106}$$

$$c = 1/I_z - \frac{1}{2}\left(\frac{1}{I_x} + \frac{1}{I_y}\right) \tag{3-107}$$

$$\sigma = (8\pi^2/h^2c)E - J(J + 1)a \tag{3-108}$$

$$\sigma_v = (8\pi^2/h^2c)E_v \tag{3-109}$$

$$G_x = (2/cI_x)\sum_{ikl}(l_{ik}^{(y)}l_{il}^{(z)} - l_{il}^{(y)}l_{ik}^{(z)})I_{kl} \tag{3-110}$$

$$G_y = (2/cI_y)\sum_{ikl}(l_{ik}^{(z)}l_{il}^{(x)} - l_{il}^{(z)}l_{ik}^{(x)})I_{kl} \tag{3-111}$$

$$G_z = (2/cI_z)\sum_{ikl}(l_{ik}^{(x)}l_{il}^{(y)} - l_{il}^{(x)}l_{ik}^{(y)})I_{kl} \tag{3-112}$$

$$I_{kl} = \int \psi_{v'}^* Q_k\left(\frac{\partial}{\partial Q_l}\right)\psi_v \, d\tau \tag{3-113}$$

The $l^{(\alpha)}$ coefficients are components of the **l** matrix and relate the normal coordinates to mass-weighted Cartesian coordinates. Wilson has extended the treatment to V, V_h, and C_{2v}-type molecules [334].

3-11. Coriolis Coupling Effects on Rotational Constants

If the conditions stated above are satisfied, a second-order or resonance Coriolis coupling can occur between nearly degenerate vibrational states. Unfortunately, the Coriolis coupling constants can be reliably evaluated by *a priori* calculations only in relatively simple molecules.

Consider a planar molecule with C_{2v} symmetry. If the in-plane modes v_i and v_j are close in frequency and belong to an allowed pair of irreducible representations, $\Gamma_i\Gamma_j$ will be an irreducible representation containing rotation about one of the axes. This will be the out-of-plane axis. In this case the out-of-plane rotational constant may show a large deviation from its value in the ground vibrational state. This is illustrated in Table 3-6 for v_3 and v_5 of F_2CO for the rotational constant C. The changes in A and B are expected from normal zero-point vibration-rotation interactions; however, a major part of the shift in C is due specifically to the Coriolis perturbation. The quantity Δ is known as the inertia defect for planar molecules. The large perturbation of the out-of-plane moment produces a very large change in Δ.

TABLE 3-6
VARIATION OF ROTATIONAL CONSTANTS PRODUCED BY
CORIOLIS COUPLING BETWEEN v_3 AND v_5 OF F_2CO^a

	Ground state	$v_3 = 1$	$v_5 = 1$
ΔA (MHz)	—	-16.93	11.90
ΔB (MHz)	—	27.75	1.42
ΔC (MHz)	—	-88.01	74.03
Δ (amu A^2)	0.1556	1.5014	-0.8648

^{a} From Ref. [423].

For a planar molecule like F_2CO the change in the perturbed moment ΔI_c can be used to calculate ζ_{ij}. From Appendix 5, when all other vibration-rotation terms are negligible,

$$\Delta I_c^i = I_c(v_i = 1) - I_c(\text{Gnd. state}) \approx \left(\frac{8K}{\omega_i}\right)\left[\frac{\omega_j^2}{(\omega_j^2 - \omega_i^2)}\right](\zeta_{ij}^c)^2 \quad (3\text{-}114)$$

where $K = h/8\pi^2 c$ and ω is the harmonic frequency in cm^{-1}. From the observed change in the moment and from infrared, Raman, or accurate relative intensity data, ζ_{ij} can be estimated. A similar equation for ΔI_c^j allows a check on the estimate. Using these approximations, values of 0.748 and 0.758 have been obtained for $v_3 = 1$ and $v_5 = 1$, respectively [423]. ζ_{ij} can also be estimated from the inertia defect (Chapter 4).

3-12. Centrifugal Distortion in Asymmetric Tops

Kivelson and Wilson [382] have extended (3-98) to account for the effects of centrifugal distortion on the energy levels of an asymmetric rotor. Using $\mathbf{H}^{(0)'}$ to represent the effective rigid rotor terms and $\mathbf{H}^{(1)'}$ to represent the centrifugal distortion contribution,

$$H = H^{(0)'} + H^{(1)'} \tag{3-115}$$

Dropping the explicit matrix-element form of (3-98),

$$H^{(0)'} = \alpha' P_z^2 + \beta' P_x^2 + \gamma' P_y^2 \tag{3-116}$$

$$H^{(1)'} = \tfrac{1}{4} \hbar^4 \sum_{\alpha\beta\gamma\delta} \tau_{\alpha\beta\gamma\delta} P_\alpha P_\beta P_\gamma P_\delta \tag{3-117}$$

where

$$\alpha' = \frac{\hbar^2}{2I_z}; \qquad \beta' = \frac{\hbar^2}{2I_x}; \qquad \gamma' = \frac{\hbar^2}{2I_y} \tag{3-118}$$

If the problem is solved exactly, the off-diagonal terms $\langle K|H|K \pm 2\rangle$ and $\langle K|H|K \pm 4\rangle$ must be included. Rather, an approximate approach based on first-order perturbation theory can be used. Vibration and rotation are separated to the second-order of approximation, and centrifugal distortion effects higher than first order are neglected.

The distortion constants $\tau_{\alpha\beta\gamma\delta}$ are given by the perturbation result

$$\tau_{\alpha\beta\gamma\delta} = \sum_{v'}{}' \frac{|\langle v|\mu_{\alpha\beta}|v'\rangle\langle v'|\mu_{\gamma\delta}|v\rangle|}{E_v - E_{v'}} \tag{3-119}$$

They are independent of the rotational quantum numbers. Kivelson and Wilson [386] have related these quartic centrifugal distortion constants to the molecular potential function and to the potential constants f_{ij}. This can be accomplished either by expanding the inertial tensor $\mathbf{I}$ or its inverse $\mathbf{\mu}$ in a set of independent general displacement coordinates δR_i. Retaining only the terms linear in the δR_i

$$\mu_{\alpha\beta} = \mu_{\alpha\beta}^{(e)} + \sum_i \mu_{\alpha\beta}^{(i)} \delta R_i \tag{3-120}$$

$$\mu_{\alpha\beta}^{(i)} = \left(\frac{\partial \mu_{\alpha\beta}}{\partial R_i} \right) \tag{3-121}$$

The derivatives are evaluated at $\delta R_i = 0$, and $\mu_{\alpha\beta}^{(e)}$ is the equilibrium value of $\mu_{\alpha\beta}$. Using orthonormal harmonic oscillator functions as a basis,

$$\langle v|\mu_{\alpha\beta}|v'\rangle = \sum_i \mu_{\alpha\beta}^{(i)}\langle v|\delta R_i|v'\rangle \tag{3-122}$$

and in terms of the linear transformation coefficients b_{ik}

$$\langle v|\delta R_i|v'\rangle = \sum_k b_{ik}\langle v|Q_k|v'\rangle \tag{3-123}$$

From the harmonic oscillator selection rules (replacing the vibrational quantum number v_k with the harmonic oscillator quantum number n_k),

$$\tau_{\alpha\beta\gamma\delta} = \sum_{ij} \mu_{\alpha\beta}^{(i)} \mu_{\gamma\delta}^{(j)} \sum_k b_{ik} b_{jk} \left[\frac{\langle n_k | Q_k | n_k + 1 \rangle \langle n_k + 1 | Q_k | n_k \rangle}{(E_{n_k} - E_{n_k+1})} \right.$$
$$\left. + \frac{\langle n_k | Q_k | n_k - 1 \rangle \langle n_k - 1 | Q_k | n_k \rangle}{(E_{n_k} - E_{n_k-1})} \right] \tag{3-124}$$

Since the f_{ij} are potential constants in the potential energy expansion

$$2V = \sum_{i,j=1}^{3N} f_{ij} \, \delta R_i \, \delta R_j \tag{3-125}$$

$$(f^{-1})_{ij} = \sum_k \frac{b_{ik} b_{jk}}{\omega_k^2} \tag{3-126}$$

The quartic distortion constant and the potential constant are then related by

$$\tau_{\alpha\beta\gamma\delta} = -\tfrac{1}{2} \sum_{ij} \mu_{\alpha\beta}^{(i)} \mu_{\gamma\delta}^{(j)} (f^{-1})_{ij} \tag{3-127}$$

Similarly, if

$$\mathbf{J}^{(i)} = \left(\frac{\partial \mathbf{I}}{\partial R_i} \right) \tag{3-128}$$

then

$$\mathbf{I} = \mathbf{I}^{(e)} + \sum_i [\mathbf{J}^{(i)}]_e \, \delta R_i \tag{3-129}$$

and

$$\mathbf{I\mu} = \mathbf{I}^{(e)}\mathbf{\mu}^{(e)} + \mathbf{I}^{(e)} \sum_i \mathbf{\mu}^{(i)} \, \delta R_i + \sum_i [\mathbf{J}^{(i)}]_e \, \delta R_i \mathbf{\mu}^{(e)} \tag{3-130}$$

This equation reduces to

$$\mathbf{\mu}^{(i)} = -\mathbf{\mu}^{(e)} [\mathbf{J}^{(i)}]_e \mathbf{\mu}^{(e)} \tag{3-131}$$

because $\mathbf{I}^{(e)}\mathbf{\mu}^{(e)} = \mathbf{I\mu}$. If the coordinate system is chosen to make $\mathbf{\mu}^{(e)}$ and $\mathbf{I}^{(e)}$ diagonal,

$$\mu_{\alpha\beta}^{(i)} = -\frac{[J_{\alpha\beta}^{(i)}]_e}{I_{\alpha\alpha}^{(e)} I_{\beta\beta}^{(e)}} \tag{3-132}$$

Finally,

$$\tau_{\alpha\beta\gamma\delta} = -\frac{\sum_{ij} [J_{\alpha\beta}^{(i)}]_e [J_{\gamma\delta}^{(j)}]_e (f^{-1})_{ij}}{2(I_{\alpha\alpha}^{(e)} I_{\beta\beta}^{(e)} I_{\gamma\gamma}^{(e)} I_{\delta\delta}^{(e)})} \tag{3-133}$$

The number of constants $\tau_{\alpha\beta\gamma\delta}$ is significantly reduced if the molecule possesses some symmetry. For orthorhombic molecules there are twenty-one nonvanishing coefficients of which only nine are different.

$$\tau_{\alpha\alpha\alpha\alpha}; \quad \tau_{\alpha\alpha\beta\beta} = \tau_{\beta\beta\alpha\alpha}; \quad \tau_{\alpha\beta\alpha\beta} = \tau_{\alpha\beta\beta\alpha} = \tau_{\beta\alpha\alpha\beta} = \tau_{\beta\alpha\beta\alpha} \tag{3-134}$$

For some symmetries off-diagonal terms involving $\langle K|K \pm 1\rangle$ and $\langle K|K \pm 3\rangle$ elements may appear. Since these terms affect the energy to second order only, they may be neglected in a first-order perturbation treatment.

By using the commutation rules governing angular momenta, terms of the type $\alpha\beta\alpha\beta$ can be removed from $\mathbf{H}^{(1)'}$ so that

$$\mathbf{H} = \mathbf{H}^{(0)} + \mathbf{H}^{(1)} \tag{3-135}$$

$$\mathbf{H}^{(0)} = \alpha\mathbf{P}_z^2 + \beta\mathbf{P}_x^2 + \gamma\mathbf{P}_y^2 \tag{3-136}$$

$$\mathbf{H}^{(1)} = \frac{1}{4}\sum_{\alpha\beta}\tau'_{\alpha\alpha\beta\beta}\mathbf{P}_\alpha^2\mathbf{P}_\beta^2 \tag{3-137}$$

Here terms of the form $\mathbf{P}_\alpha^2$ have been incorporated into $\mathbf{H}^{(0)}$. The connecting relations are

$$\alpha = \alpha' + (3\tau_{\alpha\beta\alpha\beta} - 2\tau_{\gamma\alpha\gamma\alpha} - 2\tau_{\beta\gamma\beta\gamma})\hbar^4/4 \tag{3-138}$$

$$\tau'_{\alpha\alpha\alpha\alpha} = \tau_{\alpha\alpha\alpha\alpha}\hbar^4 \tag{3-139}$$

$$\tau'_{\alpha\alpha\beta\beta} = (\tau_{\alpha\alpha\beta\beta} + 2\tau_{\alpha\beta\alpha\beta})\hbar^4 \tag{3-140}$$

The total angular momentum $\mathbf{P}^2$ commutes with $\mathbf{H}$ and $\mathbf{H}^{(0)}$ and also with $\mathbf{P}_x^2$ and $\mathbf{P}_y^2$. Useful operator products are ($\hbar$ implicit)

$$\mathbf{P}_\alpha^2\mathbf{P}^2 + \mathbf{P}^2\mathbf{P}_\alpha^2 = 2J(J+1)\mathbf{P}_\alpha^2 = 2\mathbf{P}_\alpha^4 + (\mathbf{P}_\alpha^2\mathbf{P}_\beta^2 + \mathbf{P}_\beta^2\mathbf{P}_\alpha^2) + (\mathbf{P}_\gamma^2\mathbf{P}_\alpha^2 + \mathbf{P}_\alpha^2\mathbf{P}_\gamma^2) \tag{3-141}$$

Squaring (3-136) gives

$$\mathbf{H}^{(0)2} = \alpha^2\mathbf{P}_z^4 + \beta^2\mathbf{P}_x^4 + \gamma^2\mathbf{P}_y^4 + \alpha\beta(\mathbf{P}_z^2\mathbf{P}_x^2 + \mathbf{P}_x^2\mathbf{P}_z^2) + \beta\gamma(\mathbf{P}_x^2\mathbf{P}_y^2 + \mathbf{P}_y^2\mathbf{P}_x^2)$$
$$+ \gamma\alpha(\mathbf{P}_y^2\mathbf{P}_z^2 + \mathbf{P}_z^2\mathbf{P}_y^2) \tag{3-142}$$

Using

$$\mathbf{P}^2 = \mathbf{P}_x^2 + \mathbf{P}_y^2 + \mathbf{P}_z^2 \tag{3-143}$$

to eliminate $\mathbf{P}_y^2$ from $\mathbf{H}^{(0)}$, squaring $\mathbf{H}^{(0)}$, and differentiating with respect to α leads to

$$\frac{\partial\mathbf{H}^{(0)2}}{\partial\alpha} = 2(\alpha - \gamma)\mathbf{P}_z^4 + (\beta - \gamma)(\mathbf{P}_x^2\mathbf{P}_z^2 + \mathbf{P}_z^2\mathbf{P}_x^2) + 2\gamma J(J+1)\mathbf{P}_z^2 \tag{3-144}$$

Similarly, by eliminating $\mathbf{P}_x^2$

$$\frac{\partial\mathbf{H}^{(0)2}}{\partial\alpha} = 2(\alpha - \beta)\mathbf{P}_z^4 + (\gamma - \beta)(\mathbf{P}_y^2\mathbf{P}_z^2 + \mathbf{P}_z^2\mathbf{P}_y^2) + 2\beta J(J+1)\mathbf{P}_z^2 \tag{3-145}$$

The diagonal element of $\mathbf{P}_z^2$ in the representation which diagonalizes $\mathbf{H}^{(0)}$ is

$$\langle \mathbf{P}_z^2 \rangle = \left\langle \frac{\partial \mathbf{H}^{(0)}}{\partial \alpha} \right\rangle = \frac{\partial E^{(0)}}{\partial \alpha} \tag{3-146}$$

where $E^{(0)}$ is given by (2-83). Also,

$$\left\langle \frac{\partial (\mathbf{H}^{(0)^2})}{\partial \alpha} \right\rangle = \frac{\partial E^{(0)^2}}{\partial \alpha} = 2E^{(0)} \langle \mathbf{P}_z^2 \rangle \tag{3-147}$$

$$\langle \mathbf{H}^{(0)^2} \rangle = E^{(0)^2} \tag{3-148}$$

Only the diagonal values of the operators appearing in $\mathbf{H}^{(1)}$ are important in a first-order treatment. Equations (3-146)–(3-148) may be considered as average value equations which can be solved to allow the quantities $\langle \mathbf{P}_x^4 \rangle$, $\langle \mathbf{P}_y^4 \rangle$, $\langle \mathbf{P}_x^2\mathbf{P}_y^2 + \mathbf{P}_y^2\mathbf{P}_x^2 \rangle$, $\langle \mathbf{P}_y^2\mathbf{P}_z^2 + \mathbf{P}_z^2\mathbf{P}_y^2 \rangle$, and $\langle \mathbf{P}_z^2\mathbf{P}_x^2 + \mathbf{P}_x^2\mathbf{P}_z^2 \rangle$ to be written in terms of $J(J + 1)\langle \mathbf{P}_x^2 \rangle$, $J(J + 1)\langle \mathbf{P}_y^2 \rangle$, $J(J + 1)\langle \mathbf{P}_z^2 \rangle$, $\langle \mathbf{P}_z^4 \rangle$, E, and $E^{(0)}\langle \mathbf{P}_z^2 \rangle$. If these relations along with

$$\langle \mathbf{P}_x^2 \rangle = [E^{(0)} - \gamma J(J + 1) - (\alpha - \gamma)\langle \mathbf{P}_z^2 \rangle]/(\beta - \gamma) \tag{3-149}$$

and a similar relation for $\langle \mathbf{P}_y^2 \rangle$ are substituted into $\mathbf{H}^{(1)}$, the nonrigid rotor energies can be written to first order as

$$E = E^{(0)} + A_1 E^{(0)^2} + A_2 E^{(0)} J(J + 1) + A_3 J^2(J + 1)^2 + A_4 J(J + 1)\langle \mathbf{P}_z^2 \rangle$$
$$+ A_5 \langle \mathbf{P}_z^4 \rangle + A_6 E^{(0)}\langle \mathbf{P}_z^2 \rangle \tag{3-150}$$

Kivelson [388] has expressed (3-150) in a form more convenient for machine calculations. Table 3-7 gives the explicit forms of the coefficients in terms of defined quantities. The A_i are independent of the rotational quantum numbers.

The A_i can be calculated for simple molecules if sufficient structural and force constant data is available. An equivalent first-order perturbation solution has been given [367, 369] using the formulation of the rotation-vibration problem of Goldsmith et al. [354]. Continued fraction methods for the approximate evaluation of $\langle \mathbf{P}_z^2 \rangle$ and $\langle \mathbf{P}_z^4 \rangle$ have been discussed by Kivelson and Wilson [382] and Allen and Cross [34]. For a near prolate rotor and a small value of the asymmetry parameter δ it is permissible to use

$$\langle \mathbf{P}_z^4 \rangle \cong \langle \mathbf{P}_z^2 \rangle^2 \approx K^4 \tag{3-151}$$

Tables of $\langle \mathbf{P}_z^2 \rangle$ and $\langle \mathbf{P}_z^4 \rangle$ as a function of κ have been published [323, 734]. If $E/J(J + 1)$ is very different from κ and the limiting K value is large, a good approximation for a prolate near-symmetric top is

$$\langle \mathbf{P}_z^4 \rangle \approx \langle \mathbf{P}_z^2 \rangle^2 = (\partial E^{(0)}/\partial \alpha)^2 \tag{3-152}$$

Similar expressions hold for near-oblate tops. Unless the molecule is very

TABLE 3-7

CENTRIFUGAL DISTORTION COEFFICIENTS USED TO EVALUATE
THE EXPANSION IN EQUATION (3-150)[a]

$$A_1 = \frac{16R_6}{(b-c)^2}$$

$$A_2 = -\left[\frac{16R_6(b+c)}{(b-c)^2} + \frac{4\delta_J}{(b-c)}\right]$$

$$A_3 = -D_J + 2R_6 + \frac{16R_6 bc}{(b-c)^2} + 2\delta_J\frac{(b+c)}{(b-c)}$$

$$A_4 = -\left[D_{JK} - 2\delta_J\sigma - 16R_6\frac{(a^2-bc)}{(b-c)^2} + 4R_6\sigma^2 + 4R_5\frac{(b+c)}{(b-c)}\right]$$

$$A_5 = -(D_K + 4R_5\sigma + 2R_6 - 4R_6\sigma^2)$$

$$A_6 = \frac{8R_5 - 16R_6\sigma}{b-c}$$

$$\sigma = \frac{2a-b-c}{b-c}$$

$$D_J = -(\tfrac{1}{32})(3\tau_{xxxx} + 3\tau_{yyyy} + 2\tau_{xxyy} + 4\tau_{xyxy})h^4$$

$$D_K = D_J - \tfrac{1}{4}(\tau_{zzzz} - \tau_{zzxx} - \tau_{yyzz} - 2\tau_{xzxz} - 2\tau_{yzyz})h^4$$

$$D_{JK} = -D_J - D_K - \tfrac{1}{4}\tau_{zzzz}h^4$$

$$R_5 = -\tfrac{1}{32}[\tau_{xxxx} - \tau_{yyyy} - 2(\tau_{xxzz} + 2\tau_{xzxz}) + 2(\tau_{yyzz} + 2\tau_{yzyz})]h^4$$

$$R_6 = \tfrac{1}{64}[\tau_{xxxx} + \tau_{yyyy} - 2(\tau_{xxyy} + 2\tau_{xyxy})]h^4$$

$$\delta_J = -\tfrac{1}{16}(\tau_{xxxx} - \tau_{yyyy})h^4$$

[a] From Ref. [382].

simple, the A_i must be determined empirically by fitting observed rotational transitions to (3-150). If a large number of transitions have been observed, a least squares fit usually gives a good account of the centrifugal distortion effects.

Centrifugal distortion contributions from terms of the sixth power in the rotational angular momentum have introduced effects larger than experimental error in several instances, and the treatment of Kivelson and Wilson can be extended to include these terms [410]. In the absence of machine calculations, terms of the form $\langle K|K \pm 2\rangle$ can be diagonalized by a continued fraction technique, and first-order perturbation theory may be used to treat the $\langle K|K \pm 4\rangle$ elements. For a near-symmetric top, the additional undetermined constants become manageable if only those constants which do not vanish in the symmetric rotor limit are retained. Following this procedure, Pierce *et al.* [410] introduced the additional terms $H_J J^3 (J + 1)^3 + H_{JK} J^2 (J + 1)^2 \langle \mathbf{P}_z^2 \rangle + H_{KJ} J (J + 1) \langle \mathbf{P}_z^4 \rangle + H_K \langle \mathbf{P}_z^6 \rangle$ for a planar molecule. The approximations used in the treatment force the H's to be empirical constants.

It has been found that inclusion of P^6-type terms generally introduces 729 sixth-order coefficients through the term $\Sigma_{\alpha\beta\gamma\delta\varepsilon\eta} [\alpha\beta\gamma\delta\varepsilon\eta] \mathbf{P}_\alpha \mathbf{P}_\beta \mathbf{P}_\gamma \mathbf{P}_\delta \mathbf{P}_\varepsilon \mathbf{P}_\eta$. Fortunately, these may be reduced to 105 terms as long as the energy is computed only to the fourth order [414]. These coefficients have been evaluated in terms of fundamental molecular constants for a nonlinear XYX molecule [415]. In this case only six constants are needed; they are the six cubic potential constants of the molecule.

A group of sum rules including the effects of centrifugal distortion have been derived for the rotational energy levels of an asymmetric rotor. Allen and Olson [402] and Hill and Edwards [409] have written a set of general expressions and the set for planar molecules, respectively. Substitutions have been given which correct these sum rules to the fourth order [369].

3-13. Fermi Resonance in Nonlinear Molecules

Fermi resonance interactions can alter the vibrational and rotational energy level structure of a nonlinear molecule in the same manner as described in Section 3-9 whenever a near degeneracy occurs between vibrational states of the same symmetry. In the vibrational spectrum these interactions usually involve a fundamental transition at v_i and a combination at $v_j + v_k$ or an overtone at nv_k. In the absence of a strong interaction an approximate sum rule can be written for the vibration-rotation constants. For v_j, v_k and the combination $v_j + v_k$

$$\alpha_j + \alpha_k = \alpha_{j+k} \tag{3-153}$$

for a particular rotational constant. The mixing indicated in (3-80) and (3-81) produces large deviations in (3-153) which indicate a possible resonance and eventually permit the calculation of the anharmonic potential constant k_{ijk} where resonance between v_i and $v_j + v_k$ has been assumed. The resulting effect on the rotational spectrum is a frequency shift of rotational transitions in the two interacting excited states away from their unperturbed locations.

CHAPTER 4 | MOLECULAR STRUCTURE

4-1. Internuclear Distances and Moments of Inertia

The accurate determination of moments of inertia or rotational constants from rotational spectra would be of little value unless some means were available for converting this data into molecular structure information. Moreover, for the calculated structure to be meaningful, it must be related to a defined molecular structure. For a better understanding of the problems involved in the determination and interpretation of molecular structure, the case of a diatomic molecule with an equilibrium bond length r_e may be considered. Using the Morse potential [7] shown in Fig. 4-1 as the potential

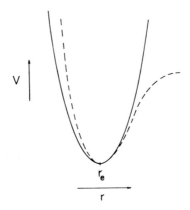

FIG. 4-1. Comparison of the Morse potential function (dashed curve) with a harmonic potential function (solid curve) for a diatomic molecule. The Morse potential has the form $V = D(1 - \exp[-k(r - r_e)])^2$ where D is the dissociation energy and k is an adjustable constant. For a harmonic oscillator $V = \frac{1}{2}kr^2$.

function for the molecule, r_e is determined by the lowest point on the potential curve. In its lowest vibrational state, the molecule does not reside at r_e due to zero-point vibrational effects. The average of the instantaneous values of r assumed by the molecule during a vibration is designated as $\langle r \rangle$. Unless the potential function is a parabola, i.e., the vibration harmonic, r_e, and $\langle r \rangle$ are not identical. Figure 4-1 compares the Morse potential function with a harmonic potential function centered at $r = r_e$.

If the potential is assumed to be parabolic, the equilibrium bond distance is equal to the average bond distance.

$$r_e = \langle r \rangle \tag{4-1}$$

The equilibrium moment of inertia I^e is proportional to r_e^2 and therefore to $\langle r \rangle^2$. However, the average moment of inertia, $\langle I \rangle$, is proportional to the instantaneous average of the square of r, i.e., to $\langle r^2 \rangle$. Since $\langle r^2 \rangle$ and $\langle r \rangle^2$ are generally not identical quantities, $\langle I \rangle$ does not equal I^e. But neither $\langle I \rangle$ nor I^e are measured in microwave spectroscopy. The effective moments of inertia I^0 obtained directly from the rotational spectrum are moments averaged over the vibrational state of the molecule.

$$I^0 \neq \langle I \rangle \tag{4-2}$$

The presence of zero-point vibrational effects prevents any simple relationship between I^0, $\langle I \rangle$ and I^e. It is possible to state relationships between I^0 and I^e, but these expressions require a knowledge of anharmonic potential constants which are known for only a few simple molecules. However, the average and effective moments of inertia can be related through correction terms which make use of the harmonic potential constants [365].

The components of the instantaneous moment of inertia tensor for a vibrating molecule may be expanded conveniently in terms of the normal coordinates Q_i:

$$I_{\alpha\beta} = I_\alpha^* \delta_{\alpha\beta} + \sum_i a_i^{\alpha\beta} Q_i + \sum_i \sum_j A_{ij}^{\alpha\beta} Q_i Q_j + \cdots \tag{4-3}$$

$\delta_{\alpha\beta}$ is the Kronecker delta which vanishes for $\alpha \neq \beta$, and the asterisk indicates an arbitrarily chosen standard configuration.

$$a_i^{\alpha\beta} = \left(\frac{\partial I_{\alpha\beta}}{\partial Q_i} \right)_* \tag{4-4}$$

$$A_{ij}^{\alpha\beta} = \left(\frac{\partial^2 I_{\alpha\beta}}{\partial Q_i \, \partial Q_j} \right)_* \tag{4-5}$$

This formulation enables perturbation expansions to be made using any convenient molecular configuration as long as it does not differ too greatly from the equilibrium configuration [476]; this is necessary to keep expansions linear in the vibrational quantum number v valid. Assuming small vibrational amplitudes, the following relationships may be written between the effective moment I^0, the average of the instantaneous moment $\langle I \rangle$, and the moment of inertia for the average configuration I^{AV} [365].

$$I_\alpha^0 = \langle I_\alpha^{-1} \rangle^{-1} - 4 \sum_i \sum_j \left[(\zeta_{ij}^\alpha)^2 \frac{\omega_i^2}{\omega_i^2 - \omega_j^2} \right] \langle Q_i^2 \rangle \qquad (4\text{-}6)$$

$$\langle I_\alpha^{-1} \rangle^{-1} = \langle I_\alpha \rangle - \sum_i \sum_\gamma [(a_i^{\alpha\gamma})^2 / I_\gamma] \langle Q_i^2 \rangle \qquad (4\text{-}7)$$

$$\langle I_\alpha \rangle = I_\alpha^* + \sum_i a_i^{\alpha\alpha} \langle Q_i \rangle + \sum_i A_{ii}^{\alpha\alpha} \langle Q_i^2 \rangle \qquad (4\text{-}8)$$

$$\langle I_\alpha \rangle = I_\alpha^{AV} + \sum_i A_{ii}^{\alpha\alpha} \langle Q_i^2 \rangle \qquad (4\text{-}9)$$

The perturbation expansion includes terms linear in the vibrational quantum numbers v_i. For example,

$$\langle Q_i^2 \rangle = \frac{2K}{d_i \omega_i} \left(v_i + \frac{d_i}{2} \right) \qquad (4\text{-}10)$$

where K is a constant and d_i is the degeneracy. In most cases, the order of the moments is given as

$$\langle I_\alpha \rangle > I_\alpha^{AV} > I_\alpha^0 > I_\alpha^e \qquad (4\text{-}11)$$

This order is dictated by the signs of the vibration-rotation terms.

The structural data available from rotational spectra usually is limited to effective moments of inertia in the ground vibrational state. For a polyatomic molecule there may be three experimental quantities: the three moments of inertia. Isotopic substitution allows more structural information to be obtained without greatly altering the molecular dimensions. When an isotopic substitution takes place in a molecule, the frequencies of vibration involving the substituted atom may change appreciably. The effect on the frequency of vibration is primarily a mass effect, because the potential energy function presumably is not very sensitive to isotopic mass changes. The product rule of Teller and Redlich is based on this assumption [21]. The main difficulty in structure calculations is that the zero-point vibrations over which the ground state rotational constants are averaged differ for each isotopic species.

4-2. r_0 Structure

The most obvious method for obtaining the molecular structure is the solution of the moment equations. The components of the inertial tensor have been defined in Chapter 2. Diagonalization of this tensor yields the principal moments of inertia designated as I_a, I_b, and I_c. The molecule-fixed axis system with origin at the COM is the x, y, z axis system. When this system is also the principal axis system, the x, y, z axes are correlated with the a, b, c axes by the permutations listed in Chapter 2. There are nine relationships which are imposed on the $3N$ atomic coordinates. These include the three diagonal moment equations similar to (2-3),

$$I_{xx} = \sum_i m_i(y_i^2 + z_i^2) \tag{4-12}$$

and the three cross-moment equations

$$I_{xy} = I_{yx} = -\sum_i m_i x_i y_i \tag{4-13}$$

(Permutation of x, y, z yields the other four relations.) The final three conditions are the center of mass equations (2-1).

$$\sum_i^{\text{atoms}} m_i q_i = 0, \qquad q = x, y, z \tag{4-14}$$

The cross-terms vanish in the principal axis system. An effective rotational constant B_0 can be defined in terms of I_b^0, the effective moment of inertia.

$$B_0 = \frac{h}{8\pi^2 I_b^0} \tag{4-15}$$

I_b^0 can be expressed as an average over the zero-point vibrations in terms of r_i, the instantaneous distance of the atoms from the b axis, or r_{0i}, the effective distance from the axis.

$$I_b^0 = \frac{1}{\langle 1/\sum_i m_i r_i^2 \rangle} = \sum_i m_i r_{0i}^2 \tag{4-16}$$

The r_0 differ slightly for each isotopic species. When the moment equations are written out for each isotope, a new set of unknowns is introduced. If the assumption is made that the r_0 are identical for each isotopic species, the set of moment equations can be solved to give the r_0 structure. There is a certain minimum number of isotopic species which must be used to solve these equations exactly. If fewer than the minimum number of species have been studied, some simplifying assumptions must be made concerning the values of bond lengths and angles in the molecule. If more data is available, it can be used as a check on the validity of the assumption that isotopic substitution causes no structural changes. It is found that large deviations in the r_0 structure occur when different isotopically substituted molecules are used in the calculation and that these deviations can be mainly attributed to zero-point vibrational effects.

4-3. r_s Structure

Kraitchman [451] has developed exact solutions for the molecular co-ordinates in terms of the equilibrium moments of inertia. These allow the calculation of the individual coordinates of the atoms. The coordinates of an isotopically substituted atom may be determined in the principal axis system of the original or parent molecule. If it is possible to isotopically substitute for each of the atoms in the parent molecule, the complete structure can be determined by elementary geometry. Unfortunately, in some situations isotopic substitution proves too insensitive to produce reliable structural information. The conditions on the center of mass and the moment equations may be used to find the coordinates of atoms for which isotopic substitutions could not be made. This r_s or "substitution" method has been discussed and compared with the r_0 method by Costain [458]. The r_s method of structure determination and its limitations will be considered for linear, symmetric, and asymmetric top molecules.

$I_x^{e'}$, $I_y^{e'}$, and $I_z^{e'}$ represent the equilibrium principal moments of the iso-topically substituted species with the unprimed moments being those of the parent molecule. The coordinates of the isotopically substituted atom in the principal axis system of the unsubstituted molecule are x, y, z. The atom of mass m is replaced by an isotope of mass $m + \Delta m$. M represents the mass of the original unsubstituted molecule. $\mathbf{R}_i$ is the distance of the ith atom from the origin of a general coordinate system with $\mathbf{R}_i^c$ being the distance of the same atom from the center of mass.

$$\mathbf{R} = \mathbf{R}_i - \mathbf{R}_i^c \tag{4-17}$$

$\mathbf{R}$ is the distance between the COM and the origin of the general coordinate system. The center of mass conditions are rewritten as

$$\sum_i^{3N} m_i \mathbf{R}_i^c = 0 \tag{4-18}$$

$$\mathbf{R} = \frac{\sum_i m_i \mathbf{R}_i}{\sum_i m_i} \tag{4-19}$$

The inertial tensor with respect to an arbitrary origin can be written as

$$\mathbf{I} = \sum_i m_i (R_i^2 \mathbf{1} - \mathbf{R}_i \mathbf{R}_i) \tag{4-20}$$

with $\mathbf{1}$ being the unit tensor. Therefore, from (4-18) and (4-19) the inertial tensor with respect to the center of mass is

$$\mathbf{I}^e = \sum_i m_i (R_i^2 \mathbf{1} - \mathbf{R}_i \mathbf{R}_i) - \left[\frac{1}{\sum_i m_i} \right] \left[\left(\sum_i m_i \mathbf{R}_i \sum_i m_i \mathbf{R}_i \right) \mathbf{1} - \left(\sum_i m_i \mathbf{R}_i \sum_i m_i \mathbf{R}_i \right) \right]$$

$$\tag{4-21}$$

For an isotopically substituted molecule, the elements of this tensor become

$$I_{xx}^{e'} = I_x^e + \Delta m(y^2 + z^2) - \frac{(\Delta my)^2}{M + \Delta m} - \frac{(\Delta mz)^2}{M + \Delta m} = I_x^e + \mu(y^2 + z^2) \quad (4\text{-}22)$$

$$I_{xy}^{e'} = -\mu xy \quad (4\text{-}23)$$

$$\mu = (\Delta mM)/(M + \Delta m) \quad (4\text{-}24)$$

Once an atom has been isotopically substituted in a molecule, its position, in principle, has been determined. If more than a single substitution is made at one atomic position, no new information concerning the positions of other atoms in the molecule can be obtained directly. However, multiple substitution can lead to estimates of the zero-point vibrational effects. A measure of these vibrational effects is obtainable because substitution of different isotopes at the same atomic position will give different calculated coordinate values.

4-4a. Linear Molecules

The following conditions hold for a linear molecule.

$$I_x^{e'} = I_y^{e'}; \qquad I_x^e = I_y^e; \qquad I_z^e = I_z^{e'} \cong 0 \quad (4\text{-}25)$$

The x' and y' axes are oriented parallel to the x and y axes. The z axis is the figure axis of the molecule and all the x, x' and y, y' coordinates are zero. By substituting these values into (4-22), the relationship between the moments in the parent and substituted molecules is

$$I_x^{e'} = I_x^e + \mu z_e^2 \quad (4\text{-}26)$$

This equation gives the absolute distance of the substituted atom from the COM of the parent molecule in terms of the mass change and the equilibrium moments.

$$z_e^2 = [\mu^{-1}(I_x^{e'} - I_x^e)] = (\mu^{-1} \Delta I_x^e) \quad (4\text{-}27)$$

From this equation, the absolute value of the z coordinate for each atom in the molecule can be calculated. Its sign must be deduced either from multiple isotopic substitution or from other sources of structural information. The sign ambiguity is a direct result of the squared dependence of the moments of inertia on the molecular coordinates.

For a linear molecule containing N atoms, the minimum number of isotopic substitutions necessary to determine the coordinates of all the atoms is $N - 2$. Once the coordinates of the $N - 2$ atoms have been calculated, they are substituted into the two equations

$$\sum_i m_i z_i = 0 \qquad (4\text{-}28)$$

$$\sum_i m_i z_i^2 = I_x^e \qquad (4\text{-}29)$$

and the remaining two coordinates are calculated. A quadratic equation results and the proper choice of roots must be made from some independent information. The only time the sign ambiguity is dangerous is when the atom lies near the COM. Then greater uncertainties are introduced by the small value of the coordinate.

The case of a symmetric top where substitution is made on the figure axis is very similar. The conditions of (4-25) are still valid with the exception that $I_z^e = I_z^{e'} \neq 0$. Since ΔI_z^e is zero, the coordinates of atoms on the axis are given by the same expression as (4-27) for linear molecules.

If the equilibrium moments of inertia were directly measurable, the only error in $|z_e|$ would result from the uncertainty in ΔI_x^e which is designated as $\delta(\Delta I_x^e)$. The uncertainty in $|z_e|$ is then given by differentiating (4-27).

$$\delta|z_e| = [2\mu|z_e|]^{-1}\delta(\Delta I_x^e) \qquad (4\text{-}30)$$

The uncertainty in $|z_e|$ increases rapidly as $|z_e| \to 0$, indicating that isotopic substitution is very unfavorable for atoms which lie near the COM. This is found to be a general conclusion applicable to any atom which lies near one or more principal axes. The error is a function of the mass difference between isotopes but is essentially independent of the mass of the atom being substituted.

The equilibrium moments of inertia are very difficult to obtain and effective moments of inertia must be used to determine the substitution coordinates. I_x^0, I_y^0, I_z^0 are the effective moments and $|z_s|$ is the absolute value of the substitution coordinate.

$$z_s^2 = \mu^{-1}(I_x^{0'} - I_x^0) = \mu^{-1} \Delta I_x^0 \qquad (4\text{-}31)$$

The effective parameters of the ground state, r_0 values, differ for each isotopic species and cannot be determined exactly by isotopic substitution.

4-4b. Comparison of r_0 and r_s Structures for Linear Molecules

Because linear molecules have the simplest molecular structure, they provide an excellent basis for a comparison of r_0 and r_s structures with each other and with the equilibrium parameters r_e. The basic assumption found in the r_0 structure requires the r_0 parameters for different isotopic species of the same molecule to be identical. This assumption is invalid for real non-rigid molecules. Isotopic substitution, particularly for hydrogen and other light atoms, can produce a significant change in the average over zero-point vibrations with the result that r_0 parameters differ for different isotopic species. Because the r_0 structure is not invariant, sizeable errors are introduced by first assuming that the r_0 parameters are identical and then forcing these parameters to fit the observed I^0. If a method were available for obtaining the correct r_0 parameters for one particular isotopic species, then the I^0 could be reproduced from these values by (4-16). The various r_0 parameters obtained by isotopic substitution cannot be expected to reproduce the I^0 of any particular isotope.

Similarly, a complete r_s structure obtained by isotopic substitution at each atomic site in a molecule allows the calculation of a substitution moment I^s which cannot be directly identified as the I^e or I^0 moments.

For a linear molecule, the effective rotational constant B_0 can be expanded in terms of the vibration-rotation constants α_i.

$$B_0 = B_e - \sum_i \alpha_i \left(v_i + \frac{d_i}{2} \right) = B_e - \bar{\alpha} \tag{4-32}$$

A parameter γ can be defined by the relation [458]

$$\left(\frac{B_e}{B'_e} \right)^\gamma = \frac{\bar{\alpha}}{\bar{\alpha}'} \tag{4-33}$$

A series of substitutions then yields a relationship between z_s and z_e.

$$\Delta I^0_x = \mu z_s^2 = \frac{h}{8\pi^2} \left[\left(\frac{1}{B'_0} \right) - \left(\frac{1}{B_0} \right) \right] = \Delta I^e_x + \frac{h}{8\pi^2} \left\{ \left[\frac{\bar{\alpha}'}{B'^2_e} \right] - \left[\frac{\bar{\alpha}}{B^2_e} \right] + \cdots \right\} \tag{4-34}$$

$$\Delta I^e_x = \frac{h}{8\pi^2} \left[\frac{1}{B'_e} - \frac{1}{B_e} \right] \tag{4-35}$$

By definition,

$$\frac{B_e}{B'_e} = \frac{I^{e'}_x}{I^e_x} = 1 + \frac{\Delta I^e_x}{I^e_x} \tag{4-36}$$

Inserting these relations into (4-34) and neglecting the terms in $(\bar{\alpha}/B_e)$ $(\Delta I^0_x / \Delta I^e_x)$,

$$\Delta I^0_x = \Delta I^e_x [1 + (2 - \gamma)\bar{\alpha}/B_e] \tag{4-37}$$

From (4-27) and (4-31) this becomes

$$|z_s| = |z_e| \{ 1 + [1 - (\gamma/2)]\bar{\alpha}/B_e \} \tag{4-38}$$

$\gamma = 1$ gives the result $|z_s| = |z_0|$ which implies that isotopic substitution has no effect on the $|z_0|$. For $\gamma = 2, |z_s| = |z_e|$ which indicates that the substitution method gives the equilibrium parameters directly. The former result is not expected to be valid because the presence of zero-point vibrational effects cannot be neglected. The latter is ruled out by the previous discussion.

Dunham [331] has shown that for a diatomic molecule

$$B'_e = \rho B_e \qquad (4\text{-}39)$$

$$\alpha'_e = \rho^3 \alpha_e \qquad (4\text{-}40)$$

where

$$\rho = \frac{v'}{v} = (\mu/\mu')^{1/2} \qquad (4\text{-}41)$$

The v's are vibrational frequencies and the μ's are reduced masses for the substituted and parent molecules. From (4-33) this gives $\gamma = \frac{3}{2}$ for a diatomic molecule and leads to the expression

$$|z_s| = (|z_e| + |z_0|)/2 \qquad (4\text{-}42)$$

The I^s which are computed from a complete r_s structure can be expected to fall between the I^0 and I^e values. Costain [458] confirmed that the average value of γ, based on experimental values, was near $\frac{3}{2}$.

For diatomic molecules the effective, average, and substitution coordinates can be related to each other by ξ, the relative deviation from the equilibrium bond length [365].

$$\xi = \frac{r - r_e}{r_e} \qquad (4\text{-}43)$$

From a series expansion in ξ, the average nth power of the bond length can be written as

$$\langle r^n \rangle^{1/n} = Kr_e \qquad (4\text{-}44)$$

where

$$K = 1 + \langle \xi \rangle - \tfrac{1}{2}(1 - n)\langle \xi^2 \rangle + \cdots \qquad (4\text{-}45)$$

$$\langle \xi \rangle = -a_1(3B_e/\omega_e)(v + \tfrac{1}{2}) \qquad (4\text{-}46)$$

$$\langle \xi^2 \rangle = (2B_e/\omega_e)(v + \tfrac{1}{2}) \qquad (4\text{-}47)$$

ω_e is the harmonic vibrational frequency, and a_1 is a dimensionless cubic anharmonic constant. Only terms linear in v are used. This gives

$$\langle r \rangle = r_e[1 + \langle \xi \rangle] \qquad (4\text{-}48)$$

$$r_0 = r_e[1 + \langle \xi \rangle - \tfrac{3}{2}\langle \xi^2 \rangle] \qquad (4\text{-}49)$$

$$r_s = r_e[1 + f(\langle \xi \rangle - \tfrac{3}{2}\langle \xi^2 \rangle)] \qquad (4\text{-}50)$$

where

$$f = (\mu/m_1)[1 + (\mu_1/\mu)^{1/2}]^{-1} + (\mu/m_2)[1 + (\mu_2/\mu)^{1/2}]^{-1} \qquad (4\text{-}51)$$

28972

The m_i are the masses of the atoms in the parent molecule, the μ_i are the reduced masses of the isotopically substituted molecules and μ is the reduced mass of the parent molecule. From the above equations it is seen that the average bond distance is larger than the effective bond length, all of which are larger than the true equilibrium value. f varies from $\sqrt{2}$ for deuterium substitution in H_2 to about $\frac{1}{2}$ when the μ_i differ negligibly from μ.

The range of the r_s structures is found to be at least an order of magnitude less than that of the r_0 structures [467]. The relationship between r_0 and r_s is apparent if it is assumed that the substituted isotope is shifted slightly to compensate for zero-point vibrational effects. Let the mass of the substituted atom be $m' = M + \Delta m$ and let the new coordinate be $r' = r_0 - \delta r$. This gives

$$\mu r_s^2 = \mu r_0^2 - 2m'r_0\,\delta r(\mu/\Delta m) \tag{4-52}$$

which is rearranged to give

$$r_s = r_0 - \left(\frac{m'\,\delta r}{\Delta m}\right) \tag{4-53}$$

Thus the r_0 coordinate is greater than the r_s coordinate by a function of mass and coordinate change with isotopic substitution.

The difference between the r_0 and r_s structures for nonlinear molecules is essentially the same as that for linear molecules, except that additional dimensions complicate the procedure. Limitations are again imposed on coordinate determinations near the center of mass or near a principal axis; nevertheless, the r_s structures are generally better than the r_0 values. Kraitchman's formulas are derived for the equilibrium moments of inertia but effective values must be used. In the following development, equilibrium values will be indicated, but it is understood that the effective values are actually used when the equilibrium values are not available.

When the I^0 equations are solved to obtain the molecular structure, the resulting solution yields the r_0 structure. When the ΔI^0 are used in Kraitchman's equations, the resulting solution yields the r_s structure.

4-5. Off-Axis Substitution in a Symmetric Top

The x axis is oriented perpendicular to a line joining the COM and the substituted atom. This completely arbitrary choice forces the substituted atom to have an x coordinate which is zero. The nonvanishing elements become

$$I_x^{e'} = I_x^e + \mu(y^2 + z^2) \tag{4-54}$$

$$I_{yy}^{e'} = I_y^e + \mu z^2 \tag{4-55}$$

$$I_{zz}^{e'} = I_z^e + \mu y^2 \tag{4-56}$$

$$I_{yz}^{e'} = -\mu yz \tag{4-57}$$

The matrix equation

$$\begin{bmatrix} I_y^e + \mu z^2 & -\mu yz \\ -\mu yz & I_z^e + \mu y^2 \end{bmatrix} = \begin{bmatrix} I_y^{e'} & 0 \\ 0 & I_z^{e'} \end{bmatrix} \tag{4-58}$$

and

$$\mu^{-1} \Delta I_x^e = y^2 + z^2 \tag{4-59}$$

are two relationships which may be solved for y and z in terms of the substituted and original moments. I_z, which cannot be determined from the rotational spectrum, can be eliminated from these equations. The resulting equations for the atomic coordinates are

$$|y_e| = \left[\frac{1}{\mu} \frac{(I_x^{e'} - I_y^{e'})(I_x^{e'} - I_z^{e'})}{(I_x^{e'} - I_y^e - I_z^e + I_y^e)} \right]^{1/2} \tag{4-60}$$

$$|z_e| = \left[\frac{1}{\mu} \frac{(I_y^{e'} - I_y^e)(I_z^{e'} - I_y^e)}{(I_y^{e'} + I_z^{e'} - I_x^{e'} - I_y^e)} \right]^{1/2} \tag{4-61}$$

For off-axis isotopic substitutions, such as in trimethylamine, $I_z^{e'}$ is very poorly determined because the isotopic species is a near symmetric top, and the coordinates are weak functions of $I_z^{e'}$. I_z^e may be calculated from the other moments in cases where a good value for $I_z^{e'}$ has been obtained.

$$I_z^e = I_z^{e'} + I_y^{e'} - I_x^{e'} \tag{4-62}$$

4-6a. Planar Asymmetric Tops

If the z axis is chosen perpendicular to the molecular plane, the z coordinates of all the atoms are zero. For a rigid planar body an interesting relation holds between the moments of inertia.

$$I_z^e = I_x^e + I_y^e \tag{4-63}$$

This equation is fully discussed in the section on inertial defect. The nonzero elements of the inertial tensor for a planar asymmetric top are

$$I_z^{e'} = I_z^e + \mu(x^2 + y^2) \tag{4-64}$$

$$I_{xx}^{e'} = I_x^e + \mu y^2 \tag{4-65}$$

$$I_{yy}^{e'} = I_y^e + \mu x^2 \tag{4-66}$$

$$I_{xy}^{e'} = -\mu xy \tag{4-67}$$

By diagonalizing the inertial tensor and solving for the coordinates, the correct substitution expressions are

$$|x_e| = \left[\frac{1}{\mu}\frac{(I_y^{e'} - I_y^e)(I_x^{e'} - I_y^e)}{(I_x^e - I_y^e)}\right]^{1/2}$$

(4-68)

$$|y_e| = \left[\frac{1}{\mu}\frac{(I_x^{e'} - I_x^e)(I_y^{e'} - I_x^e)}{(I_y^e - I_x^e)}\right]^{1/2}$$

(4-69)

4-6b. Nonplanar Asymmetric Tops

For the nonplanar class of asymmetric molecules, the planar dyadic used by Kraitchman [451] makes the derivation of coordinate expressions more straightforward. The planar dyadic is defined with respect to the center of mass.

$$\mathbf{P} = \sum_i m_i\mathbf{R}_i\mathbf{R}_i - \frac{(\Sigma_i m_i\mathbf{R}_i)(\Sigma_i m_i\mathbf{R}_i)}{\Sigma_i m_i}$$

(4-70)

When the origin lies at the COM, the elements of $\mathbf{P}$ in the principal axis system take a simplified form.

$$P_{xx} = \sum_i^N m_i x_i^2 = P_x$$

(4-71)

$$P_{xy} = \sum_i^N m_i x_i y_i = 0$$

(4-72)

The relationships between $\mathbf{P}$ and $\mathbf{I}$ are then

$$P_x = \tfrac{1}{2}(I_y + I_z - I_x)$$

(4-73)

$$I_x = P_y + P_z$$

(4-74)

For the substituted molecule the elements of the planar dyadic are given by the expressions

$$P'_{xx} = P_x + \mu x^2$$

(4-75)

$$P'_{xy} = \mu xy$$

(4-76)

The secular equation for the planar principal moments P'_x, P'_y, and P'_z can be expanded as a cubic in P' and the coefficients can be equated to the corresponding coefficients in (4-78) where they are expressed explicitly in terms of P'_x, P'_y, and P'_z.

$$\begin{bmatrix} P_x + \mu x^2 - P' & \mu xy & \mu xz \\ \mu xy & P_y + \mu y^2 - P' & \mu yz \\ \mu xz & \mu yz & P_z + \mu z^2 - P' \end{bmatrix} = 0 \quad (4\text{-}77)$$

$$P'^3 - (P'_x + P'_y + P'_z)P'^2 + (P'_xP'_y + P'_xP'_z + P'_yP'_z)P' - P'_xP'_yP'_z = 0 \quad (4\text{-}78)$$

By reinserting relations (4-75) the coordinates can be evaluated in terms of the principal moments of inertia.

$$|x_{el}| = \{(2\mu)^{-1}[\Delta I_y^e + \Delta I_z^e - \Delta I_x^e][1 + (\Delta I_x^e + \Delta I_z^e - \Delta I_y^e)/2(I_x^e - I_y^e)]$$
$$\times [1 + (\Delta I_x^e + \Delta I_y^e - \Delta I_z^e)/2(I_x^e - I_z^e)]\}^{1/2} \qquad (4\text{-}79)$$

The y and z coordinates are obtained by a proper permutation of x, y, and z, and the distance of the substituted atom from the center of mass of the original or parent molecule is given by $|R|$.

$$|R| = [(2\mu)^{-1}(\Delta I_x^e + \Delta I_y^e + \Delta I_z^e)]^{1/2} \qquad (4\text{-}80)$$

Kraitchman's basic equations have been extended to treat simultaneous isotopic substitutions of symmetrically equivalent nuclei in molecules with proper C_{nv} or improper S_{nv} symmetry [484]. Formulas have been derived for examples of C_{2v}, C_{3v}, D_{6h}, C_s, C_{2h}, and D_{3d} symmetry.

4-7. Structure Determinations When All Atoms Are Not Isotopically Substituted

It is not always possible to substitute isotopically at each atomic position in a molecule. For some atoms like fluorine only one isotope is available. In cases like this, either the moment conditions or the center of mass relations must be employed to determine all the coordinates. The minimum number of isotopic substitutions necessary to give a complete structure is determined by considering each type of molecule separately.

Consider a linear molecule with N atoms. If $N - 2$ of the atoms are isotopically substituted then only two coordinates remain undetermined. These may be calculated by using the equations

$$\sum_i m_i z_i = 0 \qquad (4\text{-}81)$$

$$\sum_i m_i z_i^2 = I_b \qquad (4\text{-}82)$$

These are the moment equations for the parent molecule. The resulting quadratics give two sets of solutions for the coordinates. The correct set must be chosen by recourse to independent information. Any fewer than $N - 2$ isotopic substitutions would force the use of assumptions or data from an independent source (e.g., electron diffraction). When all N atoms can be isotopically substituted, the r_s coordinates of all N atoms are determined. The moment of inertia which is calculated from these coordinates is designated I_b^s. Since the ΔI^0 values are used in the ΔI^e equations for the r_s coordinates, $I_b^s \neq I_b^0$.

When only $N - 1$ isotopic substitutions can be made, for example, in a molecule containing a single fluorine atom, either (4-81) or (4-82) is employed to determine the Nth coordinate. If, for instance, (4-82) for the moment of inertia is used, the whole difference between I_b^0 and I_b^s must be absorbed by the Nth coordinate. The Nth coordinate will be larger than $r_s(N)$ by $\delta r_s(N)$.

$$\delta r_s(N) = \frac{I_b^0 - I_b^s}{2m_N r_s(N)} \tag{4-83}$$

$\delta r_s(N)$ is inversely proportional to m_N, the mass of the Nth atom. The coordinate shift required for a structure determination is largest for a hydrogen atom and results in a notable difference between $X-H$ and $X-D$ bonds determined by this procedure. For minimum error the unsubstituted atom should be the heaviest, although this cannot always be controlled. Coordinates of light atoms should always be determined by isotopic substitution. If (4-81) is used instead, the coordinate shift from $r_s(N)$ will be

$$\delta r_s(N) = \sum_i m_i r_{si}/m_N \tag{4-84}$$

The deviation is again inversely proportional to m_N but is essentially independent of the coordinate value. This gives the first moment equation an advantage over the moment of inertia relation, since it can be used with greater reliability for atoms located near principal axes. Unfortunately, the error is again dependent upon m_N and this makes it a poor choice for light atoms. It is interesting to note that the isotopic substitution method and the first moment equation used with $N - 1$ substitutions are complementary, in the sense that the former is independent of the mass and inversely proportional to r whereas the latter is independent of r and inversely proportional to m.

In planar asymmetric top molecules, $N - 2$ isotopic substitutions are again the minimum number needed. The coordinates of the remaining two atoms can be obtained from the moment equations of the parent molecule.

$$\sum_i m_i x_i = 0; \qquad \sum_i m_i y_i = 0; \qquad \sum_i m_i x_i^2 = I_y^e \tag{4-85}$$

$$\sum_i m_i x_i y_i = I_{xy}^e = 0; \qquad \sum_i m_i y_i^2 = I_x^e$$

As in the other cases, the signs of the coordinates are determined from other sources of structural information. The correct one of the two sets of solutions given by (4-85) must be chosen from the other considerations.

Only $N - 3$ substitutions are needed to determine the coordinates of all the atoms in a nonplanar asymmetric top. This is possible because nine moment relations given in (4-12)–(4-14) are available. Simultaneous solution of these equations may prove to be a lengthy process.

4-8a. Determination of Coordinates near Principal Axes: Linear Molecules

Pierce [464] has proposed a method independent of the first moment equations for the determination of atomic coordinates located near one or more principal axes. This is very convenient in situations where the first moment equations do not yield a complete structure. This may occur when two or more atoms lie near a principal axis or when one or more atoms cannot be isotopically substituted. The effect of zero-point vibrations on small coordinates is well exemplified by the behavior of the N_2O molecule with isotopic substitution. Because of the mass distribution, the central nitrogen atom lies very near the center of mass for all isotopic species. The B_0 values [1091] for $N^{15}N^{14}O^{16}$ and $N^{15}N^{15}O^{16}$ are 12,137.30 MHz and 12,137.39 MHz, respectively. From (4-31) this gives a negative ΔI_x^0 which in turn yields an imaginary nitrogen coordinate. The imaginary coordinate is a direct result of the zero-point vibrational effects which cause Kraitchman's equations to be unreliable for small coordinates. Zero-point effects may produce large errors for coordinates which are less than about 0.15 Å [458].

If α represents the contribution of zero-point vibrations to I^0,

$$\alpha = \frac{h\bar{\alpha}}{8\pi^2 B_e^2} + \cdots \tag{4-86}$$

then

$$I_{jk\cdots}^0 = I_{jk\cdots}^e + \alpha_{jk\cdots} \tag{4-87}$$

where the subscripts run over all substituted atoms. $\alpha_{jk\cdots}$ can be expanded in terms of the mass changes with isotopic substitution $\Delta m_j, \Delta m_k, \Delta m_l, \ldots$

$$\alpha_{jk\cdots} = \alpha + [\alpha_j^{(1)} \Delta m_j + \alpha_k^{(1)} \Delta m_k + \cdots] + [\alpha_{jj}^{(2)} \Delta m_j^2 + \alpha_{kk}^{(2)} \Delta m_k^2$$
$$+ \alpha_{jk}^{(2)} \Delta m_j \Delta m_k + \cdots] + \cdots \tag{4-88}$$

Using (4-31) for a substitution of atom j in a linear molecule

$$\Delta I_j^0 = \mu_j z_j^2 + \alpha_j^{(1)} \Delta m_j + \alpha_{jj}^{(2)} \Delta m_j^2 + \cdots \tag{4-89}$$

If the kth atom is substituted, the center of mass is shifted by

$$\Delta z_k = \Delta m_k z_k / (M + \Delta m_k) \tag{4-90}$$

The absolute value notation has been suppressed.[†]

The coordinate of the jth atom is changed by Δz_k,

$$z_j' = z_j - \Delta z_k \tag{4-91}$$

[†] In all cases it must be remembered that only the magnitudes of the coordinates and coordinate changes are known without the benefit of some independent information.

Therefore,

$$\Delta I^0_{jk} = \mu'_j(z_j - \Delta z_k)^2 + \alpha_j^{(1)}\,\Delta m_j + \alpha_{jj}^{(2)}\,\Delta m_j^2 + \alpha_{jk}^{(2)}\,\Delta m_j\,\Delta m_k + \cdots \qquad (4\text{-}92)$$

$$\Delta I^0_{jk} = I^0_{jk} - I^0_k \qquad (4\text{-}93)$$

$$\mu'_j = \frac{(M + \Delta m_k)\,\Delta m_j}{M + \Delta m_j + \Delta m_k} \qquad (4\text{-}94)$$

By neglecting cross terms in the mass changes, the second difference expression becomes

$$\Delta\Delta I^0_{jk,j} = \Delta I^0_{jk} - \Delta I^0_j = (\mu'_j - \mu_j)z_j^2 - 2(\mu'_j\,\Delta z_k)z_j + \mu'_j\,\Delta z_k^2 \qquad (4\text{-}95a)$$

This expression is valid to the same degree of approximation for symmetric top molecules when the j and k atoms are on the symmetry axis. The success of (4-95a) can be tested by multiple isotopic substitutions, although this may prove to be very difficult experimentally. The validity of (4-31) for large coordinates is based on the assumption that the moments of inertia are much more sensitive to the isotope effect than are the zero-point terms. In an analogous manner this justifies the assumption in (4-95a) for large values of Δz_k. z_j may be reliably fixed if z_k is sufficiently large.

An alternative to (4-95a) has been suggested. (4-91) gives the coordinate shift for the jth atom after a substitution for the kth atom. If an isotopic substitution is then made at the jth position using the molecule substituted at the kth position as the parent, the z'_j coordinate can be determined from (4-31). z_k then follows from (4-91).

$$z_k = \left[\frac{M + \Delta m_k}{\Delta m_k}\right](z_j - z'_j) \qquad (4\text{-}95b)$$

This is equivalent to (4-95a).

4-8b. Near Axis Coordinates in Asymmetric Tops

The second-difference method has been extended to determine in-plane coordinates in asymmetric tops with a plane of symmetry [466]. Four isotopic species are necessary for the coordinate calculation just as they were in the linear case. These four species can be denoted as X, X', Y, Y' where X and Y are two parent species and X' and Y' are isotopically substituted at the atom whose coordinate is being calculated.

$$\Delta I_b(X) = I_b(X') - I_b(X) \qquad (4\text{-}96)$$

$$\Delta I_b(Y) = I_b(Y') - I_b(Y) \qquad (4\text{-}97)$$

Let the c axis be perpendicular to the plane of symmetry. The a coordinate is to be determined. The b coordinate is assumed to be large enough for determination by Kraitchman's first difference method. From (4-68) for planar asymmetric tops, where a_x is the a coordinate in X,

$$\Delta I_b(X) = \mu_x a_x^2 \{1 + [\Delta I_a(X)/(I_a(X) - I_b(X))]\}^{-1} = k_x a_x^2 \qquad (4\text{-}98)$$

$$\Delta I_b(Y) = \mu_y a_y^2 \{1 + [\Delta I_a(Y)/(I_a(Y) - I_b(Y))]\}^{-1} = k_y a_y^2 \qquad (4\text{-}99)$$

If the transformation from the X system to the Y system is known, and A and B are the center of mass coordinates of Y in the X system,

$$a_y = (a_x - A)\cos\theta - (b_x - B)\sin\theta \qquad (4\text{-}100)$$

$$b_y = (a_x - A)\sin\theta + (b_x - B)\cos\theta \qquad (4\text{-}101)$$

θ is the angle of rotation from the X to Y principal axis system. Rewriting (4-100) which states the relationship between a_y and a_x in terms of known parameters,

$$a_y = a_x \cos\theta + C \qquad (4\text{-}102)$$

where C is known.

The second-difference relation allows a_x to be calculated from a quadratic.

$$\Delta\Delta I_b = \Delta I_b(Y) - \Delta I_b(X) = k_y a_y^2 - k_x a_x^2$$
$$= (k_y \cos^2\theta - k_x)a_x^2 + (2k_y C \cos\theta)a_x + k_y C^2 \qquad (4\text{-}103)$$

If either I_a or I_b cannot be accurately determined, an alternative relation in terms of the out-of-plane moment I_c may be solved.

$$\Delta\Delta I_c = \Delta I_c(Y) - \Delta I_c(X) = \mu_y[(b_x - B)^2 + (a_x - A)^2] - \mu_x[a_x^2 + b_x^2]$$

$$(4\text{-}104)$$

The second-difference approach can also be applied to the calculation of coordinates of atoms which do not lie in a plane of symmetry; however, the equations are more complex and the calculations more involved. The transformation between the two basis systems generally requires a three-dimensional rotation as well as a translation, and the other two coordinates of the atom must be well determined prior to the calculation.

4-8c. Coordinates of Atoms near the COM in an Asymmetric Top with a Plane of Symmetry

The case where a and b are both small can be treated if it is assumed that the effect of coordinate rotation, in going from (X, Y) to (X', Y'), is negligible. When this assumption is valid

$$\Delta I_b(X) = \mu_x a_x^2 \qquad (4\text{-}105)$$

$$\Delta I_b(Y) = \mu_y a_y^2 \qquad (4\text{-}106)$$

and

$$\Delta \Delta I_b = \mu_y a_y^2 - \mu_x a_x^2 \qquad (4\text{-}107)$$

It is also possible to solve a set of simultaneous equations (obtained by using the method of the previous section) for a and b. The coordinate b would not be absorbed into a constant in (4-102) and two equations would result.

4-9a. The Inertia Defect

Consider the principal axis system located in a rigid planar body of infinitesimal thickness. A basic mathematical relationship between the moments of inertia of the body is

$$I_c = I_a + I_b \qquad (4\text{-}108)$$

where I_a and I_b are the two in-plane moments of inertia and I_c is the out-of-plane moment. The in-plane axes need not be principal axes. This relationship can be assumed to hold for a rigid planar molecule. Because real molecules are not rigid, this equation does not hold exactly. The inertia defect for a planar molecule is defined as

$$\Delta = I_c^0 - I_a^0 - I_b^0 \qquad (4\text{-}109)$$

and is a measure of the deviation from rigid planarity.

In the general case of a nonrigid molecule (4-73) gives

$$I_\alpha + I_\beta - I_\gamma = 2P_\gamma - \Delta_\gamma \qquad (4\text{-}110)$$

where Δ_γ primarily represents the nonrigid contributions of the vibrations. A special significance is attached to Δ_γ in the planar case since P_γ vanishes, giving (4-109).

There are several direct advantages in being able to calculate and measure Δ besides the ability to further test vibration-rotation theory. Δ can be used to determine the moments of inertia of a planar molecule when insufficient spectral data is available. When two of the moments are known, the third can be calculated from (4-109) and a knowledge of Δ. The inertia defect is a strong function of the vibrational force constants. These constants may be estimated for simple planar molecules. The inertia defect is also important in molecular structure determination in molecules which are nearly planar but whose potential function has a small hump in the planar configuration. Here the experimentally determined value of Δ may be misleading because it may lie very near to zero. In these cases, a comparison of the calculated and observed values of Δ is helpful. Finally, excited vibrational states may be identified by their inertia defects because Δ is usually a strong function of the vibrational state of a molecule.

Darling and Dennison [1034] were first to attempt a theoretical calculation of the inertia defect. They found that to second order, Δ is independent of any anharmonic vibrational constants. Oka and Morino [471] have derived a general expression for the inertia defect (Appendix 5).

Herschbach and Laurie [481] have given a general treatment of inertia defects for both planar molecules and nonplanar molecules with a plane of symmetry.

As shown in Appendix 5, Oka and Morino have written the contributions to the inertia defect as a sum of vibrational, centrifugal, and electronic terms.

$$\Delta_y = \Delta(\text{vib}) + \Delta(\text{cent}) + \Delta(\text{elect}) \qquad (4\text{-}111)$$

Table 4-1 lists the calculated contributions of each of these effects and compares the total calculated and observed values for some C_{2v} triatomic

TABLE 4-1

GROUND STATE INERTIAL DEFECTS FOR C_{2v} TRIATOMIC MOLECULES [a]

	$\Delta_{\text{vib.}}$	$\Delta_{\text{C.D.}}$	Δ_e	$\Delta^c_{\text{calculated}}$	Δ_{observed}
H_2O^{16}	0.0460	0.0008	0.0000	0.0467	0.0486
D_2O^{16}	0.0627	0.0008	0.0000	0.0635	0.0648
H_2S^{32}	0.0631	0.0007	0.0001	0.0639	0.0660
H_2Se	0.0736	0.0008	0^b	0.0744	0.0595
D_2Se	0.1034	0.0008	0^b	0.1042	0.1045
O_3	0.1107	0.0011	-0.0104	0.1014	0.1017
$O^{18}O_2$	0.1148	0.0011	-0.0104	0.1055	0.1046
$S^{32}O_2$	0.1376	0.0004	-0.0037	0.1343	0.1348
$S^{34}O_2$	0.1395	0.0004	-0.0037	0.1362	0.1365
$Cl^{35}O_2$	0.160	0.001	-0.004^b	0.157	0.168
F_2O	0.131	0.001	0^b	0.132	0.217
$Cl_2^{35}O$	0.187	0.001	0^b	0.187	0.197

[a] From Oka and Morino [478].
[b] Assumed values.
[c] For error limits see Oka and Morino [478].

molecules. These values indicate, to a good approximation, that the inertia defect may be estimated by the vibrational contributions alone. In turn, the vibrational term separates conveniently into harmonic and anharmonic contributions.

$$\Delta_y(\text{vib}) = \Delta_y^{\text{har}} + \Delta_y^{\text{anh}} \qquad (4\text{-}112)$$

Using the small amplitude vibration approximation [481], these terms are

$$\Delta_\gamma^{har} = 3 \sum_i [A_{ii}^{\alpha\alpha} + A_{ii}^{\beta\beta} - A_{ii}^{\gamma\gamma}]\langle Q_i^2 \rangle - 4 \sum_i \sum_j [(\zeta_{ij}^\alpha)^2 + (\zeta_{ij}^\beta)^2$$

$$- (\zeta_{ij}^\gamma)^2] \left[\frac{\omega_j^2}{\omega_j^2 - \omega_i^2} \right] \langle Q_i^2 \rangle \tag{4-113}$$

$$\Delta_\gamma^{anh} = - \sum_i [a_i^{\alpha\alpha} + a_i^{\beta\beta} - a_i^{\gamma\gamma}]\langle Q_i \rangle \tag{4-114}$$

The coefficients are the derivatives of the instantaneous moments of inertia with respect to the normal coordinates.

4-9b. Planar Molecules

The anharmonic contributions to the inertia defect in (4-114) vanish for a planar molecule because

$$[a_i^{\alpha\alpha} + a_i^{\beta\beta} - a_i^{\gamma\gamma}] = 4 \sum_j m_j \gamma_j \left(\frac{\partial \gamma_j}{\partial Q_i} \right) = 0 \tag{4-115}$$

where γ_j represents the out-of-plane coordinate of the jth atom (all $\gamma_j = 0$).

$$\Delta_\gamma = \Delta_\gamma^{har} = \Delta(i) + \Delta(o) \tag{4-116}$$

$\Delta(i)$ and $\Delta(o)$ are the defect terms arising from in-plane and out-of-plane vibrations, respectively. If s and s' represent in-plane vibrations and t stands for out-of-plane modes,

$$\Delta(i) = 4 \sum_s \left[\sum_{s'} (\zeta_{ss'}^\gamma)^2 \left(\frac{\omega_s^2}{\omega_s^2 - \omega_{s'}^2} \right) - \sum_t [(\zeta_{st}^\alpha)^2 + (\zeta_{st}^\beta)^2] \right.$$

$$\left. \times \left(\frac{\omega_t^2}{\omega_t^2 - \omega_s^2} \right) \right] \langle Q_s^2 \rangle \tag{4-117}$$

$$\Delta(o) = 6 \sum_t \left[1 - \frac{2}{3} \sum_s [(\zeta_{st}^\alpha)^2 + (\zeta_{st}^\beta)^2] \left(\frac{\omega_s^2}{\omega_s^2 - \omega_t^2} \right) \right] \langle Q_t^2 \rangle \tag{4-118}$$

Certain simplifications are often possible; e.g., $\Delta(o)$ vanishes for triatomic molecules where out-of-plane modes are nonexistent.

4-9c. Inertia Defect and Molecular Structure of Planar Molecules

In molecules more complex than a linear molecule, additional complications appear in the structure determination. It is still true that the replacement of the ΔI^e by ΔI^0 in Kraitchman's formula yields an r_s structure, but because of the averages over zero-point vibrations, the effective r_0 coordinates differ slightly for rotations about different axes. For planar molecules the inertia defect in terms of the effective moments of inertia invalidates relations which held for the equilibrium moments. There are three sets of data from which the r_0 structure can be determined [458]:

1. I_a^0 and I_b^0,
2. I_b^0 and I_c^0 or I_b^0 and $I_a = I_a^0 + \Delta$,
3. I_a^0 and I_c^0 or I_a^0 and $I_b = I_b^0 + \Delta$.

It is not certain which set of parameters gives a structure nearest to the equilibrium values.

Different considerations apply for the r_s structure. Equations (4-68)–(4-69) may be expressed in the form

$$x_s^2 = \left(\frac{1}{\mu}\right) \Delta I_b^0 \left(1 + \frac{\Delta I_a^0}{I_a^0 - I_b^0}\right) \tag{4-119}$$

$$y_s^2 = \left(\frac{1}{\mu}\right) \Delta I_a^0 \left(1 + \frac{\Delta I_b^0}{I_b^0 - I_a^0}\right) \tag{4-120}$$

x_s lies along the a axis and y_s along the b axis. Now

$$\Delta I_c^0 - \Delta I_a^0 - \Delta I_b^0 = \Delta' - \Delta = \tilde{\Delta} \tag{4-121}$$

where

$$I_c^{0'} - I_a^{0'} - I_b^{0'} = \Delta' \tag{4-122}$$

and $\tilde{\Delta}$ is the change in inertial defect with isotopic substitution. Again three sets of ΔI^0 are available, but the variation in the three solutions for the r_s coordinates depends on $\tilde{\Delta}$ instead of the inertia defect. Generally, the magnitude of the inertial defect is larger than the magnitude of $\tilde{\Delta}$ and one may expect more consistent r_s parameters.

An empirical rule has been devised for planar X_2YZ type molecules. If Δ_{xx} is the inertia defect for the X_2YZ molecule and Δ_{ww} is the defect for a W_2YZ molecule, then

$$\Delta_{xw} = (\Delta_{xx}\Delta_{ww})^{1/2} \tag{4-123}$$

where Δ_{xw} is the inertia defect for the $XWYZ$ molecule. Oka and Morino [483] have shown that this approximation leads to a good estimate of Δ_{xw}.

4-9d. Inertia Defect in Nonplanar Molecules

From the definition of (4-110), no restriction of planarity has been placed on the inertial defect Δ_y although its greatest usefulness occurs for planar molecules. Despite the fact that the implications of Δ_y would be far too complicated to yield useful information for large molecules with no symmetry, it can be of value for molecules which have a plane of symmetry.

Consider the class of molecules which possesses a plane of symmetry and n equivalent pairs of out-of-plane hydrogen atoms. The effective distance between the hydrogens in each pair is given by

$$nm_H(r_{HH}^0)^2 = I_a^0 + I_b^0 - I_c^0 \qquad (4\text{-}124)$$

For a molecule like acetaldehyde (4-124) can be rewritten in terms of the out-of-plane coordinate z_0.

$$4m_H z_0^2 = I_a^0 + I_b^0 - I_c^0 \qquad (4\text{-}125)$$

This equation is not valid for the equilibrium z coordinate since $4m_H z_0^2$ contains the effects of zero-point vibrations which are produced by the planar part of the molecule. From (4-124), the inertial defect is negative for a nonplanar molecule, and from Table 4-1, the planar portion of the molecule makes a positive contribution to $4m_H z_0^2$. This causes the z_0 coordinate to be reduced considerably.

For the r_s coordinates obtained from deuterium substitution

$$4\Delta m z_s^2 = (I_a^0 + I_b^0 - I_c^0)_D - (I_a^0 + I_b^0 - I_c^0)_H \qquad (4\text{-}126)$$

and $4\Delta m z_s^2$ is reduced only by $\tilde{\Delta}$. If $\tilde{\Delta}$ vanishes, the usual z_s coordinate is obtained. For a positive $\tilde{\Delta}$ the z_s coordinate can approach the equilibrium value of z.

If (4-124) is used indiscriminately to compare r_{HH}^0 and r_{DD}^0, large apparent increases in the H-H distance would occur upon isotopic substitution. Let Δ'' be defined by

$$I_a^0 + I_b^0 - I_c^0 = I_a^e + I_b^e - I_c^e - \Delta'' \qquad (4\text{-}127)$$

This discrepancy can be reduced by assuming that the major contributions to Δ'' come from the vibrations of in-plane atoms. Hence Δ'' should not be greatly affected by out-of-plane deuterium substitution. Laurie [459] has calculated Δ'' and r_{HH} in an attempt to verify this assumption and the results give a favorable indication. It can also be noted that the values of Δ'' obtained by these calculations are of the same magnitude as the inertia defects given by planar molecules. This again adds validity to the assumption that the in-plane atoms make the major contribution to Δ''.

Several general observations can be made concerning molecules with a plane of symmetry whose only out-of-plane atoms are symmetrically equivalent pairs [481]. Let $(+)$ and $(-)$ refer to vibrations which are symmetric and antisymmetric with respect to the plane of symmetry, and assume that all off-diagonal terms introduced into the inertial tensor by vibration-rotation interactions are vanishingly small. Then the in-plane atoms give no contribution to Δ_γ^{anh} nor do they add to Δ_γ^{har} for $(+)$ vibrations. However, for $(-)$ vibrations the in-plane atoms do contribute to Δ_γ^{har} as do the out-of-plane atoms in $(-)$ modes. Δ_γ^{anh} vanishes for the latter. The only anharmonic terms are produced by the out-of-plane atoms in $(+)$ vibrational modes. These modes also contribute terms to Δ_γ^{har}. The effects are summarized in Table 4-2.

TABLE 4-2

CONTRIBUTIONS TO THE HARMONIC AND ANHARMONIC PARTS OF THE INERTIAL DEFECT[a]

	In-plane $(+)$	In-plane $(-)$	Out-of-plane $(+)$	Out-of-plane $(-)$
Δ_γ^{har}	none	yes	yes	yes
Δ_γ^{anh}	none	none	yes	none

[a] The contributions are from in-plane and out-of-plane atoms for a molecule which has a plane of symmetry and out-of-plane atoms which only occur in symmetrically equivalent pairs. $(+)$ and $(-)$ refer to vibrations symmetric or antisymmetric with respect to the plane of symmetry [481].

Since the effect of the anharmonic terms $\langle Q_i \rangle$ is to displace the coordinates of the average configuration of a molecule from the equilibrium coordinates, (4-110) can be rewritten by choosing the average configuration as the standard in (4-3).

$$I_a^0 + I_b^0 - I_c^0 = 4 \sum_i m_i \langle z_i \rangle^2 - \Delta_\gamma^{har} \tag{4-128}$$

From the average value of the out-of-plane coordinates, the inertial defect can be calculated without a knowledge of the anharmonic force constants.

4-10. Variation of Bond Length with Isotopic Substitution

One very important assumption which was made in the substitution method for structure determination is the invariance of bond length with isotopic substitution. However, the structures of some related diatomic molecules in Table 4-3 indicate that large variations in bond distances can occur with isotopic substitution. This is particularly true when deuterium is substituted for hydrogen. The twofold mass change causes a 0.003–0.005 Å decrease on going from $X-H$ to $X-D$ bonds. For heavier atoms where the relative change in mass with isotopic substitution is much smaller, the changes in bond length are on the order of 0.0001 Å. It should be noted that when a heavy atom bonded to a hydrogen atom is substituted isotopically, the bond distance to the hydrogen can be assumed to be identical for both isotopic species. This results from the fact that the small mass of a hydrogen atom forces it to do most of the moving during a small amplitude vibration.

One of the effects of the assumption that bond lengths are independent of isotopic substitution is that the apparent distance usually is shorter than the

TABLE 4-3

COMPARISON OF r_0, r_e, AND $\langle r \rangle$ BOND LENGTHS IN DIATOMIC MOLECULES[a]

Molecule	r_0	r_e	$\langle r \rangle$
HF	0.9257	0.9170	0.9326
DF	0.9234	0.9171	0.9284
TF	0.9230	0.9177	0.9272
$O^{16}H$	0.9800	0.9707	0.9873
$O^{16}D$	0.9772	0.9700	0.9825
$C^{12}H$	1.1303	1.1198	1.1388
$C^{12}D$	1.1265	1.1188	1.1327
HCl^{35}	1.2837	1.2745	1.2904
HCl^{37}	1.2837	1.2746	1.2904
DCl^{35}	1.2813	1.2744	1.2858
DCl^{37}	1.2813	1.2744	1.2858
TCl^{35}	1.2800	1.2746	1.2853
TCl^{37}	1.2800	1.2746	1.2853
$C^{12}O^{16}$	1.1309	1.1282	1.1323
$C^{13}O^{16}$	1.1308	1.1282	1.1322
$C^{12}O^{18}$	1.1308	1.1282	1.1322
$C^{12}S^{32}$	1.5377	1.5349	1.5392
$C^{13}S^{32}$	1.5376	1.5349	1.5391
$C^{12}S^{34}$	1.5377	1.5349	1.5392
$I^{127}Cl^{35}$	2.3236	2.3209	2.3246
$I^{127}Cl^{37}$	2.3235	2.3209	2.3245

[a] From Ref. [476].

average bond length and in some cases even shorter than the equilibrium length. For a linear XYZ molecule [476] where substitution occurs on one of the end atoms, only a 0.01% change in bond length introduces a 0.2% error in the coordinate. This error grows much larger as the atom approaches one of the principal axes.

Another interesting effect which illustrates the importance of small changes in bond length is isotopic substitution in molecules like CO_2 or SO_2. For a rigid structure the insertion of C^{13} or S^{34} would be expected to produce no change in the moment of inertia I_b. However, the average and effective moments both decrease. A decrease in the average equilibrium bond lengths is also reported for $CS^{32}S^{34}$ over CS_2^{32}. If the assumption of no change in bond length is invoked in the case of C_2H_2 and C_2D_2, it is necessary to conclude that the C–H distance becomes shorter in excited vibrational states. Certainly this is not compatible with the present knowledge of excited state structures.

It has been suggested [476] that the usual assumption $r_{XH} = r_{XD}$ be replaced by an expression of the form

$$r_{XH} = r_{XD} + \eta \qquad (4\text{-}129)$$

where η varies between about 0.003 and 0.005 Å. From the large amount of data supporting the magnitude of η, it can be concluded that more consistent structures would be obtained from (4-129).

4-11. Values and Limitations of the Average Structure

Although the equilibrium bond distances are probably the most important structural parameters, the average structure of a molecule is very valuable. The average parameters can be used in direct comparisons with data from other experimental sources; notably, electron diffraction studies. To a good approximation, it has been shown that the average moments of inertia of a molecule can be related to the effective moments with a knowledge of the harmonic potential constants. For the ground vibrational state, the effective moment of inertia may be written as

$$I^0 = I^e + \tfrac{1}{2} \sum_i d_i \alpha_i \qquad (4\text{-}130)$$

where d_i represents the degeneracy of the vibrational mode, and α_i is the rotation-vibration interaction constant. The average moment is

$$\langle I \rangle = I^e + \tfrac{1}{2} \sum_i d_i \alpha_{ia} \qquad (4\text{-}131)$$

where α_{ia} is the anharmonic contribution to α_i, and α_{ih} is the set of harmonic terms.

$$\alpha_i = \alpha_{ia} + \alpha_{ih} \qquad (4\text{-}132)$$

This gives an average moment which is independent of α_{ia}.

$$\langle I \rangle = I^0 - \tfrac{1}{2} \sum_i d_i \alpha_{ih} \qquad (4\text{-}133)$$

The α_{ih} are complex functions of the atomic masses, molecular geometry, and harmonic force constants.

When molecular structures are being investigated, the average moments have several advantages over the experimentally determined effective moments. The substitution parameters are primarily defined by the methods used for their evaluation; average parameters have a physically well-defined meaning. The inconsistencies generated by the effective moments used in relations meant only for the equilibrium values are greatly reduced by the use of average moments. This is particularly evident for the inertia defect (Table 4-1).

The average parameters can also be used quite satisfactorily in a comparison of microwave and electron diffraction data. For diatomic molecules, $\langle r \rangle$ and the electron diffraction parameter r_g are substantially identical. However, for polyatomic molecules the definitions differ. r_g is essentially an average of the instantaneous distance between atoms and $\langle r \rangle$ is the average projection of the distances along the direction of the undisplaced bond. r_g shows a strong dependence on the anharmonic potential constants while $r_g - \langle r \rangle$ has a very mild anharmonic dependence. Relations have been derived between r_g and $\langle r \rangle$. They allow a direct comparison of the average parameters from electron diffraction and microwave spectroscopy. The relationships between r_s and r_g parameters are very complex and $r_s - r_g$ is still a strong function of the anharmonic force constants.

CHAPTER 5

NUCLEAR QUADRUPOLE COUPLING

5-1. Quadrupole Nuclei in Molecules

Nuclei possess a spin angular momentum $\mathbf{I}$ which is represented by an integral or half-integral quantum number I whose value is dependent on the composition and structure of the nucleus. A nucleus can have $2I + 1$ spin states; the magnitude of $\mathbf{I}$ is $[I(I + 1)]^{1/2}h$ where I is the maximum component of $\mathbf{I}$ in any direction. The properties of nuclear spin have been extensively and are discussed in most treatments of quantum mechanics. Under proper conditions, the nuclear spin angular momentum can couple with rotational angular momentum to produce a hyperfine structure in the rotational spectrum. For a quadrupole interaction, it is necessary that the nucleus possess a nonvanishing nuclear quadrupole moment which results from a nonspherical charge distribution in the nucleus. Such a distribution is found in nuclei with a spin angular momentum greater than $\frac{1}{2}h$ [566]. The interaction between the quadrupole moment Q and the electric field gradient of the molecule at the quadrupole nucleus provides a mechanism through which $\mathbf{I}$ and $\mathbf{J}$ can couple. Q may be either positive or negative if the nucleus has a prolate (elongated charge distribution) or an oblate (flattened charge distribution) charge shape, respectively. Q serves to measure the departure of the nuclear charge distribution from a spherical shape.

Nuclear quadrupole effects in molecules were first observed by Kellogg et al. [493] through the use of molecular beam techniques. Since then, quadrupole interactions have been observed as hyperfine structure in the rotational spectra of many molecules, in pure quadrupole resonance spectra using radio-frequency methods, and in Mössbauer spectra.

The most important parameter obtained in a nuclear quadrupole analysis is the electric field gradient, which provides valuable information concerning the electronic environment of the quadrupole nucleus. The vector model for the quadrupole interaction in the absence of an external field shows that the nuclear spin angular momentum $\mathbf{I}$ couples with the rotational angular momentum $\mathbf{J}$ to produce a resultant total angular momentum $\mathbf{F}$:

$$F = I + J \tag{5-1}$$

I and J remain as good quantum numbers whose vector sum is also quantized.

$$F = J + I, J + I - 1, \ldots, |J - I| \tag{5-2}$$

However, M_I and M_J, which are the projection quantum numbers of $\mathbf{I}$ and $\mathbf{J}$ in the uncoupled representation, are no longer constants of the motion. These relationships are illustrated in the vector diagram of Fig. 5-1 for the limiting zero-field case. It is observed that $\mathbf{I}$ and $\mathbf{J}$ precess about $\mathbf{F}$ and form fluctuating projections along the space-fixed direction.

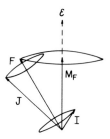

FIG. 5-1. A vector model illustrating the coupling of rotational angular momentum $\mathbf{J}$ and nuclear spin angular momentum $\mathbf{I}$ to form the resultant $\mathbf{F}$. M_F is the projection of $\mathbf{F}$ along the space-fixed axis represented by the electric field ε. Figure 8-5 illustrates the effects of ε on the coupling of $\mathbf{I}$ and $\mathbf{J}$.

The selection rules governing transitions between these energy levels are

$$\Delta I = 0; \qquad \Delta J = 0, \pm 1; \qquad \Delta F = 0, \pm 1 \tag{5-3}$$

These are the usual rigid rotor selection rules with the additional condition that the nuclear spin does not change during the transition. M_F replaces M as the projection quantum number. In order to make use of these selection rules, it is necessary to calculate the energy level splittings produced by the quadrupole interaction. This can be accomplished by developing the interaction Hamiltonian and its matrix elements in an appropriate representation.

5-2. Origin of the Quadrupole Interaction

A quadrupole moment interaction appears in the series expansion of a nuclear charge distribution which determines the potential at some distance from the nucleus. The electrostatic interaction between the nuclear charge density $\rho_n(\mathbf{r}_n)$ and the external charge density $\rho_e(\mathbf{r}_e)$ can be described in terms of the radius vectors $\mathbf{r}_n$ and $\mathbf{r}_e$ originating at the center of the nucleus (Fig. 5-2).

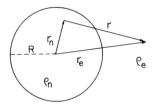

FIG. 5-2. Model used to calculate the quadrupole interaction. The charge densities ρ_e and ρ_n are functions of r_e and r_n, respectively.

If R is the effective radius of the nucleus, $\rho_n(\mathbf{r}_n)$ is negligible when $r_n > R$.

$$\mathbf{r} + \mathbf{r}_n = \mathbf{r}_e \tag{5-4}$$

where $\mathbf{r}$ is the vector distance between $\mathbf{r}_e$ and $\mathbf{r}_n$ and $\mathbf{r}_e > \mathbf{r}_n$. The magnitudes of these vectors can be related by the law of cosines. It follows that the charge interaction energy is given by

$$H = \int \frac{\rho_e(\mathbf{r}_e)\rho_n(\mathbf{r}_n)\, d\tau_e\, d\tau_n}{r} \tag{5-5}$$

Using the binomial theorem, an expansion of $1/r$ can be written in terms of a power series in r_n/r_e.

$$\frac{1}{r} \approx \frac{1}{r_e} + \frac{r_n}{r_e^2}P_1(\cos\theta) + \frac{r_n^2}{r_e^3}P_2(\cos\theta) + \cdots \tag{5-6}$$

θ is the angle between $\mathbf{r}_e$ and $\mathbf{r}_n$, and the P_l are Legendre polynomials. They are defined as

$$P_l(\Lambda) = \frac{1}{2^l l!}\frac{d^l(\Lambda^2 - 1)^l}{d\Lambda^l} \tag{5-7}$$

$$P_0(\cos\theta) = 1; \qquad P_1(\cos\theta) = \cos\theta; \qquad P_2(\cos\theta) = \tfrac{1}{2}(3\cos^2\theta - 1)$$

Each of the terms in (5-6) may be identified with a multiple moment of order 2^l. The first term in the expansion is the electrostatic potential at a distance r_e from the origin due to the nuclear charge located at the origin. Here the nuclear charge is treated as a point charge located at the origin. The second term is the nuclear electric dipole moment which effectively vanishes due to symmetry considerations [566]. The $l = 2$ term is the nuclear quadrupole contribution. Higher order terms are sufficiently smaller so that the quadrupole term dominates.

Several interesting observations can be made concerning electric multipole moments. For a nucleus with spin I the largest observable multipole effect is of the order 2^{2I} when $2I$ is even. If there is no nuclear degeneracy in I, if all the electrical effects come from electrical charges, and if the nuclear forces conserve parity, all of the odd multipoles vanish and the highest order multipole observed is $2^{(2I-1)}$ when $2I$ is an odd integer.

The quadrupole interaction energy can be obtained from the expansion of $1/r$.

$$H_Q = \int \frac{\rho_e(\mathbf{r}_e)\rho_n(\mathbf{r}_n)r_n^2(3\cos^2\theta - 1)\, d\tau_e\, d\tau_n}{2r_e^3}$$

$$= \int \frac{\rho_e(\mathbf{r}_e)\rho_n(\mathbf{r}_n)[3(\mathbf{r}_e\cdot\mathbf{r}_n)^2 - r_e^2 r_n^2]\, d\tau_e\, d\tau_n}{2r_e^5} \qquad (5\text{-}8)$$

The quantity in brackets in the integral may be expressed in terms of its coordinate components x_n and x_e.

$$[3(\mathbf{r}_e\cdot\mathbf{r}_n)^2 - r_e^2 r_n^2] = \tfrac{1}{3}\sum_{ij}(3x_{ni}x_{nj} - \delta_{ij}r_n^2)(3x_{ei}x_{ej} - \delta_{ij}r_e^2) \qquad (5\text{-}9)$$

δ_{ij} is the Kronecker delta. Now H_Q can be separated into two factors aside from the constant $\tfrac{1}{6}$.

$$H_Q = \tfrac{1}{6}\sum_{ij}Q_{ij}\nabla E_{ij} \qquad (5\text{-}10)$$

$$Q_{ij} = \int \rho_n(\mathbf{r}_n)[3x_{ni}x_{nj} - \delta_{ij}r_n^2]\, d\tau_n \qquad (5\text{-}11)$$

$$\nabla E_{ij} = \int \frac{\rho_e(\mathbf{r}_e)[3x_{ei}x_{ej} - \delta_{ij}r_e^2]\, d\tau_e}{r_e^5} \qquad (5\text{-}12)$$

The summation in (5-10) is equivalent to the scalar product of two tensors and can be written in dyadic notation.

$$H_Q = -\tfrac{1}{6}\mathbf{Q}:\nabla\mathbf{E} \qquad (5\text{-}13)$$

The tensors $\mathbf{Q}$ and $\nabla\mathbf{E}$ are symmetric and have zero trace. Because all the matrix elements of $\mathbf{Q}$ which are diagonal in I have the same dependence on M_I [566, 492], it follows that

$$Q_{ij} = \frac{eQ}{I(2I-1)}[\tfrac{3}{2}(\mathbf{I}_i\mathbf{I}_j + \mathbf{I}_j\mathbf{I}_i) - \delta_{ij}I^2] \qquad (5\text{-}14)$$

where Q is a scalar with the units of area called the quadrupole coupling constant.

$$eQ = \langle M_I = I|\rho_n(\mathbf{r}_n)(3z_n^2 - r_n^2)|M_I = I\rangle \qquad (5\text{-}15)$$

Similarly, the electric field gradient tensor can be expressed as

$$\nabla E_{ij} = \frac{q_{zz}}{J(2J-1)}[\tfrac{3}{2}(\mathbf{J}_i\mathbf{J}_j + \mathbf{J}_j\mathbf{J}_i) - \delta_{ij}J^2] \qquad (5\text{-}16)$$

for matrix elements diagaonal in J . q_{ZZ} is the electric field gradient along the space-fixed Z axis averaged over the state $M_J = J$.

$$q_{ZZ} = \left\langle M_J = J \left| \left| \frac{\partial^2 V}{\partial Z^2} \right| \right| M_J = J \right\rangle = \left\langle \left| \frac{\partial^2 V}{\partial Z^2} \right| \right\rangle_{av} \qquad (5\text{-}17)$$

Casimir [492] has simplified (5-13) for atomic nuclei, and the resulting first-order Hamiltonian in the molecular case is

$$H_Q = \sum_i eQ_i \left\langle \left| \frac{\partial^2 V}{\partial Z^2} \right| \right\rangle_{i\,/av} \left[\frac{3(\mathbf{J} \cdot \mathbf{I}_i)^2 + \frac{3}{2}(\mathbf{J} \cdot \mathbf{I}_i) - \mathbf{J}^2 \mathbf{I}_i^2}{2J(2J-1)I_i(2I_i-1)} \right] \qquad (5\text{-}18)$$

The indicated average of $(\partial^2 V/\partial Z^2)$ required in the first-order energy correction is over the unperturbed wave function $\psi^{(0)}$. The $\mathbf{J}$ are the overall rotational angular momentum operators, and the $\mathbf{I}_i$ are the nuclear spin angular momentum operators. The summation is over the quadrupole nuclei of the molecule. e is the unit electronic charge, and Q_i is considered constant for a given nucleus because its average has no rotational dependence. Since the electric field gradient $\langle (\partial^2 V/\partial Z^2) \rangle_{av}$ depends on the electronic environment of the quadrupole nucleus, the nucleus acts as a probe which samples the field strength in the molecule. When only one nucleus possesses a quadrupole moment, the factor containing the scalar products of the vectors $\mathbf{J}$ and $\mathbf{I}$ can be simplified to a scalar quantity which is an explicit function of the quantum numbers.

$$\mathbf{I} \cdot \mathbf{J} = \frac{1}{2}[F(F + 1) - I(I + 1) - J(J + 1)] \qquad (5\text{-}19)$$

$$H_Q = eQ \left\langle \left| \frac{\partial^2 V}{\partial Z^2} \right| \right\rangle_{av} \left[\frac{\frac{3}{4}C(C + 1) - I(I + 1)J(J + 1)}{J(2J-1)2I(2I-1)} \right] \qquad (5\text{-}20)$$

C is a function of F, I, and J; Z represents the space-fixed axis.

$$C = F(F + 1) - I(I + 1) - J(J + 1) \qquad (5\text{-}21)$$

C is the diagonal matrix element of the operator $2\mathbf{I} \cdot \mathbf{J}$. It is observed from (5-20) that H_Q is undefined for $I = 0$ and $I = \frac{1}{2}$. This verifies the requirement $I \geqslant 1$. It also follows that the quadrupole interaction vanishes for $J = 0$.

The gradient of the electric field can be described by the potential e/r. For a nucleus at the center of a Cartesian coordinate system, the electric field gradient arising from a charge e located on the Z axis a distance r from the origin can be written in terms of the potential as

$$\frac{\partial^2 V}{\partial Z^2} = \frac{2e}{r^3} \qquad (5\text{-}22)$$

If the charge is off the Z axis through an angle θ,

$$\frac{\partial^2 V}{\partial Z^2} = e\left(\frac{3\cos^2\theta - 1}{r^3}\right) \tag{5-23}$$

For a group of charges

$$\left\langle\frac{\partial^2 V}{\partial Z^2}\right\rangle_{av} = \left\langle\sum_i e_i\left[\frac{3\cos^2\theta_i - 1}{r_i^3}\right]\right\rangle_{av} \tag{5-24}$$

θ_i is the angle between $\mathbf{r}_i$ and the space-fixed Z axis. The summation in (5-24) is over all extranuclear charge and can be expressed as an integral over ρ_e, the extranuclear charge density.

$$q_{zz} = \int \rho_e \left(\frac{3\cos^2\theta - 1}{r^3}\right) d\tau \tag{5-25}$$

This is equivalent to integrating over e and over the square of the wave function which specifies the probability distribution of the electrons contributing to $\langle\partial^2 V/\partial Z^2\rangle_{av}$.

$$q_{zz} = \int \psi^*(q)_i \psi \, d\tau = e \int \psi^* \left(\frac{3\cos^2\theta_i - 1}{r_i^3}\right) \psi \, d\tau \tag{5-26}$$

$(q)_i$ refers to the contribution of the ith electron.

The quadrupole interaction can be developed in a general manner based on the coupling of angular momentum vectors. The charge interaction producing H_Q has been conveniently expressed in terms of Legendre polynomials. These may be written as products of second-order spherical harmonics, because any function which is well-behaved in the spherical coordinates θ and ϕ can be expressed as a linear combination of these functions. For the Legendre polynomial P_l, the spherical harmonic addition theorem gives a convenient relationship in terms of second-order spherical harmonics.

$$P_l(\cos\theta) = \frac{4\pi}{2l + 1} \sum_{m=-l}^{m=l} (-1)^m Y_m^l(\theta_1, \phi_1) Y_{-m}^l(\theta_2, \phi_2) \tag{5-27}$$

For the spherical harmonics to be single-valued, m must be an integer with $0 \le |m| \le l$. This relationship allows the separation of nuclear and electronic coordinates. The spherical harmonics for $l = 2$ can then be related to the quadrupole moment and the electric field gradient. Identifying θ_1, ϕ_1 with the nuclear coordinates and θ_2, ϕ_2 with the electronic coordinates, $Y(\omega_n)$ can be defined in terms of the nuclear quadrupole moment Q, and $Y(\omega_e)$ can be defined in terms of q_{zz}. Equations (5-6) and (5-27) lead to the connecting relationships

$$Q = \left[\frac{16\pi}{5e^2}\frac{I(2I - 1)}{(I + 1)(2I + 3)}\right]^{1/2} \langle I\|r_n^2 Y^2(\omega_n)\|I\rangle \tag{5-28}$$

and

$$q_{zz} = \left[\frac{16\pi}{5e^2} \frac{J(2J-1)}{(J+1)(2J+3)} \right]^{1/2} \langle J \| r_e^{-3} Y^2(\omega_e) \| J \rangle \qquad (5\text{-}29)$$

The reduced matrix elements identified by the double bar notation are formed by removing some specific quantum number dependence from the original matrix elements (Appendix 6).

Although Q has been determined for a large number of nuclei, it is convenient to define a composite term χ_{ij}, the nuclear quadrupole coupling constant.

$$\chi_{ij} = eq_{ij}Q \qquad (5\text{-}30)$$

The subscripts ij are determined by the coordinate system and by the symmetry of the extranuclear charge distribution. Once Q has been determined for a particular nucleus, χ_{ij} offers a direct measure of the field gradient q_{ij}.

Another important result of electromagnetic theory is Laplace's equation, which restricts the potential in a charge free region such as that very near but not including a nucleus.

$$\nabla^2 V = \frac{\partial^2 V}{\partial x^2} + \frac{\partial^2 V}{\partial y^2} + \frac{\partial^2 V}{\partial z^2} = 0 \qquad (5\text{-}31)$$

This relationship leads directly to a boundary condition on the nuclear coupling constants and confirms the zero trace of ∇E_{ij}

$$\chi_{xx} + \chi_{yy} + \chi_{zz} = 0 \qquad (5\text{-}32)$$

The quadrupole coupling constant can be viewed as a measure of the variation in electrostatic energy with respect to the relative orientation of the quadrupole moment of the nucleus. This is important in the evaluation of $\partial^2 V/\partial Z^2$. Consider a spherical charge distribution about the quadrupole nucleus such as that provided by the s electrons in a free atom. A charge density ρ results at the nucleus. Poisson's equation gives (ε is the dielectric constant)

$$\nabla^2 V = -4\pi\rho/\varepsilon \qquad (5\text{-}33)$$

However, the spherical symmetry does not permit a change in energy with nuclear orientation; this, in turn, prohibits any quadrupole interaction. Therefore, the $-4\pi\rho/\varepsilon$ contribution is specifically omitted and Laplace's equation is used. The directional dependence of the quadrupole coupling constants χ_{ij} suggests a tensor relationship to specify the anisotropy.

$$\chi = \begin{bmatrix} \chi_{xx} & \chi_{xy} & \chi_{xz} \\ \chi_{yx} & \chi_{yy} & \chi_{yz} \\ \chi_{zx} & \chi_{zy} & \chi_{zz} \end{bmatrix} \qquad (5\text{-}34)$$

Diagonal elements of this tensor expressed in a principal axis system are the experimentally measured quantities obtained from the first-order hyperfine structure of the rotational spectrum. The off-diagonal elements vanish when the principal inertial axis system and the principal quadrupole axis system coincide. Nonvanishing off-diagonal elements in the principal axis system contribute to the second-order energy correction.

5-3. Matrix Elements of H_Q

Because M_I and M_J are no longer constants of the motion, it is convenient to express the matrix elements of H_Q in a symmetric rotor representation which is diagonal in $I, F,$ and M_F. For a single quadrupole nucleus, the matrix elements may be written in a general form requiring only an evaluation of the rotational dependence of the electric field gradient along the space-fixed Z axis. To express these general matrix elements τ is used to represent the internal projection quantum numbers. For a linear rotor, it does not enter into the evaluation; for a symmetric rotor, it expresses the K dependence; for an asymmetric rotor, it signifies the τ or $K_{-1}K_1$ dependence in an asymmetric rotor representation. Because these matrix elements are diagonal in K in a symmetric rotor representation, it is their J dependence which introduces the off-diagonal elements found in the second-order correction term:

$$\langle J\tau|H_Q|J\tau'\rangle = \frac{eQ\langle J\tau M = J|\nabla E_{ZZ}|J\tau'M = J\rangle}{8I(2I-1)J(2J-1)}$$

$$\times \left[3C(C+1) - 4I(I+1)J(J+1)\right] \qquad (5\text{-}35)$$

$$\langle J\tau|H_Q|J+1, \tau'\rangle = \frac{eQ\langle J\tau M = J|\nabla E_{ZZ}|J+1, \tau'M = J\rangle}{8I(2I-1)J(2J+1)^{1/2}}[F(F+1)$$

$$-(I+1)I - J(J+2)][(I+J+F+2)(I-J+F)$$

$$\times (J-I+F+1)(J+I-F+1)]^{1/2} \qquad (5\text{-}36)$$

$$\langle J\tau|H_Q|J+2, \tau'\rangle = \frac{eQ\langle J\tau M = J|\nabla E_{ZZ}|J+2, \tau'M = J\rangle}{16I(2I-1)[(2J+1)(J+1)]^{1/2}}[(I+J+F+2)$$

$$\times (I+J+F+3)(I-J+F-1)(I-J+F)$$

$$\times (J-I+F+1)(J-I+F+2)(I+J-F+1)$$

$$\times (I+J-F+2)]^{1/2} \qquad (5\text{-}37)$$

These equations also give the $\langle J|J-1\rangle$ and $\langle J|J-2\rangle$ elements because H_Q is Hermitian. ∇E_{ZZ} represents the electric field gradient $\partial^2 V/\partial Z^2$.

In terms of reduced matrix elements involving the spherical harmonics, the general matrix elements of H_Q may be expressed as

$$\langle IJ\tau|H_Q|IJ'\tau'\rangle = (-1)^{I+J-F}[(2I+1)(2J+1)]^{1/2}W(IJIJ';2F)$$

$$\times (4\pi/5)[\langle I\|r_n^2 Y^2(\omega_n)\|I\rangle \langle J\|r_e^{-3}Y^2(\omega_e)\|J'\rangle] \qquad (5\text{-}38)$$

These matrix elements are diagonal in F and M_F. The $W(IJIJ;2F)$ are Racah coefficients which find important use in vector coupling problems [496, 497].

$$W(IIJJ;2F) = 6(-1)^{F-I-J}\left[\frac{(2J-2)!(2I-2)!}{(2J+3)!(2I+3)!}\right]^{1/2}$$

$$\times [C(C+1) - \tfrac{4}{3}I(I+1)J(J+1)] \qquad (5\text{-}39)$$

Use has been made of the symmetry property $W(IIJJ;2F) = W(IJIJ;F2)$.

5-4. First-Order Quadrupole Energy

For a single quadrupole nucleus, the first-order quadrupole energy reduces to the problem of averaging the field gradient over the proper unperturbed wave functions of the molecule. In the case of a linear molecule, the appropriate wave functions are given by (2-43) and the average is

$$\langle J, M = J|\nabla E_{zz}|J, M = J\rangle = \left(\frac{\partial^2 V}{\partial a^2}\right)\int \psi^*_{J,M=J}\left(\frac{3\cos^2\theta - 1}{2}\right)\psi_{J,M=J}\, d\tau$$

$$= \frac{-J}{2J+3}\left(\frac{\partial^2 V}{\partial a^2}\right) \qquad (5\text{-}40)$$

This equation makes use of the fact that for a rigid linear or symmetric top molecule

$$\chi_{xx} = \chi_{yy} = -\tfrac{1}{2}\chi_{zz} \qquad (5\text{-}41)$$

because the charge distribution is symmetric about the figure axis. This requirement forces the principal axis system of the molecule to be coincident with the principal quadrupole axis system in which the quadrupole tensor is diagonal (after translation to the COM).

$$\chi_{zz} = \chi_{aa} \qquad (5\text{-}42)$$

$$\chi_{cc} = \chi_{bb} = \chi_{xx} = \chi_{yy} \qquad (5\text{-}43)$$

$$\chi_{ij} = 0 \qquad (i \neq j) \qquad (5\text{-}44)$$

If the interaction between I and J is stronger than the interaction of either one with any other field, the quadrupole energy is given by (5-35) and (5-40) as

$$E_Q^{(1)} = -\chi_{aa} f(I, J, F) \tag{5-45}$$

where

$$f(I, J, F) = \left[\frac{\frac{3}{4}C(C + 1) - I(I + 1)J(J + 1)}{2I(2I - 1)(2J - 1)(2J + 3)} \right] \tag{5-46}$$

$f(I, J, F)$ is often referred to as Casimir's function and has been extensively tabulated [20]. Once the quadrupole coupling constant χ_{aa} has been determined from experimental data, the other two constants are given by (5-41). This form holds as long as no degenerate vibrational bending modes are excited. (5-45) vanishes if J is zero or I is less than one. Illustrating nuclear quadrupole splitting in a linear molecule, Fig. 5-3 shows the quadrupole pattern of the $J = 1 \to 2$ transition in $O^{17}C^{12}S^{32}$ where the O^{17} nucleus has a nuclear spin of $\frac{5}{2}$.

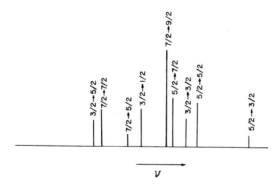

FIG. 5-3. Relative quadrupole splittings and component line strengths of the $J = 1 \to 2$ transition in $O^{17}C^{12}S^{32}$ [540]. $eqQ = -1.32$ MHz.

Casimir's function has several interesting properties. For $F = J + I$ or $F = J - I$, $f(I, J, F)$ is independent of I. When $F = J$ and $I = 1$, $f(I, J, F)$ takes the value -0.25. It is also found that for the maximum and minimum values of F, $f(I, J, F)$ is positive, while for most intermediate values of F, $f(I, J, F)$ has a negative value.

Some representative values of nuclear quadrupole coupling constants in linear molecules containing single quadrupole nuclei are listed in Table 5-1.

TABLE 5-1

eqQ VALUES IN SOME LINEAR MOLECULES

Quadrupole nucleus	Molecule	eqQ(MHz)	References
Cl^{35}	H^2Cl^{35}	67.3	[1417]
	H^3Cl^{35}	67.0	[1310]
	FCl^{35}	-145.99	[1096]
	$Tl^{203}Cl^{35}$	-15.795	[1156]
Cl^{37}	H^2Cl^{37}	53.0	[1417]
	H^3Cl^{37}	53.0	[1310]
	FCl^{37}	-114.92	[1096]
	$Tl^{203}Cl^{37}$	12.446	[1156]
Br^{79}	H^2Br^{79}	530.5	[1417]
	H^3Br^{79}	527.6	[1334]
	$Tl^{205}Br^{79}$	130.	[1327]
	FBr^{79}	1089.0	[1143]
	Li^7Br^{79}	37.2	[1281]
Br^{81}	H^2Br^{81}	443.5	[1417]
	H^3Br^{81}	442.1	[1334]
	FBr^{81}	909.2	[1143]
I^{127}	H^2I^{127}	-1823.3	[1417]
	H^3I^{127}	-1822.6	[1334]
	$Tl^{205}I^{127}$	$-550.$	[1327]
N^{14}	FCN^{14}	-2.67	[1510]
	HCN^{14}	-4.58	[1141]
O^{17}	CO^{17}	4.43	[584]
	$O^{17}CS$	-1.32	[540]
S^{33}	CS^{33}	12.835	[1330]
	OCS^{33}	-29.13	[929]
S^{35}	OCS^{35}	21.90	[942]

Although some nuclei, such as deuterium, have nonzero quadrupole moments, their interaction is too weak to be resolved, except under conditions of very high resolution. These conditions may be obtained in molecular beam studies where the effects of Doppler broadening are considerably reduced. The variation in sign and magnitude of eqQ for a particular nucleus reflects its charge environment through the value of the electric field gradient.

For a symmetric top, the first-order averaging is done with the wave functions in (2-67) and the resulting expression is a function of K.

$$\langle JKM = J|\nabla E_{zz}|JKM = J\rangle = \frac{3K^2 - J(J+1)}{(J+1)(2J+3)}\left(\frac{\partial^2 V}{\partial c^2}\right) \qquad (5\text{-}47)$$

The symmetric rotor quadrupole energy can be expressed in terms of the quadrupole coupling constant as

$$E_Q^{(1)} = \left[\frac{3K^2}{J(J+1)} - 1 \right] f(I, J, F)\chi_{cc} \tag{5-48}$$

For $K = 0$, this expression reduces to the one given above for a linear molecule in the ground state. As in the case of a linear molecule, the single quadrupole nucleus must lie on the figure axis. It is possible for a symmetric top to possess three equivalent off-axis quadrupole nuclei, but this problem requires the use of vector coupling coefficients and is discussed in Section 5-7.

Once χ_{cc} is determined, χ_{aa} and χ_{bb} can be obtained from (5-41). Table 5-2 lists the eqQ values for some symmetric top molecules which have one quadrupole nucleus, and Fig. 5-4 illustrates the relatively simple quadrupole hyperfine structure of the $J = 0 \rightarrow 1$ transition in a symmetric rotor.

When a degenerate bending mode is excited in a linear molecule, a component of angular momentum along the molecular axis results. In such a state, the molecule acts like a near-symmetric top. In this case the symmetric

TABLE 5-2

eqQ Values in Some Symmetric Top Molecules

Molecule	Quadrupole nucleus	eqQ(MHz)	References
CH_3Cl^{35}	Cl^{35}	-74.740	[1056]
CH_3Cl^{37}	Cl^{37}	-58.921	[1056]
CH_3Br^{79}	Br^{79}	577.15	[564]
CH_3Br^{81}	Br^{81}	482.16	[564]
CH_3I^{125}	I^{125}	2179.	[587]
CH_3I^{127}	I^{127}	1934.	[587]
CH_3I^{129}	I^{129}	1422.	[587]
CH_3I^{131}	I^{131}	973.	[587]
CF_3Cl^{35}	Cl^{35}	-77.98	[404]
CF_3Cl^{37}	Cl^{37}	-61.44	[1092]
CF_3Br^{79}	Br^{79}	619.	[1204]
CF_3Br^{81}	Br^{81}	517.	[1204]
CF_3I^{127}	I^{127}	-2143.8	[1137]
CH_3CCCl^{35}	Cl^{35}	-79.6	[1311]
CH_3CCCl^{37}	Cl^{37}	-62.6	[1311]
CH_3CCBr^{79}	Br^{79}	647.	[1205]
CH_3CCBr^{81}	Br^{81}	539.	[1205]
CH_3CCI^{127}	I^{127}	$-2230.$	[1205]
$(CH_3)_3N^{14}$	N^{14}	-5.47	[690]
$N^{14}SF_3$	N^{14}	1.19	[1560]
$Sb^{121}H_3$	Sb^{121}	458.7	[1321]
$Sb^{121}D_3$	Sb^{121}	465.4	[1321]

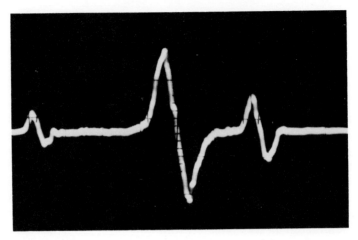

FIG. 5-4. Oscilloscope trace of the $J = 0 \rightarrow 1$ transition in trimethylamine, illustrating the quadrupole hyperfine structure produced by the N^{14} nucleus. The Stark components (up) are just becoming resolved from the zero-field lines (down). The two outer components are separated by 4.10 MHz [690]. Frequency is increasing to the left.

top K is replaced by l, the vibrational angular momentum along the axis. The expression for the gradient is analogous to that for a symmetric top molecule and is independent of the sign of l.

$$\langle JlM = J|\nabla E_{ZZ}|JlM = J\rangle = \frac{-J}{2J + 3}\left[1 - \frac{3l^2}{J(J + 1)}\right]\left(\frac{\partial^2 V}{\partial a^2}\right) \quad (5\text{-}49)$$

Quadrupole hyperfine structure has been observed on the l-type doublets of BrCN [581]. Discussion of the vibrational dependence of the quadrupole coupling constant is given in Section 5-8 where a linear XYZ molecule in a degenerate bending mode is considered. For excited vibrational states such as the degenerate bending mode of a symmetric rotor which contributes a component of angular momentum along the figure axis, the resultant angular momentum along the axis is substituted for K in (5-49).

The best approach for an asymmetric rotor is to relate $(\partial^2 V/\partial Z^2)$ to the electric field gradients along the molecular principal axes. This relationship is written in terms of the direction cosines between the space-fixed Z axis and the molecule-fixed principal axes.

$$\begin{aligned}
\frac{\partial^2 V}{\partial Z^2} &= \left[\phi_{Za}\left(\frac{\partial V}{\partial a}\right) + \phi_{Zb}\left(\frac{\partial V}{\partial b}\right) + \phi_{Zc}\left(\frac{\partial V}{\partial c}\right)\right]^2 \\
&= \phi_{Za}^2\left(\frac{\partial^2 V}{\partial a^2}\right) + \phi_{Zb}^2\left(\frac{\partial^2 V}{\partial b^2}\right) + \phi_{Zc}^2\left(\frac{\partial^2 V}{\partial c^2}\right) + 2\phi_{Za}\phi_{Zb}\left(\frac{\partial^2 V}{\partial a\,\partial b}\right) \\
&\quad + 2\phi_{Za}\phi_{Zc}\left(\frac{\partial^2 V}{\partial a\,\partial c}\right) + 2\phi_{Zb}\phi_{Zc}\left(\frac{\partial^2 V}{\partial b\,\partial c}\right)
\end{aligned} \quad (5\text{-}50)$$

The known matrix elements of the direction cosines make this expression relatively easy to evaluate. First-order averaging takes place over the state $M_J = J$. The last three terms in (5-50) do not contribute to the first-order energy, and the gradient may be expressed as

$$\langle J\tau M = J | \nabla E_{ZZ} | J\tau M = J \rangle = \langle \phi_{Za}^2 \rangle \left(\frac{\partial^2 V}{\partial a^2} \right) + \langle \phi_{Zb}^2 \rangle \left(\frac{\partial^2 V}{\partial b^2} \right)$$
$$+ \langle \phi_{Zc}^2 \rangle \left(\frac{\partial^2 V}{\partial c^2} \right) \tag{5-51}$$

As an example, for an oblate rotor, the matrix elements of ϕ_{Za} and ϕ_{Zb} have only $\langle K|K \pm 1 \rangle$ terms in the symmetric rotor representation. Thus the terms $\phi_{Za}\phi_{Zc}$ and $\phi_{Zb}\phi_{Zc}$ have no diagonal elements in the asymmetric rotor representation, since this representation possesses no terms connecting even and odd K. The term containing $\phi_{Za}\phi_{Zb}$ vanishes in both representations because it is imaginary. Subscripts a and c are interchanged for a prolate rotor. Matrix elements of the squared direction cosines can be expressed in terms of tabulated quantities such as the transition strength. The transition strength has been defined in Chapter 2 as

$$^gS_{J_\tau J'_{\tau'}} = \sum_{F,M,M'} |\langle J\tau M | \phi_{Fg} | J'\tau'M' \rangle|^2$$
$$= 3|\langle J | \phi_{Zg} | J' \rangle|^2 \cdot |\langle J\tau | \phi_{Zg} | J'\tau' \rangle|^2 \cdot \sum_{MM'} |\langle JM | \phi_{Zg} | J'M' \rangle|^2 \tag{5-52}$$

The direction-cosine elements in the principal axis system have been squared and summed over F, M, and M'. In the absence of a perturbing external field, the three space-fixed directions are equivalent and the summation over F can be done simply by multiplying the squared elements for any given F by three. F should not be confused with the resultant momentum in (5-2).

$$^gS_{J\tau J'_{\tau'}} = 3 \sum_{MM'} |\langle J\tau M | \phi_{Fg} | J'\tau'M' \rangle|^2 \tag{5-53}$$

In terms of the transition strengths, the gradient can be written as

$$\langle J\tau M = J | \nabla E_{ZZ} | J\tau M = J \rangle = \frac{2J}{(2J + 1)(2J + 3)} \sum_{\tau'} \left[\left(\frac{\partial^2 V}{\partial a^2} \right)^a S_{J_\tau J_{\tau'}} \right.$$
$$\left. + \left(\frac{\partial^2 V}{\partial b^2} \right)^b S_{J_\tau J_{\tau'}} + \left(\frac{\partial^2 V}{\partial c^2} \right)^c S_{J_\tau J_{\tau'}} \right] \tag{5-54}$$

$\langle \partial^2 V/\partial Z^2 \rangle$ is most conveniently expressed in terms of the reduced energy $E(\kappa)$ [516].

$$\langle J\tau M = J|\nabla E_{ZZ}|J\tau M = J\rangle$$

$$= \frac{1}{(J+1)(2J+3)}\left(\frac{\partial^2 V}{\partial a^2}\right)\left[J(J+1) + E(\kappa) - (\kappa+1)\frac{\partial E(\kappa)}{\partial \kappa}\right]$$

$$+ \frac{2}{(J+1)(2J+3)}\left(\frac{\partial^2 V}{\partial b^2}\right)\frac{\partial E(\kappa)}{\partial \kappa} + \frac{1}{(J+1)(2J+3)}\left(\frac{\partial^2 V}{\partial c^2}\right)$$

$$\times \left[J(J+1) - E(\kappa) + (\kappa-1)\frac{\partial E(\kappa)}{\partial \kappa}\right] \tag{5-55}$$

or more generally in terms of the change in the energy with respect to the rotational constants.

$$\langle J\tau M = J|\nabla E_{ZZ}|J\tau M = J\rangle$$

$$= \frac{2}{(J+1)(2J+3)}\left[\frac{\partial^2 V}{\partial a^2}\left(\frac{\partial E}{\partial A}\right) + \frac{\partial^2 V}{\partial b^2}\left(\frac{\partial E}{\partial B}\right) + \frac{\partial^2 V}{\partial c^2}\left(\frac{\partial E}{\partial C}\right)\right] \tag{5-56}$$

Changes in energy with respect to the rotational constants can be evaluated by differentiating the energy expression (2-83) and obtaining the $\partial E(\kappa)/\partial \kappa$ terms from published tables of $E(\kappa)$.

Using the expansion in terms of b for the near-symmetric top energy levels given in (2-104)[297],

$$\langle J\tau M = J|\nabla E_{ZZ}|J\tau M = J\rangle$$

$$= \frac{1}{(J+1)(2J+3)}\left\{\left[3K^2_{-1} - J(J+1) + 3\sum_{n=0}(1-n)C_n b_p^n\right]\right.$$

$$\times \left(\frac{\partial^2 V}{\partial a^2}\right) - \left[\sum_{n=0}(n+1)C_{n+1}b_p^n\right]\left(\frac{\partial^2 V}{\partial b^2} - \frac{\partial^2 V}{\partial c^2}\right)\right\} \tag{5-57}$$

for a near-prolate rotor. For a near-oblate top K_1^2 and $\partial^2 V/\partial c^2$ are used in the first term and $((\partial^2 V/\partial a^2) - (\partial^2 V/\partial b^2))$ is used in the second term. b_p is replaced by b_o. From (5-57) for a prolate rotor

$$\frac{\partial E}{\partial A} = K^2_{-1} + \sum_{n=0}(1-n)C_n b_p^n \tag{5-58}$$

$$\frac{\partial E}{\partial B} = \tfrac{1}{2}[J(J+1) - K^2_{-1}] + \tfrac{1}{2}\sum_{n=0}[(n-1)C_n - (n+1)C_{n+1}]b_p^n \tag{5-59}$$

$$\frac{\partial E}{\partial C} = \tfrac{1}{2}[J(J+1) - K^2_{-1}] + \tfrac{1}{2}\sum_{n=0}[(n-1)C_n + (n+1)C_{n+1}]b_p^n \tag{5-60}$$

Similar expressions neglecting terms with $n > 2$ have been derived by Knight and Feld[511] and Townes and Schawlow[20].

The first-order quadrupole energy for an asymmetric rotor with a single quadrupole nucleus is given by substituting the appropriate matrix element of ∇E_{ZZ} in the diagonal matrix element (5-35). Generally, the principal inertial axis system does not coincide with the axis system defined by the quadrupole nucleus. The coupling constant tensor possesses some non-vanishing off-diagonal elements in all but accidental cases. If a plane of symmetry containing the quadrupole nucleus is present, two of the off-diagonal elements vanish and the determination of the quadrupole axis orientation is simplified. Formulating the problem as a matrix equation

$$\chi = \mathbf{T}^{-1}\chi_p\mathbf{T} \tag{5-61}$$

where

$$\chi_p = \begin{pmatrix} \chi_\alpha & 0 & 0 \\ 0 & \chi_\beta & 0 \\ 0 & 0 & \chi_\gamma \end{pmatrix} \tag{5-62}$$

χ_p is a diagonal tensor expressed in the quadrupole axis system with the diagonal elements χ_α, χ_β, and χ_γ. χ is also a symmetric tensor of second rank with zero trace and expresses the quadrupole constants in the inertial principal axis system. $\mathbf{T}$ and $\mathbf{T}^{-1}$ are rotational operators which diagonalize χ by rotating the quadrupole constants in the principal inertial axis system to the quadrupole axis system. For a molecule with a plane of symmetry perpendicular to the a axis, $\mathbf{T}$ takes the form

$$\mathbf{T} = \begin{pmatrix} 1 & 0 & 0 \\ 0 & \cos\theta & \sin\theta \\ 0 & -\sin\theta & \cos\theta \end{pmatrix} \tag{5-63}$$

In this case, the relations between the diagonal elements of χ and χ_p are

$$\chi_\alpha = \chi_{aa} \tag{5-64}$$

$$\chi_\beta = \frac{\chi_{bb}\cos^2\theta - \chi_{cc}\sin^2\theta}{\cos^2\theta - \sin^2\theta} \tag{5-65}$$

$$\chi_\gamma = \frac{\chi_{cc}\cos^2\theta - \chi_{bb}\sin^2\theta}{\cos^2\theta - \sin^2\theta} \tag{5-66}$$

θ is the angle between the c axis and the γ axis. Conversely,

$$\chi_{cc} = \chi_\gamma \cos^2\theta + \chi_\beta \sin^2\theta \tag{5-67}$$

$$\chi_{bb} = \chi_\gamma \sin^2\theta + \chi_\beta \cos^2\theta \tag{5-68}$$

$$\chi_{bc} = (\chi_\beta - \chi_\gamma)\sin\theta\cos\theta \tag{5-69}$$

The problem of determining the orientation of the principal quadrupole axis system can be studied by considering an asymmetric top in which a single quadrupole nucleus is connected by one bond to the rest of the molecule. X is the quadrupole nucleus and M represents the remaining atoms in the molecule. If $M-X$ possesses a single plane of symmetry, the $M-X$ bond must lie in the plane. For molecules which possess two planes of symmetry perpendicular to each other, the $M-X$ bond can only lie along the line formed by the intersection of the two planes. In asymmetric tops with no symmetry elements, the $M-X$ bond may take any orientation relative to the principal quadrupole axes. One common method for determining χ_α, χ_β, and χ_γ is through the use of isotopic substitution. The same quadrupole nucleus is studied in two isotopic species of a particular molecule, and the orientation of the principal inertial axis system generally differs in the two isotopic species. Substitution should be made with an isotope which does not possess a nuclear quadrupole moment or with an atom whose quadrupole interaction is too small to be detected. Because the charge distribution is relatively unchanged after isotopic substitution, the principal quadrupole axes can be assumed to remain stationary. The experimentally determined quadrupole constants χ_{aa}, χ_{bb}, and χ_{cc} differ for the two molecules. Using the matrix equation

$$\mathbf{T}\chi\mathbf{T}^{-1} = \chi' \qquad (5\text{-}70)$$

where χ and χ' are the quadrupole tensors for the original and isotopically substituted molecules and the rotation operator $\mathbf{T}$ is determined by the principal axis rotation produced by the isotopic substitution, the off-diagonal elements of χ and χ' can, in principle, be determined. Once this is done, it is a simple matter to diagonalize one of these tensors to determine the diagonal elements of χ_p. The position of the principal quadrupole axis system can then be found. The off-diagonal element χ_{ij} may also be determined from the second-order quadrupole effect, provided the proper near degeneracy is present. This possibility is discussed in Section 5-5.

When these methods cannot be used, it may be necessary to make one or more additional assumptions. A possibility is to assume that one of the principal quadrupole axes lies along the $M-X$ bond. This assumption is based on the presence of charge symmetry about the bond to the quadrupole nucleus. In particular, if the molecule has a plane of symmetry, this premise allows the angle between the two sets of axes to be calculated. This specifies $\mathbf{T}$ in (5-70). When no symmetry is present, the calculation of $\mathbf{T}$ is more complicated. (5-61) can then be used to find χ_p.

Another approach is to assume that two of the diagonal values of χ_p are equal. This would mean that the electrostatic potential is cylindrically symmetric at the quadrupole nucleus but does not necessarily infer that the potential is cylindrically symmetric with respect to the $M-X$ bond. A parameter η can be defined to measure the deviation from cylindrical symmetry in the quadrupole axis system.

$$\eta = \frac{\chi_\alpha - \chi_\beta}{\chi_\gamma} \tag{5-71}$$

Here the γ axis is assumed to lie along the $M-X$ bond. When a plane of symmetry is present, the elements of χ_p can be obtained from (5-64) and (5-41). θ is then found from (5-65) and (5-66). Additional information is necessary when no symmetry exists. These assumptions have been applied to ethyl chloride [1578] and chloromethylsilane [1579], and the results are given in Table 5-3; Column I assumes that the γ axis is colinear with the $C-Cl$ bond, and column II assumes that $\chi_\alpha = \chi_\beta$.

TABLE 5-3

QUADRUPOLE DATA FOR ETHYL CHLORIDE[a] AND CHLOROMETHYL SILANE[b]

Molecule	Parameter	I	II
$C_2H_5Cl^{35}$	χ_γ	-68.80 ± 0.15 MHz	-71.24 ± 0.19 MHz
	θ	$26°\,0'$	$27°\,0' \pm 5'$
	η	0.035 ± 0.003	0
$CH_2Cl^{35}SiH_3$	χ_γ	-68.7 ± 1.6 MHz	-72.0 ± 0.6 MHz
	θ	$36.7°$	$37.2 \pm 0.2°$
	η	0.048 ± 0.016	0

[a] From Ref. [1578].
[b] From Ref. [1579].

5-5. Second-Order Quadrupole Energy

When the first-order correction was applied to molecules like BrCN and ICN [508], discrepancies between the observed and calculated spectra were noted. These discrepancies arise from the assumption that the quadrupole splitting is much smaller than the spacing of the rotational energy levels. When this is not the case, it is necessary to calculate the second-order correction.

$$E_Q^{(2)} = \sum_{J'\tau'}{}' \frac{|\langle IJ\tau FM_F|H_Q|IJ'\tau'FM_F\rangle|^2}{E_{J\tau} - E_{J'\tau'}} \tag{5-72}$$

Nonvanishing off-diagonal matrix elements connect energy levels with identical F and M_F but different J. Summation over the various J' levels which connect with J forces a mixing of states, and the rotational states of the molecule are no longer strictly specified by the quantum number J because J is no longer a constant of the motion.

Only evaluation of the matrix elements of ∇E_{ZZ} is necessary for the calculation of the second-order energy. For an oblate symmetric rotor

$$\langle JKM = J|\nabla E_{ZZ}|J + 1, KM = J\rangle$$

$$= \frac{3K[(J + 1)^2 - K^2]^{1/2}}{(J + 1)(J + 2)[2J + 3]^{1/2}} \left(\frac{\partial^2 V}{\partial c^2}\right) \tag{5-73}$$

$$\langle JKM = J|\nabla E_{ZZ}|J + 2, KM = J\rangle$$

$$= \frac{3[\{(J + 1)^2 - K^2\}\{(J + 2)^2 - K^2\}]^{1/2}}{(J + 2)(2J + 3)[(J + 1)(2J + 5)]^{1/2}} \left(\frac{\partial^2 V}{\partial c^2}\right) \tag{5-74}$$

and the off-diagonal matrix elements are

$$\langle JK|H_Q|J + 1, K\rangle$$

$$= 3eqQC'K\left[\left(1 - \frac{K^2}{(J + 1)^2}\right) \frac{(I + J + F + 2)(J + F - I + 1)}{(2J + 1)(2J + 3)}\right.$$

$$\left. \times (I + F - J)(I + J - F + 1)\right]^{1/2} \tag{5-75}$$

$$\langle JK|H_Q|J + 2, K\rangle$$

$$= \frac{3eqQ}{16I(2I - 1)(2J + 3)} \left[\left(1 - \frac{K^2}{(J + 1)^2}\right)\left(1 - \frac{K^2}{(J + 2)^2}\right)\right.$$

$$\left. \times \frac{(I + F - J - 1)(I + F - J)(I + J + F + 3)(I + J + F + 2)}{(2J + 1)(2J + 5)}\right]^{1/2} \tag{5-76}$$

$$C' = \frac{F(F + 1) - I(I + 1) - J(J + 2)}{8I(2I - 1)J(J + 2)} \tag{5-77}$$

For a linear molecule in the ground state, $K = 0$ and only the $\langle J|J + 2\rangle$ elements are necessary. If the linear molecule is in an excited bending mode which produces an angular momentum component along the figure axis, l is used in place of K in (5-75) and (5-76).

For an asymmetric rotor it is necessary to evaluate the off-diagonal elements of ∇E_{ZZ}. In general

$$\langle J'\tau'M = J|\nabla E_{ZZ}|J\tau M = J\rangle = \left[\frac{16\pi}{5}\right]^{1/2}$$

$$\times \langle J'\tau'M = J|\rho_e(\mathbf{r}_e)r_e^{-3}Y_0^2(\omega_e)|J\tau M = J\rangle \tag{5-78}$$

The off-diagonal coupling constants χ_{ij} contribute to the second-order energy through the direction-cosine crossterms $\phi_{Zi}\phi_{Zj}$ in the expansion of $\partial^2 V/\partial Z^2$ in (5-50). Matrix elements of the direction-cosine products required for second-order quadrupole calculations have been characterized by Schwendeman [602] in the Wang symmetric rotor basis. The terms $\phi_{Zi}\phi_{Zj}$ which connect the Wang blocks $E^{\pm}$, $O^{\pm}$ for $J' = J$, $J + 1$, $J + 2$ are listed explicitly.

Appreciable second-order effects occur for asymmetric rotors when near degeneracies are present between rotational energy levels of the proper symmetry. $E_{J_\tau} - E_{J'_{\tau'}}$ in (5-72) may be small for accidental near degeneracies or when the K doubling becomes small. The nonvanishing interactions can be determined from the symmetry properties of the direction cosines and the asymmetric rotor wave functions of the two levels. Symmetries of the direction-cosine elements in the asymmetric rotor representation are given in Table 2-12. Since the overall symmetry of the matrix element must belong to the totally symmetric representation A of the rotation group V, the direct product of the rotational symmetries is required to be identical with that of the direction cosine product $\phi_{Zi}\phi_{Zj}$. From a nonvanishing term of the form $\phi_{Zi}\phi_{Zj}(\partial^2 V/\partial i \partial j)$, the off-diagonal element χ_{ij} $(i \neq j)$ of the quadrupole tensor may be determined by establishing a simple linear relationship between Δ (a frequency deviation from the predicted first-order splitting) and χ_{ij}^2 [591, 592].

5-6. Molecules with Two Quadrupole Nuclei

When more than one quadrupole nucleus is present in a molecule, there exists the possibility of coupling between the individual quadrupole moments by way of molecular rotation. The resulting hyperfine structure can become very complicated. In an uncoupled representation, the Hamiltonian is just the sum of two individual quadrupole terms given by (5-13).

$$H_Q(\mathbf{I}_1, \mathbf{I}_2) = H_Q(\mathbf{I}_1, \mathbf{J}) + H_Q(\mathbf{I}_2, \mathbf{J}) \tag{5-79}$$

I_1 and I_2 are the nuclear spins of the quadrupole nuclei. Methods used to treat this problem depend on the relative degrees of coupling of the two nuclei; one of the nuclei couples much more strongly than the other or their degrees of coupling are of the same order of magnitude. In the first instance, the major contribution to the hyperfine splitting is made by the nucleus which is strongly coupled. The weakly coupled nucleus can be treated as a perturbation on these splittings. When the nuclear coupling is similar for both nuclei, the treatment is more involved.

Several different vector models may be used to construct an appropriate representation. For example, when I_1 is strongly coupled and I_2 is weakly coupled

$$\mathbf{F}_1 = \mathbf{J} + \mathbf{I}_1 \tag{5-80}$$

$$\mathbf{F} = \mathbf{F}_1 + \mathbf{I}_2 \tag{5-81}$$

F still represents the total angular momentum of the molecule, including spin. $\psi(F, F_1)$ is the set of wave functions for the states which are defined by F and F_1. If J is combined with I_2 and the resultant F_2 added to I_1, the set of functions $\psi(F, F_2)$ is generated.

$$\mathbf{F}_2 = \mathbf{J} + \mathbf{I}_2 \tag{5-82}$$

$$\mathbf{F} = \mathbf{F}_2 + \mathbf{I}_1 \tag{5-83}$$

These sets of wave functions are linearly related by a unitary transformation.

$$\psi(F, F_1) = \sum_{F_2} C(F_1, F_2)\psi(F, F_2) \tag{5-84}$$

$$\psi(F, F_2) = \sum_{F_1} C(F_1, F_2)\psi(F, F_1) \tag{5-85}$$

The unitary character of $C(F_1, F_2)$ allows the phases to be chosen so that the coefficients are real. Note that there are identical values of F for several different values of F_1 and therefore different values of $H_Q(\mathbf{I}_1, \mathbf{J})$ for the same F. States are also specified by a value of F_1 and a different F. If the perturbation resulting from I_2, i.e., $H_Q(\mathbf{I}_2, \mathbf{J})$, is negligible, those states are degenerate and the problem reduces to that of one nucleus. However, the degeneracy is lifted when $H_Q(\mathbf{I}_2, \mathbf{J})$ is significant. The transformation coefficients $C(F_1, F_2)$ can be evaluated in a closed form after Racah's formulation [496, 497].

$$C(F_1, F_2) = \langle I_1 J(F_1) I_2 F | I_1 J I_2(F_2) F \rangle$$
$$= [(2F_1 + 1)(2F_2 + 1)]^{1/2} W(I_1 J F I_2; F_1 F_2) \tag{5-86}$$

Bardeen and Townes [507] have evaluated the $C(F_1, F_2)$ for the two important cases of $I_1 = I$, $I_2 = 1$ and $I_1 = I$, $I_2 = \frac{3}{2}$.

When $H_Q(\mathbf{I}_1, \mathbf{J})$ is the dominant interaction and $H_Q(\mathbf{I}_2, \mathbf{J})$ can be treated as a perturbation on $H_Q(\mathbf{I}_1, \mathbf{J})$, the appropriate eigenfunctions for evaluation of the first-order energy are the $\psi(F, F_1)$.

$$E_Q^{(1)} = \langle F, F_1 | H_Q(\mathbf{I}_1, \mathbf{J}) + H_Q(\mathbf{I}_2, \mathbf{J}) | F, F_1 \rangle$$
$$= \psi(F, F_1) H_Q(\mathbf{I}_1, \mathbf{J})\psi(F, F_1) + \psi(F, F_1) H_Q(\mathbf{I}_2, \mathbf{J})\psi(F, F_1) \tag{5-87}$$

Using (5-84),

$$E_Q^{(1)} = E_Q(I_1) + \sum_{F_2} C(F_1, F_2)^2 E_Q(I_2) \tag{5-88}$$

where $E_Q(I_1)$ is the eigenvalue of $H_Q(\mathbf{I}_1, \mathbf{J})$ for the eigenfunction $\psi(F, F_1)$.

If the interactions $H_Q(\mathbf{I}_1, \mathbf{J})$ and $H_Q(\mathbf{I}_2, \mathbf{J})$ are comparable, neither the $\psi(F, F_1)$ nor the $\psi(F, F_2)$ are valid wave functions for the system. The $I_1I_2IJFM_F$ representation is the most convenient. It is formed by coupling $\mathbf{I}_1$ and $\mathbf{I}_2$ to produce the total nuclear spin $\mathbf{I}$ which is then coupled with $\mathbf{J}$ to form $\mathbf{F}$. Flygare and Gwinn [593] have expressed the matrix elements in terms of Racah coefficients and reduced matrix elements similar to (5-38).

$$\langle I_1 I_2 I' J' F M_F | H_Q(\mathbf{I}_1, \mathbf{I}_2) | I_1 I_2 I J F M_F \rangle$$

$$= \frac{4\pi}{5}(-1)^{I'+J-F}[(2I'+1)(2J'+1)]^{1/2}$$

$$\times W(I'IJ'J, 2F)\Big[\langle I_1 I_2 I' \| r_n^2 Y^2(\omega_n)_1 \| I_1 I_2 I \rangle$$

$$\times \langle J' \| r_e^{-3} Y^2(\omega_e)_1 \| J \rangle + \langle I_1 I_2 I' \| r_n^2 Y^2(\omega_n)_2 \| I_1 I_2 I \rangle$$

$$\times \langle J' \| r_e^{-3} Y^2(\omega_e)_2 \| J \rangle \Big] \tag{5-89}$$

Since I_1 commutes with $r_n^2 Y^2(\omega_n)_2$ and I_2 commutes with $r_n^2 Y^2(\omega_n)_1$, the matrix elements for nucleus 1 can be expressed as

$$\langle I_1 I_2 I' \| r_n^2 Y^2(\omega_n)_1 \| I_1 I_2 I \rangle = (-1)^{I_2 - I_1 - I'}[(2I+1)(2I_1+1)]^{1/2}$$

$$\times W(I_1 I_1 I' I, 2I_2)\langle I_1 \| r_n^2 Y^2(\omega_n)_1 \| I_1 \rangle \tag{5-90}$$

For the second nucleus a similar relationship results.

$$\langle I_1 I_2 I' \| r_n^2 Y^2(\omega_n)_2 \| I_1 I_2 I \rangle = (-1)^{I_1 - I_2 - I'}[(2I+1)(2I_2+1)]^{1/2}$$

$$\times W(I_2 I_2 I' I, 2I_1)\langle I_2 \| r_n^2 Y^2(\omega_n)_2 \| I_2 \rangle \tag{5-91}$$

Equation (5-28) relates these reduced matrix elements to the nuclear quadrupole moments. The relation for the field gradient q_J is obtained from (5-29) and from the definition

$$\langle J'\tau' M = J | \nabla E_{ZZ} | J\tau M = J \rangle$$

$$= \left(\frac{16\pi}{5}\right)^{1/2} \langle J'\tau' M = J | \rho(\mathbf{r}_e) r_e^{-3} Y_0^2(\omega_e) | J\tau M = J \rangle \tag{5-92}$$

where $\rho(\mathbf{r}_e)$ is electronic charge density.

$$\langle J' \| \rho(\mathbf{r}_e) r_e^{-3} Y^2(\omega_e) \| J \rangle = \frac{\langle J'\tau' M = J | \rho(\mathbf{r}_e) r_e^{-3} Y_0^2(\omega_e) | J\tau J \rangle}{C(J2J', J0J)}$$

$$= \left[\frac{5}{16\pi}\right]^{1/2} [C(J2J', J0J)]^{-1}\langle J'\tau' M = J | \nabla E_{ZZ} | J\tau M = J \rangle \tag{5-93}$$

Use has been made of the Wigner–Eckart conditions discussed in Appendix 6.

$C(J2J', J0J)$ is a vector coupling coefficient which has been tabulated by Condon and Shortley [1].

$$C(J2J', J0J) = \left[\frac{J(2J + 1)}{(J + 1)(2J + 3)}\right]^{1/2} \tag{5-94a}$$

$$C(J2, J + 1, J0J) = \left[\frac{3J}{(J + 1)(J + 2)}\right]^{1/2} \tag{5-94b}$$

$$C(J2, J + 2, J0J) = \left[\frac{6}{(2J + 3)(J + 2)}\right]^{1/2} \tag{5-94c}$$

$$\langle I_1 I_2 I'J'FM_F | H_Q(\mathbf{I}_1, \mathbf{I}_2) | I_1 I_2 IJFM_F \rangle$$

$$= \tfrac{1}{4}(-1)^{I'+J-F}[(2I' + 1)(2J' + 1)(2I + 1)]^{1/2} W(I'IJ'J, 2F)$$

$$\times [C(J2J', J0J)]^{-1}\left\{eQ_1\langle J'\tau M = J | \nabla E_{zz} | J\tau M = J\rangle_1 (-1)^{I'}\right.$$

$$\times \left[\frac{(2I_1 + 1)(I_1 + 1)(2I_1 + 3)}{I_1(2I_1 - 1)}\right]^{1/2} W(I_1 I_1 I'I, 2I_2) + eQ_2$$

$$\times \langle J'\tau M = J | \nabla E_{zz} | J\tau M = J\rangle_2 (-1)^{I}\left[\frac{(2I_2 + 1)(I_2 + 1)(2I_2 + 3)}{I_2(2I_2 - 1)}\right]^{1/2}$$

$$\times \left. W(I_2 I_2 I'I, 2I_1)\right\} \tag{5-95}$$

Nonvanishing matrix elements occur for $J' = J, J \pm 1, J \pm 2$ and $I' = I$, $I \pm 1, I \pm 2$. If $I_1 = I_2$ and the coupling constants are identical, the $\langle I | I \pm 1\rangle$ matrix elements of H_Q vanish. The matrix elements $\langle I | H_Q | I\rangle$ and $\langle I | H_Q | I \pm 2\rangle$ for identical spins have been given by Foley [501] and revised by Myers and Gwinn [545]. $\langle I | H_Q | I \pm 1\rangle$ elements were given by Robinson and Cornwell [557]. Flygare and Gwinn [593] have tabulated the matrix elements for $I_1 = I_2 = \tfrac{3}{2}$.

Rather than calculate the matrix elements directly, the problem may be developed in the form of a secular equation. Because $\psi(F, F_1)$ and $\psi(F, F_2)$ are inadequate when the quadrupole interactions are of the same order of magnitude, a linear combination of either set of wave functions must be used to form an appropriate basis [507].

$$\psi(F) = \sum_{F_1} a(F_1)\psi(F, F_1) \tag{5-96}$$

or

$$\psi(F) = \sum_{F_2} a(F_2)\psi(F, F_2) \tag{5-97}$$

The first-order energy is then

$$E_Q^{(1)} = \langle F | H_Q(\mathbf{I}_1, \mathbf{J}) + H_Q(\mathbf{I}_2, \mathbf{J}) | F\rangle \tag{5-98}$$

which leads to a secular equation of the form

$$\left[\sum_{F_2} C(F_1, F_2)^2 E(F_2) + E(F_1) - E_Q^{(1)} \right] a(F_1)$$

$$+ \sum_{F_1' \neq F_1} \sum_{F_2} C(F_1, F_2) C(F_1', F_2) E(F_2) a(F_1') = 0 \qquad (5\text{-}99)$$

Instead of using the coupling coefficients, the matrix elements of $H_Q(I_2, J)$ may be evaluated directly if the elements of the $I_2 \cdot J$ operator are known. These have been given by Condon and Shortley [1].

$$\langle F_1 I_2 F | I_2 \cdot J | F_1 I_2 F \rangle = \tfrac{1}{2} [F(F + 1) - F_1(F_1 + 1) - I_2(I_2 + 1)]$$

$$\times \langle F_1 | J | F_1 \rangle \qquad (5\text{-}100)$$

$$\langle F_1 I_2 F | I_2 \cdot J | F_1 - 1, I_2 F \rangle = -\tfrac{1}{2} [(F + F_1 - I_2)(F + I_2 - F_1 + 1)$$

$$\times (F + F_1 + I_2 + 1)(F_1 + I_2 - F)]^{1/2}$$

$$\times \langle F_1 | J | F_1 - 1 \rangle \qquad (5\text{-}101)$$

$$\langle F_1 I_2 F | I_2 \cdot J | F_1 + 1, I_2 F \rangle = -\tfrac{1}{2} [(F + F_1 - I_2 + 1)(F + I_2 - F_1)$$

$$\times (F + F_1 + I_2 + 2)(F_1 + I_2 - F + 1)]^{1/2}$$

$$\times \langle F_1 | J | F_1 + 1 \rangle \qquad (5\text{-}102)$$

where

$$\langle F_1 | J | F_1 \rangle = \frac{J(J + 1) - I_1(I_1 + 1) + F_1(F_1 + 1)}{2F_1(F_1 + 1)} \qquad (5\text{-}103)$$

$$\langle F_1 | J | F_1 - 1 \rangle$$

$$= \left\{ \frac{(F_1 - J + I_1)(F_1 + J - I_1)(F_1 + J + I_1 + 1)(J + I_1 - F_1 + 1)}{4F_1^2(2F_1 - 1)(2F_1 + 1)} \right\}^{1/2} \qquad (5\text{-}104)$$

$$\langle F_1 | J | F_1 + 1 \rangle$$

$$= \left[\frac{(F_1 - J + I_1 + 1)(F_1 + J - I_1 + 1)(F_1 + J + I_1 + 2)(J + I_1 - F_1)}{4(F_1 + 1)^2(2F_1 + 1)(2F_1 + 3)} \right]^{1/2} \qquad (5\text{-}105)$$

The elements of $(I_2 \cdot J)^2$ are found by squaring the matrix for $(I_2 \cdot J)$.

5-7. Molecules with Three Quadrupole Nuclei

The vector coupling formalism of Racah can be extended to treat molecules with three or more quadrupole nuclei. Generalizing to three different spins, the Hamiltonian for the uncoupled case can be written as

$$H = H_R + H_Q(\mathbf{I}_1, \mathbf{J}) + H_Q(\mathbf{I}_2, \mathbf{J}) + H_Q(\mathbf{I}_3, \mathbf{J}) = H_R + H_Q(\mathbf{I}_1, \mathbf{I}_2, \mathbf{I}_3) \quad (5\text{-}106)$$

The problem of coupling three nuclear spins to overall rotation was treated by Bersohn [525]. The resulting complexity of the energy level structure led Mizushima and Ito [536] to apply group theoretical techniques to the problem of calculating the hyperfine structure of $J = 0 \to 1$ transitions in XYZ_3 molecules for three identical spins of 1, $\frac{3}{2}$, 2 and $\frac{5}{2}$.

In one possible vector-coupling representation pictured in Fig. 5-5

$$\mathbf{I}_i = \mathbf{I}_1 + \mathbf{I}_2, \qquad \mathbf{I} = \mathbf{I}_i + \mathbf{I}_3, \qquad \text{and} \qquad \mathbf{F} = \mathbf{I} + \mathbf{J} \quad (5\text{-}107)$$

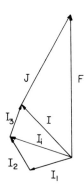

FIG. 5-5. Static vector model illustrating the coupling scheme for three quadrupolar nuclei given in (5-107).

Molecules containing three identical quadrupole nuclei usually have C_{3v} symmetry. By applying a transformation, the matrix of $H_Q(\mathbf{I}_1, \mathbf{I}_2, \mathbf{I}_3)$ can be factored into submatrices of symmetry A_1, A_2, and E corresponding to the irreducible representations of C_{3v}. This operation is equivalent to transforming from an I_iI representation to an SI representation where S indicates the symmetry. Wolfe [1371] has written the first-order matrix elements of $H_Q(\mathbf{I}, \mathbf{J})$ in the SI representation in terms of the reduced matrix elements for ∇E and Q (j labels one of the identical quadrupole nuclei):

$$\langle SIJKF|H_Q(\mathbf{I}, \mathbf{J})|SI'JKF\rangle = (-1)^{I+J-F}\lambda(SII')\langle I_j\|Q_j\|I_j\rangle$$

$$\times \langle JK\|\nabla E_{ZZ}^{(j)}\|JK\rangle W(IJI'J; F2) \quad (5\text{-}108)$$

where the transformation coefficients $\lambda(SII')$ have been tabulated by Bersohn [525], Mizushima and Ito [536], and Wolfe [1371]. Using (5-28) and (5-29) in (5-38) for the three-nucleus representation and referencing ∇E to the figure axis of the symmetric rotor through (5-47), it follows that

$$\langle SIJKF|H_Q(\mathbf{I},\mathbf{J})|SI'JKF\rangle$$

$$= (-1)^{I+J-F}\lambda(SII')eq_{zz}Q[3K^2 - J(J+1)]$$

$$\times \left[\frac{5(2J+1)}{(J+1)(4J)(2J+3)(2J-1)}\right]^{1/2}W(IJI'J;F2) \tag{5-109}$$

The usual symmetric rotor selection rules are supplemented by additional restrictions on S and F.

$$S \to S$$
$$F \to F, \quad F \pm 1 \tag{5-110}$$

If β is the angle between the YZ bond and the figure axis of the molecule, these matrix elements can be expressed in terms of the electric field gradient along the YZ bond through the substitution

$$q_{ZZ} = \tfrac{1}{2}(3\cos^2\beta - 1)q_{\text{bond}} \tag{5-111}$$

which follows from (5-22) and (5-23). Bersohn [525, 20] first derived the general form of the matrix elements for $H_Q(\mathbf{I}_1,\mathbf{I}_2,\mathbf{I}_3)$; in the I_iIJKFM_F representation,

$$\langle I_iIJKFM_F|H_Q(\mathbf{I}_1,\mathbf{I}_2,\mathbf{I}_3)|I_i'I'JKFM_F\rangle$$

$$= (-1)^{I_2+I_3-I_1-I_i-I_i'+J-F}[64J(2J-1)I_1(2I_1-1)]^{-1/2}e\langle I_1|Q_1|I_1\rangle$$

$$\times \langle JK|\nabla E_{ZZ}^{(1)}|JK\rangle\Big[(2I_i+1)(2I_i'+1)(2I+1)(2I'+1)(2I_1+1)$$

$$\times (2I_1+2)(2I_1+3)(2J+1)(2J+2)(2J+3)\Big]^{1/2}$$

$$\times W(I_1I_1I_iI_i';2I_2)W(I_iI_i'II';2I_3)W(I_iI_i'JJ;2F)$$

$$+(-1)^{I_1+I_3-I_2-I_i-I_i'+J-F}[64J(2J-1)I_2(2I_2-1)]^{-1/2}e\langle I_2|Q_2|I_2\rangle$$

$$\times \langle JK|\nabla E_{ZZ}^{(2)}|JK\rangle[(2I_i+1)(2I_i'+1)(2I+1)(2I'+1)(2I_2+1)$$

$$\times (2I_2+2)(2I_2+3)(2J+1)(2J+2)(2J+3)]^{1/2}$$

$$\times W(I_2I_2I_iI_i';2I_1)W(I_iI_i'II';2I_3)W(I_iI_i'JJ;2F)$$

$$+ (-1)^{I_i-I_3+I-I'+J-F}\delta_{I_iI_i'}[J(2J-1)I_3(2I_3-1)]^{-1/2}$$

$$\times e\langle I_3|Q_3|I_3\rangle\langle JK|\nabla E_{ZZ}^{(3)}|JK\rangle[(2I+1)(2I'+1)(2I_3+1)$$

$$\times (2I_3+2)(2I_3+3)(2J+1)(2J+2)(2J+3)]^{1/2}$$

$$\times W(I_3I_3II';2I_i)W(II'JJ;2F) \tag{5-112}$$

This form may be obtained by expanding (5-109) after transforming back to the I_iI representation. This matrix element can be generalized to include elements off-diagonal in J which enter into second-order corrections; however, corrections higher than first-order are rarely useful because of the difficulties involved in resolving and comparing the complex hyperfine structure with first-order calculations [1495].

The complexity of the quadrupole splitting increases with J; therefore, it is advantageous to study the $J = 0 \rightarrow 1$ transition despite the decrease in intensity characteristic of lower frequencies. In the simplest case of $I_1 = 1$ for a symmetric rotor $J = 0 \rightarrow 1$ transition, there are six hyperfine transitions; for $I_1 = \frac{5}{2}$ the number of components increases to 25 [536]. Figure 5-6 illustrates the calculated hyperfine structure resulting from three identical quadrupole nuclei in a symmetric rotor.

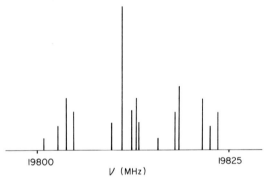

FIG. 5-6. Calculated quadrupole splitting of the $J = 2 \rightarrow 3$, $K = 2$ transition of $CHCl_3^{35}$ [1371].

5-8. Quadrupole Hyperfine Structure in Excited Vibrational States

For a linear XYZ molecule, the charge distribution about the quadrupole nucleus Z would be symmetric about the molecular axis in a rigid molecule but becomes slightly asymmetric in the excited bending mode which characteristically produces l-type doubling. The degree of asymmetry can be estimated by the asymmetry parameter η in (5-71). This parameter appears in the matrix element of H_Q which connects the two states $\pm l$.

$$\langle J, l = \pm 1, F | H_Q | J, l = \mp 1, F \rangle = -\tfrac{1}{2}\eta eqQ f(I, J, F) \qquad (5\text{-}113)$$

The resultant splitting of the l-type doublets then becomes

$$\Delta v = 2q_l J(J + 1) + \eta eqQ[f(I, J + 1, F_f) - f(I, J, F_i)] \qquad (5\text{-}114)$$

q is the electric field gradient and q_l is the l-type doubling constant. Subscripts i and f stand for initial and final states. The centers of the l-type doublets are independent of η. q_l is identical to q in (3-31).

The field asymmetry at the quadrupole nucleus also gives a second-order contribution through the matrix elements off-diagonal in J and of the form $\langle JlF|H_Q|J \pm 1, \pm 2; l \pm 2; F\rangle$. Being off-diagonal in l, these matrix elements only contribute to the doublet splitting and not to a displacement of the center of the doublet. This causes the centers of the doublets to be independent of η to at least second order. If η is very small, the second-order contribution is negligible. The observable interaction comes from cross terms due to matrix elements diagonal and off-diagonal in l which give a correction term of the order $[\eta(eqQ)^2/B] \times 10^{-3}$. After factoring out contributions which depend only on overall rotation, the matrix elements

$$\langle JlM = J|\nabla E_{zz}|J \pm 1, \pm 2; l \pm 2; M = J\rangle$$

can be evaluated either by direct integration over the rotational wave functions or by the use of Racah coefficients.

$$\langle JlJ|\nabla E_{zz}|J + 1, l - 2, J\rangle$$

$$= \frac{-\eta eqQ}{2(J + 2)(J + 1)}\left[\frac{(J - l + 1)(J - l + 2)(J - l + 3)(J + l)}{2J + 3}\right]^{1/2} \tag{5-115}$$

$$\langle JlJ|\nabla E_{zz}|J + 1, l + 2, J\rangle$$

$$= \frac{\eta eqQ[J + l + 3]}{2(J + 2)(J + 1)}\left[\frac{(J + l + 2)(J + l + 1)(J - l)}{(2J + 3)(J + l + 3)}\right]^{1/2} \tag{5-116}$$

$$\langle JlJ|\nabla E_{zz}|J + 2, l - 2, J\rangle$$

$$= \frac{-\eta eqQ}{2(2J + 3)(J + 2)}\left[\frac{(J - l + 1)(J - l + 2)(J - l + 3)(J - l + 4)}{(J + 1)(2J + 5)}\right]^{1/2}$$

$$\langle JlJ|\nabla E_{zz}|J + 2, l + 2, J\rangle \tag{5-117}$$

$$= \frac{-\eta eqQ[(J + l)^2 + 7(J + l) + 12]}{2(2J + 3)(J + 2)}$$

$$\times \left[\frac{(J + l + 1)(J + l + 2)}{(J + 1)(2J + 5)(J + l + 3)(J + l + 4)}\right]^{1/2} \tag{5-118}$$

For the J, F, $l = \pm 1$ energy levels, the second-order energy correction becomes

$$E^{(2)} = \sum_{J'l'} \frac{|\langle J, l = \pm 1, F|H_Q|J'l'F\rangle\langle J'l'F|H_Q|Jl = \pm 1, F\rangle|}{E_J - E_{J'}} \tag{5-119}$$

In a molecule like ICN where a second quadrupole moment is present a more complex interaction occurs. For the particular case of nitrogen and iodine coupling in the same molecule, the effects of η on the nitrogen splitting are usually negligible compared to those on the iodine splitting. However, if the two quadrupole nuclei have similar magnitudes of coupling, both nuclei must be included in a detailed treatment.

Although variation of eqQ with vibrational state has been observed for some linear molecules, the quadrupole coupling constant is not particularly sensitive to the lower vibrational states of symmetric and asymmetric top molecules. Only when the electron distribution near the quadrupole nucleus is affected by a molecular vibration would any serious deviation in ∇E_{ZZ} be expected. The excited states which can be observed in microwave spectroscopy are usually limited to torsional and low frequency bending modes; the higher vibrational states which might be expected to show some variation in eqQ have not been experimentally observed.

5-9. Relative Intensities of Quadrupole Components

In most cases, rotational transitions are identified by their Stark effect and by their rigid rotor frequency expressions. In a few situations [595], the quadrupole hyperfine structure has been used to assign rotational quantum numbers to transitions. Although first-order quadrupole splittings are easily calculated, the interpretation of observed transitions is simplified when the relative intensities are known. The introduction of nuclear spin does not change the total intensity of a rotational transition and the sum of the intensities of the resolved components is just the intensity of the unsplit line.

In Chapter 2, the asymmetric rotor intensity problem was solved by applying the transformation which diagonalizes the asymmetric rotor energy matrix to the direction-cosine matrix in a symmetric rotor representation; the transition strengths are the squares of the elements of the transformed direction-cosine matrix summed over the M components and multiplied by three. To calculate the relative intensities of quadrupole hyperfine components it is necessary to find the transformation which diagonalizes the energy matrix in a representation that accounts for the quadrupole interaction.

For a single quadrupole nucleus, relative intensities can be obtained from a consideration of similar vector-coupling problems in atoms. Relative intensities of multiplet components in atomic spectra have been discussed by Hill [489], Pauling and Goudsmit [490], White [491], and Condon and Shortley [1]. Intensity formulas have been derived for the atomic case as a function of the resultant electronic angular momentum $\mathbf{L}$, the resultant spin angular momentum $\mathbf{S}$, and the vector sum $\mathbf{J} = \mathbf{L} + \mathbf{S}$. By changing the identities of these vectors to suit the molecular case with nuclear quadrupole coupling, these formulas become valid for pure rotational spectra as long as the hyperfine splittings are small enough so that the frequency dependence of intensity can be neglected. The modified relative intensity formulas appear in Table 5-4. The proportionality constants A and B contain intensity factors which may be neglected when only the relative

TABLE 5-4

RELATIVE INTENSITY EXPRESSIONS FOR QUADRUPOLE HYPERFINE COMPONENTS[a]

Transition	Component	Relative intensity
$J - 1 \rightarrow J$	$F - 1 \rightarrow F$	$\dfrac{A(J + F + I + 1)(J + F + I)(J + F - I)(J + F - I - 1)}{F}$
	$F \rightarrow F$	$\dfrac{-A(J + F + I + 1)(J + F - I)(J - F + 1)(J - F - I - 1)(2F + 1)}{F(F + 1)}$
	$F + 1 \rightarrow F$	$\dfrac{A(J - F + I)(J - F + I - 1)(J - F - I - 1)(J - F - I - 2)}{F + 1}$
$J \rightarrow J$	$F - 1 \rightarrow F$	$\dfrac{-B(J + F + I + 1)(J + F - I)(J - F + I + 1)(J - F - I)}{F}$
	$F \rightarrow F$	$\dfrac{B[J(J + 1) + F(F + 1) - I(I + 1)]^2(2F + 1)}{F(F + 1)}$
	$F + 1 \rightarrow F$	$\dfrac{-B(J + F + I + 2)(J + F - I + 1)(J - F + I)(J - F - I - 1)}{F + 1}$

[a] From Ref. [489].

intensities of closely spaced hyperfine components are being calculated; these constants are readily evaluated from known values of the total asymmetric rotor transition strength.

If two quadrupole nuclei are present, it is advantageous to consider similar and dissimilar degrees of coupling separately. When one nucleus couples strongly relative to the second nucleus, the $I_1 J F_1 I_2 F$ representation is appropriate. Because the splittings of I_2 appear as perturbations on the components produced by I_1, the total relative intensities of the I_1 components are obtained from Table 5-4, and then the relative intensities of the I_2 structure are obtained from Table 5-4 by replacing J by F_1 and I by I_2 [507].

For cases where the couplings are identical or nearly identical, the relative intensities may be calculated by determining the transformation which diagonalizes the energy matrix in the two-nucleus representation [557]. This transformation is then applied to the properly formed dipole moment matrix. For the $I_1 J F_1 I_2 F$ representation, the coefficients $a(F_1)$ in (5-99) may be calculated from the known energy values. The relative intensity of a transition $i \rightarrow f$ connecting the initial and final hyperfine levels is

$$I(i \rightarrow f) \propto \left| \sum_{F_i'} \sum_{F_1} a_i(F_1) a_f(F_1') S^{1/2}(I_1 J F_1 | I_1 J' F_1') S^{1/2}(J_2 F_1 F | I_2 F_1' F') \right| \quad (5\text{-}120)$$

The $S(I_1 J F_1 | I_1 J' F_1')$ are proportional to the relative intensities given in Table 5-4; the $S(I_2 F_1 F | I_2 F_1' F')$ also can be obtained from Table 5-4 by identifying I_2, F_1 and F with I, J and F, respectively. Because the transition strengths in (5-120) are proportional to the squares of dipole matrix elements similar to those discussed in Chapter 2, a proper choice of phase consistent with the energy level calculation must be made.

If only approximate relative intensities are needed, they may be obtained by interpolating between the two limiting cases of strong–weak and weak–strong coupling. The limiting intensities are given by the product $S(I_1 J F_1 | I_1 J' F_1') S(I_2 F_1 F | I_2 F_1' F')$ where I_1 is the strongly coupled nuclear spin. Similar considerations hold for three or more quadrupole nuclei; however, the complex energy level structure makes it difficult to apply approximate methods for the calculation of intensities.

CHAPTER 6 | INTERNAL ROTATION

6-1a. Introduction

A large portion of the work in microwave spectroscopy has been directed toward the study of barriers that restrict free internal motions in molecules. The mechanism which allows this type of observation is a coupling between the overall rotational angular momenta and the momentum associated with the restricted internal motion. One of the restricted motions of interest is the hindered internal rotation of a methyl group with respect to the bond it forms with the remainder of the molecule. The magnitude of the forces and distances involved place the investigation of hindered internal rotation of a methyl group sufficiently within the resolution available to microwave spectroscopy and allow the measurement of both relatively high and very low barriers. Under the proper conditions barriers up to the order of 4 kilocalories can be studied. Barriers hindering the free rotation of methyl groups are usually less than this value. Presumably, the measured barrier values may then be used to obtain a clearer understanding of the related molecular forces. Although the quantum-mechanical nature of hindered rotation is of basic importance, the major part of this chapter is concerned with the analysis of the microwave spectrum and subsequent calculation of the barrier height. More detailed discussions of the interpretation of these results and of the nature of the barrier are referenced in the bibliography.

6-1b. Physical Models

The model employed in the internal rotation problem can be formulated from the symmetry of the molecule being studied. The simplest case is that of a symmetric top with only one internal rotor. The internal rotor must lie on the symmetry axis of the molecule, and the degree of internal motion is a relative rotation of the two symmetric parts of the molecule. One of the two rotating groups is designated the top and the other is called the frame. In an asymmetric rotor, the frame is generally asymmetric; the top may be either

145

symmetric or asymmetric. A lack of symmetry in both the top and frame greatly complicates the barrier determination.

When the top has threefold or higher symmetry, the moments of inertia of the molecule are independent of the internal rotation angle. This occurs because the locus traced by the top in the plane perpendicular to its symmetry axis is a circle. When the top is also asymmetric, the moments of inertia of the molecule become functions of the angle of internal rotation.

The above models are pictured in Fig. 6-1. Also shown is a model for the double rotor case, e.g., dimethylsulfide. The symmetry characteristics of these models are reflected in the Hamiltonians which are derived from them. As in most physical problems, the degree of difficulty involved in the calculations is inversely related to the degree of symmetry present. In the discussions to follow it is assumed that the hindered internal rotor is a methyl group.

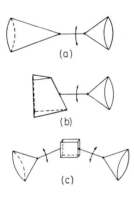

FIG. 6-1. Some schematic models for the internal rotation problem: (a) symmetric rotor, (b) asymmetric rotor, and (c) asymmetric rotor with two equivalent internal rotors. The arrows indicate the internal degrees of freedom.

6-1c. Potential Energy and Hindered Rotation

Figure 6-2 shows the general form of a threefold potential barrier. This potential energy function can be described in terms of the barrier height and the relative angle of internal rotation α. For a symmetric rotor the potential energy must be N-fold periodic as α goes through 2π, where N represents the degree of symmetry of the rotor. A Fourier expansion can be used for the potential with the angular reference placed to eliminate all sine terms.

$$V(\alpha) = \sum_i a_i \cos i N\alpha \qquad (6\text{-}1)$$

A more convenient form is given in (6-2) where the reference level with respect to the energy has been shifted. Defining the coefficients explicitly,

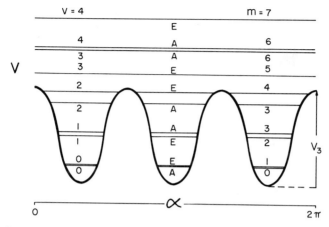

FIG 6-2. Torsional energy levels for a rotor hindered by a threefold potential barrier. Each level can be labeled by its torsional state v, its internal rotation sublevel (A or E), and its free rotation quantum number m.

$$V(\alpha) = \sum_i \frac{V_{Ni}}{2}(1 - \cos i N\alpha) \tag{6-2}$$

Experience has shown that the series in (6-2) converges rapidly and the first term in the summation is usually sufficient. Attempts to evaluate $2N$-fold contributions to the barrier have been made, but they show that these effects are small compared to the contribution of the N-fold term. In the case where the internal rotor has the threefold symmetry of a methyl group, a good approximation of the potential is

$$V(\alpha) = \frac{V_3}{2}(1 - \cos 3\alpha) \tag{6-3}$$

The theory of single-top internal rotors has been developed by several investigators [655, 668, 670, 673]. The potential function resembles that of Fig. 6-2. V_3 is the barrier height. From Fig. 6-2 and the analysis for a single internal rotor to follow, it is found that a threefold potential barrier splits the torsional energy levels into a nondegenerate (A) level and a doubly degenerate (E) level. For a barrier of sufficient size, the ground torsional state of the molecule lies below the top of the barrier. Classically, a rotation of 120° by the methyl group can only be executed if sufficient energy is applied to lift it over the barrier. Therefore, in a classical model, the rotation of the methyl group with respect to the remainder of the molecule would be effectively frozen for molecules below the top of the barrier, while molecules with enough energy to overcome the barrier would rotate freely. A quantum-mechanical approach shows that it is possible for hindered internal rotation to take place even when the molecule has insufficient energy to pass over the barrier. Quantum-mechanical tunneling permits the molecule to tunnel through the barrier at a rate governed by the effective barrier height. The tunneling process is detectable because it perturbs the rotational energy structure by removing the degeneracy of the A and E levels. It is the accurate determination of this splitting which provides a measure of V_3. Other means based on relative intensities and vibration-rotation interactions may be of importance in special situations.

Figure 6-3 shows the evolution of the torsional levels of a single-top molecule for changes in asymmetry and barrier height. The added complexity is caused by the introduction of the pure rotational characteristics of the

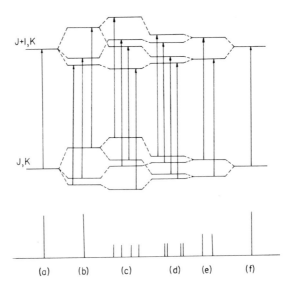

FIG. 6-3. Torsional energy levels as a function of asymmetry and barrier height. Representative splittings are shown for a symmetric rotor (a), a hindered symmetric rotor (b), a hindered asymmetric rotor with an intermediate barrier (c), a hindered asymmetric rotor with a high barrier (d), an asymmetric rotor with an infinite barrier (e), and a symmetric rotor (f). The appearance of the spectrum is shown at the bottom of the figure.

molecule. When hindered internal rotation is introduced in a symmetric rotor, the energy levels are split into triplets. However, the three transition frequencies are identical. When asymmetry and an intermediate barrier are introduced, K doubling produces four levels which form a doublet for a high barrier. Figure 6-3 should be referred to as the various symmetry types are treated.

For two equivalent internal rotors, the torsional energy level structure becomes more complicated. Potential energy terms arise not only from interactions with the molecular frame but also from possible interactions with the other top. Using α_1 and α_2 to designate the relative internal rotation angles and $V_3^{(1)}$ and $V_3^{(2)}$ to represent the barrier heights, the total hindering potential can be expanded in a Fourier series in α_1 and α_2

$$V(\alpha_1,\alpha_2) = V_0 + \tfrac{1}{2}V_3^{(1)}(1 - \cos 3\alpha_1) + \tfrac{1}{2}V_3^{(2)}(1 - \cos 3\alpha_2) + V_3^{(12)}\cos 3\alpha_1 \cos 3\alpha_2$$

$$+ V_3^{(12)*} \sin 3\alpha_1 \sin 3\alpha_2 + \text{higher terms} \qquad (6\text{-}4)$$

$V_3^{(12)}$ and $V_3^{(12)*}$ are measures of the top-top interaction and are smaller than $V_3^{(1)}$ and $V_3^{(2)}$. These crossterms represent a relative gearing of the two internal rotors. The fact that these terms are small is physically justifiable because the distance between the two methyl groups is usually large enough to prevent any direct interactions, such as steric effects. Ignoring V_0, recognizing that $V_3^{(1)} = V_3^{(2)}$ if the two internal rotors are equivalent, and ignoring the coupling and higher terms,

$$V(\alpha_1, \alpha_2) = \tfrac{1}{2}V_3(2 - \cos 3\alpha_1 - \cos 3\alpha_2) \qquad (6\text{-}5)$$

This represents the potential for the pure torsional problem independent of top-top coupling.

The $\cos 3\alpha_1 \cos 3\alpha_2$ coupling can be important in coupling between states such as vv' and $v \pm 2; v' \mp 2$. The $\sin 3\alpha_1 \sin 3\alpha_2$ term can couple states like vv' and $v \pm 1; v' \mp 1$. The positions of these coupling terms are shown in Fig. 6-4.

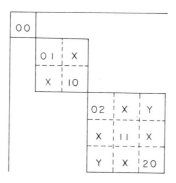

FIG. 6-4. Part of the torsional energy matrix for a molecule with two equivalent methyl groups. The nearly degenerate states are grouped into blocks labeled by $W = v_1 + v_2 = 0, 1, 2 \ldots$. Diagonal subblocks are labeled by the torsional quantum numbers v_1 and v_2. Positions of the off-diagonal connecting elements $p_1 p_2$ and $\sin 3\alpha_1 \sin 3\alpha_2$ are identified by X and the $\cos 3\alpha_1 \cos 3\alpha_2$ term is identified by Y. Elements which lie outside these blocks can be included as correction terms by applying a Van Vleck transformation.

Another interesting case occurs when the frame of a single-top molecule is planar as in CH_3BF_2 and CH_3NO_2. The potential energy then has the form[†]

$$V(\alpha) = \frac{V_6}{2}(1 - \cos 6\alpha) + \frac{V_{12}}{2}(1 - \cos 12\alpha) + \cdots \qquad (6\text{-}6)$$

The two contributions to $V(\alpha)$ from opposite sides of the C_{2v} frame are $180°$ out-of-phase and force a cancellation of the odd-order contributions to $V(\alpha)$. This can be visualized in Fig. 6-5 by holding the three-fold rotor stationary and rotating the frame. It is apparent that the potential experienced by the A half of the frame is a maximum when the potential acting on the B half of the frame is a minimum.

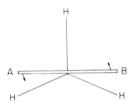

FIG. 6-5. Molecular model illustrating the low sixfold potential hindering internal rotation between a symmetric methyl group and a planar frame. A and B identify the two ends of the frame. Symmetry cancellation of the threefold barrier term is exact if the frame has C_{2v} symmetry.

6-2. High Potential Barriers

There have been two general approaches to the high barrier problem in single top molecules. The method chosen depends on the reference axis system because the kinetic energy terms in the Hamiltonian take a form dependent upon the axis system. In one case the principal axis system of the molecule is used because it removes interaction terms between the overall angular momenta of the molecule. In the other case the axis of the internal rotor is chosen as one of the reference axes and the other two axes are placed to take advantage of any molecular symmetry. This choice allows a reduction of the interaction terms between overall rotation and internal torsion. The latter method is commonly called the internal axis method or IAM; the former is the principal axis method or PAM. Each system has advantages and disadvantages relative to the other. The proper choice is determined by a consideration of the molecule being treated. The principal axis method has been developed by Wilson, Herschbach, and others [655, 662, 670]. Nielsen [604] and Dennison (see Hecht and Dennison [668]) are credited with the initial development of the internal axis approach. This work has been

---

[†] The even terms V_6 and V_{12} are redefined as twice their values in (6-2).

summarized in an excellent review of hindered internal rotation in single-top molecules by Lin and Swalen [703]. Notation consistent with their paper is employed here whenever possible.

6-3a. Energy Levels, Selection Rules, and Intensities for a High Barrier

The Hamiltonian of a rigid molecule is invariant under twofold rotations about its principal axes, and its energy levels belong to the irreducible representations of the four group $V(a, b, c)$. Hindered internal rotation introduces coupling terms of the form $p_i P_j$ which indicate the presence of an interaction between internal and overall rotation. This requires that appropriate changes in α take place during the twofold rotations to allow the Hamiltonian to remain unchanged. A special set of operations must be formulated which constitute a new symmetry group for the molecule and take into account the presence of internal degrees of freedom. The selection rules and relative intensities then follow from a group-theoretical analysis.

6-3b. A Single Internal Rotor

A mathematical analysis reveals that the torsional motion splits the energy levels into a nondegenerate level and a degenerate level. This result can be obtained more elegantly by applying group-theoretical methods. The CH_3 group rotations are governed by the symmetry point group C_3 and the torsional wave functions belong to the irreducible representations A and E of C_3. For a molecule with no overall symmetry, the Hamiltonian remains invariant under the operations E, C_3 and C_3^2 when they are applied only to the methyl group.[†] These operations do not alter the dipole moment of the molecule which transforms with the symmetry A. Because the dipole moment belongs to species A, a nonvanishing transition can occur only between two levels of the same degeneracy.

$$A \leftrightarrow A; \qquad E \leftrightarrow E; \qquad A \nleftrightarrow E \qquad (6\text{-}7)$$

For the molecules with some symmetry elements, more detailed selection rules can be written. However, the general rules in (6-7) will always be valid, i.e., degenerate and nondegenerate levels do not combine.

As an example, the selection rules are derived here for a molecule with a single plane of symmetry. It is first necessary to determine the set of symmetry operations which leaves the Hamiltonian invariant. These operations may be defined by transformations of the coordinates or angular momenta of the molecule [712] and are listed in Table 6-1. The P_i are rotational angular

---

[†] E is the identity operation and C_3 is a rotation of $2\pi/3$ about the threefold symmetry axis.

TABLE 6-1

SYMMETRY OPERATIONS FOR MOLECULES WITH ONE OR TWO INTERNAL ROTORS[a]

Single rotor (D_3):	$P_x, P_y, P_z, p; \theta, \phi, \chi, \alpha$
E	No change
C_x	$P_y \to -P_y, P_z \to -P_z, p \to -p; \chi \to \chi + \pi, \alpha \to -\alpha$
C_3	$\alpha \to \alpha + \dfrac{2\pi}{3}$
C_3^2	$\alpha \to \alpha + \dfrac{4\pi}{3}$
$C_x C_3$	$P_y \to -P_y, P_z \to -P_z, p \to -p; \chi \to \chi + \pi, \alpha \to -\alpha - \dfrac{2\pi}{3}$
$C_x C_3^2$	$P_y \to -P_y, P_z \to -P_z, p \to -p; \chi \to \chi + \pi, \alpha \to -\alpha - \dfrac{4\pi}{3}$

Double rotor (C_{2v}):	$P_x, P_y, P_z, p_1, p_2; \theta, \phi, \chi, \alpha_1, \alpha_2$
E	No change
C_z	$P_x \to -P_x, P_y \to -P_y, p_1 \to -p_2, p_2 \to -p_1; \chi \to \chi + \pi, \alpha_1 \to -\alpha_2,$ $\alpha_2 \to -\alpha_1$
C_y	$P_x \to -P_x, P_z \to -P_z, p_1 \to -p_1, p_2 \to -p_2; \theta \to \pi - \theta, \phi \to \phi + \pi,$ $\chi \to \pi - \chi, \alpha_1 \to -\alpha_1, \alpha_2 \to -\alpha_2$
C_x	$P_y \to -P_y, P_z \to -P_z, p_1 \to p_2, p_2 \to p_1; \theta \to \pi - \theta, \phi \to \phi + \pi,$ $\chi \to -\chi, \alpha_1 \to \alpha_2, \alpha_2 \to \alpha_1$
$C_3(1)$	$\alpha_1 \to \alpha_1 + \dfrac{2\pi}{3}$
$C_3(2)$	$\alpha_2 \to \alpha_2 + \dfrac{2\pi}{3}$

Double rotor (C_s):	$P_x, P_y, P_z, p_1, p_2; \theta, \phi, \chi, \alpha_1, \alpha_2$
E	No change
C_z	$P_y \to -P_y, P_x \to -P_x, p_1 \to -p_2, p_2 \to -p_1; \chi \to \chi + \pi, \alpha_1 \to -\alpha_2,$ $\alpha_2 \to -\alpha_1$
$C_3(1)$	$\alpha_1 \to \alpha_1 + \dfrac{2\pi}{3}$
$C_3(2)$	$\alpha_2 \to \alpha_2 + \dfrac{2\pi}{3}$

[a] After each operation only the momenta and coordinates which change are listed. The remaining ones are invariant.

momenta and p represents the angular momentum of the torsional motion. These symmetry operations satisfy the group properties of the point group D_3 [21] and the energy levels belong to the irreducible representations A_1, A_2, and E of D_3. Since the molecule has only a plane of symmetry, the dipole moment is restricted to lie in the plane. Because the dipole moment transforms in the same manner as the Cartesian coordinates x, y, z, it must belong to the irreducible representation having the correct Cartesian transformation properties. This is A_2. For the dipole moment integral to have A_1 symmetry, the selection rules must be

$$A_1 \leftrightarrow A_2, \qquad E \leftrightarrow E \tag{6-8}$$

These rules reduce to (6-7) when the plane of symmetry is removed. In a similar manner, the selection rules

$$A \leftrightarrow B_z, \qquad B_x \leftrightarrow B_y, \qquad E_1 \leftrightarrow E_1, \qquad E_2 \leftrightarrow E_2 \tag{6-9}$$

hold for molecules with a C_{2v} frame (dipole moment restricted to the twofold axis) in which the proper symmetry operations form a group isomorphic with D_{6h} [21]. g and u restrictions also apply to (6-9).

To determine the relative intensities of the A and E components, it is noted that the CH_3 group protons have eight spin functions to be combined with the torsional wave functions. These combinations are governed by the restriction that the overall wave function is antisymmetric with respect to the exchange of two protons. For the operations of C_3, which always exchanges an even number of pairs of protons, ψ_{total} must belong to A. The symmetries of the nuclear spin functions are determined by the torsional group character table. The characters of the eight spin functions are [21, 703] just the number of these functions left unaltered by the operations of the group, i.e., E, C_3, and C_3^2.

$$\chi_E = 8; \qquad \chi_{C_3} = 2; \qquad \chi_{C_3^2} = 2 \tag{6-10}$$

The symmetry is then determined by the standard reduction formula

$$n_k = \frac{1}{g} \sum_c g_c \chi_c^{(k)*} \chi_c \tag{6-11}$$

n_k is the weight, g is the number of symmetry elements in the subgroup[†] C_3 which interchanges protons of the methyl group, g_c is the number of elements in the class c of species of the subgroup, and $\chi_c^{(k)}$ is the character of the kth irreducible representation of C_3 for class c. The result is $\Gamma = 4A + 2E_1 + 2E_2$. The nuclear spin weight of a level is given by the weight of the representation A in the product $\psi_T \psi_S$ where ψ_T is the symmetry of the torsional wave

---

[†] For a molecule with no overall symmetry, C_3 comprises the entire group.

function. For the nondegenerate torsional levels

$$\psi_T \psi_S = A \times (4A + 2E_1 + 2E_2) = 4A + 2E_1 + 2E_2 \qquad (6\text{-}12)$$

For the degenerate levels

$$\psi_T \psi_S = (E_1 + E_2) \times (4A + 2E_1 + 2E_2) = 4A + 6E_1 + 6E_2 \qquad (6\text{-}13)$$

Thus the A and E transitions have equal intensities. A deuterated methyl group CD_3 has twenty-seven spin functions with a reduced symmetry of $11A + 8E_1 + 8E_2$. Therefore,

$$A \times (11A + 8E_1 + 8E_2) = 11A + 8E_1 + 8E_2 \qquad (6\text{-}14)$$

$$(E_1 + E_1) \times (11A + 8E_1 + 8E_2) = 16A + 19E_1 + 19E_2 \qquad (6\text{-}15)$$

This gives a relative intensity ratio of $11:16$ for the $A:E$ transitions.

6-3c. Two Equivalent Internal Rotors

For a molecule with two equivalent internal rotors belonging to the point group C_{2v} or C_s, a twofold rotation about any of the principal axes will not leave the Hamiltonian invariant because of changes in α_1 and α_2. Myers and Wilson [712] have derived the proper symmetry for C_{2v}-type double rotor molecules and Sage [723] has given the results for the C_s case. These new groups do not conform to any of the 32 symmetry point groups; however, they can be conveniently expressed as direct products of these point groups. For C_{2v} molecules the new group I is isomorphic with the direct product $C_{3v} \times C_{3v}$. For C_s symmetry, the new group S is isomorphic with $C_3 \times C_{3v}$. The direct product of the two point groups is just the product of the corresponding irreducible representations, symmetry operations, and characters.

I contains 36 symmetry operations and S contains 18 symmetry operations. These are all the distinct products formed by the appropriate symmetry operations which leave the Hamiltonian invariant. The correct operations which generate S and I are listed in Table 6-1. The sign convention for α_1 and α_2 is established by viewing the methyl groups from the center of the molecule. α_1 and α_2 are positive for clockwise rotations. As an example, the group I will be treated in some detail. Group I possesses nine irreducible representations as indicated by the character table in Table 6-2.

The four nondegenerate species $A_1 A_1$, $A_1 A_2$, $A_2 A_1$, $A_2 A_2$ correspond to the irreducible representations A, B_x, B_y, B_z of the four group which describes the symmetry of the asymmetric rotor functions. Operations E, $C_3(1)C_3(2)$, $C_3^2(1)C_3^2(2)$, C_z, $C_z C_3(1)C_3(2)$, $C_z C_3^2(1)C_3^2(2)$ correspond to C_{3v} for the angle $\frac{1}{2}(\alpha_1 + \alpha_2)$ and the operations E, $C_3(1)C_3^2(2)$, $C_3^2(1)C_3(2)$, C_x, $C_x C_3(1)C_3^2(2)$, $C_x C_3^2(1)C_3(2)$ form the group C_{3v} for the angle $\frac{1}{2}(\alpha_1 - \alpha_2)$. The xz plane is

TABLE 6-2
CHARACTER TABLE OF THE INTERNAL ROTATION GROUP I^a

	EE	$2EC_3$	$3E\sigma_v$	$2C_3E$	$4C_3^2$	$6C_3\sigma_v$	$3\sigma_v E$	$6\sigma_v C_3$	$9\sigma_v^2$
A_1A_1	1	1	1	1	1	1	1	1	1
A_1A_2	1	1	-1	1	1	-1	1	1	-1
A_1E	2	-1	0	2	-1	0	2	-1	0
A_2A_1	1	1	1	1	1	1	-1	-1	-1
A_2A_2	1	1	-1	1	1	-1	-1	-1	1
A_2E	2	-1	0	2	-1	0	-2	1	0
EA_1	2	2	2	-1	-1	-1	0	0	0
EA_2	2	2	-2	-1	-1	1	0	0	0
EE	4	-2	0	-2	1	0	0	0	0

^{a} From Refs. [705, 712].

chosen to contain the internal rotor axes with the x axis forming their bisector. Correlation with the principal axis system is made through the I^r representation in Table 2-1.

$$\alpha_\pm = \tfrac{1}{2}(\alpha_1 \pm \alpha_2) \qquad (6\text{-}16)$$

These groups are designated as C_{3v}^+ for α_+ and C_{3v}^- for α_-. C_{3v}^+ leaves α_- invariant and C_{3v}^- leaves α_+ invariant.

The selection rules can be obtained by finding the symmetry species to which the dipole operator belongs. In symmetry group C_{3v}^+, μ_b belongs to A_2 but in C_{3v}^- it belongs to A_1. This may be verified by checking the transformation properties of μ_b under the operations of C_{3v}^+ and C_{3v}^-. Thus μ_b belongs to A_1A_2 of I. Table 6-3 gives the character table and multiplication properties of point group C_{3v}.

TABLE 6-3
CHARACTER TABLE AND MULTIPLICATION RULES OF THE POINT GROUP C_{3v}

C_{3v}	E	$2C_3$	$3\sigma_v$
A_1	1	1	1
A_2	1	1	-1
E	2	-1	0

$$A_1 \times A_1 = A_1$$
$$A_2 \times A_2 = A_1$$
$$A_1 \times A_2 = A_2 \times A_1 = A_2$$
$$A_1 \times E = A_2 \times E = E \times A_1 = E \times A_2 = E$$
$$E \times E = A_1 + A_2 + E$$

The product of the species of the two combining energy levels and $A_1 A_2$ must belong to $A_1 A_1$, the completely symmetric irreducible representation. This results in the selection rules shown in Table 6-4. The results for C_s are also given.

TABLE 6-4

SELECTION RULES FOR C_{2v} AND C_s DOUBLE ROTORS

C_{2v}	$A_1 A_1 \leftrightarrow A_1 A_2$
	$A_2 A_1 \leftrightarrow A_2 A_2$
	$A_1 E \leftrightarrow A_1 E$
	$A_2 E \leftrightarrow A_2 E$
	$E A_1 \leftrightarrow E A_2$
	$E E \leftrightarrow E E$
C_s	$A A_1 \leftrightarrow A A_2$
	$A E \leftrightarrow A E$
	$E_0 A_1 \leftrightarrow E_0 A_2$
	$E_0 E \leftrightarrow E_0 E$

For a very high barrier, the torsional wave functions can be approximated by the product of two harmonic oscillator functions in α_+ and α_- [712].

$$U_{v\sigma}(\alpha_1) U_{v\sigma}(\alpha_2) \sim H_{n-}(\alpha_- + ka) H_{n+}(\alpha_+ + la) \qquad (6\text{-}17)$$

$a = 2\pi/3$, and k, $l = 0$, ± 1. H_n is the nth harmonic oscillator function. Subgroup C_{3v}^- operates on H_{n-} and C_{3v}^+ operates on H_{n+}. The species to which a given harmonic oscillator function H_n belongs is $A_1 + E$ if n is even and $A_2 + E$ if n is odd. Possible parity combinations are given in Table 6-5.

TABLE 6-5

SYMMETRY SPECIES FOR PARITIES OF n_+ AND n_-

n_+	n_-	Symmetry species
even	even	$A_1 A_1 + A_1 E + E A_1 + E E$
even	odd	$A_2 A_1 + A_2 E + E A_1 + E E$
odd	odd	$A_2 A_2 + A_2 E + E A_2 + E E$
odd	even	$A_1 A_2 + A_1 E + E A_2 + E E$

These species confirm that the energy levels in the ground torsional state are ninefold degenerate in the limit of an infinite barrier and that a quartet is produced as the barrier is lowered. The first-order perturbation terms which tend to remove the degeneracy of $A_i E$ and $E A_j$ species are often negligible, with the result that triplets instead of quartets are observed in the spectrum.

In excited torsional states, the torsional quantum numbers v and v' may not be equal and states such as $v = 0$, $v' = 1$ and $v = 1$, $v' = 0$ may interact strongly. Defining the indexing quantum number $W = v + v'$ [738], the solution to the torsional equation in the high barrier limit is ninefold degenerate for $W = 0$, eighteen-fold degenerate for $W = 1$, and twenty-seven-fold degenerate for $W = 2$. These states are represented in Fig. 6-4 along with off-diagonal matrix elements which connect them.

The statistical weights of the torsional levels can be determined by considering the subgroup of I which causes the interchange of equivalent nuclei. This group is formed by removing the operation C_z from I.

$$II = C_{3v}^- \times C_3^+ \qquad (6\text{-}18)$$

The group C_3^+ is now used in place of C_{3v}^+ and its character table is listed in Table 6-6. The correlation between C_3 and C_{3v} is $A_1 \leftrightarrow A$, $A_2 \leftrightarrow A$, and $E \leftrightarrow E_1 + E_2$. For C_s molecules, the subgroup S' which interchanges equivalent nuclei on the internal rotors is $C_3 \times C_3$.

TABLE 6-6
CHARACTER TABLE OF THE POINT GROUP C_3

	E	C_3	C_3^2	
A	1	1	1	
$E_0 \begin{cases} E_1 \\ E_2 \end{cases}$	1 1	ω ω^2	ω^2 ω	$(\omega = -\tfrac{1}{2} + i\sqrt{3}/2)$

Statistical weights are given by the standard formula (6-11). The overall function has species $\Gamma_i \Gamma_j$. χ_c is the character of the species formed by the total functions which belong to $\Gamma_i \Gamma_j$ for class c. In effect, the reduction formula determines the statistical weight for a level by reducing, on the group II, the set of overall wave functions produced by taking the product of the functions belonging to $\Gamma_i \Gamma_j$ and all possible spin functions appropriate to the exchange of identical nuclei. n_k is the number of times the irreducible representation of the overall wave function appears in the reduction. This irreducible representation for the interchange of identical Fermions is $A_1 A$ if an even number are exchanged and $A_2 A$ if an odd number are exchanged. For Bosons like deuterium the species is always $A_1 A$. Because II is the direct product of two point groups, the quantities in (6-11) will be just the product of those for C_{3v} and C_3.

$$g_c = g_c^- g_c^+$$
$$\chi_c^{(k)} = \chi_c^{(k^-)} \chi_c^{(k^+)} = \pm 1 \qquad (6\text{-}19)$$

The ± 1 is determined by whether the operation $c^- c^+$ interchanges an even or odd number of identical hydrogen nuclei.

χ_c is given by

$$\chi_c = \chi_c^{\Gamma_i} \chi_c^{\Gamma_j} \prod_i (2s_i + 1)_{c^- c^+} \qquad (6\text{-}20)$$

Any operation $c^- c^+$ results in a permutation of identical nuclei. As in the single-top case, the contribution to χ_c from the nuclear spin function is the number of spin functions which are left unaltered by the permutation, i.e., $\prod_i (2s_i + 1)_{c^- c^+}$ where s_i is the spin of one of the equivalent nuclei in the ith set. The contributions from the rest of the wave function (exclusive of spin) are given by the first two factors in (6-20). These are the characters of the appropriate species in group I.

For C_{2v} molecules like dimethylsulfide, the theoretical statistical weights for ground state rotational transitions $A \leftrightarrow B_b$ are $6:16:2:4$ for $A_1 A_1 : EE : A_1 E : EA_1$. For $B_a \leftrightarrow B_c$ transitions the weights are $10:16:6:4$. For C_s molecules like cis-2,3 epoxybutane the intensities are $2:4:1:1$ for $A A_1 : E_0 E : A E : E_0 A_1$. Relative weights have also been obtained for deuterated methyl groups and excited torsional states [705, 712, 723].

6-4. The PAM for a Symmetric-Top Molecule

For a symmetric top with only a single internal rotor, the methyl group axis necessarily lies along the figure axis of the molecule. Molecules such as methyl silane and methyl germane fall into this category. The Hamiltonian for any conservative molecular system can be written as the sum of the kinetic and potential energies.

$$H = T + V \qquad (6\text{-}21)$$

A general expression for kinetic energy is

$$2T = \omega^+ I \omega \qquad (6\text{-}22)$$

where I is the inertial tensor and ω is the angular velocity vector. In its most general form I also contains the contribution of the internal rotor.

$$\omega = \begin{bmatrix} \omega_a \\ \omega_b \\ \omega_c \\ \dot{\alpha} \end{bmatrix} ; \qquad I = \begin{bmatrix} I_a & 0 & 0 & 0 \\ 0 & I_b & 0 & 0 \\ 0 & 0 & I_c & I_\alpha \\ 0 & 0 & I_\alpha & I_\alpha \end{bmatrix} \qquad (6\text{-}23)$$

The off-diagonal terms have the form $\lambda_g I_\alpha$ where λ_g is the direction cosine between the internal rotor axis and the g principal axis. Removing the α terms from I and ω gives

$$2T = \omega^+ I \omega + \dot{\alpha}^+ I_\alpha \dot{\alpha} + \omega^+ I_\alpha \dot{\alpha} + \dot{\alpha}^+ I_\alpha \omega \qquad (6\text{-}24)$$

Expanding the kinetic energy gives

$$2T = I_a\omega_a^2 + I_b\omega_b^2 + I_c\omega_c^2 + I_\alpha\dot{\alpha}^2 + 2I_\alpha\dot{\alpha}\omega_c \tag{6-25}$$

where $\dot{\alpha}$ is the time derivative of the internal rotation angle α, the ω_i are the angular velocity components about the three principal axes, and I_α is the moment of the internal rotor (methyl group) about its symmetry axis. In this case the c axis has been chosen as the figure axis.

The kinetic energy can be expressed more conveniently in terms of the angular momenta of the system.

$$\mathbf{P} = \mathbf{I\omega} \tag{6-26}$$

This leads to

$$2T = \mathbf{P}^+\mathbf{I}^{-1}\mathbf{P} \tag{6-27}$$

where

$$\mathbf{P} = \begin{bmatrix} P_a \\ P_b \\ P_c \\ p \end{bmatrix} \tag{6-28}$$

The relationships between the angular momenta and the angular velocities are given by

$$P_a = \frac{\partial T}{\partial \omega_a} = I_a\omega_a \tag{6-29}$$

$$P_b = \frac{\partial T}{\partial \omega_b} = I_b\omega_b \tag{6-30}$$

$$P_c = \frac{\partial T}{\partial \omega_c} = I_c\omega_c + I_\alpha\dot{\alpha} \tag{6-31}$$

$$p = \frac{\partial T}{\partial \dot{\alpha}} = I_\alpha\omega_c + I_\alpha\dot{\alpha} \tag{6-32}$$

With these definitions the kinetic energy becomes

$$2T = \frac{P_a^2}{I_a} + \frac{P_b^2}{I_b} + \frac{P_c^2}{(I_c - I_\alpha)} + \frac{I_c}{I_\alpha(I_c - I_\alpha)}p^2 - \frac{2P_cp}{(I_c - I_\alpha)} \tag{6-33}$$

The P_i are total components of angular momentum (including any contributions from the internal rotation) and p is the total angular momentum of the internal top (including any contribution from overall rotation). Substitution of (6-33) and (6-3) into (6-21) yields the Hamiltonian for the system. This Hamiltonian can be subdivided into three parts.

$$H = H_r + H_{ir} + H_{r,ir} \tag{6-34}$$

H_r represents the pure rotational terms and H_{ir} represents the internal rotation terms. $H_{r,ir}$ is the coupling between overall rotation and internal rotation. Because $I_a = I_b$, H_r can be simplified and expressed in terms of rotational constants.[†]

$$H_r = A(P_a^2 + P_b^2) + C_i P_c^2 \tag{6-35}$$

$$A = \frac{\hbar^2}{2I_a} = \frac{\hbar^2}{2I_b}; \qquad C = \frac{\hbar^2}{2I_c} \tag{6-36}$$

$$C_i = \frac{\hbar^2}{2(I_c - I_a)} \tag{6-37}$$

H_{ir} is a function of the angular momentum p and the internal rotation angle α.

$$H_{ir} = Fp^2 + V(\alpha) \tag{6-38}$$

$$F = \frac{\hbar^2 I_c}{2I_\alpha(I_c - I_\alpha)} = \frac{\hbar^2}{2rI_\alpha} \tag{6-39}$$

$$r = \frac{I_c - I_\alpha}{I_c} \tag{6-40}$$

The coupling term $H_{r,ir}$ allows the rotational energy levels of the molecule to be perturbed by the internal motion.

$$H_{r,ir} = -2C_i P_c p \tag{6-41}$$

Subdivision of the Hamiltonian in this manner permits the convenient application of perturbation theory. The first two terms in (6-34) can be used as the zero-order Hamiltonian and $H_{r,ir}$ can be treated as the perturbation.

$$(H_r + H_{ir})\psi^{(0)} = (E_r + E_{ir})\psi^{(0)} \tag{6-42}$$

$\psi^{(0)}$ is the product of the symmetric rotor eigenfunctions and the appropriate internal rotor eigenfunctions.

$$\psi^{(0)} = S_{JKM}(\theta, \phi)e^{iK\chi}U_{v\sigma}(\alpha) \tag{6-43}$$

The eigenvalues for a rigid symmetric rotor are given in Chapter 2.

$$E_r = AJ(J + 1) + (C_i - A)K^2 \tag{6-44}$$

[†] The rotational constants are expressed in energy units.

The pure internal rotation equation is

$$\left[Fp^2 + \frac{V_N}{2}(1 - \cos N\alpha) \right] U_{v\sigma}(\alpha) = E_{v\sigma} U_{v\sigma}(\alpha) \qquad (6\text{-}45)$$

In the present case N is equal to three. The $U_{v\sigma}(\alpha)$ are the eigenfunctions for the internal rotation equation and the quantum-mechanical equivalent of p is

$$p \equiv -i\left(\frac{\partial}{\partial \alpha}\right)_{\theta,\phi,\chi} \qquad (6\text{-}46)$$

Equation (6-45) is analogous to the Mathieu differential equation whose solutions for the threefold periodic case have long been known. Equation (6-47) shows the Mathieu equation in an appropriate form followed by the proper transformations relating it to (6-45).

$$\left(\frac{d^2}{dx^2} - s\cos^2 x\right)y = -b_{v\sigma}y \qquad (6\text{-}47)$$

$$2x = N\alpha + \pi \qquad (6\text{-}48)$$

$$E_{v\sigma} = \frac{N^2 F b_{v\sigma}}{4} \qquad (6\text{-}49)$$

$$V_N = \frac{N^2 F s}{4} \qquad (6\text{-}50)$$

Appendix 9 gives a detailed discussion of the Mathieu equation.

The three solutions satisfying the torsional equation can be expressed in a Fourier series.

$$U_{v\sigma}(\alpha) = \sum_k A^v_{3k+\sigma} \exp[i(3k + \sigma)\alpha] \qquad (6\text{-}51)$$

where v is the torsional quantum number in the limit of harmonic oscillations (i.e., an infinite barrier), and σ is an index identifying the torsional sublevels. The eigenfunctions $U_{v\sigma}(\alpha)$ are dependent on the reduced barrier height s and are available in tabulated form [624].

Equation (6-45) describes the motion of a threefold rotor of the symmetry group C_3. The solutions conform to the irreducible representations of C_3; namely, A and E. The A solution is obtained by setting σ equal to zero and the degenerate E solution results from setting σ equal to ± 1. The non-degenerate solution has a period of π in x; the degenerate solution has a period of 3π in x.

It now becomes necessary to diagonalize the energy matrix H. The matrix elements of H are

$$\langle JKMv\sigma|H|JKMv\sigma\rangle = AJ(J + 1) + (C_i - A)K^2 + E_{v\sigma} \qquad (6\text{-}52)$$

$$\langle JKMv\sigma|H|JKM, v \pm 1, \sigma\rangle = -2C_iK\langle v|p|v \pm 1\rangle \qquad (6\text{-}53)$$

The pure rigid rotor term H_r and the torsional term H_{ir} are diagonal in J, K, M and σ. It remains for the off-diagonal elements of $H_{r,ir}$ to be removed. They result from the fact that the operator p is not diagonal in v, the pseudo-torsional quantum number. The off-diagonal property of v is caused by the finite size of the barrier V_3. Additional contributions to $H_{r,ir}$ result if the V_6 term is included in the potential energy. The matrix elements off-diagonal in v may be reduced to second order by a Van Vleck transformation (Appendix 7). Such a transformation reduces to fourth order the off-diagonal contributions to the energy. This effectively separates the overall rotational terms from the internal rotor matrix elements. The result is a factoring of the original matrix pictured in Fig. 6-6 into a series of rotational submatrices

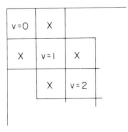

FIG. 6-6. Torsional energy matrix for a single top molecule prior to applying a Van Vleck transformation. X represents the off-diagonal elements produced by the internal angular momentum p connecting v with $v \pm 1$. Any contribution from a V_6 term (not shown) will connect levels with the same parity of v.

for the individual torsional states. These submatrices are effectively diagonal in both v and σ.

$$H_{v\sigma} = A(P_a^2 + P_b^2) + C_{v\sigma}P_c^2 - 2C_iP_c\langle v\sigma|p|v\sigma\rangle + E_{v\sigma} \tag{6-54}$$

$$C_{v\sigma} = C + 4C^2 \sum_v{}' \frac{|\langle v\sigma|p|v', \sigma\rangle|^2}{E_{v\sigma} - E_{v',\sigma}} \tag{6-55}$$

$$\langle v\sigma|p|v', \sigma\rangle = \int_0^{2\pi} U_{v\sigma}^*(\alpha)\frac{1}{i}\frac{d}{d\alpha}U_{v',\sigma}(\alpha)\,d\alpha \tag{6-56}$$

Equations (6-55) and (6-56) indicate that the correction terms added onto the diagonal are similar to second-order perturbation corrections.

For an infinitely high barrier, each of the three potential wells will approximate a harmonic oscillator potential and the torsional states labeled by v are triply degenerate. As the barrier is lowered, tunneling takes place between the minima, causing a separation of each torsional level into its A and E components. The splitting is a strong function of the barrier height. The energy from (6-54) is

$$E = AJ(J + 1) + (C_{v\sigma} - A)K^2 - 2C_iK\langle v\sigma|p|v\sigma\rangle + E_{v\sigma} \qquad (6\text{-}57)$$

$E_{v\sigma}$ is the pure torsional energy and is not a function of the rotational quantum numbers. This prevents the splitting from directly affecting the spectrum. The correction terms may be carried to a higher order and expressed as a power series in ρK where

$$\rho = \left[\sum_g \left(\frac{\lambda_g I_\alpha}{I_g} \right)^2 \right]^{1/2} = \frac{I_\alpha}{I_c} \qquad (6\text{-}58)$$

$$E = AJ(J + 1) + (C - A)K^2 + F\sum_n W_{v\sigma}^{(n)}(\rho K)^n \qquad (6\text{-}59)$$

The $W_{v\sigma}^{(n)}$ are perturbation coefficients. The symmetry of the solution forces the odd-order perturbation coefficients to vanish for the A levels. In general, the odd-order terms do not vanish for the E levels and deviations from a rigid rotor spectrum occur for the $E \rightarrow E$ transitions. Another consequence of the torsional motion is the torsional dependence of the rotational constant C.

The selection rules are those of a symmetric top (neglecting inversion) and the additional restriction that σ does not change.

$$\Delta J = \pm 1; \qquad \Delta K = 0; \qquad \Delta \sigma = 0 \qquad (6\text{-}60)$$

The A levels remain doubly degenerate with respect to K (except for $K = 0$), because the odd coefficients in (6-59) vanish. The existence of odd powers of K due to odd perturbation coefficients tends to lift the K degeneracy of the E levels. Three sets of rotational transitions result; all exhibit a double degeneracy.

$$J(\pm K, \sigma = 0) \rightarrow (J + 1)(\pm K, \sigma = 0) \qquad (6\text{-}61)$$

$$J(+K, \sigma = \pm 1) \rightarrow (J + 1)(+K, \sigma = \pm 1) \qquad (6\text{-}62)$$

$$J(-K, \sigma = \pm 1) \rightarrow (J + 1)(-K, \sigma = \pm 1) \qquad (6\text{-}63)$$

Calculation of the frequencies of these transitions indicates that the three spectral lines are coincident despite the fact that the energy levels are split. The magnitude of the splitting is identical in the upper and lower states, and the ground state spectrum shows no internal rotation effects. The energy level splittings and transitions are shown in Fig. 6-3 for a hindered symmetric rotor.

6-5. The IAM for a Symmetric-Top Molecule

In the IAM the axis of the internal rotor is chosen as one of the coordinate axes. This choice has the advantage of lessening the interaction between internal and overall rotation. It possesses the disadvantage of not necessarily being a principal axis system. With a symmetric-top molecule, the internal rotor axis is coincident with a principal axis. The resulting kinetic energy is the same as that in the PAM given in (6-33). p does not vanish in the limit of an infinite barrier and the Hamiltonian cannot be separated into terms for a rigid rotor and an internal rotor. The problem can be seen more easily by looking at the explicit form of p.

$$p = \frac{\partial T}{\partial \dot{\alpha}} = I_a \omega_c + I_a \dot{\alpha} \tag{6-64}$$

When $V_3 \to \infty$, $\dot{\alpha} \to 0$, and $p \to I_a \omega_c$ which is not zero.

A transformation proposed by Nielsen [604] removes the crossterm between P_c and p and forces p to depend only on $\dot{\alpha}$.

$$p' = p - \left(\frac{I_a}{I_c}\right) P_c \tag{6-65}$$

The Hamiltonian is then

$$H = \frac{P_a^2}{2I_a} + \frac{P_b^2}{2I_b} + \frac{P_c^2}{2I_c} + \frac{I_c}{2I_a(I_c - I_a)} p'^2 + V(\alpha) \tag{6-66}$$

This transformation does not make p' the internal angular momentum since $p' \neq I_a \dot{\alpha}$. The internal angular momentum associated with the relative motion of the top and frame of the molecule has been removed. The new coordinate system produced by the Nielsen transformation is rotating in space in such a way as to remove this relative motion.[†] The orientation of the internal rotation axes depends on $\dot{\alpha}$ and if $\dot{\alpha} \to 0$ the axes remain fixed with respect to the molecule.

If θ, ϕ, and χ are the Eulerian angles in the original coordinate system, the transformation results in the following changes.

$$\theta' = \theta, \qquad \phi' = \phi, \qquad \chi' = \chi + (I_a/I_c)\alpha \tag{6-67}$$

If χ_1 and χ_2 are Eulerian angles of the frame and top, respectively,

$$\alpha' = \chi_2' - \chi_1', \qquad \chi' = \chi_1' \tag{6-68}$$

These relations are unchanged from those holding before the transformation since $\alpha = \alpha'$.

The Nielsen transformation upsets the commutation rules among the various angular momenta. p' does not commute with P_a or P_b, although it does commute with $P_a^2 + P_b^2$. P_a and P_b do not commute with p' because their matrix elements are a function of the quantum number of internal torsion.

[†] Hecht and Dennison [668] refer to the new coordinate system as the molecule-fixed axis system; Lin and Swalen [703] name it the internal rotation axis system.

This dependence can be removed by a transformation which affects P_a and P_b but not $P_a^2 + P_b^2$.

$$\begin{bmatrix} P_a' \\ P_b' \\ P_c' \end{bmatrix} = \begin{bmatrix} \cos\tau & \sin\tau & 0 \\ -\sin\tau & \cos\tau & 0 \\ 0 & 0 & 1 \end{bmatrix} \begin{bmatrix} P_a \\ P_b \\ P_c \end{bmatrix} \qquad (6\text{-}69)$$

$$\tau = \frac{I_a}{I_c}\alpha = \rho\alpha \qquad (6\text{-}70)$$

The Hamiltonian is now

$$H = A(P_a'^2 + P_b'^2) + CP_c'^2 + Fp'^2 + V(\alpha) \qquad (6\text{-}71)$$

$$A = \frac{\hbar^2}{2I_a} = \frac{\hbar^2}{2I_b}; \qquad F = \frac{\hbar^2 I_c}{2I_a(I_c - I_a)}; \qquad C = \frac{\hbar^2}{2I_c} \qquad (6\text{-}72)$$

The Nielsen transformation allows the wave functions to be written as

$$\psi = S_{JKM}(\theta', \phi')e^{iK\chi'}M(\alpha') \qquad (6\text{-}73)$$

As a result of the transformation, the boundary conditions no longer allow use of the periodic Mathieu functions $U_{v\sigma}(\alpha)$. $M(\alpha')$ now represents non-periodic solutions of the equation [660]

$$[Fp'^2 + V(\alpha')]M(\alpha') = EM(\alpha') \qquad (6\text{-}74)$$

The wave function must remain unaltered for 2π changes in χ_1 and χ_2 or χ' and α'.

$$M(\alpha') = e^{if\alpha'}P(\alpha') \qquad (6\text{-}75)$$

$P(\alpha')$ is periodic in the angle α' and f is a constant determined by the boundary conditions. These conditions are

$$\chi' \rightarrow \chi' + 2\pi\left[\frac{I_a}{I_c}n_2 + \frac{(I_c - I_a)}{I_c}n_1\right] \qquad (6\text{-}76)$$

$$\alpha' \rightarrow \alpha' + 2\pi(n_2 - n_1) \qquad (6\text{-}77)$$

n_1 and n_2 are integers defined by the boundary conditions

$$\chi_1 \rightarrow \chi_1 + 2\pi n_1; \qquad \chi_2 \rightarrow \chi_2 + 2\pi n_2 \qquad (6\text{-}78)$$

which held before the transformation. The wave function will be invariant for the transformation of (6-76) and (6-77) if

$$K\left[\frac{I_a}{I_c}n_2 + \frac{(I_c - I_a)}{I_c}n_1\right] + f(n_2 - n_1) = n \qquad (6\text{-}79)$$

n is an integer. This relationship is valid for either of the two following values of f [608, 703].

$$f = -K\frac{I_a}{I_c} = -\rho K \tag{6-80}$$

$$f = \frac{(I_c - I_a)}{I_c}K = (1 - \rho)K \tag{6-81}$$

In the latter case

$$\psi = S_{JKM}(\theta', \phi')e^{iK\chi'} e^{-i\rho K\alpha'}P(\alpha') \tag{6-82}$$

The torsional part of the wave function now shows a K dependence but is not a function of θ', ϕ', or χ' which represent overall rotation. The solutions of the torsional equation can again be expressed in a Fourier expansion.

$$M_{Kv\sigma}(\alpha) = e^{-i\rho K\alpha'} \sum_k A^{Kv}_{3k+\sigma} \exp[i(3k + \sigma)\alpha'] \tag{6-83}$$

In explicit form the torsional equation is found to have imaginary coefficients

$$-F\left(\frac{d^2 P(\alpha')}{d\alpha'^2}\right) + 2i\rho KF\left(\frac{dP(\alpha')}{d\alpha'}\right) + \frac{V_3}{2}(1 - \cos 3\alpha')P(\alpha') = (E - F\rho^2 K^2)P(\alpha') \tag{6-84}$$

and the eigenfunctions for $\sigma = +1$ are not degenerate with those for $\sigma = -1$. However, the relationships between the complex conjugates are

$$M_{Kv\sigma}(\alpha') = M^*_{-K,v,-\sigma}(\alpha') \tag{6-85}$$

$$P_{Kv\sigma}(\alpha') = P^*_{-K,v,-\sigma}(\alpha') \tag{6-86}$$

Only for $K = 0$ are the $\sigma = \pm 1$ functions degenerate. For $K \neq 0$ there are three torsional levels for each torsional state. When overall and internal rotation are considered, both the PAM and IAM predict the same energy level structure. This must be true because the physical problem is unchanged.

Using the selection rules in (6-60), the energy levels are doubly degenerate in K, and transitions fall into three categories.

$$J(\pm K, \sigma = +1) \to (J + 1)(\pm K, \sigma = +1) \tag{6-87}$$

$$J(\pm K, \sigma = 0) \to (J + 1)(\pm K, \sigma = 0) \tag{6-88}$$

$$J(\pm K, \sigma = -1) \to (J + 1)(\pm K, \sigma = -1) \tag{6-89}$$

A continued fraction technique can be used to determine the solutions to the torsional problem. In the case of a high barrier, the eigenvalues may be expressed in a Fourier series and considered as periodic functions of $(2\pi/3)(\rho K - \sigma)$ because the $M(\alpha')$ are unchanged when $\rho K - \sigma + 3$ is substituted for $\rho K - \sigma$.

$$E_{Kv\sigma} = F \sum_n a_n^{(v)} \cos(2\pi n/3)(\rho K - \sigma) \tag{6-90}$$

The relationship between the torsional energy and the Mathieu eigenvalue b is

$$E(\rho K - \sigma = x) = b(3\pi/x) \qquad (6\text{-}91)$$

The total energy of a symmetric top exhibiting hindered internal rotation is then

$$E = AJ(J + 1) + (C - A)K^2 + F \sum_n a_n^{(v)} \cos \frac{2\pi n}{3}(\rho K - \sigma) \qquad (6\text{-}92)$$

For a high barrier value, the Fourier series can be expanded in terms of the sine and cosine of $2\pi\sigma/3$. The resulting expansions for $\sigma = 0$ and $\sigma = \pm 1$ agree with the results of the PAM. Again the rotational spectrum is shown to be unaffected by the internal torsion.

6-6. PAM for Asymmetric Molecules with Symmetric Internal Rotors

An asymmetric molecule with an attached methyl group is an example of the most common type of molecule whose internal rotation has been studied. The frame of the molecule may have any of the symmetry elements of an asymmetric rotor such as a twofold axis or a plane of symmetry. The axis of the top is no longer colinear with a threefold molecular axis (or generally with any of the principal axes).

The kinetic energy is still given by (6-22) but with a more complex form of inertial tensor. If λ_i represents the direction cosine of the top axis with respect to the ith principal axis, the expanded kinetic energy is

$$2T = \sum_i I_i \omega_i^2 + I_\alpha \dot\alpha^2 + 2I_\alpha \dot\alpha \sum_i \lambda_i \omega_i \qquad (6\text{-}93)$$

In terms of angular momenta the Hamiltonian becomes

$$H = \sum_i \mathscr{A}_i P_i^2 + F p^2 + \tfrac{1}{2} \sum_{i \neq j} D_{ij}(P_i P_j + P_j P_i)$$

$$-2 \sum_i Q_i P_i p + V(\alpha) \qquad (i, j = a, b, c)$$

$$\mathscr{A}_i = \frac{h^2}{8\pi^2 I_i}\left[1 + \frac{\lambda_i^2 I_\alpha}{r I_i}\right] \qquad (\mathscr{A}_i = A, B, C)$$

$$F = \frac{h^2}{8\pi^2 r I_\alpha}$$

$$r = 1 - \sum_i \frac{\lambda_i^2 I_\alpha}{I_i} \qquad (6\text{-}94)$$

$$D_{ij} = \frac{h^2 \lambda_i \lambda_j I_\alpha}{8\pi^2 r I_i I_j}$$

$$Q_i = \frac{h^2 \lambda_i}{8\pi^2 r I_i}$$

The Hamiltonian can also be written in a more condensed form.

$$H = H_r + F(p - \mathscr{P})^2 + V(\alpha) \tag{6-95}$$

H_r represents the rigid rotor terms and

$$\mathscr{P} = \sum_i P_i \lambda_i I_\alpha / I_i \tag{6-96}$$

In order to preserve the simplified boundary conditions of the problem, a perturbation treatment is applied. It is possible to employ a transformation which approximately separates the overall and internal rotation terms, but this complicates the boundary conditions of r and K [703] on the torsional wave functions.

The Hamiltonian is separated into three terms for the perturbation treatment.

$$H^{(0)} = \left(\frac{A + B}{2}\right)P^2 + \left(C - \frac{A + B}{2}\right)P_z^2 + Fp^2 + \frac{V_3}{2}(1 - \cos 3\alpha) \tag{6-97}$$

$$H^{(1)} = -2 \sum_i Q_i P_i p \tag{6-98}$$

$$H^{(2)} = \left(\frac{A - B}{2}\right)(P_x^2 - P_y^2) + \tfrac{1}{2} \sum_{i \neq j} D_{ij}(P_i P_j + P_j P_i) \tag{6-99}$$

$H^{(0)}$ consists of independent symmetric rigid rotor and internal rotor terms. The eigenfunction of $H^{(0)}$ is just the product of the symmetric rotor wave function and the Mathieu function.

$$\psi^{(0)} = S_{JKM}(\theta, \phi)e^{iK\chi}U_{v\sigma}(\alpha) \tag{6-100}$$

As in the symmetric top case, the Hamiltonian is diagonal in J, M, and σ but nondiagonal in K and v. $H^{(1)}$ contributes off-diagonal terms in K and v; $H^{(2)}$ has off-diagonal terms in K only. Terms off-diagonal in v can also arise from any V_6 corrections to the barrier. To approximately diagonalize the energy in v, a Van Vleck transformation can be applied to the Hamiltonian. This diagonalization is effective when the torsional (vibrational) levels are widely spaced with respect to the rotational levels. The transformed Hamiltonian is then diagonal in v to second order. This allows a factoring into rotational submatrices for each torsional state $v\sigma$.

$$H_{v\sigma} = H_r + FW_{v\sigma} \tag{6-101}$$

$W_{v\sigma}$ now includes the correction terms which have been introduced onto the diagonal by the Van Vleck transformation. This parameter may be expressed as a power series in the reduced angular momentum $\mathscr{P}$.

$$W_{v\sigma} = \sum_n W_{v\sigma}^{(n)} \mathscr{P}^n \tag{6-102}$$

Consistent with Herschbach's notation [670] this summation may be expressed to fourth order as

$$W_{v\sigma} = \tfrac{9}{4}b'_{v\sigma} - 2\xi_v\mathscr{P} + \eta_{v\sigma}\mathscr{P}^2 + \zeta_v\mathscr{P}^3 + \tau_{v\sigma}\mathscr{P}^4 + \cdots \quad (6\text{-}103)$$

The value of this expansion arises from the fact that the perturbation coefficients have been tabulated [670, 718].[†] Odd order coefficients in (6-103) vanish for the A levels as indicated by the missing σ subscripts. $b'_{v\sigma}$ is related to $b_{v\sigma}$ by an expansion in V_6/V_3 [670].

To second order, the matrix elements of $H_{v\sigma}$ can be written in terms of new, effective rotational constants and the perturbation terms $W_{v\sigma}^{(n)}$.

$$\langle JKM|H_{v\sigma}|JKM\rangle = \left(\frac{A_{v\sigma} + B_{v\sigma}}{2}\right)J(J + 1) + \left[C_{v\sigma} - \left(\frac{A_{v\sigma} + B_{v\sigma}}{2}\right)\right]K^2$$

$$+ Q_c W_{v\sigma}^{(1)} K + E_{v\sigma} \quad (6\text{-}104)$$

$$\langle JKM|H_{v\sigma}|J, K \pm 1, M\rangle = \tfrac{1}{2}[(D_{bc} \pm iD_{ac})W_{v\sigma}^{(2)}(2K \pm 1) + (Q_b \pm iQ_a)W_{v\sigma}^{(1)}]$$

$$\times [J(J + 1) - K(K \pm 1)]^{1/2} \quad (6\text{-}105)$$

$$\langle JKM|H_{v\sigma}|J, K \pm 2, M\rangle = -\tfrac{1}{4}[A_{v\sigma} - B_{v\sigma} \pm 2iD_{ab}W_{v\sigma}^{(2)}][J(J + 1)$$

$$- K(K \pm 1)]^{1/2}[J(J + 1) - (K \pm 1)(K \pm 2)]^{1/2}$$

$$(6\text{-}106)$$

The modified constants have the form

$$A_{v\sigma} = \frac{h^2}{8\pi^2 I_a}\left[1 + \frac{\lambda_a^2 I_a}{r I_a}W_{v\sigma}^{(2)}\right] \quad (6\text{-}107)$$

The diagonal term $E_{v\sigma}$ is included for completeness but does not affect the rotational energy level splittings, since it is independent of the rotational quantum numbers.

In terms of the integral,

$$\langle v\sigma|p|v'\sigma\rangle = -i\int_0^{2\pi} U_{v\sigma}^*(\alpha)\frac{\partial}{\partial\alpha}U_{v'\sigma}(\alpha)\,d\alpha \quad (6\text{-}108)$$

the first and second order perturbation coefficients can be written as

$$W_{v\sigma}^{(1)} = -2\langle v\sigma|p|v\sigma\rangle \quad (6\text{-}109)$$

$$W_{v\sigma}^{(2)} = 1 + \frac{16}{9}\sum_{v'}\frac{|\langle v\sigma|p|v'\sigma\rangle|^2}{b_{v\sigma} - b_{v'\sigma}} \quad (6\text{-}110)$$

In most cases, the perturbation expansion need only be considered to second order. The A levels follow a pseudorigid rotor form because $\langle v0|p|v0\rangle = 0$ and $\mathscr{P}^2$ is quadratic in the P_i. When these quadratic terms are combined with

---

[†] A table of the $W_{v\sigma}^{(n)}$ can be found in Appendix 12.

those in H_r, the A and E sublevels of a torsional state have different effective rotational constants, and the orientation of the principal axes is altered by the crossterms $P_i P_j + P_j P_i$. Rotation of the principal axis system is usually small enough to be neglected; however, successive 2×2 rotations can be employed to reach the true principal axis system.

If the odd-order terms for the E levels are negligible, the E levels also follow a pseudorigid rotor form. The rotational constants take the form

$$A_{v\sigma} = A + F\alpha^2 \eta_{v\sigma} \tag{6-111}$$

where

$$\alpha = \frac{\lambda_a I_a}{I_a} \tag{6-112}$$

The difference of the rotational constants for the A and E levels results in a splitting of the rotational transitions. Since the coupling perturbation differs for the A and E states, tunneling between A and E levels will occur at different rates. As V_3 approaches infinity, the perturbation coefficients (except that of zero order) vanish and the A and E levels become degenerate.

For relatively high barriers, the energy level splitting can be expressed as an expansion in the rotational constant differences.

$$\Delta E = \left(\frac{\partial E}{\partial A}\right) \Delta A + \left(\frac{\partial E}{\partial B}\right) \Delta B + \left(\frac{\partial E}{\partial C}\right) \Delta C \tag{6-113}$$

$$E = \frac{A + C}{2} J(J + 1) + \frac{A - C}{2} E(\kappa) \tag{6-114}$$

$$2\left(\frac{\partial E}{\partial A}\right) = J(J + 1) + E(\kappa) - (\kappa + 1)\left[\frac{\partial E(\kappa)}{\partial \kappa}\right] \tag{6-115}$$

$$\left(\frac{\partial E}{\partial B}\right) = \frac{\partial E(\kappa)}{\partial \kappa} \tag{6-116}$$

$$2\left(\frac{\partial E}{\partial C}\right) = J(J + 1) - E(\kappa) + (\kappa - 1)\left(\frac{\partial E(\kappa)}{\partial \kappa}\right) \tag{6-117}$$

$$\Delta A = A_A - A_E = F\alpha^2 \Delta\eta_v \tag{6-118}$$

The $\Delta\eta_v$ have been tabulated for various values of the parameter s [670] in (6-47). Once s is known, V_3 may be calculated from (6-50).

For an asymmetric rotor with a high barrier, the odd-order terms are usually small enough to be ignored. Only when these terms are of the same order of magnitude or larger than the asymmetry must they be considered. In an extensive analysis, the ξ and ζ terms can be treated as perturbations to the pseudorigid rotor terms. The odd-order terms must be treated directly in cases where the molecule is a near-symmetric top or in the high K levels of an asymmetric rotor. With the latter, the asymmetry splittings diminish with increasing K for the high J levels.

Some additional transitions between the degenerate torsional levels may be observed in situations where the torsional splittings are of the same order of magnitude as the asymmetry doubling. If a representation is chosen which diagonalizes the asymmetric rotor energy, the odd-order correction terms for the E torsional levels appear off-diagonal. Moreover, when a symmetric rotor representation is used, the asymmetry terms are off-diagonal. Both representations break down when the two effects are similar in magnitude, and a quadratic secular equation must be solved. The new wave functions are linear combinations of the original asymmetric rotor functions.

Consider the case of propylene oxide where this effect has been observed [682]. At low K values, the asymmetry doubling exceeds the magnitude of the odd-order internal rotor terms for the E levels. For large K values, the situation is reversed and the internal rotation terms dominate. Figure 6-7 shows the effects of mixing for a perpendicular transition between a pair of K doublets for intermediate K in propylene oxide. For low K, the four allowed transitions are observed. As K increases, the forbidden transitions gain in intensity giving six lines. In the limit of high K values, the allowed E transitions tend to vanish. The mixing undoes the Wang transformation

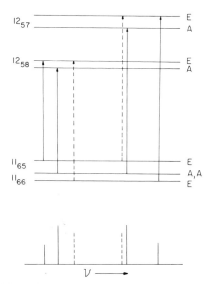

Fig. 6-7. Example of forbidden transitions (dashed lines) among torsional sublevels in propylene oxide as a result of comparable internal rotation and asymmetry splitting [688]. The two allowed A transitions are separated by 10.34 MHz.

and effectively imposes the C_3 symmetry of a hindered symmetric rotor on the wave functions. Therefore, the A levels tend to become degenerate in the symmetric rotor limit and only three transitions are observed. The E levels remain separated since the odd-order K terms are still present.

The fourth-order terms $\tau_{v\sigma}\mathscr{P}^4$ can be important for low barriers or transitions with high K. They are analogous to the fourth-order terms introduced in the centrifugal distortion treatment (Chapter 3). Using the commutation rules for angular momentum, part of the fourth-order contribution can be reduced to terms in $\mathscr{P}^2$ which, in turn, alter the rotational constants in (6-111).

$$A_{v\sigma} = A + F\alpha^2\eta_{v\sigma} + F(3\beta^2\gamma^2 - 2\alpha^2\beta^2 - 2\alpha^2\gamma^2)\tau_{v\sigma} \qquad (6\text{-}119)$$

The remaining fourth-order terms give a first-order six term energy correction analogous to that in (3-150). The coefficients A_1 through A_6 have been tabulated by Herschbach [670].

6-7. IAM for Asymmetric Top Molecules

Hecht and Dennison [668, 669] applied the IAM to an asymmetric rotor with a plane of symmetry. The kinetic energy in terms of the elements of the inertial tensor gives a Hamiltonian of the form

$$H = AP_y^2 + BP_x^2 + CP_z^2 + D(P_xP_z + P_zP_x) - 2DP_xp$$
$$- 2CP_zp + Fp^2 + V(\alpha) \qquad (6\text{-}120)$$

where

$$A = \frac{h^2}{2I_{yy}} \qquad\qquad C = \frac{I_{xx}h^2}{2r(I_{xx}I_{zz} - I_{xz}^2)}$$

$$B = \frac{(I_{zz} - I_\alpha)h^2}{2r(I_{xx}I_{zz} - I_{xz}^2)} \qquad D = \frac{I_{xz}h^2}{2r(I_{xx}I_{zz} - I_{xz}^2)} \qquad (6\text{-}121)$$

$$F = \frac{h^2}{2rI_\alpha} \qquad\qquad r = \frac{I_{xx}(I_{zz} - I_\alpha) - I_{xz}^2}{I_{xx}I_{zz} - I_{xz}^2}$$

The y axis is perpendicular to the plane of symmetry and the internal rotor axis lies in the plane of symmetry. Acetaldehyde, CH_3CHO, is an example of a molecule meeting these requirements. The treatment for a molecule whose frame is completely asymmetric is much more difficult algebraically. P_y, P_x, and P_z are components of the total angular momentum about an axis system fixed in the frame of the molecule. The z axis is collinear with the internal rotor axis. Again p does not merely express the momentum of the relative motion of top and frame but is the total angular momentum of the internal rotor. The origin of the coordinate system lies at the COM.

To reduce the coupling between internal and overall rotation, a transformation to the internal rotation axes must be employed. The form of the transformation depends on the orientation of the internal axis in the plane of symmetry. If it does not lie on one of the principal axes, terms in $P_x p$ and $P_z p$ must be removed. A rotation in the x, z plane can remove the $P_x p$ term, and a modified Nielsen transformation may be used to remove the $P_z p$ term. A third transformation similar to (6-69) is needed to force the internal angular momentum to zero. These three transformations may be expressed as

$$P''_y = P_y$$

$$P''_x = (I_{xx}P_x - I_{xz}P_z)(I^2_{xx} + I^2_{xz})^{-1/2} \qquad (6\text{-}122)$$

$$P''_z = (I_{xz}P_x + I_{xx}P_z)(I^2_{xx} + I^2_{xz})^{-1/2}$$

and

$$p' = p - \rho P''_z \qquad (6\text{-}123)$$

and

$$P'_y = (\cos \rho\alpha)P_y + (\sin \rho\alpha)P_x$$

$$P'_x = (-\sin \rho\alpha)P_y + (\cos \rho\alpha)P_x \qquad (6\text{-}124)$$

$$P'_z = P_z$$

where

$$B'' = \frac{I_{xx}h^2}{2(I^2_{xx} + I^2_{xz})}$$

$$C'' = \frac{h^2}{2}\left[\frac{I_{xx} + I_{zz}}{I_{xx}I_{zz} - I^2_{xz}} - \frac{I_{xx}}{I^2_{xx} + I^2_{xz}}\right] \qquad (6\text{-}125)$$

$$D'' = \frac{I_{xz}h^2}{2(I^2_{xx} + I^2_{xz})}$$

$$\rho = \frac{I_\alpha(I^2_{xx} + I^2_{xz})^{1/2}}{(I_{xx}I_{zz} - I^2_{xz})}$$

The transformed Hamiltonian is

$$H' = \left(\frac{A + B''}{2}\right)(P'^2_y + P'^2_x) + C''P'^2_z + Fp^2 + V(\alpha) + \left(\frac{A - B''}{2}\right)$$

$$\times [(P'^2_y - P'^2_x)\cos 2\rho\alpha - (P'_y P'_x + P'_x P'_y)\sin 2\rho\alpha] + D''$$

$$\times [(P'_x P'_z + P'_z P'_x)\cos \rho\alpha + (P'_y P'_z + P'_z P'_y)\sin \rho\alpha] \qquad (6\text{-}126)$$

As a result of the last transformation, the P'_i obey commutation rules (2-14) and commute with the new internal angular momentum p' which is a function of the relative motion of the two parts of the molecule. The relationships between the new Euler angles of the internal axis system θ', ϕ', χ' and the old Euler angles θ, ϕ, χ are

$$\cos \theta' = \frac{I_{xx}}{(I_{xx}^2 + I_{xz}^2)^{1/2}} \cos \theta + \frac{I_{xz}}{(I_{xx}^2 + I_{xz}^2)^{1/2}} \sin \theta \cos \chi_1 \qquad (6\text{-}127)$$

$$\tan \phi' = \frac{\tan \phi[\sin \theta - (I_{xz}/I_{xx})\cos \theta \cos \chi_1] - (I_{xz}/I_{xx})\sin \chi_1}{[\sin \theta - (I_{xz}/I_{xx})\cos \theta \cos \chi_1] + (I_{xz}/I_{xx})\sin \chi_1 \tan \phi} \qquad (6\text{-}128)$$

$$\tan\left[\chi' + \frac{I_\alpha(I_{xx}^2 + I_{xz}^2)^{1/2}\alpha}{I_{zz}(I_{xx}I_{zz} - I_{xz}^2)}\right] = \frac{\sin \chi_1(I_{xx}^2 + I_{xz}^2)^{1/2}}{I_{xx}\cos \chi_1 - I_{xz}\cot \theta} \qquad (6\text{-}129)$$

$$\alpha' = \alpha \qquad (6\text{-}130)$$

The angular momenta P_i' can be defined in terms of the new set of canonically conjugate variables p_θ', p_ϕ', p_χ', θ', ϕ', and χ'. The transformations have removed all the $P_i'p'$ terms. When $\dot{\alpha}' \to 0$, this changes the Hamiltonian to one of a rigid rotor plus a hindered rotor.

The Hamiltonian is first divided into $H^{(0)}$ and $H^{(1)}$.

$$H^{(0)} = \left(\frac{A + B''}{2}\right)(P_y'^2 + P_x'^2) + C''P_z'^2 + Fp'^2 + V(\alpha) \qquad (6\text{-}131)$$

$$H^{(1)} = \left(\frac{A - B''}{2}\right)[(P_y'^2 - P_x'^2)\cos 2\rho\alpha - (P_y'P_x' + P_x'P_y')\sin 2\rho\alpha]$$
$$+ D''[(P_x'P_z' + P_z'P_x')\cos \rho\alpha + (P_z'P_y' + P_z'P_y')\sin \rho\alpha] \qquad (6\text{-}132)$$

$H^{(0)}$ can be solved exactly with basis functions consisting of the symmetric rotor functions and the solution of the torsional equation. The matrix elements are

$$\langle JKMv\sigma|H|JKMv'\sigma\rangle = \left(\frac{A + B''}{2}\right)[J(J + 1) - K^2] + C''K^2 + E_{v\sigma} \qquad (6\text{-}133)$$

$$\langle JKMv\sigma|H|J, K + 1, Mv'\sigma\rangle = D''(K + \tfrac{1}{2})[J(J + 1) - K(K + 1)]^{1/2} \\ \times I_{K+1,v'\sigma}^{Kv\sigma} \qquad (6\text{-}134)$$

$$\langle JKMv\sigma|H|J, K + 2, Mv'\sigma\rangle = -\left(\frac{A - B''}{4}\right)[J(J + 1) - K(K + 1)]^{1/2} \\ \times [J(J + 1) - (K + 1)(K + 2)]^{1/2} \\ \times I_{K+2,v'\sigma}^{Kv\sigma} \qquad (6\text{-}135)$$

$$I_{K'v'\sigma}^{Kv\sigma} = \int_0^{2\pi} Q_{Kv\sigma}^*(\alpha)Q_{K'v'\sigma}(\alpha)\,d\alpha \qquad (6\text{-}136)$$

$$M_{Kv\sigma}(\alpha') = \exp(-i\rho K\alpha')Q_{Kv\sigma}(\alpha') \qquad (6\text{-}137)$$

The torsional functions could also be defined as

$$M_{Kv\sigma}(\alpha') = \exp[i(1 - \rho)K\alpha']Q_{Kv\sigma}(\alpha') \qquad (6\text{-}138)$$

The matrix elements concerned with the rigid rotor terms have not been constructed in a principal axis system. A transformation to the principal axis system is possible and would result in a removal of the $\langle K|K + 1 \rangle$ terms. However, this would prevent factoring of the energy matrix into three submatrices for each value of σ, and it is usually preferable to treat the $\langle K|K + 1 \rangle$ elements. Also, the off-diagonal elements in v are very small and give negligible contributions to the energy.

The complicated boundary conditions make calculation of the integrals $I_{K'v'\sigma}^{Kv\sigma}$ difficult. In the limit of an infinite hindering potential $I_{K'v'\sigma}^{Kv\sigma} \to 0$ for $v' \neq v$ and $\to 1$ for $v' = v$. The terms $\delta_{K+1,v\sigma}^{Kv\sigma}$ and $\delta_{K+2,v\sigma}^{Kv\sigma}$ are introduced to take advantage of these limiting properties.

$$\delta_{K+1,v\sigma}^{Kv\sigma} = 1 - \int_0^{2\pi} Q_{Kv\sigma}^*(\alpha) Q_{K+1,v\sigma}(\alpha) \, d\alpha \tag{6-139}$$

$$\delta_{K+2,v\sigma}^{Kv\sigma} = 1 - \int_0^{2\pi} Q_{Kv\sigma}^*(\alpha) Q_{K+2,v\sigma}(\alpha) \, d\alpha \tag{6-140}$$

When the barrier is very high, the problem is simplified by using the harmonic oscillator approximation for the torsional functions. In this case, the hindered internal motion can be treated by small oscillations about the bottom of a parabolic potential. The harmonic oscillator functions $H_v(\alpha)$ can be used in place of the torsional functions. There are three torsional functions; one is centered at the bottom of each minimum in the hindering potential. The results are

$$e^{-i\rho K\alpha} \to 1 \tag{6-141}$$

$$M_{Kv\sigma}(\alpha) \to P_{Kv\sigma}(\alpha) \tag{6-142}$$

$$M_{Kv,0}(\alpha) = \frac{1}{\sqrt{3}}[H_v^{(1)} + H_v^{(2)} + H_v^{(3)}] \tag{6-143}$$

$$M_{Kv,1}(\alpha) = \frac{1}{\sqrt{3}}[H_v^{(1)} + \omega H_v^{(2)} + \omega^2 H_v^{(3)}] \tag{6-144}$$

$$M_{Kv,-1}(\alpha) = \frac{1}{\sqrt{3}}[H_v^{(1)} + \omega^2 H_v^{(2)} + \omega H_v^{(3)}] \tag{6-145}$$

$$\omega = \exp[2\pi i/3] \tag{6-146}$$

The torsional eigenvalues are approximated as

$$E_v = 3(V_3 F)^{1/2}(v + \tfrac{1}{2}) \tag{6-147}$$

The small off-diagonal elements in v can be removed by a Van Vleck transformation just as in the PAM, or they may be neglected if they are sufficiently small. A transformation is then applied to diagonalize the rigid rotor part of the Hamiltonian.

$$H' = S^{-1}HS \tag{6-148}$$

H' is diagonal in the limit of an infinite barrier. S is a unitary matrix and can be factored into the product of two matrices S_1 and S_2.

$$S = S_1 S_2 \tag{6-149}$$

S_1 removes the $\langle K|K + 1\rangle$ matrix elements and transforms the Hamiltonian to that of a rigid rotor in the principal axis system with only $\langle K|K + 2\rangle$ off-diagonal elements. S_2 diagonalizes the asymmetric rotor Hamiltonian in a principal axis system.

Hecht and Dennison have written S explicitly for the $J = 1$ case.

$$S = \begin{bmatrix} \dfrac{1+\gamma}{2} & \dfrac{\beta}{\sqrt{2}} & \dfrac{1-\gamma}{2} \\[2mm] \dfrac{-\beta}{\sqrt{2}} & \gamma & \dfrac{\beta}{\sqrt{2}} \\[2mm] \dfrac{1-\gamma}{2} & \dfrac{-\beta}{\sqrt{2}} & \dfrac{1+\gamma}{2} \end{bmatrix} \begin{bmatrix} -\dfrac{1}{\sqrt{2}} & 0 & \dfrac{1}{\sqrt{2}} \\[2mm] 0 & 1 & 0 \\[2mm] \dfrac{1}{\sqrt{2}} & 0 & \dfrac{1}{\sqrt{2}} \end{bmatrix} \tag{6-150}$$

$$\left\{\begin{matrix} \gamma^2 \\ \beta^2 \end{matrix}\right\} = \frac{1}{2} \pm \frac{1}{2} \frac{(I_{xx} - I_{zz})(I_{xx}^2 - I_{xz}^2) + 4I_{xx}I_{xz}^2}{(I_{xx}^2 + I_{xz}^2)[(I_{xx} - I_{zz})^2 + 4I_{xz}^2]^{1/2}} \tag{6-151}$$

$$\gamma\beta = \frac{I_{xz}(I_{xx}I_{zz} - I_{xz}^2)}{(I_{xx}^2 + I_{xz}^2)[(I_{xx} - I_{zz})^2 + 4I_{xz}^2]^{1/2}} \tag{6-152}$$

$$\gamma^2 + \beta^2 = 1 \tag{6-153}$$

γ and β are the direction cosines of the z principal axis with respect to the z' and x' internal rotation axes. The S_2 matrices are obtained from the treatment of a rigid asymmetric rotor.[†] The elements of S_1 are a little more difficult to obtain. S_1 is a function of γ and β alone. The total angular momentum components about the principal axes are related to those in the internal axis system by the following relations.

$$P_a = P'_y; \qquad P_b = \gamma P'_x - \beta P'_z; \qquad P_c = \beta P'_x + \gamma P'_z \tag{6-154}$$

Let ψ_{JKM} represent the solutions of the symmetric rigid rotor part of $H^{(0)}$ in the nonprincipal axis system. ψ_{JK_pM} represents the same solutions in a principal axis system.

[†] For $J = 1$, S_2 is just the Wang transformation X.

$$\psi_{JK_p} = \sum_{K=-J}^{K=+J} a_{K_pK}\psi_{JK} \qquad (6\text{-}155)$$

The a_{K_pK} are the matrix elements of $(S_1)^{-1}$. These elements may be determined from the properties of the angular momentum operators (Chapter 2).

$$\langle JKM|P_z'|JKM\rangle = Kh \qquad (6\text{-}156)$$

$$\langle JKM|P_x'|J, K\pm 1, M\rangle = \frac{h}{2}[(J\mp K)(J\pm K+1)]^{1/2} \qquad (6\text{-}157)$$

$$\langle JK_pM|P_c|JK_pM\rangle = K_ph \qquad (6\text{-}158)$$

$$\langle JK_pM|P_b|J, K_p\pm 1, M\rangle = \frac{h}{2}[(J\mp K_p)(J\pm K_p+1)]^{1/2} \qquad (6\text{-}159)$$

These relations and (6-155) give

$$(\beta P_x' + \gamma P_z' - hK_p)(a_{K_pJ}\psi_{JJ} + a_{K_p(J-1)}\psi_{J(J-1)}\cdots) = 0 \qquad (6\text{-}160)$$

The linear independence of the ψ_{JK} forces the coefficient of each ψ_{JK} to be zero, resulting in $2J+1$ equations for the coefficients. These equations may be used to solve for the a_{K_pK}.

$$a_{K_pK} = \sum_n (-1)^n \frac{[(J+K)!(J-K)!(J+K_p)!(J-K_p)!]^{1/2}}{(J-K_p-n)!(J+K-n)!n!(n+K_p-K)!}$$

$$\times \left(\cos\frac{\beta}{2}\right)^{2J+K-K_p-2n}\left(\sin\frac{\beta}{2}\right)^{2n+K_p-K} \qquad (6\text{-}161)$$

The summation is from the larger of 0 or $(K-K_p)$ to the smaller of $(J-K_p)$ or $(J-K)$. As $\beta \to 0$ and $\alpha \to 1$, S_1 becomes the identity matrix.

The structure of the energy matrix is now very similar to that in the PAM. The energy submatrices for $\sigma = \pm 1$ are identical. The matrix is diagonal in σ and essentially diagonal in v and may be written as $H_{v\sigma}$ for each torsional sublevel. The selection rule $\Delta\sigma = 0$ predicts two transitions, an A and an E transition. Because the physical problem has not changed, the rate of tunneling through the barrier is governed by considerations similar to those used in the PAM treatment.

Hindered internal rotation also produces a slight shift in the positions of the limiting rigid rotor levels. These shifts are produced not only by the torsional motion but also may be due, in part, to other modes of vibration in the molecule. The quantities δ and I are effectively independent of K and σ in the high barrier limit. After the transformation S the δ's are found to add correction terms to the rotational constants which are identical for the A and E levels. These corrections produce the resulting frequency shifts.

The hindered internal rotation splittings have been calculated explicitly for levels up to $J = 3$ [668]. Appendix 8 gives these expressions in terms of the rotational constants and three molecular parameters: Δ_0, β, and ρ.

$$\Delta_K = \Delta_0 \cos\left(\frac{2\pi}{3} K\rho\right) \qquad (6\text{-}162)$$

β and ρ depend only on the mass and geometry, while Δ_0 is a function of the barrier height. Using the W.K.B. approximation, the relation between Δ_0 and V for the ground torsional state is given by

$$\Delta_0 = \tfrac{9}{4}F\,\Delta b = 7.05(V')^{3/4}\,e^{-1.324(V')^{1/2}} \qquad (6\text{-}163)$$

with

$$V' = V \bigg/ \frac{h^2}{2} \frac{(I_{xx}I_{zz} - I_{xz}^2)}{I_\alpha(I_{xx}I_f - I_{xz}^2)} \qquad (6\text{-}164)$$

where I_f is the moment of inertia of the frame along the symmetry axis of the top. Equation (6-163) is generally good over the range $50 \le V' \le 200$. The value of V can be determined from the molecular structure and enough observed splittings to evaluate Δ_0, β, and ρ. Woods [748] has reported a computer routine which enables the use of higher J transitions for the barrier calculations. For small values of β, Lide and Mann [676] have developed approximate expressions (truncated at β^2) for the $A - E$ splittings.

6-8. Low Barriers

When the barrier is of the order of several hundred calories or less, the perturbation techniques applied in the high barrier case must be revised. It is convenient in this case to consider the limit of free internal rotation as the source of the unperturbed Hamiltonian. The potential energy $V(\alpha)$ goes to zero in the limit of free rotation and the kinetic energy constitutes the entire Hamiltonian. For a symmetric rotor, the energy becomes

$$H = A(P_a^2 + P_b^2) + C_i P_c^2 + Fp^2 - 2C_i pP_c \qquad (6\text{-}165)$$

where the rotational constants A, C_i, and F have been defined in (6-36), (6-37), and (6-39), respectively. The torsional equation is

$$(Fp^2 - 2C_i pP_c)e^{im\alpha} = E'_{ir}e^{im\alpha} \qquad (6\text{-}166)$$

E'_{ir} is the energy of free rotation and m is an integer which is a good quantum number in the limit of free rotation. The basis functions for free internal rotation are

$$\psi^{(0)} = S_{JKM}(\theta, \phi)\,e^{iK\chi}\,e^{im\alpha} \qquad (6\text{-}167)$$

The energy is given by the diagonal matrix elements.

$$\langle JKMm|H|JKMm\rangle = AJ(J + 1) + (C_i - A)K^2 + Fm^2 - 2C_iKm \quad (6\text{-}168)$$

Because the dipole moment does not depend on α, the additional selection rule $\Delta m = 0$ is required along with the usual symmetric rotor selection rules. Application of these selection rules to (6-168) yields the transition frequencies.

$$v = 2A(J + 1)/h \quad (6\text{-}169)$$

These transitions are identical with those of a rigid symmetric rotor. The symmetry properties of a symmetric rotor prevent free internal rotation from perturbing its rotational spectrum.

Free internal rotation does affect the spectrum of an asymmetric rotor. The diagonal matrix elements are essentially the same as those in the symmetric rotor case; off-diagonal elements are introduced by the asymmetry. This is apparent when the Hamiltonian is written as

$$H = H^{(0)} + H^{(1)} \quad (6\text{-}170)$$

$$H^{(0)} = \left(\frac{A + B}{2}\right)(P_a^2 + P_b^2) + C_iP_c^2 + Fp^2 - 2C_ipP_c \quad (6\text{-}171)$$

$$H^{(1)} = \left(\frac{A - B}{2}\right)(P_a^2 - P_b^2) \quad (6\text{-}172)$$

Using the same basis functions as in the symmetric rotor case, the matrix elements are

$$\langle JKMm|H|JKMm\rangle = \left(\frac{A + B}{2}\right)J(J + 1) + \left[C_i - \frac{A + B}{2}\right]K^2$$

$$+ Fm^2 - 2C_iKm \quad (6\text{-}173)$$

$$\langle JKMm|H|J, K \pm 2, Mm\rangle = -\left(\frac{A - B}{4}\right)[J(J + 1) - K(K \pm 1)]^{1/2}$$

$$\times [J(J + 1) - (K \pm 1)(K \pm 2)]^{1/2} \quad (6\text{-}174)$$

For a given J, M, and m, the energy matrix, which is $2J + 1$ in dimension, can be factored into separate submatrices for even and odd K. This results from the absence of odd-order off-diagonal connecting elements.

These matrix elements can be compared to those of a rigid asymmetric rotor. The off-diagonal elements are identical and terms in the quantum number m have been added to the diagonal. For $m = 0$, the diagonal elements become similar to those of a rigid asymmetric rotor with the rotational constant for the figure axis altered by I_α. When m does not vanish, terms linear in K are introduced onto the diagonal. The squared term in m is of lesser importance since it serves as an additive constant; however, the linear term in K prevents full utilization of the Wang transformation which would otherwise lead to a further factoring of the energy matrix.

Diagonalization of the energy matrix can be done exactly for low J values. For large values of the quantum numbers second-order perturbation theory can be used to produce an approximate diagonalization.

$$
\begin{aligned}
E = {}& \left(\frac{A+B}{2}\right) J(J+1) + \left[C_i - \frac{A+B}{2}\right] K^2 + Fm^2 - 2C_i K m \\
& + \frac{(A-B)^2 [J^2 - (K-1)^2][(J+1)^2 - (K-1)^2]}{64\{[C_i - \frac{1}{2}(A+B)](K-1) - C_i m\}} \\
& - \frac{(A-B)^2 [J^2 - (K+1)^2][(J+1)^2 - (K+1)^2]}{64\left\{\left[C_i - \dfrac{A+B}{2}\right](K+1) + C_i m\right\}}
\end{aligned}
\tag{6-175}
$$

For nonvanishing values of m, all the energy levels will be doubly degenerate in $\pm m$. The selection rules for an asymmetric rotor are still valid along with an additional restriction on m.

$$
\Delta m = 0 \tag{6-176}
$$

The selection rules governing the symmetric rotor quantum number K are identical with those for a rigid rotor. For example, if the dipole moment lies along the pseudofigure axis c, the parity of K can not change.

The spectrum has some characteristic features. For a transition of the form $J \to J + 1$, $\Delta K = 0$ (K being even or odd), each value of m gives rise to two transitions symmetrically spaced about $(A + B)(J + 1)$. As the values of m increase, the transitions converge to the band head at $(A + B)(J + 1)$. The intensities of the transitions for large m values fall off considerably as a consequence of the Boltzmann factor and the band head is not always well defined.

When the barrier to internal rotation becomes finite, the Hamiltonian must be reevaluated. m is no longer a good quantum number, but for low barriers it can be retained to label the levels. The first term of (6-6) can be used in the Hamiltonian and can be expressed in exponential form

$$
V(\alpha) = \frac{V_6}{4}(2 - e^{i6\alpha} - e^{-i6\alpha}) \tag{6-177}
$$

The matrix elements $\langle JKMm|H|JKMm\rangle$ and $\langle JKMm|H|J, K \pm 2, Mm\rangle$ are identical to those in (6-173) and (6-174); however, an additional term off-diagonal in m is introduced by the barrier.

$$
\langle JKMm|H|JKM, m \pm 6\rangle = -V_6/4 \tag{6-178}
$$

The $V_6/2$ term in the potential is not a function of the quantum numbers and can be disregarded. If V_6 is small, the terms off-diagonal in m can be effectively removed by a Van Vleck transformation. The new matrix elements are

$$\langle JKMm|H|JKMm \rangle = \left(\frac{A+B}{2}\right)J(J+1) + \left[C_i - \frac{A+B}{2}\right]K^2 + Fm^2$$

$$- 2mKC_i + \frac{FV_6^2}{32[(C_iK - Fm)^2 - 9F^2]} \tag{6-179}$$

$$\langle JKMm|H|J, K \pm 2, Mm \rangle = -\left(\frac{A-B}{4}\right)\{[J(J+1) - K(K \pm 1)]$$

$$\times [J(J+1) - (K \pm 1)(K \pm 2)]\}^{1/2} \tag{6-180}$$

If V_6 is small, the correction term added to the diagonal produces only a small effect on the spectrum. An investigation of the denominator of the correction term indicates that the degeneracy is lifted for $m = \pm 3$.

$$\frac{FV_6^2}{32[(C_iK - Fm)^2 - 9F^2]} = \frac{V_6^2}{192[C_iK - F(m+3)]} - \frac{V_6^2}{192[C_iK - F(m-3)]}$$

$$\tag{6-181}$$

The other levels remain doubly degenerate in $\pm m$. This peculiar situation for $|m| = 3$ allows the barrier to split the m degeneracy of these levels. This leads to a method for determining the value of V_6. For a particular J and parity of K, the energy matrix for all $|m| = 3$ must be considered. The m degeneracy is theoretically lifted for all m values which are a whole number multiple of 3. This can be shown if a higher-order Van Vleck transformation is used because the splittings decrease with increasing m.

The degeneracy which characterizes the levels with $m \neq 0, \pm 3, \ldots$ results in a first-order Stark effect when $K \neq 0$ (Chapter 8). The levels with $m = 0$, $\pm 3, \ldots$ in the presence of a low barrier show a second-order Stark pattern. These effects aid the assignment of m values to the spectrum.

CH_3BF_2 presents an excellent example of the sensitivity of $|m| = 3$ transitions to the barrier height. The $J = 1 \rightarrow 2$ transition for K odd consists of four components. Diagonalization of the energy matrices for these two levels permits V_6 to be calculated. These matrices are found to be symmetric about the antidiagonal which allows a further factoring into two sub-matrices.[†] The symmetry may be expressed by

$$\langle 3, K|H| \pm 3, K' \rangle = \langle -3, -K|H| \mp 3, -K' \rangle \tag{6-182}$$

[†] The resulting transformation [655] is equivalent to choosing wave functions of the form $\psi^{\pm}(K, m) = (1/\sqrt{2})[\psi(K, m) \pm \psi(-K, -m)]$.

For the $J = 1$, K odd levels, the matrix has been given as [679]

$$
\begin{bmatrix}
a' & b + V_6/4 & 0 & 0 \\
b + V_6/4 & a & 0 & 0 \\
0 & 0 & a' & b - V_6/4 \\
0 & 0 & b - V_6/4 & a
\end{bmatrix}
\tag{6-183}
$$

where

$$
a = \frac{A + B}{2} - 5C_i + 9F - \frac{V_6^2}{192(6F - C)}
\tag{6-184}
$$

$$
a' = \frac{A + B}{2} + 7C_i + 9F + \frac{V_6^2}{192(6F + C)}
\tag{6-185}
$$

$$
b = \frac{B - A}{2}
\tag{6-186}
$$

Table 6-7 gives the observed transitions for $J = 1 \rightarrow 2$, K odd. The transitions occur in pairs symmetrically spaced about the band head at $2(A + B)$. The very large splittings which are observed tend to make the assignment of the spectrum somewhat difficult but also give an accurate barrier height. In the case of CH_3BF_2, Naylor and Wilson [679] obtained a barrier value of 13.77 ± 0.03 calories.

TABLE 6-7

$J = 1 \rightarrow 2$, K ODD TRANSITIONS IN $CH_3BF_2{}^a$

$|m|$	Frequency	$|m|$	Frequency
0	22280.6	3	23999.7
0	29637.6	3	24278.8
1	26590.5	3	27625.8
2	25635.5	3	27904.3
2	26276.7		

^{a} From Ref. [679].

The rotational constants are determined from the $m = 0$ transitions which are nondegenerate in m and have the characteristics of a rigid rotor spectrum.

For two equivalent internal rotors, the low barrier is again treated as a perturbation to the free rotor problem. The basis functions are

$$
\psi^{(0)} = S_{JK}(\theta, \phi) \, e^{iK\chi} \, e^{im_1\alpha_1} \, e^{im_2\alpha_2}
\tag{6-187}
$$

where the symmetric rotor functions are used and the subscripts 1 and 2 refer to the two internal rotors. Because each individual top does not "see" a planar frame, the threefold contributions to $V(\alpha_1, \alpha_2)$ do not cancel. The dipole moment does not depend on α_1 or α_2 and the selection rules again require no change in m_1 or m_2.

Swalen and Costain [705] have given the appropriate matrix elements for a molecule with C_{2v} symmetry and have illustrated the connections between the infinite barrier and free rotation limits.

A class of molecules which has a low threefold barrier is represented by the prototypes methylacetylene and dimethylacetylene. Molecules such as $CH_3-C\equiv C-CF_3$ [647], $CH_3-C\equiv C-CH_2Cl$ [701], and $CH_3-C\equiv C-SiH_3$ [752] show almost completely free internal rotation. Small deviations from the spectrum of free rotation often allow an upper limit to be placed on the barrier height. The matrix elements for 1-chloro-2-butyne-type molecules are discussed by Laurie and Lide [701], while the matrix elements for a double rotor similar to methylsilylacetylene are treated by Kirchhoff and Lide [752]. In the former case, the maximum barrier was estimated from the effective rotational constants of the $m = 0$ state, and in the latter case, deviations in the $m = 1$ and $m = 2$ states led to an upper barrier limit.

6-9. Completely Asymmetric Molecules

When both the top and frame of a molecule undergoing a hindered torsional motion are asymmetric in nature, the problem of formulating the quantum-mechanical Hamiltonian and of solving for the rotational energy levels is more complex than in cases where the top has threefold symmetry. Burkhard and Irwin [642] developed solutions of the wave equation for an asymmetric molecule with an asymmetric top, but their results take a complicated form. The approach of Quade and Lin [739] lends itself more readily to the analysis of a spectrum.

The main complication in this treatment is the fact that the moments of inertia of the molecule are functions of α. The development of the quantum-mechanical Hamiltonian is very similar to that derived by Wilson and Howard [335] for vibration-rotation interactions. Again the classical Hamiltonian is developed first and the transition to the quantum-mechanical operator form is made afterward.

Only a qualitative discussion of the spectrum is given, because the mathematical treatment is lengthy. Let the frame of the molecule possess a plane of symmetry. For a molecule like acetaldehyde, a single isotopic substitution on the methyl group gives rise to two rotational configurations. In the CH_2DCOH molecule, the deuterium atom can occupy a symmetrical position in the plane, opposing the oxygen atom, or an asymmetrical position out of the plane. The torsional part of the Hamiltonian is no longer invariant for a rotation of $2\pi/3$. This effectively removes the degeneracy of the E

torsional levels and each torsional state is characterized by three nondegen-erate sublevels. Using the notation n_σ, the ground state levels may be labeled as 0_0, 0_+, and 0_-. The 0_0 state represents the symmetrical con-figuration; the 0_+, 0_- states are the two asymmetric or out-of-plane states in the limit of an infinite barrier. The latter two become degenerate in this limit. For a finite barrier, the resulting microwave spectrum shows the transi-tions for each torsional state. The splitting of the transitions associated with 0_+ and 0_- levels gives a measure of the barrier height because terms of the form $\langle 0_+|H|0_-\rangle$ are nonvanishing and 0_0 does not connect with either 0_+ or 0_-.

6-10. Internal Rotation Barriers from Intensities

When the splitting method cannot be used to evaluate the internal barrier, less accurate estimates can be obtained by measuring the relative intensities of ground and excited torsional state transitions. The intensities will be related by the Boltzmann factor.

$$\frac{I_{ex}}{I_{gnd}} = \left(\frac{g_{ex}}{g_{gnd}}\right) e^{-\Delta E/kT} \tag{6-188}$$

The g's are statistical weights, and ΔE is the torsional energy separation. Once ΔE has been calculated, it may be used with F, which must be deter-mined from the structure, to evaluate $\Delta b_{v\sigma}$ where $b_{v\sigma}$ is defined by (6-49). From $\Delta b_{v\sigma}$ the reduced barrier parameter s can be obtained from tables of solutions to the Mathieu equation. (6-50) then gives the barrier height.

6-11. Internal Barriers from Vibration-Rotation Interactions

The shift of excited state transitions from those of the ground state is the result of nonrigid effects in the molecule. Frequency shifts of excited torsional states can be used to evaluate the potential hindering the torsional motion in cases where the splitting method cannot be used and relative intensity measurements are inaccurate. This is most useful in symmetric top molecules where the number of parameters to be evaluated is not prohibitively large. Kivelson [634] has treated the problem of internal rotation in nonrigid symmetric and asymmetric rotors [645, 646]. For simplicity, the symmetric rotor case will be outlined briefly; extension to the more complex asymmetric rotor can be obtained from the literature.

The rigid symmetric rotor has been treated in Chapter 2. Earlier in this chapter, the model was modified to include a torsional motion, and the moments of inertia of this semirigid model are not functions of the angle α

if the torsional group is symmetric. Thus, for a rigid top and frame, the internal torsion affects the rotational constants only through higher-order interactions involving other molecular vibrations. Let the Hamiltonian **H** be written as

$$\mathbf{H} = \tfrac{1}{2} \sum_{\alpha\beta} \mu_{\alpha\beta} \mathbf{P}_\alpha \mathbf{P}_\beta + \mathbf{H}_{ir} + \mathbf{H}_v \tag{6-189}$$

$\mathbf{H}_{ir}$ represents the torsional terms, $\mathbf{H}_v$ represents the remaining vibrational modes, and $\mathbf{P}_z$ is the component of total angular momentum along the α principal axis.[†] $\mu_{\alpha\beta}$ is a component of the instantaneous inertia tensor. For a rigid top and frame, $\mathbf{H}_{ir}$ is naturally independent of any vibrational modes other than the torsion, and $\mathbf{H}_v$ vanishes. However, for the actual nonrigid case, $\mathbf{H}_{ir}$ is a function of the other vibrations, and $\mathbf{H}_v$ is a function of the torsion. $\mu_{\alpha\beta}$ is a function of the vibrational coordinates (Chapter 3). From the above discussion, **H** has terms off-diagonal in the vibrational quantum numbers. As in previous cases, a Van Vleck transformation can be used to effect an approximate diagonalization of $\mathbf{H}_v$ under proper conditions. The barrier dependent rotational constant $B_{v\sigma}$ and the rotational transition frequency as a function of vibrational state can be calculated in terms of a number of empirical constants and the expectation values of the kinetic and potential energy. For the rotational constant

$$B_{v\sigma} = B_v + F_v \langle 1 - \cos 3\alpha \rangle + G_v \langle p'^2 \rangle \pm L_v K \langle p' \rangle \tag{6-190}$$

B_v, F_v, G_v, and L_v are independent of the rotational quantum numbers. These parameters are then evaluated from observed satellite frequencies corresponding to excited torsional states. Assuming the usual threefold cosine potential function, the barrier can be estimated by equating the torsional terms in (6-190) to $-\alpha_T(v + 1)$ where α_T is a function of V_3.

6-12. Excited Torsional States

In a large number of asymmetric molecules, the barrier hindering internal rotation is too high to permit any observable splitting in the ground vibrational state. This makes the observation of rotational transitions in excited torsional states very important. Because the excited torsional levels are nearer to the crest of the barrier, tunneling occurs at a much higher rate. Excited torsional states allow resolvable internal rotation splittings for much larger values of s than the ground state. For example, if in a parallel transition the largest value of s which might produce a splitting in the ground state $v = 0$ is $s = 50$, then the $v = 1$ and $v = 2$ torsional states may allow splittings to be observed for s values of approximately 90 and 130. Perpendicular

---

[†] The subscript α should not be confused with the angle of internal rotation.

transitions allow observable splittings for larger values of s than do parallel transitions in the same torsional state. Fortunately, the torsional vibrations are usually among the lowest frequency modes in a molecule, and the excited states are appreciably populated. Vibration-rotation interactions cause the transitions in excited torsional states to be displaced from the ground state transitions. Figure 6-8a illustrates these features for propylene oxide [688], assuming no torsional fine structure. In Figure 6-8b the effects

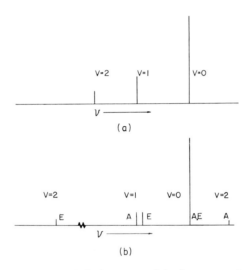

FIG. 6-8. Relative intensities and displacements of the first two excited torsional states of the $1_{01} \rightarrow 2_{12}$ transition in propylene oxide: (a) in the hypothetical case of no internal rotation structure and (b) with structure included [688].

of tunneling are shown. The appropriate internal rotation parameters have been tabulated for the first two excited torsional states [670, 718]. The semirigid model used in the analysis of ground state splittings can also be applied because only the A-E separations are of interest. For the most part, barriers determined from excited torsional splittings are in good agreement with those obtained from the ground state [737]. When two torsional modes are present, the increased number of perturbation terms and possible near degeneracies illustrated in Fig. 6-5 must be taken into account.

6-13a. Coriolis Interactions and Internal Rotation in Symmetric Top Molecules

As shown in Chapter 3, Coriolis interactions appear as first-order effects in symmetric rotors, but the selection rule $\Delta K = 0$ prevents the spectrum from exhibiting the Coriolis splitting. However, the second-order l-type doubling effect can produce an observable splitting which results from the matrix elements given in (3-26). Because symmetric rotors do not show the internal rotation fine structure characteristic of asymmetric rotors, a Coriolis interaction might be used to determine the internal rotation energy and the potential barrier [743]. It has been shown [668] that for a sufficiently high barrier, the matrix elements for the A and E states of a symmetric rotor are

$$\langle JKl | H_{vA} | JKl \rangle = -\tfrac{2}{3} \Delta_0 \cos \theta(K) \tag{6-191}$$

$$\langle JKl | H_{vE} | JKl \rangle = -\tfrac{2}{3} \Delta_0 \cos\left(\theta \pm \frac{2\pi}{3}\right)$$

$$= \tfrac{1}{3} \Delta_0 \cos \theta(K) \pm 3^{-1/2} \Delta_0 \sin \theta(K) \tag{6-192}$$

where Δ_0 is defined in (6-163) and

$$F = \frac{\hbar^2 I_f I_\alpha}{2I_z} \tag{6-193}$$

$$\theta(K) = \frac{2\pi K I_\alpha}{3I_z} \tag{6-194}$$

I_f and I_α are the moments of inertia along the symmetry axis of the frame and top, respectively.[†] The total axial moment $I_z = I_f + I_\alpha$.

For the $K = \pm 1$, $l = \pm 1$ states, the energy matrix with off-diagonal elements from (3-27) gives

$$E_A = E_r + E_v - \tfrac{2}{3} \Delta_0 \cos \theta(K) \pm 2qJ(J + 1) \tag{6-195}$$

for the A levels, and

$$E_E = E_r + E_v + \tfrac{1}{3} \Delta_0 \cos \theta(K) \pm [4q^2 J^2(J + 1)^2 + \tfrac{1}{3} \Delta_0^2 \sin^2 \theta(K)]^{1/2} \tag{6-196}$$

for the E levels of the first excited degenerate vibrational state (not the excited torsional state). E_r is the rotational energy, and E_v is the vibrational energy. For the A levels, the internal rotation term is not a function of J; but for the E levels, the $\sin \theta(K)$ term is dependent on the sign of K, and the internal rotation term shows a J dependence. The splitting of the E states can be used to determine the barrier height as long as the internal rotation term and the Coriolis term have the right relative magnitudes. To the degree of approximation used in this treatment, Fig. 3-5 for C_{3v} molecules shows that the $K = \pm 1$, $l = \mp 1$ levels are not split by the Coriolis interaction, and that the internal rotation terms produce only higher order effects on these levels. Therefore, for a $J \to J + 1$, $|K| = 1$ transition, a minimum of five lines

---

[†] These are often referred to as I_2 and I_1 [665] or C_1 and C_2 [668].

can be expected. Two additional forbidden transitions may occur if the $\Delta K = 0$ selection rule breaks down due to a mixing of K states. However, these transitions may not all be resolvable. Table 6-8 lists the transition frequencies of a $J \to J + 1$ transition.

TABLE 6-8

FREQUENCY EXPRESSIONS FOR THE INTERNAL ROTATION COMPONENTS
OF A SYMMETRIC TOP IN THE PRESENCE OF A CORIOLIS INTERACTION[a]

Symmetry	Frequency
A	$2B(J + 1) \pm 8qJ$
A	$2B(J + 1)$
E	$2B(J + 1) \pm [4q^2(J + 1)^2(J + 2)^2 + \frac{1}{3}\Delta_0^2 \sin^2 \theta]^{1/2}$ $\mp [4q^2 J^2 (J + 1)^2 + \frac{1}{3}\Delta_0^2 \sin^2 \theta]^{1/2}$
E	$2B(J + 1)$
(forbidden)	$2B(J + 1) \pm [4q^2(J + 1)^2(J + 2)^2 + \frac{1}{3}\Delta_0^2 \sin^2 \theta]^{1/2}$ $\pm [4q^2 J^2 (J + 1)^2 + \frac{1}{3}\Delta_0^2 \sin^2 \theta]^{1/2}$

[a] From Ref. [743].

The relative magnitudes of the internal rotation and Coriolis terms govern the splittings. The E lines move toward the center as the internal rotation energy is increased and move toward the A lines as it is decreased with respect to the Coriolis term.

6-13b. Coriolis Interactions in Excited Torsional States of Asymmetric Rotors

With a significant number of internal barriers being determined by splitting measurements in excited torsional states, the possibility of Coriolis interactions between the torsional mode v_α and another low-lying vibration v_q should be considered. It is most important to determine the effect of the Coriolis coupling on the A and E components because their splitting fixes the barrier. The Hamiltonian can be expressed as

$$H = H_r + H_v + H_{ir} + H_{r,ir} + H_{ir,v} \qquad (6\text{-}197)$$

where vibration-rotation interactions with all but the torsional mode have been neglected. $H_{ir,v}$ represents the interaction between a vibrational mode v and the internal torsion.

Laurie [700] has developed an explicit expression for (6-197) by assuming a molecular model with a plane of symmetry and an interacting vibration which is in the symmetry plane.

For a near symmetric rotor, the energy matrix is conveniently written in a basis consisting of the symmetric rotor functions, the periodic Mathieu function, and the harmonic oscillator functions in the coordinate q. Coriolis terms in $H_{ir,v}$ give matrix elements $\langle v_q v_\alpha | H | v_q \pm 1, v_\alpha \mp 1 \rangle$ that connect states of v_q and v_α. A Van Vleck transformation can be used to remove terms connecting these groups of elements, thereby producing an energy matrix similar to that in Fig. 6-9. The energy matrix can be factored into one sub-matrix for the A levels and one submatrix for the E levels. The Coriolis terms

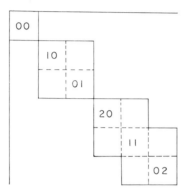

FIG. 6-9. A portion of the energy matrix showing the origin of possible Coriolis interaction terms. The diagonal blocks give the vibrational quantum numbers for v_α^σ and v_q. The unnumbered off-diagonal blocks may contain terms leading to a strong Coriolis interaction [700].

connect $v_\alpha^\sigma = 1$, $v_q = 0$ states to $v_\alpha^\sigma = 0$, $v_q = 1$ levels. If the internal rotation splitting is negligible in the ground vibrational state, the matrix elements in $v_\alpha^\sigma = 0$, $v_q = 1$ are similar in form to those in the ground state. Elements of $v_\alpha^\sigma = 1$, $v_q = 0$ are analogous to those of the ground state (if it were split by internal rotation). It is assumed that the ground state internal rotor splittings are unresolved and those in $v_\alpha^\sigma = 1$, $v_q = 0$ are resolvable. The off-diagonal elements are

$$\langle JKv|H|JKv'\rangle = g_z^\sigma K \qquad (6\text{-}198)$$

$$\langle JKv|H|J, K+1, v'\rangle = (\tfrac{1}{2}ig_x^\sigma)[J(J+1) - K(K+1)]^{1/2} \qquad (6\text{-}199)$$

The g_i^σ are functions of geometry and elements of the form $\langle JKv|qp_\alpha|JKv'\rangle$ where v and v' refer to any combination of v_α^σ and v_q.

Even and odd K can be grouped together by the Wang transformation. For the A levels, factoring into two subgroups[†] $\langle E_v^+, O_v^+|E_{v'}^-, O_{v'}^-\rangle$,

---

[†] The I^r representation of Chapter 2 is used. These matrix elements are characteristic of a near-prolate top [279].

$\langle E_v^-, O_v^- | E_{v'}^+, O_{v'}^+ \rangle$ occurs; for the E states the $\langle E_v^+ | E_v^- \rangle$ and $\langle O_v^+ | O_v^- \rangle$ elements prevent the factoring. Matrix elements introduced by the Coriolis coupling have the form

$$\langle E_v^+, K | E_{v'}^-, K \rangle = \langle O_v^+, K | O_{v'}^-, K \rangle = \langle E_v^-, K | E_{v'}^+, K \rangle$$

$$= \langle O_v^-, K | O_{v'}^+, K \rangle = g_z^\sigma K \qquad (6\text{-}200)$$

$$\langle E_v^+, K | O_{v'}^-, K + 1 \rangle = \langle O_v^-, K | E_{v'}^+, K + 1 \rangle = \langle O_v^+, K | E_{v'}^-, K + 1 \rangle$$

$$= \langle E_v^-, K | O_{v'}^+, K + 1 \rangle = \tfrac{1}{2} i g_x^\sigma [2J(J + 1)]^{1/2} \qquad (K = 0)$$

$$= \tfrac{1}{2} i g_x^\sigma [J(J + 1) - K(K + 1)]^{1/2} \qquad (K \neq 0) \qquad (6\text{-}201)$$

It is evident that Coriolis effects on both the rigid rotor spectrum and the torsional splittings must be taken into account in a complete treatment. To second order, the terms diagonal in K contribute $(g_z^\sigma K)^2 / \Delta E_v$ where ΔE_v is the vibrational energy difference. The rotational energy difference has been neglected. This results in a small correction to the effective rotational constant for the near symmetric rotor axis. For the terms off-diagonal in K it is not possible to neglect the rotational energy differences of the connected states and no simple K dependence occurs. The energy levels are complex functions of the g_i^σ.

Some qualitative observations of the spectrum often verify the presence of a Coriolis interaction. A large change in the rotational constant can indicate an interaction. Furthermore, in most cases the excited torsional satellites fall at lower frequencies than the ground state lines for parallel transitions of low J. When an interaction is present [700], the torsional satellites may be observed at higher frequencies.

For a high barrier and a small asymmetry, contributions of the Coriolis coupling to the relative positions of the A and E transitions are small. The terms to be considered are: (a) Coriolis terms dependent upon σ which are introduced by the Van Vleck transformation; (b) the difference between the matrix elements $\langle v_\alpha^A = 0 | p_\alpha | v_\alpha^A = 1 \rangle$ and $\langle v_\alpha^E = 0 | p_\alpha | v_\alpha^E = 1 \rangle$; and (c) the modification of the odd-order internal rotation terms for E levels by large off-diagonal Coriolis elements. The presence of a strong Coriolis coupling might result in a splitting of the A and E levels for all observed transitions in an excited torsional state even when the barrier is not low enough to produce the splitting itself.

6-14. V_6 Contributions to the Torsional Barrier

The general success of the Fourier expansion for the potential energy in which only the V_3 term is retained has led to the conclusion that the contributions of the higher terms, e.g., V_6 are very small. Few attempts have been made to measure V_6, and in all cases V_6/V_3 tends toward zero. For the low barrier problem in CH_3NO_2 and CH_3BF_2, V_6 has been measured accurately and found to be of the order of only a few calories. These determinations were facilitated by the fact that V_3 vanishes because of symmetry considerations. Table 6-9 lists some values of V_6 which have been estimated from microwave and far infrared spectra. V_6 is usually less than 3 % of V_3 and may make either a positive or negative contribution to $V(\alpha)$.

TABLE 6-9

ESTIMATES OF SOME V_6 CONTRIBUTIONS TO THE
TORSIONAL BARRIER SHAPE

Molecule	V_6 (cal/mole)	References
CH_3NO_2	6.03^a	[665]
CF_3NO_2	74.4^a	[757]
CH_3BF_2	13.77^a	[679]
$CH_3CH=CH_2$	-45	[736]
$CH_3CF=CH_2$	11	[736]
	<50	[1467]
$CH_3\underset{\diagdown\diagup}{\underset{O}{CHCH_2}}$	-26	[736]
	<30	[688]
CH_3CH_2Cl	~0	[736]
CH_3SH	<11	[1487]
CH_3OH	<11	[694]
$CH_3C_6H_4F(p$-fluorotoluene$)$	13.82^a	[755a]

^{a} Molecular symmetry forces V_3 to vanish.

It is valuable to note the effect of a finite V_6 contribution on the hindering potential. Since the $(V_6/2)(1 - \cos 6\alpha)$ term possesses nodes at both the minimum and maximum positions of the V_3 term, it does not change the actual height of the barrier. Instead it tends to alter its shape. Figure 6-10 shows the effects of positive and negative contributions of the V_6 term. For $V_6 > 0$, the potential becomes narrower, forcing the torsional levels below

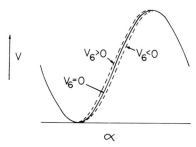

FIG. 6-10. Effect of a V_6 term on the shape of a threefold barrier hindering internal rotation [736].

the top of the barrier to become more widely separated. The top of the barrier suffers a broadening. If $V_6 < 0$, the levels tend to be closer together and the top of the barrier narrows.

Herschbach [698] has shown that an evaluation of V_6 usually requires information from several torsional states. It has been observed that the effect of V_6 on the torsional splitting increases significantly with the torsional quantum number. However, the increase in the V_3 contribution may be even greater, effectively forcing the V_6 dependence to decrease with v. The V_6 dependence can be conveniently introduced in a power series expansion of the perturbation coefficients in the parameter $X = V_6/V_3$ [670].

$$b'_{v\sigma} = b_{v\sigma} + X\frac{s}{2}[1 - \langle v|\cos 6\alpha|v\rangle]$$

$$+ X^2\frac{s^2}{4}\sum_{v'}' \frac{\langle v|\cos 6\alpha|v'\rangle\langle v'|\cos 6\alpha|v\rangle}{(b_{v\sigma} - b_{v'\sigma})} + \cdots \qquad (6\text{-}202)$$

A more concise notation is often preferred for expansions of this type [670].

$$b'_{v\sigma} = b_{v\sigma} + X\frac{s}{2}(1 - 6_{vv}) + X^2\frac{s^2}{4}\left(\frac{66}{\Delta}\right) + X^3\frac{s^3}{8}\left(6_{vv}\frac{66}{\Delta^2} - \frac{1}{3}\frac{666}{\Delta\Delta'}\right) + \cdots$$
$$(6\text{-}203)$$

Estimates of V_6 can also be made by observing several transitions between excited torsional levels in the far infrared.[†] Fateley and Miller [736] have assumed that F is identical for all the transitions and have adjusted V_6 to obtain consistent results for V_3. These values are also shown in Table 6-9. This approach seems to be more successful than one where the variation in V_3 between torsional states is absorbed by F.

6-15. Internal Rotation and Nuclear Quadrupole Coupling

A large number of molecules with hindered internal rotors also possess quadrupolar nuclei. In a general form, the Hamiltonian can be written as

$$H = H_r + H_{ir} + H_{r,ir} + H_Q \qquad (6\text{-}204)$$

The approach used to solve this Hamiltonian depends on the relative contribution of each term and the symmetry of the molecule. Because H_Q is diagonal in the torsional quantum number v, the energy matrix can be established using matrix elements which are already known and then diagonalized to obtain the energy levels. The form of H_Q also allows the Van Vleck transformation to be used without modification to effect an approximate diagonalization.

[†] Note that when microwave parameters such as F are applied to the analysis of far infrared torsional transitions, they become values averaged over the connected torsional levels.

When the internal rotation splittings are much larger than the quadrupole splittings, the latter can be treated as a perturbation on the internal rotation problem. For large quadrupole splittings and a high internal barrier, the reverse is true.

First-order matrix elements for a quadrupole nucleus in the molecular frame of an asymmetric rotor have been given using the IAM basis for a molecule containing a plane of symmetry [793]. The direction-cosine matrices are calculated in the representation used for the internal rotation problem.

$$\langle JKv|\nabla E_{ZZ}|JKv\rangle = \frac{3K^2 - J(J + 1)}{(J + 1)(2J + 3)}q_{zz} \tag{6-205}$$

$$\langle JKv|\nabla E_{ZZ}|J, K + 1, v\rangle = \frac{(2K + 1)[J(J + 1) - K(K + 1)]^{1/2}}{2(J + 1)(2J + 3)}$$

$$\times (1 - \delta_{Kv\sigma}^{K+1,v\sigma})q_{yz} \tag{6-206}$$

$$\langle JKv|\nabla E_{ZZ}|J, K + 2, v\rangle$$

$$= \frac{[(J - K)(J - K - 1)(J + K + 1)(J + K + 2)]^{1/2}}{2(J + 1)(2J + 3)}$$

$$\times (1 - \delta_{Kv\sigma}^{K+2,v\sigma})(q_{yy} - q_{xx}) \tag{6-207}$$

The x, y, z axis system is the molecule-fixed system used in the IAM. The x axis is perpendicular to the plane of symmetry and $q_{xy} = q_{xz} = 0$. Quadrupole effects can produce an important interaction if an appropriate near degeneracy is present. For example, the $\langle K|K \pm 2\rangle$ elements connect the $K = 1$ levels which may be nearly degenerate in a near symmetric top.

A simple approach can be used for molecules whose quadrupole energy is much larger than the internal rotation splittings. Let $E_{R'}$ and $E_{Q'}$ be the rotational and quadrupole energies for the upper level of the K doublet and E_R and E_Q be the analogous quantities for the lower level. $\Delta E_R = E_{R'} - E_R$ and $\Delta E_Q = E_{Q'} - E_Q$. The internal rotation splitting is given by [702]

$$E_E - E_A = \pm\{[\tfrac{1}{4}(\Delta E_R + \Delta E_Q)^2 + \delta_K^2]^{1/2} - \tfrac{1}{2}(\Delta E_R + \Delta E_Q)\} \tag{6-208}$$

The $+$ refers to the upper K level and the $-$ refers to the lower K level.

$$\delta_K = 3^{-1/2}\Delta_0 K\rho \sin\left(\frac{2\pi}{3}\right) \tag{6-209}$$

For $\Delta E_R \gg |\Delta E_Q|$, (6-208) may be expanded to

$$E_E - E_A = \pm\frac{1}{2}\left\{[\Delta E_R^2 + 4\delta_K^2]^{1/2} - \Delta E_R - \Delta E_Q\left[1 - \frac{\Delta E_R}{[\Delta E_R^2 + 4\delta_K^2]^{1/2}}\right]\right\} \tag{6-210}$$

This expression is not valid if the K doubling is too small. To determine the barrier height ΔE_R and ΔE_Q are evaluated from the A transitions, and the measured splitting of the A and E levels is used to find δ_K.

If a near degeneracy makes a second-order quadrupole effect important, the $\langle J|J + 1\rangle$ and $\langle J|J + 2\rangle$ elements of ∇E_{ZZ} must be included in the energy matrix.

6-16a. Molecules with Two Equivalent Methyl Groups

The double rotor problem introduces the possibility of coupling between two hindered rotors as well as torsion overall-rotation interactions. The Hamiltonian and energy levels are necessarily more complex than in the single rotor case.

The first approach to the double rotor suggests an extension of the single top methods to include two methyl groups and rotor-rotor interactions. The IAM reduces the coupling terms between internal and overall rotation by choosing one of the symmetry axes colinear with the top axis. This method is used by Woods in a discussion of the n-top problem [1710]. The PAM lends itself to this type of problem because the new interaction terms are amenable to a perturbation treatment. The symmetry statistics are also more complex due to the presence of more torsional sublevels and different combinations of excited torsional states. Perturbation coefficients which have been tabulated for the single rotor problem can be of use if the top-top coupling terms are small [721]. In this case the basis functions assume that there is no coupling between the tops in the zeroth order of approximation. If excited torsional states are treated, the possibility of direct interactions between nearly degenerate states must be considered, e.g., the 01 and 10 states in Fig. 6-4 which are almost degenerate in the high barrier limit.

6-16b. Kinetic Energy

The kinetic energy may be expanded in terms of a generalized inertial tensor $\mathbf{I}$ and composite angular velocities which include the overall angular velocities ω_a, ω_b, and ω_c and the angular velocities of the internal rotors $\dot{\alpha}_1$ and $\dot{\alpha}_2$.

If the two rotors are geometrically equivalent, at least one plane of symmetry must exist in the molecule. The algebra is considerably simplified for molecules like acetone and dimethylsulfide in which two planes of symmetry are found. Molecules in the ground torsional state with C_{2v} symmetry are discussed here. Extension to molecules belonging to symmetry group C_s is straightforward.

Let the a and b principal axes lie in the plane of symmetry containing the two methyl group axes. The b axis is defined by the intersection of the two symmetry planes. Because the c axis is normal to both internal rotor axes, there are no coupling terms between ω_c and $\dot{\alpha}_1$ or $\dot{\alpha}_2$. For molecules where the same isotope of hydrogen is used in both methyl groups $I_{\alpha 1} = I_{\alpha 2} = I_\alpha$.

$$2T = I_a\omega_a^2 + I_b\omega_b^2 + I_c\omega_c^2 + I_\alpha(\dot{\alpha}_1^2 + \dot{\alpha}_2^2) + I_\alpha\lambda_a\omega_a(\dot{\alpha}_1 - \dot{\alpha}_2)$$
$$+ I_\alpha\lambda_b\omega_b(\dot{\alpha}_1 + \dot{\alpha}_2) \tag{6-211}$$

The simplification imposed by equating $I_{\alpha 1}$ and $I_{\alpha 2}$ is not restrictive in most cases. In molecules which contain two isotopically different methyl groups, e.g., $(CH_3)(CD_3)X$, the tunneling rate of the CD_3 group is so much less than that of the CH_3 group that the molecule can usually be treated as a single top molecule in the high barrier limit. Torsion of the CD_3 group is frozen out.

It is convenient to express the kinetic energy in terms of the generalized angular momentum in (6-96).

$$T = H_r + F[(p_1 - \mathscr{P}_1)^2 + (p_2 + \mathscr{P}_2)^2] + F'[(p_1 - \mathscr{P}_1)(p_2 - \mathscr{P}_2)$$
$$+ (p_2 - \mathscr{P}_2)(p_1 - \mathscr{P}_1)] \tag{6-212}$$

The subscripts 1 and 2 identify the two internal rotors. H_r is the rigid rotor Hamiltonian expressed in uncorrected rotational constants and F and F' are inverse reduced moments of inertia. $p_1 - \mathscr{P}_1$ and $p_2 - \mathscr{P}_2$ are the angular momentum components of the two tops with respect to the molecular frame. F and F' are defined by the equation

$$F \pm F' = \hbar^2/2(r \pm q)I_\alpha \tag{6-213}$$

where

$$r = 1 - \sum_i \lambda_{ik}^2 I_\alpha/I_i \tag{6-214}$$

$$q = - \sum_i \lambda_{i1}\lambda_{i2} I_\alpha/I_i \tag{6-215}$$

If it is assumed that the barrier to internal rotation is relatively high, F will be much greater than F'. Contributions higher than threefold to the hindering potential are neglected for the same reasons used in the single top case. The Hamiltonian for the high barrier can be written in symmetrized form.

$$H = H_r + 2F_+(p_+ - \mathscr{P}_+)^2 + 2F_-(p_- - \mathscr{P}_-)^2 + V(\alpha_1, \alpha_2) \tag{6-216}$$

$$\mathscr{P}_\pm = \tfrac{1}{2}(\mathscr{P}_1 \pm \mathscr{P}_2) \tag{6-217}$$

$$p_\pm = \tfrac{1}{2}(p_1 \pm p_2) \tag{6-218}$$

$$F_\pm = F \pm F' \tag{6-219}$$

$$V(\alpha_1, \alpha_2) = \tfrac{1}{2}V_3(2 - \cos 3\alpha_1 - \cos 3\alpha_2) + V_3^{(12)}(1 - \cos 3\alpha_1)$$
$$\times (1 - \cos 3\alpha_2) + V_3^{(12)*} \sin 3\alpha_1 \sin 3\alpha_2 \tag{6-220}$$

The Hamiltonian is now ready to be separated into zeroth order terms and perturbing terms. The energy matrix could be divided into a purely torsional part and a purely rotational part with only the terms $-4F_{\pm}p_{\pm}\mathscr{P}_{\pm}$ connecting the two submatrices. These terms could be diagonalized by an appropriate transformation. Unfortunately, this approach would not take advantage of the tabulated perturbation coefficients developed in the single top theory. To accomplish this the top-top coupling terms are also treated by perturbation theory [722]. The Hamiltonian becomes

$$H = H^{(0)} + H^{(1)} \tag{6-221}$$

$$H^{(0)} = H_r + F(p_1^2 + p_2^2) + \tfrac{1}{2}V_3(2 - \cos 3\alpha_1 - \cos 3\alpha_2) \tag{6-222}$$

$$H^{(1)} = 2F_+\mathscr{P}_+^2 + 2F_-\mathscr{P}_-^2 - 4F_+p_+\mathscr{P}_+ - 4F_-p_-\mathscr{P}_- + F'(p_1p_2 + p_2p_1)$$
$$+ V_3^{(12)}(1 - \cos 3\alpha_1)(1 - \cos 3\alpha_2) + V_3^{(12)*} \sin 3\alpha_1 \sin 3\alpha_2 \tag{6-223}$$

The asymmetric terms in H_r could be placed in $H^{(1)}$. However, to emphasize the torsional problem, asymmetric rotor functions are used in the basis set along with the Mathieu functions [624]. The torsional equation is

$$[F(p_1^2 + p_2^2) + \tfrac{1}{2}V_3(2 - \cos 3\alpha_1 - \cos 3\alpha_2)]U_{v_1\sigma_1}(\alpha_1)U_{v_2\sigma_2}(\alpha_2)$$
$$= [E_{v_1\sigma_1}(\alpha_1) + E_{v_2\sigma_2}(\alpha_2)]U_{v_1\sigma_1}(\alpha_1)U_{v_2\sigma_2}(\alpha_2) \tag{6-224}$$

The symmetries of appropriate combinations of the torsional functions are shown in Table 6-10 [738] for $v = v'$ and $v \neq v'$.

The energy level structure for a high but finite barrier should lead to quartets when $v = v'$ and octets when $v \neq v'$; however, coupling terms are often too small to allow complete separation of all the transitions. Pierce [721] and Pierce and Hayashi [722] have treated the case $v = v'$. If the top-top coupling terms are neglected and a Van Vleck transformation is used to diagonalize the energy matrix to second order in v, the Hamiltonian can be written as

$$H_{vv} = H_r + F \sum_n [\omega_{vv}^{(+n)}\mathscr{P}_+^n + \omega_{vv}^{(-n)}\mathscr{P}_-^n], \qquad n = 0, 1, 2 \tag{6-225}$$

Equation (6-225) omits the term $F\omega^{(x2)}(\mathscr{P}_+\mathscr{P}_- + \mathscr{P}_-\mathscr{P}_+)$. $\omega^{(x2)}$ is zero for all terms except those of EE symmetry where it is $W_{v1}^{(2)} - W_{v0}^{(2)}$. The $\omega_{vv}^{(\pm n)}$ are linear combinations of the single top perturbation terms tabulated by Herschbach [670] and Hayashi and Pierce [718]. The actual relations are given in Table 6-11 [721].

If the Van Vleck transformation is used when the top-top terms are included in $H^{(1)}$, H_{vv} can be expressed in terms of the parameter $W_{vv}^{(\pm n)}$.

TABLE 6-10

SYMMETRY OF TORSIONAL FUNCTIONS $\langle v\sigma, v'\sigma'|$ FOR C_{2v} MOLECULES
WITH TWO EQUIVALENT INTERNAL ROTORS FOR $v = v'$ AND $v \neq v'$

Torsional state	Torsional function	Symmetry	
$v = v'$	$\langle v0, v0|$	$A_1 A_1$	
	$\langle v0, v1|, \langle v-1, v0| \atop \langle v1, v0|, \langle v0, v-1|$	EE	
	$\langle v1, v1|, \langle v-1, v-1|$	$A_1 E$	
	$\langle v1, v-1|, \langle v-1, v1|$	EA_1	

		$+$	$-$
$v \neq v'$	$\dfrac{1}{\sqrt{2}}(\langle v0, v'0| \pm \langle v'0, v0|)$	$A_1 A_1$ or^a $A_1 A_2$	$A_2 A_2$ $A_2 A_1$
	$\dfrac{1}{\sqrt{2}}(\langle v1, v'1| \pm \langle v'1, v1|)$ $\atop$ $\dfrac{1}{\sqrt{2}}(\langle v-1, v'-1| \pm \langle v'-1, v-1|)$	$A_1 E$	$A_2 E$
	$\dfrac{1}{\sqrt{2}}(\langle v1, v'-1| \pm \langle v'1, v-1|)$ $\atop$ $\dfrac{1}{\sqrt{2}}(\langle v-1, v'1| \pm \langle v'-1, v1|)$	EA_1	EA_2
	$\langle v'0, v1|, \langle v-1, v'0| \atop \langle v1, v'0|, \langle v'0, v-1|$	EE	
	$\langle v0, v'1|, \langle v'-1, v0| \atop \langle v'1, v0|, \langle v0, v'-1|$	EE	

^{a} The upper pair apply when v and v' are of the same parity and the lower pair is valid for v and v' of opposite parity.

$$H_{vv} = H_r + F \sum_n [W_{vv}^{(+n)} \mathscr{P}_+^n + W_{vv}^{(-n)} \mathscr{P}_-^n], \qquad n = 0, 1, 2 \quad (6\text{-}226)$$

$$W_{vv}^{(\pm n)} = \omega_{vv}^{(\pm n)} + xX_{vv}^{(\pm n)} + yY_{vv}^{(\pm n)} + zZ_{vv}^{(\pm n)} \qquad (6\text{-}227)$$

$$x = F'/F \qquad (6\text{-}228)$$

$$y = V_3^{(12)}/V_3 \qquad (6\text{-}229)$$

$$z = V_3^{(12)*}/V_3 \qquad (6\text{-}230)$$

TABLE 6-11

EVALUATION OF THE $\omega_{vv}^{(\pm n)a}$

Γ_{vv}	$\omega_{vv}^{(1)}$	$\omega_{vv}^{(-1)}$	$\omega_{vv}^{(\pm 2)}$
A_1A_1	0	0	$2W_{v0}^{(2)}$
A_1E	$2W_{v1}^{(1)}$	0	$2W_{v1}^{(2)}$
EA_1	0	$2W_{v1}^{(1)}$	$2W_{v1}^{(2)}$
EE	$W_{v1}^{(1)}$	$W_{v1}^{(1)}$	$W_{v0}^{(2)} + W_{v1}^{(2)}$

[a] From Ref. [721].

$Z_{vv}^{(\pm n)}$ vanishes through second order, and $X_{vv}^{(\pm n)}$ may be expressed in terms of the $W_{vv}^{(n)}$ (Table 6-12). The $Y_{vv}^{(\pm n)}$ are much more difficult to evaluate and empirical formulas have been given to calculate them [721].

TABLE 6-12

DEFINITION OF THE $X_{vv}^{(\pm n)}$ IN TERMS OF THE $W_{v\sigma}^{(n)a}$

Γ_{vv}	$X_{vv}^{(1)}$	$X_{vv}^{(-1)}$	$X_{vv}^{(\pm 2)}$
A_1A_1	0	0	$\pm 2[W_{v0}^{(2)}]^2$
A_1E	$2W_{v1}^{(2)}W_{v1}^{(1)}$	0	$\pm 2[W_{v1}^{(2)}]^2 + 3W_{v1}^{(1)}W_{v1}^{(3)} \mp 2[W_{v1}^{(1)}]^2 W_{v1}^{(d)}$
EA_1	0	$-2W_{v1}^{(2)}W_{v1}^{(1)}$	$\pm 2[W_{v1}^{(2)}]^2 - 3W_{v1}^{(1)}W_{v1}^{(3)}$ $\mp 2[W_{v1}^{(1)}]^2 W_{v1}^{(d)}$
EE	$W_{v0}^{(2)}W_{v1}^{(1)}$	$-W_{v0}^{(2)}W_{v1}^{(1)}$	$\pm 2W_{v0}^{(2)}W_{v1}^{(2)} \mp [W_{v1}^{(1)}]^2 W_{v0}^{(d)}$

[a] From Ref. [721]. $W_{v\sigma}^{(d)}$ is the denominator correction discussed by Herschbach [670] and Stelman [746].

Matrix elements of p, p^2, $\cos 3\alpha$, $\sin 3\alpha$, and $\cos 6\alpha$ have been extensively tabulated by Hayashi and Pierce [718] for a threefold barrier and can be applied directly to the double rotor problem to allow calculation of top-top coupling effects. They have also computed the perturbation coefficients necessary for a rotational analysis.

When $v \neq v'$, the $\sin 3\alpha_1 \sin 3\alpha_2$, $\cos 3\alpha_1 \cos 3\alpha_2$, and $p_1 p_2$ terms can be much more important than in the $v = v'$ case, because they may connect nearly degenerate torsional states. In a vv' torsional state, the nearly degenerate torsional sublevels are not connected; however, levels with the same $\sigma\sigma'$ may be nearly degenerate and are connected by top-top coupling terms within a torsional block labeled by $W = v + v'$ (Fig. 6-4). The problem can then be treated either by degenerate perturbation theory or by applying a Van Vleck transformation to fold correction terms into each W block and then treating each block individually [705].

In the ground torsional state, triplets have been observed in $(CH_3)_2SiH_2$, $(CH_3)_2O$ and *cis* 2,3 epoxybutane; quartets have been observed in acetone and in the 01 and 10 excited torsional states of dimethylamine.

6-17. Symmetric Tops with Three Methyl Groups

The interactions related to hindered internal rotation grow more complex as the number of methyl groups is increased. However, the amount of available information and complexity of the spectrum may be reduced and simplified if the degree of symmetry of the molecule is enhanced. Upon addition of a third methyl group to an asymmetric rotor like dimethylsilane, a threefold axis of symmetry is introduced, reducing the complex asymmetric rotor spectrum to that of a symmetric top with at least C_3 and probably C_{3v} symmetry. Except for a high-order interaction, the ground vibrational state does not reflect the effects of hindered rotation. In $(CH_3)_3CH, (CH_3)_3CF$, $(CH_3)_3P$, and $(CH_3)_3N$ the internal barrier is sufficiently high to prevent any internal rotation structure in either the ground or first excited vibrational states. However, molecules with lower barriers such as $(CH_3)_3SiH$ [1506] have exhibited some apparent torsional fine structure in excited vibrational states.

It is evident that a careful assignment of the excited state spectrum in a symmetric top with three internal rotors is essential for an accurate barrier calculation. The excited states which are sufficiently populated to be observed in the microwave spectrum usually are restricted to the torsional modes and deformation or rocking vibrations of the heavy atoms in the framework. Nontorsional frequencies ordinarily can be assigned by infrared and Raman studies. Degenerate and nondegenerate modes may be distinguished by the presence or absence of *l*-type doubling which affects only the degenerate states. Lide and Mann [691] have proposed a set of empirical rules based on qualitative comparisons of the vibration-rotation constants α_v in sets of $(CH_3)_3AB$ molecules: (1) deformation modes fall on the high frequency side of the ground state line; (2) torsional modes fall on the low frequency side of the ground state; and (3) the degenerate torsional state occurs at a lower frequency than the nondegenerate torsional state.

After Pitzer and Gwinn [610] and Lide and Mann [690], the classical Hamiltonian in momentum form may be written as

$$H = \left(\frac{1}{2I_x}\right)(P_x^2 + P_y^2) + \left(\frac{1}{2I_z}\right)P_z^2 + \left(\frac{1}{2I_a}\right)p_1^2 + \left(\frac{1}{2I_e}\right)(p_2^2 + p_3^2) + V \quad (6\text{-}231)$$

A transformation has been utilized to remove the coupling terms p_iP_j. P_x, P_y, and P_z are the components of net angular momentum of the molecule and z represents the figure axis. p_1, p_2, and p_3 are angular momenta conjugate to the angular coordinates α_1, α_2, and α_3.

$$\alpha_1 = \frac{1}{\sqrt{3}}(\phi_1 + \phi_2 + \phi_3) \tag{6-232}$$

$$\alpha_2 = \frac{1}{\sqrt{6}}(2\phi_1 - \phi_2 - \phi_3) \tag{6-233}$$

$$\alpha_3 = \frac{1}{\sqrt{2}}(\phi_2 - \phi_3) \tag{6-234}$$

ϕ_1, ϕ_2, and ϕ_3 give the relative orientations of the methyl groups with respect to the molecular frame. If I_α is the moment of the methyl group and m is the angle between the top axis and the figure axis,

$$I_a = I_\alpha[1 - (3I_\alpha/I_z)\cos^2 m] \tag{6-235}$$

$$I_e = I_\alpha[1 - (3I_\alpha/2I_x)\sin^2 m] \tag{6-236}$$

A reasonable potential function is

$$2V = V_0 - V_1 \sum_{i=1}^{3} \cos 3\phi_i - V_2 \sum_{i>j} \cos 3\phi_i \cos 3\phi_j - V_3 \cos 3\phi_1 \cos 3\phi_2$$

$$\times \cos 3\phi_3 + V_4 \sum_{i>j} \sin 3\phi_i \sin 3\phi_j + V_5 \sum_{i\neq j\neq k} \cos 3\phi_i \sin 3\phi_j \sin 3\phi_k \tag{6-237}$$

It should be noted that some of the terms in the Fourier expansion for V vanish in the case of C_{3v} symmetry. The term V_0 can be dropped because it is an additive constant. The V_1 term represents the usual potential for three independent methyl groups and the remaining terms describe the interactions between the internal rotors. For a high barrier and assuming small torsional oscillations, V can be expanded about the equilibrium configuration giving

$$2V = K \sum_i \phi_i^2 + 2L \sum_{i>j} \phi_i \phi_j \tag{6-238}$$

where

$$K = (\tfrac{9}{2})(V_1 + 2V_2 + V_3) \tag{6-239}$$

$$L = (\tfrac{9}{2})(V_4 + V_5) \tag{6-240}$$

This leads to

$$2V = (K + 2L)\alpha_1^2 + (K - L)(\alpha_2^2 + \alpha_3^2) \tag{6-241}$$

It is necessary to discuss the symmetry properties of the torsional oscillations. The normal modes of vibration which are predominantly the torsional vibrations belong to the irreducible representations A_2 and E of C_{3v} and may be designated as v_a and v_e. Using the simplified potential, the frequencies of these vibrations are

$$\omega_a = [2\Gamma_a(K + 2L)]^{1/2} \tag{6-242}$$

$$\omega_e = [2\Gamma_e(K - L)]^{1/2} \tag{6-243}$$

where

$$\Gamma_i = (\hbar^2/2I_i) \tag{6-244}$$

These equations are used to evaluate K and L. The ω_i may be obtained from either far infrared measurements or relative intensities of the satellite lines. If V_1 is the dominant term, the approximate barrier height is given by

$$V_1 \approx (\tfrac{2}{9})K \tag{6-245}$$

From the approximations which have been employed and the necessity of using far infrared or relative intensity measurements, it is apparent that this approach is not as accurate as one which uses torsional splittings.

A possible interpretation of the interaction constant L is to assume that it represents the forces between hydrogen atoms of different methyl groups. In this case, $L > 0$ is attractive and $L < 0$ is repulsive. Usually [690] L is less than zero causing $\omega_a < \omega_e$. This corroborates a repulsion between hydrogens, because in the A_2 mode the methyl groups oscillate in phase and keep a greater average distance apart than they do in the E mode where one top moves out-of-phase with the other two.

6-18. Rotational Isomerism

Many polyatomic molecules are known to exist as different rotational isomers called the *cis*, *trans*, and *gauche* forms. The most stable form is determined by the potential function hindering the torsional motion which tends to interchange these rotamers. Figure 6-11 shows the potential function for normal propyl fluoride [725]. It has the general form

$$V = \sum_n (\tfrac{1}{2}V_n)[1 - \cos(n\theta)] \tag{6-246}$$

θ is the angle of rotation about the central C—C bond. Unlike the potential

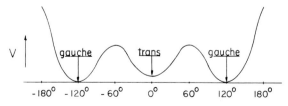

FIG. 6-11. Potential function for normal propyl fluoride.

for a methyl group with threefold symmetry, the terms in (6-246) which are not a multiple of three are nonzero and may be very important. Relative intensity measurements are used to ascertain which rotational form is the most stable and to estimate the energy differences. An interesting complication results in $XH_2C—CH_2Y$ if either X or Y is a methyl group. The excited torsional states of the methyl group as well as the molecular $C—C$ torsions appear as satellite lines near the ground state spectrum of each rotamer. Characteristic internal rotation splitting may occur in the torsional states of the CH_3 group and splittings in the molecular torsional states may be caused by interactions between the $C—C$ and CH_3 modes. The coupling of these motions seems to have only a slight effect on the internal rotation splittings in the methyl torsional state.

For two equivalent forms of the *gauche* rotamer, an additional splitting may be observed in the ground state rotational spectrum. This splitting, which is small in propionaldehyde, seems to be caused by a coupling between overall rotation and the angular momentum associated with the molecular torsion [1633].

6-19. Barriers Determined from Rotational Spectra

If a molecule possesses a permanent dipole moment and a conveniently observable rotational spectrum, microwave spectroscopy presents one of the most accurate methods available for barrier determination. By obtaining barrier information for a series of related molecules, it is possible to make some qualitative statements on the effects of group substitution at different molecular positions. At the present time, no adequate theory is available for the calculation of barrier heights from the first principles of molecular structure. In any case, a large group of well-determined barriers will provide the first true test of forthcoming theories.

Appendix 9 lists a large number of the internal barriers determined by microwave techniques. The barriers are listed by bond type according to the periodic table. Inspection of the values for a particular series of compounds usually allows a rough estimate of barrier heights in other related compounds. However, an exception can usually be found to any general empirical rule for predicting these barriers.

7-1. Characteristics of the Inversion Motion

Another hindered internal mode which can perturb the rotational spectrum of a molecule is the inversion motion. This degree of freedom may exist whenever a molecule has two energetically equivalent configurations which cannot be reached by a set of simple molecular rotations. All nonplanar molecules fall into this category. Inversion is not important in planar molecules because the two equivalent forms can be reached by simple rotations about the principal axes.

The two configurations of an inverting molecule are separated by a potential barrier which hinders interconversion of the two forms. The nature of the inversion barrier not only affects the quantum-mechanical behavior of the molecule but also may produce some macroscopic effects. If the barrier is large enough, the inversion can be neglected and in the case of asymmetric molecules stable enantiomers may result.

Figure 7-1 shows the evolution of the potential energy diagram as a barrier is introduced. The effect of an inversion barrier on the vibrational energy levels of a molecule can be analyzed, using the harmonic oscillator potential function as a basis. In the absence of a perturbing potential, the harmonic oscillator energy levels are equally spaced. n is the harmonic oscillator quantum number. As a barrier is introduced at the bottom of the potential well, the vibrational energy levels draw together in pairs; the two lowest levels are displaced the most. In the case of an infinitely high barrier, the pairs of levels coalesce and no inversion doubling is apparent. Classically, the molecule is isolated in one of two identical potential wells, and its vibrational levels are doubly degenerate. This is true for most nonplanar molecules whose potential energy barriers are much larger than the energies of the lower vibrational levels.

Let the harmonic oscillator function represent the potential function for the out-of-plane bending motion of a planar molecule and assume a small amplitude of vibration. With a planar equilibrium structure, the two

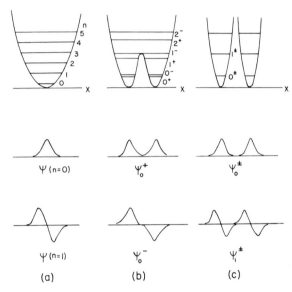

FIG. 7-1. Potential functions and wave functions for the two lowest levels of (a) a harmonic oscillator, (b) a finite inversion barrier, and (c) an infinite inversion barrier.

equivalent molecular configurations obtained by inverting the molecule, e.g., by performing a reflection of the nuclei through a plane normal to the molecular plane, can be connected by simple rotations. The eigenfunctions of the energy levels are characterized by their symmetry. They are alternately symmetric and antisymmetric with respect to inversion. The symmetric levels are designated by a + and the antisymmetric levels are identified by a −. If the equilibrium structure becomes nonplanar, the symmetric and antisymmetric levels draw together, and each pair of vibrational levels consists of a + and a − component. Because the lowest vibrational level of a molecule is always symmetric, the lower member of each pair of levels is symmetric and the upper member is antisymmetric. Alternatively, each vibrational level for a high inversion barrier may be thought of as two inversion sublevels; one is symmetric and the other is antisymmetric to inversion. Using the latter description for the vibrational energy levels in Fig. 7-1, they can be labeled by a vibrational quantum number and by the inversion symmetry. In this notation, the four lowest levels are 0^+, 0^-, 1^+, and 1^-.

In the case of a high barrier where rotation is neglected, two different types of transitions are important. The first is a transition from one sublevel of one vibrational state to a sublevel of another vibrational state. The other is simply a transition between the two sublevels of the same vibrational state. The first type of transition is approximately the vibrational frequency corresponding to the normal coordinate which most nearly describes the classical inversion motion. The second is properly called a pure inversion transition and is not approximated by any of the normal vibrations of the molecule. This inversion frequency can be further explained by a consideration of the proper potential function.

For a high barrier, the lower vibrational levels lie below the top of the potential barrier. The two minima in the potential function represent the two energetically equivalent equilibrium forms of the inverting molecule. When the molecule resides in a vibrational state below the top of the barrier, it is classically impossible for it to invert to its other form. This would restrict inversion to molecules in vibrational states above the top of the barrier. However, the quantum-mechanical tunnel effect allows molecules to tunnel through the barrier at a rate which is a function of the height of the barrier. The pure inversion frequency is related to the rapidity of this classically-forbidden motion. When the rotational levels of the molecule are included, they also occur as pairs of $+$ and $-$ inversion levels. For a resolvable inversion doubling, the rotational spectrum will be complicated by an increased number of transitions and by an additional selection rule for the inversion symmetry.

7-2. Properties of the Inversion Wave Functions

The quantum-mechanical behavior of a molecule under the influence of inversion is described by the properties of the vibrational wave functions governing the inversion mode. In particular, the symmetry properties of the wave functions determine the selection rules. Figure 7-1 shows qualitative plots of the wave functions for the two lowest states of a harmonic oscillator, a double minimum potential, and an infinite potential barrier. The wave function for the harmonic oscillator state $n = 0$ has its maximum at $x = 0$; the function for the state $n = 1$ has a node at $x = 0$. Similarly, for a one-dimensional problem, all the wave functions for odd values of n possess nodes at $x = 0$. As a symmetrical potential barrier is introduced at $x = 0$, the levels with even n are perturbed much more than those where n is odd. The 0^+, 1^+, 2^+,... levels are displaced from their harmonic oscillator positions toward the 0^-, 1^-, 2^-,... levels. The latter are also perturbed but to a smaller extent. Larger values of n undergo much smaller shifts than the $n = 0$ level. However, in the limit of an infinite barrier, all values of n are affected.

Classically, a molecule under the influence of an inversion barrier is expected to oscillate in one of the two potential minima and to execute inversion by passage from one minimum to the other minimum only when sufficient energy is available. This is not the case when the time dependence of the wave functions is included. The molecule is rarely associated with either potential minimum but is "distributed" across both minima as indicated by the wave functions in Fig. 7-1. If ψ_R and ψ_L are oscillator functions describing the molecule in the left and right minima of Fig. 7-1,

$$\psi_0^+ = (\tfrac{1}{2})^{1/2}[\psi_L + \psi_R] \tag{7-1}$$

$$\psi_0^- = (\tfrac{1}{2})^{1/2}[\psi_L - \psi_R] \tag{7-2}$$

ψ_0^+ is symmetric and ψ_0^- is antisymmetric for an inversion. The time-dependent wave function is [20, 1018]

$$\psi(t) = (\tfrac{1}{2})^{1/2}[\psi_0^+ + \psi_0^- \, e^{2\pi i v t}] \, e^{2\pi i E_0^+ t/h} \tag{7-3}$$

$\psi(t)$ indicates that the tunneling process is continuous in nature. E_0^+ is the energy of the ψ_0^+ state and hv is the energy difference between the two inversion states. Because $\psi(t)$ is a function of time, it does not correspond to a constant energy value. Rather, $\psi(t)$ gives a measure of the rate of tunneling in terms of the energy separation of the two inversion levels.

A well-known illustration can be used to demonstrate the symmetric-antisymmetric properties of the inversion wave functions. Let H_{inv} be the operator which inverts the molecule; this inversion is not the same as a center of inversion but consists of a coordinate sign change of only one suitable dimension. For a properly chosen coordinate system and an inversion motion along the x direction, the center of inversion takes x, y, z into $-x, -y, -z$, while the inversion motion takes x, y, z into $-x, y, z$. The energy of the system and the Hamiltonian must be unchanged by this inversion. Because the energy of the molecule is unchanged by H_{inv}, for a nondegenerate state the wave function which describes the new configuration of the molecule can differ from the original wave function only by a constant multiplier.

$$\psi_i = a\psi \tag{7-4}$$

For a degenerate system, the transformed wave functions are formed by linear combinations of the original functions.

A second inversion of the coordinates returns the molecule to its original configuration, and

$$\psi_{ii} = a\psi_i = a^2\psi \tag{7-5}$$

Because ψ_{ii} must be identical to ψ, $a^2 = 1$ and $a = \pm 1$. The $a = +1$ solution leads to the symmetric inversion functions, and the $a = -1$ solution gives the antisymmetric functions.

7-3. Inversion in Symmetric Top Molecules

The most famous example of a symmetric top which exhibits detectable inversion splittings is the ammonia molecule. Classical inversion may be pictured as a tunneling of the nitrogen atom through the plane formed by the three hydrogen atoms or as a movement of the hydrogens past a stationary nitrogen atom. The rotational selection rules for a symmetric top require that $\Delta J = 0, \pm 1$ and $\Delta K = 0$.

The intensity of a transition depends on the behavior of the dipole matrix element

$$\langle i|\mathbf{\mu}|j \rangle = \int \psi_i^* \mathbf{\mu} \psi_j \, d\tau \qquad (7\text{-}6)$$

ψ represents the appropriate normalized wave function, and $\mathbf{\mu}$ is the dipole moment operator. For a pure inversion transition, $\Delta J = 0$ and the ψ are just the inversion wave functions. For the matrix element $\langle i|\mathbf{\mu}|j \rangle$ to be non-zero, the integral must be totally symmetric with respect to an inversion of the coordinates. Because the dipole moment is restricted to lie along the symmetry axis of a symmetric top, it changes direction during the inversion, and $\mathbf{\mu}$ is antisymmetric with respect to this operation. Therefore, the inversion functions ψ_i^* and ψ_j must be of opposite symmetry to make $\langle i|\mathbf{\mu}|j \rangle$ totally symmetric and a pure inversion transition is allowed in a symmetric rotor.

$$+ \leftrightarrow - ; \qquad \pm \nleftrightarrow \pm \qquad (7\text{-}7)$$

For transitions with $\Delta J = \pm 1$ the behavior of the rotational wave functions must be considered. (7-6) becomes

$$\langle i|\mathbf{\mu}|j \rangle = \int \psi_{i,R}^* \psi_{i,\text{inv}}^* \mathbf{\mu} \psi_{j,R'} \psi_{j,\text{inv}} \, d\tau \qquad (7\text{-}8)$$

In a totally symmetric electronic and vibrational state, the rotational wave function is symmetric if K is even and antisymmetric if K is odd. Because $\Delta K = 0$, the rotational wave functions for energy levels connected by a transition must have the same symmetry. Therefore, the selection rules (7-7) also hold for symmetric top transitions involving rotation and inversion.

The pure inversion spectrum of NH_3 occurs in the microwave region near 24 GHz. These transitions are very intense and were among the first observed in the microwave region [1008]. The vibration-inversion spectrum lies in the infrared region near 950 cm^{-1} [2].

The energy levels and statistics of symmetric top molecules, exclusive of inversion, have been discussed in Chapter 2. Symmetric top transitions involving finite inversion splittings are shown in Fig. 7-2. The selection rules for a rigid symmetric top remain valid; however, for molecules like NH_3, alternate levels for $K = 0$ or a multiple of three vanish as a result of the Pauli exclusion principle. The total wave function must be antisymmetric

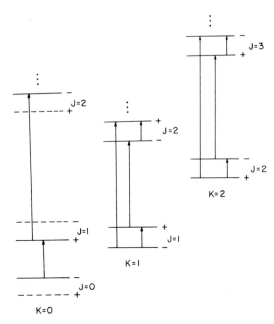

FIG. 7-2. Symmetric top transitions involving inversion. The dashed levels may or may not be present.

for the interchange of two protons. Because spin functions of symmetry A_2 do not exist for NH_3, levels which have even J values possess only antisymmetric inversion levels and odd J levels have only symmetric inversion levels. For ND_3 both A_1 and A_2 spin functions exist and none of the levels vanish for $K = 0$. The levels for $|K| = 3$ are treated in Section 7-8.

7-4a. Some Potential Functions for the Twofold Inversion Barrier

Interest in the inversion spectrum of the ammonia molecule has led a number of investigators to postulate potential functions which attempt to fit the experimental results of the observed spectrum. The ammonia molecule has been the object of this effort because NH_3 is a symmetric top and the inversion motion can be assumed to occur parallel to or symmetrically about the symmetry axis. This approximation allows the problem to be reduced to one dimension, a suitable coordinate along the molecular axis. The inversion problem can be formulated in terms of a single particle moving under the influence of a twofold potential but restrained to a single coordinate.

Hund [759] first approached this type of molecular model and showed that the vibrational levels of such a system occur in pairs when under the influence of a twofold potential. It is important to relate observables such as the pure inversion frequency, the energy separation of the pairs of levels, and the details of the equilibrium molecular structure to the shape and height of the potential barrier. The next sections review some methods which have been used to formulate a twofold potential for ammonia.

7-4b. Morse–Stuckelberg Potential

One of the first functions to be applied to the double-minimum problem has the algebraic form [760]

$$V(X) = \frac{X^6}{12X_0^4} - \frac{1}{4}X^2 + \frac{1}{6}X_0^2 \tag{7-9}$$

X is a dimensionless coordinate related to the physical coordinate x by

$$x = \left[\frac{\hbar}{2\pi\mu v} \right]^{1/2} X \tag{7-10}$$

μ and v are the reduced mass and vibrational frequency, respectively. X_0 represents the coordinate of the equilibrium position. The main disadvantage of this potential function is its tendency to cause x_0 to increase to large values as the barrier height increases. Near the minima, (7-9) shows large deviations from a parabola, and an agreement for the energy levels occurs only with physically unreasonable combinations of barrier height and x_0 values [814].

7-4c. Dennison–Uhlenbeck Potential

Dennison and Uhlenbeck have treated the double minimum problem through the Wentzel–Kramers–Brillouin approximation [761]. The W.K.B. approach involves the coupling of two separate solutions of the wave equation at the boundaries between regions of classical and nonclassical behavior. Let

$$P = +[2\mu|E - V|]^{1/2} \tag{7-11}$$

E is the total energy, V is the barrier height, and μ is the mass of the system. In the classically allowed regions of the potential function, the eigenfunction is oscillatory in nature.

$$\psi(x) = \frac{c}{\sqrt{P}} \cos\left[\frac{1}{\hbar} \int P \, dx + \gamma \right] \tag{7-12}$$

In the classically forbidden regions, the solution has an exponential form.

$$\psi(x) = \frac{a}{\sqrt{P}} \exp\left[\frac{1}{\hbar} \int P \, dx\right] + \frac{b}{\sqrt{P}} \exp\left[-\frac{1}{\hbar} \int P \, dx\right] \qquad (7\text{-}13)$$

a, b, c, and γ are arbitrary constants, and x is the coordinate of the system. The relationships between the adjustable parameters which fit the solutions at the boundary regions are the Kramers connection formulas [994].

The potential function is an even function of x, and the eigenfunctions are either even or odd functions of x. Even functions are denoted as $\psi^+_{(x)}$ and the odd functions as $\psi^-_{(x)}$. The energy values corresponding to these solutions are E^+ and E^-. The inversion splitting of any pair of these levels is $\Delta = E^- - E^+$. After satisfying the odd and even solutions at the boundaries, it is possible to derive an expression for Δ_n of the nth pair of levels.

$$\Delta_n = \frac{\hbar}{\mu A_n^2} \int_{x_1}^{x_2} \frac{dx}{[2\mu|E_n - V|]^{1/2}} \qquad (7\text{-}14)$$

$$A_n = \exp\left[\frac{1}{\hbar} \int_0^{x_1} P_n \, dx\right] \qquad (7\text{-}15)$$

x_1 and x_2 are the intersection points of the energy level with energy E and the potential function which is symmetrical about $x = 0$. The two innermost intersections occur at $\pm x_1$ and the outermost intersections occur at $\pm x_2$. If the potential function is assumed to be harmonic between x_1 and x_2, then a classical frequency v may be designated as the frequency of transition between each adjacent pair of levels. For such a harmonic system

$$2\mu \int_{x_1}^{x_2} \frac{dx}{[2\mu|E - V|]^{1/2}} = \frac{1}{v} \qquad (7\text{-}16)$$

$$\frac{\Delta_n}{hv} = \frac{1}{\pi A_n^2} \qquad (7\text{-}17)$$

The inversion splitting in this degree of approximation does not depend on the shape of the potential function but does depend on the area in the nonclassical region between $x = 0$ and $x = x_1$. v_2, the parallel vibration which is directly associated with the inversion, Δ_0, and Δ_1 are used to fit the potential. v_2 must be used to determine the shape of the potential near the two minima and Δ_0 and Δ_1 are used to determine the area under the curve in the classically forbidden region. The potential function consists of a pair of parabolae connected by a straight line (Fig. 7-3). $2(x_0 - \alpha)$ is the length of the joining line, and $2x_0$ is the distance between the minima. This curve allows the calculation of Δ_n as a function of α and x_0.

$$\frac{\Delta_n}{hv_2} = \frac{1}{\pi}\left[\frac{\alpha + (\alpha^2 - 2n - 1)^{1/2}}{(2n + 1)^{1/2}}\right]^{2n+1} \exp[-(2x_0 - \alpha)(\alpha^2 - 2n - 1)^{1/2}] \qquad (7\text{-}18)$$

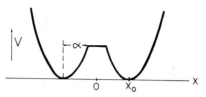

Fɪɢ. 7-3. Dennison–Uhlenbeck potential function for ammonia [761].

Success of the W.K.B. approximation in this case can be checked against asymptotically correct solutions for Δ_0 and Δ_1.

$$\Delta_0 = \frac{2\alpha h v_2}{\pi^{1/2}} \exp[-\alpha^2 - 2(x_0 - \alpha)(\alpha^2 - 1)^{1/2}] \qquad (7\text{-}19)$$

$$\Delta_1 = \frac{h v_2(4\alpha^3 - 4\alpha)}{\pi^{1/2}} \exp[-\alpha^2 - 2(x_0 - \alpha)(\alpha^2 - 3)^{1/2}] \qquad (7\text{-}20)$$

In the case of ammonia the agreement between (7-18) and (7-19–20) is within 10 percent; for large values of x_0 and α the agreement is considerably improved. The W.K.B. approximation is best applied to energy states with large values of the quantum number n. It is not optimum for lower energy states or in cases where the upper state of an inversion pair is near the top of the barrier.

7-4d. Rosen–Morse Potential

The W.K.B. method was employed by Dennison and Uhlenbeck because the normal use of perturbation theory on any exact solutions of the Schroedinger equation would have involved excessively large perturbation energies. Rosen and Morse [762] proposed developing exact solutions for potential fields more closely resembling those present in the real molecule. Their potential field, using the constants B, C, and d, has the form

$$V(x) = B \tanh\left(\frac{x}{d}\right) - C \operatorname{sech}^2\left(\frac{x}{d}\right) \qquad (7\text{-}21)$$

and is pictured in Fig. 7-4. The wave equation is

$$\frac{d^2\psi}{dz^2} + (-e - \beta \tanh z + \gamma \operatorname{sech}^2 z)\psi = 0 \qquad (7\text{-}22)$$

$z = (x/d)$ and e is a constant related to the energy. The solution is a function of the hypergeometric series $F(z)$.

$$\psi(z) = (\cosh^{-b} x)F(z)\exp(az) \qquad (7\text{-}23)$$

a, b, β, and γ are constants. For $\gamma \gg 1$ and small values of the vibrational

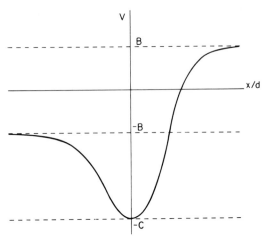

FIG. 7-4. Form of the Rosen–Morse potential function given in (7-21). B and C are positive. The conditions governing B, C, k and d are discussed by Rosen and Morse [762].

quantum number n, the energy levels can be expressed as an expansion in $(n + \frac{1}{2})$.

$$E_n = V(x_0) + hv_0\left(n + \frac{1}{2}\right) - \left(\frac{h^2}{2\mu d^2}\right)\left(1 + \frac{3B^2}{8C^2}\right)\left(n + \frac{1}{2}\right)^2 + \cdots \quad (7\text{-}24)$$

μ is related to the reduced mass and v_0 is the classical frequency of oscillation about the minimum at x_0.

The wave functions are assumed to satisfy a one-dimensional wave equation along the x axis.

$$\frac{d^2\psi}{dx^2} + \left(\frac{8\pi^2\mu}{h^2}\right)(E - V(x))\psi = 0 \quad (7\text{-}25)$$

The potential function consists of two curves $V(x)$ which are joined symmetrically.

$$V(x) = \begin{cases} B\tanh\left(\dfrac{x}{d} - k\right) - C\operatorname{sech}^2\left(\dfrac{x}{d} - k\right), & x \geq 0 \quad (7\text{-}26) \\[2ex] -B\tanh\left(\dfrac{x}{d} + k\right) - C\operatorname{sech}^2\left(\dfrac{x}{d} + k\right), & x \leq 0 \end{cases}$$

$$x_0 = kd - \tanh^{-1}\left(\frac{B}{2C}\right) \quad (7\text{-}27)$$

The energies of the inversion sublevels are

$$E_n^{\pm} = E_n + \int_0^{\infty} [\psi_n(x + kd)]^2 V(x)\, dx \pm \int_0^{\infty} \psi_n(x - kd)V(x)\psi_n(-x - kd)\, dx \quad (7\text{-}28)$$

where E_n is the vibrational energy. If the levels lie well below the top of the barrier, Δ_n is much less than the separation between the sets of levels.

$$\Delta_n = 2 \int_0^\infty \psi_n(x - kd) V(x) \psi_n(-x - kd) \, dx \tag{7-29}$$

This splitting can be calculated because the form of ψ_n is known. Using the gamma function,

$$\Delta_0 = \frac{4\Gamma(2b) \exp(-2ak)}{\Gamma(a + b)\Gamma(a - b)(2 \cosh k)^{2b}} \left[\frac{2C \tanh k}{b + 1} - \frac{B}{b} \right] \tag{7-30}$$

$$\Delta_1 = \frac{2\Gamma(2b + 2)}{\Gamma(a + b)\Gamma(a - b)(2 \cosh k)^{2b}} \left[\frac{\exp(-2ak)}{(2a^2 + b)(b + 1)^2 - a^2 b(1 + 2b)} \right]$$

$$\times \left\{ 2C \left[\left(\frac{a^2 - (b + 1)^2}{b + 1} + \frac{(b + 1)^2}{b + 2} \right) \tanh k + \frac{2a(b + 1)}{b + 2} \tanh^2 k \right. \right.$$

$$\left. + \frac{(b + 1)^2}{b + 2} \tanh^3 k \right]$$

$$\left. - B \left[\frac{a^2 - b - 1}{b} + 2a \tanh k + (b + 1) \tanh^2 k \right] \right\} \tag{7-31}$$

The energy separation between the first two sets of inversion levels is

$$E_1 - E_0 = 2g(C + g^2/4)^{1/2} - 2g^2 - \left(\frac{B^2}{4} \right) \frac{g(4C + g^2)^{1/2} - g^2}{C + g^2 - g(4C + g^2)^{1/2}} \tag{7-32}$$

where

$$g^2 = \frac{\hbar^2}{4\mu \, d^2} \tag{7-33}$$

7-4e. Manning Potential

With improved experimental data available for NH_3 and ND_3, Manning [763] proposed a potential function which has the expected physical form and allows an exact solution of the Schroedinger equation (Fig. 7-5).

$$V(x) = \frac{1}{k\rho^2} \left[-\frac{\beta}{2} \left(\frac{\beta}{2} + \frac{1}{2} \right) \mathrm{sech}^2 \frac{x}{2\rho} - D \left(\mathrm{sech}^2 \frac{x}{2\rho} - \mathrm{sech}^4 \frac{x}{2\rho} \right) \right] \tag{7-34}$$

ρ, β, and D are arbitrary constants and x is the distance between the nitrogen atom and the plane of the hydrogen atoms.

$$k = \frac{8\pi^2 c\mu}{h} \tag{7-35}$$

μ is the reduced mass related to the inversion motion. The barrier height

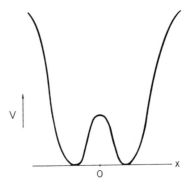

Fig. 7-5. Form of the Manning potential function given by (7-34).

V is zero at $x = \pm\infty$ and

$$V = -\frac{1}{k\rho^2}\frac{\beta}{2}\left(\frac{\beta}{2} + \frac{1}{2}\right) \qquad (7\text{-}36)$$

at $x = 0$. The minimum values of V occur at $\pm x_0$.

$$\text{sech}^2\frac{x_0}{2\rho} = \frac{(\beta/2)(\beta/2 + \frac{1}{2}) + D}{2D} \qquad (7\text{-}37)$$

This makes the effective barrier height

$$V_{\text{eff}} = \frac{1}{k\rho^2}\frac{[D - (\beta/2)(\beta/2 + \frac{1}{2})]^2}{4D} \qquad (7\text{-}38)$$

Using continued fraction techniques it was found that (7-34) gives energy level differences in good agreement with those observed experimentally for NH_3 and ND_3. Approximate barrier heights of 2072 cm^{-1} for NH_3 and 2068 cm^{-1} for ND_3 were obtained.

7-4f. Wall–Glocker Potential

The potential function [764]

$$V(x) = \tfrac{1}{2}k[|x| - l]^2 \qquad (7\text{-}39)$$

has been applied to the ammonia molecule for an approximate calculation of the inversion splitting. Figure 7-6 shows the singularity at $x = 0$. The wave functions for the two lowest sets of levels are

$$\psi_0^\pm = N_0^\pm[\exp(-b(x - l)^2) \pm \exp(-b(x + l)^2)] \qquad (7\text{-}40)$$

$$\psi_1^\pm = N_1^\pm[(x - l)\exp(-b(x - l)^2) \mp (x + l)\exp(-b(x + l)^2)]$$

$$\pm \frac{l\exp(-2bl^2)}{1 \pm \exp(-2bl^2)}[\exp(-b(x - l)^2) \pm \exp(-b(x + l)^2)] \qquad (7\text{-}41)$$

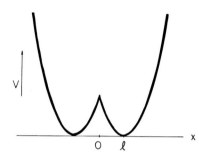

FIG. 7-6. Wall–Glocker potential function [764].

In (7-40) and (7-41) the $+$ refers to the symmetric wave function and the $-$ labels the antisymmetric function. The last term in (7-41) preserves the orthogonality condition. N represents the normalizing factor, k is a force constant, and

$$b = \frac{\pi}{h}(k\mu)^{1/2} \tag{7-42}$$

for a harmonic oscillator. If the last term in (7-41) is neglected, and

$$q^2 = 2bl^2 \tag{7-43a}$$

$$v_0 = \frac{1}{2\pi}\left(\frac{k}{\mu}\right)^{1/2} \tag{7-43b}$$

the first four energy levels are given as

$$E_0^+ = \frac{hv_0}{2}\left[1 + \frac{2q^2 - (4q^2/(\pi)^{1/2})\int_0^q \exp(-n^2)\,dn - (4/(\pi)^{1/2})q\exp(-q^2)}{1 + \exp(-q^2)}\right] \tag{7-44}$$

$$E_0^- = \frac{hv_0}{2}\left[1 + \frac{2q^2 - (4q^2/(\pi)^{1/2})\int_0^q \exp(-n^2)\,dn}{1 - \exp(-q^2)}\right] \tag{7-45}$$

$$E_1^+ = \frac{3hv_0}{2}\left[1 + \frac{2q^2 - (4q^2/(\pi)^{1/2})\int_0^q \exp(-n^2)\,dn - (4q^3/(\pi)^{1/2})\exp(-q^2)}{3[1 - (1 - 2q^2)\exp(-q^2)]}\right] \tag{7-46}$$

$$E_1^- = \frac{3hv_0}{2}$$

$$\times\left[1 + \frac{\begin{array}{c}2q^2 - (4q^2/(\pi)^{1/2})\int_0^q \exp(-n^2)\,dn \\ -(8/(\pi)^{1/2})q\exp(-q^2) + (4q^3/(\pi)^{1/2})\exp(-q^2)\end{array}}{3[1 + (1 - 2q^2)\exp(-q^2)]}\right] \tag{7-47}$$

The barrier height is

$$V(x = 0) = \frac{hv_0}{2} q^2 \qquad (7\text{-}48)$$

Results obtained from this potential are very approximate; it yields a potential barrier for ammonia which is about 50% too high.

7-4g. Newton–Thomas Potential

Newton and Thomas [771] have applied a general treatment for the separation of low and high frequency vibrations to the inversion of ammonia. The motion is assumed to consist of high frequency vibrations taking place in a system whose configuration is slowly changing. The double-minimum vibrational frequency is assumed to be low compared to the other vibrations in the molecule. Through the use of a one-dimensional Sturm-Liouville equation and the associated Mathieu equation, the potential function has the form

$$V(x) = \frac{K(a + bx^2)^2}{(1 + x^2)^2} \qquad (7\text{-}49)$$

K, a, and b are constants and $V(x)$ has its maximum at $x = 0$.

$$V_{max} = Ka^2 \qquad (7\text{-}50)$$

The minimum falls at $V = 0$ for $x = (a/b)^{1/2}$. As $x \to \infty$, V approaches

$$V_\infty = Kb^2 \qquad (7\text{-}51)$$

A fit comparable to that from the Manning potential was obtained for ammonia. However, the values calculated for the first excited state are not satisfactory.

7-4h. Sutherland–Costain Potential

For ammonia-type molecules, Costain and Sutherland formulated a potential function based on vibrational force constants. The inversion motion for pyramidal XY_3 symmetric tops is chosen as the symmetrical deformation in which the apical $Y-X-Y$ angle opens symmetrically to 120° in the planar configuration. Only minor changes are assumed to take place in the bond lengths. The potential takes the form [779]

$$V = \tfrac{3}{2}[K_l(\Delta l)^2 + K_\delta(\Delta\alpha)^2] \qquad (7\text{-}52)$$

Δl is the change in $X-Y$ bond length and $\Delta\alpha$ is the change in the apex angle. The force constants K_l and K_δ are obtained from vibrational data. A relationship between Δl and $\Delta\alpha$ displacements allows the potential to be written as

$$V = A(\Delta\alpha)^2 \tag{7-53}$$

A is to be determined. $(\Delta\alpha)_{max}$ is the difference between 120° and the equilibrium bond angle; the barrier height is the change in V between these two angles. Relations between the $X-Y$ stretching frequency ω_1, the symmetrical deformation ω_2, and the force constants are

$$4\pi^2(\omega_1^2 + \omega_2^2)m_y = K_l\left(1 + \frac{3m_y}{m_x}\cos^2\beta\right) + \frac{K_\delta}{l^2}\frac{12\cos^2\beta}{(1 + 3\cos^2\beta)}\left(1 + \frac{3m_y}{m_x}\sin^2\beta\right)$$

$$\tag{7-54}$$

and

$$16\pi^4\omega_1^2\omega_2^2 = \frac{K_l K_\delta}{l^2}\frac{12\cos^2\beta}{(1 + 3\cos^2\beta)}\left(1 + \frac{3m_y}{m_x}\right) \tag{7-55}$$

β is the angle between the symmetry axis and the $X-Y$ bond. Choosing the symmetry coordinates S_1 and S_2 so that

$$\Delta l = pS_1 - sS_2 \tag{7-56}$$

and

$$\Delta\beta = dS_2 - fS_1 \tag{7-57}$$

the value of A can be calculated. p, s, d, and f are functions of the molecular constants. For NH_3 this gives (in cm^{-1}),

$$V(\alpha) = 3.89 \times 10^4(\Delta\alpha)^2 \tag{7-58}$$

If the potential function is transformed so that the energy can be plotted as a function of pyramid height h, the Costain–Sutherland potential follows the Manning potential form very closely. The values of Δ_0 and Δ_1 calculated from $V(\alpha)$ compare favorably with the experimentally observed quantities. Also, (7-52) has been used to predict the inversion splittings and barrier heights in phosphine and arsine.

7-4i. Harmonic Oscillator Perturbed by a Gaussian Barrier

It is convenient to write the vibrational potential energy as a power series in the coordinate x.

$$V(x) = \sum_n \tfrac{1}{2}a_n x^n \tag{7-59}$$

Because the potential energy governing the inversion motion treated in this chapter is assumed to be symmetrical about $x = 0$, the odd coefficients in V vanish. The factor $\frac{1}{2}$ has been included so that a_2 can be directly identified with the harmonic potential constant which is usually expressed as k.

Matrix elements for the harmonic oscillator problem are well known [21]. In terms of x and its conjugate momentum p, the harmonic oscillator energy is

$$H = \frac{\hbar^2}{2\mu}p^2 + \tfrac{1}{2}kx^2 \tag{7-60}$$

By perturbing the harmonic oscillator with a Gaussian barrier term, the double-minimum problem can be treated in a way which is adaptable to high speed machine calculations. The Gaussian-perturbed potential energy is then

$$V(x) = \tfrac{1}{2}kx^2 + v\exp(-cx^2) \tag{7-61}$$

Because vibrations associated with double-minimum potentials may be highly anharmonic, it may be necessary to add higher terms in x to the potential function. The Hamiltonian for the problem then becomes

$$H = \frac{\hbar^2 p^2}{2\mu} + \frac{1}{2}kx^2 + \frac{1}{2}bx^4 + v\exp(-cx^2) \tag{7-62}$$

k, b, c and v are potential constants. The problem may be nondimensionalized by applying a transformation to form a new set of variables. One possible transformation is given by

$$P = \left(\frac{\hbar^2}{\mu k}\right)^{1/4} p \tag{7-63}$$

and

$$X = \left(\frac{\mu k}{\hbar^2}\right)^{1/4} x \tag{7-64}$$

The dimensionless Hamiltonian is then obtained by dividing (7-62) by the harmonic oscillator energy $h\nu_0$.

$$H = \tfrac{1}{2}P^2 + \tfrac{1}{2}X^2 + \tfrac{1}{2}BX^4 + V\exp(-CX^2) \tag{7-65}$$

$$B = b\varepsilon/k^2 \tag{7-66a}$$

$$V = v/\varepsilon \tag{7-66b}$$

$$C = c\varepsilon/k \tag{7-66c}$$

$$\varepsilon = h\nu_0 = (k\hbar^2/\mu)^{1/2} \tag{7-66d}$$

If desired, the factor $\tfrac{1}{2}$ of P^2 and X^2 could be removed by including it in the transformation. The matrix elements of P^2, X^2, and X^4 in the harmonic oscillator representation are known.

$$\langle n|P^2|n\rangle = n + \tfrac{1}{2} \tag{7-67a}$$

$$\langle n|X^2|n\rangle = n + \tfrac{1}{2} \tag{7-67b}$$

$$\langle n|X^4|n\rangle = \tfrac{1}{4}(6n^2 + 6n + 3) \tag{7-67c}$$

$$\langle n|P^2|n + 2\rangle = -\tfrac{1}{2}[(n + 1)(n + 2)]^{1/2} \tag{7-67d}$$

$$\langle n|X^2|n + 2\rangle = \tfrac{1}{2}[(n + 1)(n + 2)]^{1/2} \tag{7-67e}$$

$$\langle n|X^4|n + 2\rangle = (2n + 3)[(n + 1)(n + 2)]^{1/2} \tag{7-67f}$$

$$\langle n|X^4|n + 4\rangle = \tfrac{1}{4}[(n + 1)(n + 2)(n + 3)(n + 4)]^{1/4} \tag{7-67g}$$

Prior to matrix diagonalization, the only remaining problem is the evaluation of matrix elements of $V \exp(-CX^2)$ in a harmonic oscillator representation. Three approaches have been used which all require a knowledge of the Hermite polynomials characteristic of harmonic oscillator problems. The matrix elements of the exponential terms may be calculated term by term through direct integration using the wave functions

$$\psi_n = N_n H_n \exp(-\tfrac{1}{2}X^2) \tag{7-68}$$

H_n is the nth Hermite polynomial, and N_n is a normalizing factor. The elements for the Gaussian barrier are then given as

$$\langle n|V \exp(-CX^2)|m\rangle = V N_n N_m \int_{-\infty}^{+\infty} H_n(X)H_m(X) \exp[-(1 + C)X^2]\, dX \tag{7-69}$$

The infinite energy matrix can be truncated to a finite order; in favorable cases the lower energy levels are relatively unaffected by the truncation.

Another method involves the use of the generating function for Hermite polynomials [1018]. The matrix elements are evaluated by matching appropriate power series expansion coefficients. Chan and Stelman [813] have simplified the method for determining the matrix elements of $\exp(-CX^2)$ in a harmonic oscillator representation. In closed form, the matrix elements are

$$\langle n|\exp(-CX^2)|m\rangle = 0 \tag{7-70}$$

for n even (odd), m odd (even), and

$$\langle n|\exp(-CX^2)|m\rangle = \left[\frac{n!\,m!}{(1 + C)2^n 2^m}\right]^{1/2} \sum_{l=0,2,\ldots}^{n} \frac{(-\theta)^{(n+m)/2-l}\kappa^l}{l!\left[\dfrac{m-l}{2}\right]!\left[\dfrac{n-l}{2}\right]!} \tag{7-71}$$

for $n < m$ and even.

$$\kappa = 2/(1 + C) \tag{7-72a}$$

$$\theta = C/(1 + C) \tag{7-72b}$$

For m and n odd, an identical expression holds with $l = 1, 3, \ldots$. A recursion relation between the matrix elements facilitates their calculation. This type of relationship is useful because the large numbers which may be encountered in evaluating the coefficients of (7-71) for large matrices can be avoided. Because the commutator of X and $\exp(-CX^2)$ vanishes, the recursion formula becomes

$$n^{1/2}\langle n - 1|\exp(-CX^2)|m\rangle + (n + 1)^{1/2}\langle n + 1|\exp(-CX^2)|m\rangle$$
$$- m^{1/2}\langle n|\exp(-CX^2)|m - 1\rangle - (m + 1)^{1/2}\langle n|\exp(-CX^2)|m + 1\rangle = 0$$
$$(7\text{-}73)$$

This follows from the matrix elements

$$\langle n|X|n\rangle = 0 \tag{7-74a}$$

$$\langle n|X|n + 1\rangle = [\tfrac{1}{2}(n + 1)]^{1/2} \tag{7-74b}$$

$$\langle n|X|n - 1\rangle = (n/2)^{1/2} \tag{7-74c}$$

The transformation connecting (7-62) and (7-65) can be used to relate these elements to p and x. The recursion formula generates the matrix through two independent lattices pictured in Fig. 7-7; however, only one of the lattices proves to be nonvanishing.

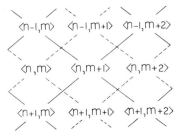

FIG. 7-7. Illustration of the matrix elements connected by the recursion relation (7-73). Even-even elements are connected to odd-odd elements and even-odd elements are connected to odd-even elements.

The classical motion undergone by NH_3 during the inversion is not described by a single normal mode but by some combination of the normal coordinates. Since the reduced mass μ is dependent on the normal mode, the ratio of the reduced masses of NH_3 and ND_3 is not exactly known. Swalen and Ibers [810] chose to carry this ratio as a variable. Data available on ammonia allowed the first fourteen energy levels to be calculated using four or five variables. The parameters were the reduced mass ratio, the harmonic force constant, the barrier height, the equilibrium angle between the

N—H bond and the plane of the hydrogens, and the quartic anharmonicity term (when a fifth variable was used). The results compared favorably with those from the Manning and Newton–Thomas potentials. The improved agreement of the Gaussian perturbed harmonic oscillator function obtained for the higher energy levels results because V is a steeper function for large x than the Manning or Newton–Thomas potentials. It was observed that the Manning potential is essentially equivalent to a harmonic oscillator potential with a Gaussian barrier [810]. For ammonia, the quartic anharmonicity term did not yield a significant improvement of the calculated energy levels.

Several advantages of using a harmonic oscillator representation are now apparent. The matrix elements of P^2, X^2, X^4, and $\exp(-CX^2)$ are known. A large number of levels may be treated in one computation which is of a very general form and easily adjusted to high speed digital computers. When the wave functions are also known, other quantities such as transition moments may be obtained.

7-4j. Quartic Oscillator

For some inversion-type vibrations, a high degree of anharmonicity is present and the problem can be conveniently approached in the quartic oscillator representation. Significant quartic contributions may be found for near-planar molecules where a small barrier can produce a highly anharmonic potential containing a dominant quartic term. Although the harmonic oscillator basis is very convenient as a result of the known matrix elements, an anharmonic contribution due to the presence of a nonzero x^4 term may become very important, particularly for higher vibrational levels. If a harmonic oscillator representation is being used, the x^4 term might force the use of a large number of harmonic oscillator basis functions to produce an effective matrix diagonalization for more than just the lowest energy levels.

To avoid this, Chan and Stelman [812] have calculated the first twenty energy levels and wave functions by diagonalizing the pure quartic oscillator

$$H = \frac{h^2}{2\mu}p^2 + \tfrac{1}{2}bx^4 \tag{7-75}$$

in a harmonic oscillator representation. In general, the quartic oscillator eigenfunctions may be expanded in terms of a set of harmonic oscillator functions.

$$\psi_Q = \mathbf{T}^{-1}\psi_H \tag{7-76}$$

where $\mathbf{T}^{-1}$ identifies the expansion coefficients. If the expansion coefficients are known, the quartic oscillator energy levels are calculated by applying this transformation to (7-75) after a change of variables analogous to (7-63) and (7-64).

$$E = sT^{-1}(P^2 + X^4)T \tag{7-77}$$

s is a scalar containing the coordinate-momentum transformation. Conversely, the problem is usually solved by determining the similarity transformation required to diagonalize $P^2 + X^4$, which can then be used to compute the quartic oscillator eigenfunctions. Matrix elements of X, X^2, X^3, X^4, and X^6 have been calculated in the quartic oscillator representation and tabulated for the first twenty levels of a quartic oscillator [812].

7-4k. Mixed Harmonic-Quartic Potential

The quartic oscillator basis can be successfully used to treat the relatively anharmonic low-frequency bending vibrations which characterize near planar molecules through a mixed harmonic-quartic potential function of the form [816a]

$$V(x) = ax^4 - bx^2 \tag{7-78}$$

a and b are positive and the $-bx^2$ term introduces the barrier. When compared with the harmonic oscillator perturbed by a Gaussian barrier, (7-78) exhibits much steeper sides and correspondingly divergent vibrational levels.

7-5. Inversion-Vibration Interactions

For the NH_3 molecule, sufficient experimental data is available to study the dependence of inversion splitting on the vibrational quantum numbers [811]. Table 7-1 lists a summary of some of the data. The potential energy consists of a double-minimum function for the inversion mode and five uncoupled harmonic oscillators representing the remaining vibrational degrees of freedom.

$$V = V_0(x) + \tfrac{1}{2}\sum_{=1}^{5} c_i q_i^2 \tag{7-79}$$

The summation is over the remaining vibrational modes excluding the inversion, and q_i is the appropriate vibrational coordinate. The form of the inversion potential used by Weeks *et al.* [811] is

$$V_0(x) = -2F \cos\left(\frac{x}{L}\right) + 2G \cos\left(\frac{2x}{L}\right) \tag{7-80}$$

for $|x| \le \pi L$ and

$$V_0(x) = 2(F + G) \tag{7-81}$$

TABLE 7-1

VIBRATION-INVERSION DEPENDENCE IN NH$_3$[a]

v_1	v_2	$v_3^{l_3}$	$v_4^{l_4}$	Δ (cm^{-1})
0	0	0^0	0^0	0.793
0	1	0^0	0^0	35.81
0	2	0^0	0^0	284.74
0	3	0^0	0^0	512.02
0	0	1^1	0^0	0.35
0	0	2^2	0^0	0.43
0	0	0^0	1^1	1.01
0	0	0^0	2^0	2.24
0	0	0^0	2^2	1.42
0	0	1^1	1^1	0.57
1	0	0^0	0^0	0.99
1	0	0^0	1^1	0.86
0	1	1^1	0^0	18.49
0	1	0^0	1^1	45.4
0	1	1^1	1^1	23.68
1	1	0^0	0^0	25.55

[a] From Ref. [811].

for $\pi L < |x| \leq \pi/2$. F, G, and L are positive, and the two minima occur at $\cos(x_0/L) = F/4G$. F and G are assumed to be mild functions of the other vibrational modes of the molecule and can be expanded in a Taylor series for small vibrational amplitudes.

The barrier height is given by $4G(1 - F/4G)^2$. This potential function generates relatively simple wave functions for a perturbation calculation; however, its behavior at large x allows it to be used only for the lowest energy levels.

7-6. Reduced Mass for NH$_3$-like Symmetric Tops

The potential function for inversion in a symmetric top molecule is a function of the reduced mass of the molecule, which, in turn, is a function of the path taken during the classical inversion motion. The possible forms of the reduced mass for NH$_3$ are of the most interest. Two extreme motions can be defined which probably set the limits for the actual inversion mode. In one case it may be assumed that the N—H bond length remains constant and only the H—N—H angle changes. The resulting expression for the reduced mass is

$$\mu = [3m/(M + 3m)](M + 3m \sin^2 \theta_e) \tag{7-82}$$

θ_e is the equilibrium H—N—H angle, M is the mass of the nitrogen, and m

is the hydrogen mass. Alternatively, it may be assumed that the hydrogen-hydrogen distance remains constant and the nitrogen-hydrogen distance changes. In this case

$$\mu = 3mM/(M + 3m) \qquad (7\text{-}83)$$

This simplified form is possible because the motion is one-dimensional. Figure 7-8 illustrates these two modes of inversion. The actual reduced

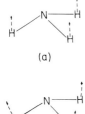

(a)

(b)

FIG. 7-8. Two possible classical inversion paths for ammonia. In (a) the H atoms form a "rigid" triangle and move normal to the plane formed by their equilibrium positions. In (b) the N–H distance remains constant.

mass is a function of some combination of these two modes. Using the reduced mass ratio k, defined by Swalen and Ibers as $\mu(ND_3)/\mu(NH_3)$, the former model gives $k = 1.3219$ and the latter gives $k = 1.3029$.

It appears that a majority of the actual reduced mass is contributed by a motion which is predominately an angle bend as shown in Fig. 7–8(b).

7-7. Rotational Dependence of Inversion Splittings in Symmetric Tops

The pure inversion transitions of ammonia were observed to have some dependence on the rotational quantum numbers J and K (similar to the dependence of the centrifugal distortion effects studied in Chapter 3). From (2-48) and (2-49) for the energy of a symmetric top, an expression

$$\Delta_{JK} = \Delta_0 + aJ(J + 1) + bK^2 + cJ^2(J + 1)^2 + dJ(J + 1)K^2 + \cdots \qquad (7\text{-}84)$$

can be written to include as many terms as are necessary to fit the observed spectrum. Most of the symmetric top potential functions discussed above can be adapted to the rotational dependence through a semiempirical function of the rotational constants. One of the best agreements for ammonia was obtained by Costain [776], who applied the exponential dependence of the inversion splittings in the Uhlenbeck–Dennison potential. From (7-18),

$$\Delta_{JK} = \Delta_0 \exp[AJ(J + 1) + BK^2 + CJ^2(J + 1)^2 + DJ(J + 1)K^2 + EK^4]$$

(7-85)

All except the $|K| = 3$ lines are well determined with this type of expression. By applying the corrections for $|K| = 3$ lines developed by Nielsen and Dennison [769] the deviations are well explained.

7-8. $|K| = 3$ Inversion Transitions in Ammonia

Semiempirical expressions used to fit the rotational dependence of pure inversion transitions of ammonia apparently fail for the $|K| = 3$ lines. When J is even for $|K| = 3$, the predicted frequency in NH_3 is low; for odd J, the predicted value is larger than the observed frequency. The magnitude of the deviation increases with J and is explained by a high order vibration-rotation interaction which lifts the K degeneracy for $|K| = 3$ levels.

For levels where K is a multiple of 3, the rotational wave functions belong to the irreducible representations A_1 and A_2 of symmetry group C_{3v}. When K is neither zero nor a multiple of 3, the wave functions are doubly degenerate and belong to E. No perturbation generated by interactions produced within the molecule itself can lift the degeneracy of the E levels. The A_1 and A_2 levels are symmetric and antisymmetric, respectively, for the interchange of two identical hydrogen atoms and can be split by a vibration-rotation interaction. Figure 7-9 shows (a) the evolution of an energy level for ND_3 through a finite inversion splitting in (b) and lifting of the K degeneracy in (c). For NH_3, one of the levels in each K doublet vanishes as a result of the Pauli principle and only one transition is observed.

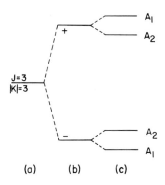

FIG. 7-9. Splitting of the $J = 3$, $|K| = 3$ level of ND_3 under the influence of inversion in (b) and as a result of K doubling in (c).

For ND_3, spin functions of both nondegenerate symmetries A_1 and A_2 can exist; for NH_3, no spin functions of A_2 symmetry are formed. In order for ψ_{total} of NH_3 to be antisymmetric for the exchange of two protons in a symmetric vibrational state, the rotational wave function ψ_R must belong to A_2 and the A_1 rotational transitions must vanish. Because both A_1 and A_2 spin functions exist for ND_3, a K doublet appears for $|K| = 3$ transitions. The energy matrix $\langle JK|H|J'K'\rangle$ is diagonal in J and K for a rigid symmetric rotor. However, nonrigid effects introduce elements connecting K and $K \pm 3i$, where i is an integer governed by $|K| \leq J$. The perturbing matrix elements $\langle JK \pm 3|H|JK \mp 3\rangle$ appear in the fourth order and are produced by the first-order correction terms for the moments of inertia and the Coriolis interaction. For $J = 3$, the matrix has the form (suppressing J)

$$\begin{bmatrix} \langle 3|H|3\rangle - \lambda & \langle 3|H|0\rangle & \langle 3|H| - 3\rangle \\ \langle 3|H|0\rangle & \langle 0|H|0\rangle - \lambda & \langle -3|H|0\rangle \\ \langle 3|H| - 3\rangle & \langle -3|H|0\rangle & \langle -3|H| - 3\rangle - \lambda \end{bmatrix} = 0 \qquad (7\text{-}86)$$

$\langle 3|H|0\rangle$-type terms contribute to the energies in sixth order and can be neglected. If the two roots for $|K| = 3$ are designated as E_3^+ and E_3^-,

$$E_3^+ \approx \langle 3|H|3\rangle + \langle 3|H| - 3\rangle \qquad (7\text{-}87a)$$

$$E_3^- \approx \langle 3|H|3\rangle - \langle 3|H| - 3\rangle \qquad (7\text{-}87b)$$

The corresponding wave functions may be defined as ψ_3^+ and ψ_3^-. When J is even, ψ_3^+ belongs to A_1 and ψ_3^- to A_2. For J odd, the reverse is true. The splitting is observable for $|K| = 3$ but is much smaller for $|K| = 6$ and for higher multiples of 3. Therefore, the apparent deviations of the $|K| = 3$ transitions in NH_3 are produced by the splitting of the two $|K| = 3$ components and vanishing of one of them as a result of the Pauli principle.

Nielsen and Dennison [769] derived a formula for the doublet splitting of the $|K| = 3$ lines.

$$\Delta v = 2\alpha J(J + 1)[J(J + 1) - 2][J(J + 1) - 6] \qquad (7\text{-}88)$$

α is a vibration-rotation constant.

For molecules where both levels are present, symmetry statistics may aid the identification of the A_1 and A_2 transitions. In ND_3 the $A_1 : A_2$ intensity ratio is $10 : 1$.

7-9a. Inversion in Asymmetric Tops

The greater number of energy levels, complexity of the classical path followed during the inversion, and possibility of more than one set of selection rules make the inversion-rotation spectrum of an asymmetric top somewhat irregular compared to the spectrum of a symmetric top. One approach to the problem is to adopt the potential functions which have been used for symmetric tops, because the basic twofold symmetry properties of the barrier are essentially unchanged. The reduced mass can then be derived for the most likely classical path. Additional information is often provided by isotopic substitution and vibrational spectra.

7-9b. Selection Rules for Asymmetric Tops

The selection rules on J are still given by $\Delta J = 0, \pm 1$, and the pseudo-quantum numbers K_{-1} and K_1 are governed by the rules in Table 2-8. The appropriate dipole matrix element is given by

$$\langle i|\mathbf{\mu}|j\rangle = \int \psi_{R,i}^* \psi_{inv,i}^* \mathbf{\mu} \psi_{R',j} \psi_{inv,j} \, d\tau \tag{7-89}$$

ψ_R represents an asymmetric rotor wave function and ψ_{inv} is a vibrational wave function for the inversion. In factored form, the matrix element becomes

$$\langle i|\mathbf{\mu}|j\rangle = \int \psi_{R,i}^* \phi_{Fg} \psi_{R',j} \, d\tau \int \psi_{inv,i}^* \mu_g \psi_{inv,j} \, d\tau \tag{7-90}$$

μ_g is averaged over the nuclear, electronic, and vibrational (except ψ_{inv}) wave functions. Both integrals in (7-90) must be nonvanishing for an inversion-rotation transition to be allowed.

First consider the inversion integral of the dipole moment

$$\langle i|\mathbf{\mu}|j\rangle_{inv} = \int \psi_{inv,i}^* \mu_g \psi_{inv,j} \, d\tau \tag{7-91}$$

$\langle i|\mathbf{\mu}|j\rangle$ must be totally symmetric. If the dipole moment reverses direction during the inversion, μ_g is antisymmetric with the result that $\psi_{inv,i}^*$ and $\psi_{inv,j}$ must have opposite symmetries.

$$+ \leftrightarrow - ; \qquad \pm \nleftrightarrow \pm \tag{7-92}$$

These are identified as type I selection rules. For a molecule in which the g component of the dipole moment does not change direction, the ψ_{inv} have identical symmetries.

$$\pm \leftrightarrow \pm ; \qquad + \nleftrightarrow - \tag{7-93}$$

These are referred to as type II selection rules. In either case, a nonzero rotational matrix element must accompany $\langle i|\mathbf{\mu}|j\rangle_{inv}$. Representing this by

$$\langle i|\phi_{Fg}|j\rangle = \int \psi_{R,i}^* \phi_{Fg} \psi_{R',j} \, d\tau \tag{7-94}$$

it is apparent that if a transition between inversion levels takes place, it must be accompanied by an allowed rotational transition. Figure 7-10 shows transitions for the two types of selection rules; it is apparent that type I selection rules may produce a spectrum quite different from that characteristic of a rigid rotor.

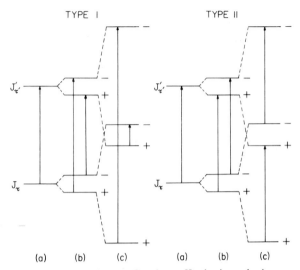

Fig. 7-10. Inversion transitions for type I and type II selection rules in asymmetric rotors: (a) infinite barrier, (b) high barrier, and (c) low barrier. The type II transitions are actually rotational transitions in distinct inversion states.

7-9c. Types of Barriers

The relative height of the inversion barrier plays an important part in determining the structure of the microwave spectrum. Barriers may be classified as high, intermediate, and low. Because the dipole moment usually has components along at least two axes, both types of selection rules for the inversion levels may occur.

If the barrier height is large, and the states being considered are well below the top of the barrier, inversion splittings will be unresolved or relatively small compared to the rotational energy level spacings. Most molecules fall into this category and the vast majority have unresolved splittings. Figure 7-10 shows the high barrier splittings for type I and type II selection rules. In the type I case two transitions, symmetrically spaced about the hypothetical unsplit line (other interactions neglected), are observed in place of every rigid rotor rotational line. The frequency difference between the two inversion-rotation transitions is the sum of the two inversion splittings. For small vibration-rotation interactions the type II lines are nearly coincident. The frequency spacing in this case is just the difference of the inversion splittings in the upper and lower rotational states.

For a barrier which is intermediate in size, the inversion splitting of the individual levels increases appreciably. The result of increased vibration-rotation interaction may lead to a splitting of the type II lines. This would allow direct measurement of the difference in the inversion doubling of the two rotational levels which are connected. The type I splittings would be very large, because the observed frequency difference is twice the rotational frequency when the inversion splitting is greater than the pure rotational spacing.

Some molecules, particularly those which are nearly planar, possess extremely small inversion barriers on the order of a few or tens of cm^{-1}. Transitions arising from type I selection rules move to the infrared. The type II lines may still be observable in the microwave region and appear as strong ground state lines accompanied by satellites. These satellites are the result of low lying vibrational states associated with the out-of-plane motion.

The high barrier case is treated first. Due to the complexity of the problem and the small number of asymmetric molecules exhibiting a resolvable inversion splitting, the theory of inversion in asymmetric tops is not as far advanced as the treatments of internal rotation. The ability to accurately calculate the barrier height is dependent on a knowledge of the vibrational frequencies related to the inversion motion and the inversion splitting in excited vibrational states.

7-9d. Application of Symmetric Top Potential Functions to Asymmetric Tops

If the form of the potential is sufficiently accurate to treat the symmetric ammonias, it seems valid to assume that the potential function does not change appreciably with isotopic substitution for one or two of the hydrogen atoms. Inversion splittings and energy level spacings change, but the height and shape of the potential should be relatively unaltered. With an increase in mass, the inversion splittings are reduced by the slower rate of tunneling through the potential barrier. Weiss and Strandberg [778] have applied the Uhlenbeck–Dennison potential to the asymmetric ammonias. Calculated values for Δ_0, the inversion splitting in the ground state, are good, although the values calculated for Δ_1 are low by 20%. Swalen and Ibers [810] obtained better agreement for the deutero-ammonias with the Gaussian perturbed harmonic oscillator, although Δ_1 was still too low.

In going from the ammonias to the methylamines, the larger mass and structure changes should cause considerable variations in the potential barrier. The potential barrier parameters of ammonia can no longer be used; however, the general form of the hindering potential is probably the same. Care must be taken in defining quantities, such as the reduced mass, which are complicated by the size and asymmetry of the molecule.

7-9e. Reduced Mass for Inversion in an Asymmetric Top

The reduced mass for inversion in an asymmetric top is a function of a more complex motion than in a symmetric top. In a symmetric top, the instantaneous positions of the atoms during the inversion can be assumed to retain the threefold symmetry of the figure axis. In an asymmetric top, the motion may be governed by a lesser symmetry element; e.g., a twofold axis or plane of symmetry, and the actual paths employed by the atoms are more ambiguous. Asymmetric top molecules such as methylamine, di-methylamine, hydrazine, and the asymmetric deuterated ammonias are all of the $X-NH_2$ or X_2-NH type. Derivation of the reduced mass for $X-NH_2$ molecules [805] is given here; extension to the X_2-NH-type follows directly.

Figure 7-11a illustrates the model used in the derivation. X may be a single atom or a group of atoms comprising the remainder of the molecule.

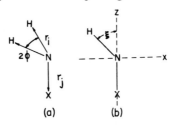

FIG. 7-11. Model for the derivation of the reduced mass of NH_2X molecules. (a) presents the vector model and (b) illustrates the molecule-fixed axis system [805].

r_i is a vector from the nitrogen atom to a hydrogen atom; r_j extends from the nitrogen atom to the center of mass of the group X. 2ϕ is the $H-N-H$ angle, and ξ is the angle between the z axis and the projection of the $N-H$ bond on the plane of symmetry. m_N, m_H, and m_X are the respective masses of N, H, and X. N and H refer to any nitrogen or hydrogen isotopes (as long as both hydrogen isotopes are identical). In the more complicated case of $NHDX$ molecules, the plane of symmetry vanishes and the following treatment must be extended. Figure 7-11b shows the orientation of the system of molecule-fixed axes. The origin lies at the nitrogen atom, the z axis is colinear with the $X-N$ bond, and y is the out-of-plane axis.

If v is the velocity vector of a hydrogen atom, then the components of v in the molecule-fixed system are ($v \cos \alpha$, $v \cos \beta$, $v \cos \gamma$) and the cosine factors are direction cosines of v in the molecule-fixed system. If i, j, and k are unit vectors in the X, Y, Z space-fixed directions, then the velocities in the space-fixed system are

$$V_H = [(v \cos \alpha - v_x k \cos \phi \cos \xi + v_x')i \pm (v \cos \beta)j$$

$$+ (v \cos \gamma - v_x k \cos \phi \sin \xi + v_z')k] \qquad (7\text{-}95)$$

$$V_N = v_x'i + v_z'k \qquad (7\text{-}96)$$

$$V_X = (v_x' + v_j)i + v_z'k \qquad (7\text{-}97)$$

The remaining terms are defined as

$$k = (r_i/r_j) \tag{7-98a}$$

$$v_x' = \{2m_H(lk \cos \phi \cos \xi - \cos \alpha) - lm_x\}\frac{v}{M} \tag{7-98b}$$

$$v_z' = 2m_H(lk \cos \phi \sin \xi - \cos \gamma)\frac{v}{M} \tag{7-98c}$$

$$v_j = lv \tag{7-98d}$$

$$M = 2m_H + m_N + m_X \tag{7-98e}$$

$$l = \{(m_X + m_N)k \cos \phi(\sin \xi \cos \gamma + \cos \xi \cos \alpha) + m_H \cos \alpha\}$$
$$\times \left\{(m_X + m_N)k^2 \cos^2 \phi + 2m_X k \cos \phi \cos \xi + m_X\left(1 + \frac{m_N}{2m_H}\right)\right\}^{-1} \tag{7-98f}$$

v_x', v_z', and v_j are determined from the conservation of linear momentum and conservation of angular momentum.

Finally, the reduced mass μ is defined by the relationship

$$\mu v^2 = 2m_H V_H^2 + m_N V_N^2 + m_X V_X^2 \tag{7-99}$$

Explicitly, in terms of the molecular parameters

$$\mu = \frac{2m_H}{M}[2m_H \cos^2 \beta - lm_X \cos \alpha + (m_X + m_N)$$

$$\times \{1 - lk \cos \phi(\sin \xi \cos \gamma + \cos \xi \cos \alpha)\}] \tag{7-100}$$

Kasuya [805] has evaluated μ for four classical paths pictured in Fig. 7-12.

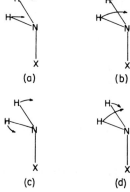

(a)   (b)

(c)   (d)

FIG. 7-12. Some classical inversion paths for the NH_2X molecule. The direction cosines $(\cos \alpha, \cos \beta, \cos \gamma)$ are: (a) $1, 0, 0$: (b) $\cos \xi, 0, \sin \xi$; (c) $\sin \phi, \cos \phi \sin \xi, 0$; and (d) $\cos \xi(1 - \sin^2 \xi \cos^2 \phi)^{1/2}$, $\sin \phi \sin \xi$, $\cos \phi \cos \xi \sin \xi$. The direction cosines are evaluated in the "equilibrium" configuration corresponding to one of the minima of the twofold potential function [805].

In (a) the hydrogens move normal to the yz plane and in (b) the N—H distance remains constant. These are similar to the two extreme motions used for ammonia in the symmetric top case.

7-9f. Rotational Dependence of the Inversion Splittings in an Asymmetric Rotor

One method for treating the rotational dependence of the inversion splittings in an asymmetric top is to modify the expressions used for a symmetric top. Weiss and Strandberg [778] have applied the equation developed by Sheng *et al.* [765] to the asymmetric deuterated ammonias NH_2D and NHD_2.

$$\Delta_{JK} = \Delta_0 - A[J(J + 1) - K^2] + BK^2 + \cdots \qquad (7\text{-}101)$$

The quantum number K for a symmetric top must be replaced because it is no longer a constant of the motion in an asymmetric rotor. In cases where the gth principal axis of the asymmetric rotor lies near the symmetry axis of the limiting symmetric top, P_g, the rotational angular momentum along the gth axis, may be used to estimate K.

$$\langle P_a^2 \rangle = \tfrac{1}{2}J(J + 1) + \frac{E(\kappa)}{2} - \left(\frac{1 + \kappa}{2}\right)\langle P_b^2 \rangle \qquad (7\text{-}102\text{a})$$

$$\langle P_b^2 \rangle = dE(\kappa)/d\kappa \qquad (7\text{-}102\text{b})$$

$$\langle P_c^2 \rangle = J(J + 1) - \langle P_a^2 \rangle - \langle P_b^2 \rangle \qquad (7\text{-}102\text{c})$$

For the asymmetric ammonias, $\langle P_c^2 \rangle$ is the proper expectation value of rotational angular momentum and is approximately equal to K_1^2. Using millimeter data, Lichtenstein *et al.* [817] obtained better agreement with the exponential dependence of (7-85). The additional assumption $\langle P_c^2 \rangle^2 = \langle P_c^4 \rangle$ was used in order to allow the inclusion of a term equivalent to a K^4 correction.

7-10. Inversion-Inversion Coupling

The molecule hydrazine [815] introduces the special possibility of coupling between two inversion-like motions in the same molecule. If $P_{\lambda 1}$ and $P_{\lambda 2}$ are the angular momenta associated with the inversion motion of the two amino groups, the pure inversion terms of the Hamiltonian may be written as

$$H_{inv} = \tfrac{1}{2}B(P_{\lambda 1}^2 + P_{\lambda 2}^2) + \tfrac{1}{2}D(P_{\lambda 1}P_{\lambda 2} + P_{\lambda 2}P_{\lambda 1}) + V(\lambda_1) + V(\lambda_2) \quad (7\text{-}103)$$

The appearance of the energy levels depends on the degree of coupling between the two modes of inversion. Figure 7-13 illustrates the splitting for four possible degrees of interaction. In I, the coefficient $D \to 0$ and the

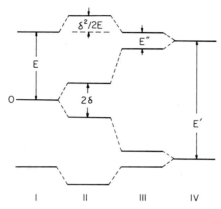

FIG. 7-13. Effects of inversion on the energy levels of a molecule with two possible inversion modes [805]. I through IV illustrate negligible, weak, medium, and strong coupling.

coupling between the two inversion motions is negligible. The equations are separable.

$$[\tfrac{1}{2}BP_{\lambda 1}^2 + V(\lambda_1)]\psi(\lambda_1) = E_1\psi(\lambda_1) \qquad (7\text{-}104)$$

$$[\tfrac{1}{2}BP_{\lambda 2}^2 + V(\lambda_2)]\psi(\lambda_2) = E_2\psi(\lambda_2) \qquad (7\text{-}105)$$

For a single inversion there are two levels governed by the wave functions $\psi^+(\lambda)$ and $\psi^-(\lambda)$. This gives

$$E_1 = E_2 = \pm E/2 \qquad (7\text{-}106)$$

for $\psi^\pm(\lambda)$. There are four levels having the wave functions $\psi^-(\lambda_1)\psi^-(\lambda_2)$, $\psi^+(\lambda_1)\psi^-(\lambda_2)$, $\psi^-(\lambda_1)\psi^+(\lambda_2)$, and $\psi^+(\lambda_1)\psi^+(\lambda_2)$ and the energies E, 0, 0, and $-E$, respectively.

When D is not negligible, the degeneracy of the $\psi^+(\lambda_1)\psi^-(\lambda_2)$ and $\psi^-(\lambda_1)\psi^+(\lambda_2)$ levels is lifted and a first-order splitting of 2δ occurs (case II in Fig. 7-13). δ is the off diagonal element in H_{inv}.

$$H_{\text{inv}} = \begin{bmatrix} -E & \delta & 0 & 0 \\ \delta & E & 0 & 0 \\ 0 & 0 & 0 & \delta \\ 0 & 0 & \delta & 0 \end{bmatrix} \qquad (7\text{-}107)$$

If D is too large to be treated by perturbation theory, it is best to introduce the transformation

$$\lambda = (\lambda_1 + \lambda_2)/\sqrt{2} \tag{7-108a}$$

$$\tilde{\lambda} = (\lambda_1 - \lambda_2)/\sqrt{2} \tag{7-108b}$$

so that

$$H_{\text{inv}} = \tfrac{1}{2}(B + D)P^2 + \tfrac{1}{2}(B - D)\tilde{P}^2 + V'(\lambda) + V'(\tilde{\lambda}) \tag{7-109}$$

Separation of variables gives

$$[\tfrac{1}{2}(B + D)P^2 + V'(\lambda)]\psi_1 = \varepsilon_1\psi_1 \tag{7-110}$$

$$[\tfrac{1}{2}(B - D)\tilde{P}^2 + V'(\tilde{\lambda})]\psi_2 = \varepsilon_2\psi_2 \tag{7-111}$$

$$\varepsilon_1 = \pm E'/2 \tag{7-112}$$

$$\varepsilon_2 = \pm E''/2 \tag{7-113}$$

Because $E' > E''$, no degeneracies result, and the energies for $\psi_1^-\psi_2^-$, $\psi_1^-\psi_2^+$, $\psi_1^+\psi_2^-$, and $\psi_1^+\psi_2^+$ are $E' + E''$, $E' - E''$, $-E' + E''$, and $-E' - E''$, respectively. This is case III.

In the most extreme case, the coupling could become very strong. This forces ε_2 to vanish and double degeneracies to occur as in IV. In essence, the molecule undergoes a single inversion composed of inversions of the two constituent groups. One group would instantaneously follow the other.

7-11. Inversion and Internal Rotation—The Methyl Amines

The microwave spectra of methylamine and dimethylamine are subject to both inversion and internal rotation effects. There is evidence for a strong coupling between inversion and internal rotation in both cases. A complete treatment of this type of problem requires a derivation of the appropriate Hamiltonian. Lide [793] treated methylamine as a molecule with two internal degrees of freedom by applying the IAM to the internal rotation and by adding a number of empirical parameters to the diagonal of the energy matrix in order to account for the inversion splitting. This approach was justified in a systematic analysis of the methylamine Hamiltonian by Kivelson and Lide [792].

The relative strength of the inversion-internal rotation coupling in methylamine can be estimated from a consideration of the molecular structure. Consider a classical inversion of the NH_2 group. As the molecule goes from one inversion configuration to the other, it is forced from a position of minimum torsional energy to a position of maximum torsional energy (Fig. 7-14a). Thus an inversion of the NH_2 group forces the methyl group to execute a rotation in order to reach a position of minimum energy. In dimethylamine (Fig. 7-14b) the inversion does not force the methyl groups

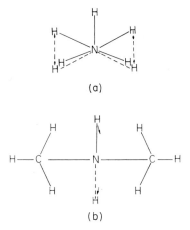

(a)

(b)

FIG. 7-14. Molecular models illustrating the relative coupling between inversion and internal rotation in (a) methylamine and (b) dimethylamine.

from their minimum energy orientations. Yet the excited torsional states show an increase in inversion splitting over that in the ground state [816].

In the formulation of the Hamiltonian for these molecules, the explicit dependence of the moments of inertia on the masses and coordinates of the system must be derived. This happens because the moments of inertia are not independent of the inversion motion. A similar derivation is used for internal rotation in molecules with asymmetric internal tops [739]. Table 7-2 compares approximate splitting constants for some amines. Note that the values for CH_3NH_2 and CD_3ND_2 are larger, respectively, than those for NH_3 and ND_3. This has been attributed to the fact that the C—N—H angle is larger than the H—N—H angle [789], and to the presence of an internal rotation term in the splitting constant [792].

TABLE 7-2

APPROXIMATE SPLITTING CONSTANTS FOR SOME AMINES IN THE GROUND STATE

Amine	Splitting (MHz)	Reference
NH_3	23805	[20]
ND_3	1600	[1223]
NH_2D	12100	[817]
NHD_2	5000	[817]
CH_3NH_2	28600	[782]
CD_3ND_2	2246	[792]
$(CH_3)_2NH$	1323	[816]
$(CH_3)_2ND$	53	[816]
$(CH_3)_3N$	<1	[690]

7-12a. Inversion in Near-Planar Molecules

If a molecule is planar in its equilibrium configuration, the potential energy for an out-of-plane vibration will increase on either side of the minimum position in the potential function. To a good approximation for harmonic or nearly harmonic potentials, the vibrational levels of a planar molecule are equally spaced and alternately symmetric and antisymmetric with respect to inversion. The lack of $\pm$ degeneracy is due to the ability of a planar molecule to reach its two inversion configurations by simple rotations.

Several important changes occur as a symmetrical potential hill is introduced at the minimum position. If the barrier is large enough, the molecule no longer possesses a planar equilibrium configuration but is forced into what is effectively a nonplanar equilibrium structure. The size of the perturbing barrier determines the separation of the two equivalent equilibrium forms and the energy level spacing. As the barrier is introduced, the evenly spaced energy levels of the harmonic vibration draw together in pairs with $+$ and $-$ symmetry. The presence of a barrier can greatly perturb the lower vibrational levels, destroying any semblance of harmonic separation, and the low-frequency out-of-plane vibration which corresponds to an inversion may be very anharmonic.

In most cases the next lowest fundamental mode of vibration is several hundred cm^{-1} higher than the out-of-plane mode. These low energy inversion levels are well populated, and rotational transitions belonging to several of these states should be observable in the form of satellite lines accompanying the ground state transition. When the degree of anharmonicity is large enough to make harmonic oscillator basis calculations difficult, it may be advantageous to use the pure quartic oscillator representation discussed in Section 7-4j. Using the most efficient basis, it is often possible to compute the eigenvalues for a sizeable number of energy levels and to fix the shape of the effective potential function with a relatively high degree of accuracy.

The low vibrational frequency associated with the out-of-plane mode is also important, because it may approach the order of magnitude of observed rotational transitions. In this respect, the usual assumption concerning separation of vibration and rotation may break down. An accurate treatment requires additional vibration-rotation terms to be included in the Hamiltonian, particularly when strongly interacting nearly degenerate levels are present.

If a pair of out-of-plane vibrations are present, the potential function must be described in terms of two normal coordinates X_a and X_b. The resulting two-dimensional potential field allows a form of pseudorotation which may be hindered if the potentials along the X_a and X_b axes are not equivalent.

From the above considerations, there are several important questions to be answered. First and probably most important, it must be determined whether a molecule is truly planar, near-planar with a small perturbing potential, or permanently bent with a high hindering barrier. It is then necessary to find the height of the barrier, if there is one, and the degree of nonplanarity.

In some cases additional information such as far infrared vibrational frequencies is available. The presence of a small out-of-plane transition moment component can sometimes be discovered through the Stark effect. Symmetry statistics govern the intensities of the rotational transitions and a careful measurement of intensities may give information concerning the equilibrium structure.

A number of molecules including formamide [800], cyanamide [796, 807], trimethylene sulfide [822b], and trimethylene oxide [798, 802, 822] have been investigated and have been shown to be either slightly nonplanar or essentially planar with a small potential hill perturbing the lower vibrational states. The various indicators provided by the microwave and far infrared spectra of these molecules are discussed in an attempt to formulate criteria which distinguish planar molecules from near-planar ones.

7-12b. Inertial Defect

In the study of inertial defects in Chapter 4 it was noted that positive values of $I_c - I_a - I_b$ are obtained for planar molecules and that negative values of $I_c - I_a - I_b$ are characteristic of nonplanar molecules. From this it is tempting to conclude that a molecule is truly planar if its inertia defect is positive. The danger in this type of assumption is indicated by the positive values of Δ obtained for six isotopic species of formamide which has been shown to be slightly nonplanar [800].[†] A positive value of Δ can be expected in nonplanar molecules when the contribution from the out-of-plane coordinate is insufficient to compensate for the inertia defect.

7-12c. Satellites and Intensities

The ground state rotational transitions of a near-planar molecule are usually accompanied by at least one, and in some cases, several nearby satellite lines. The number of satellites which are observable depends on the frequency of the out-of-plane bending motion. Displacement of the satellite lines from the main transition is a function of the degree of rotation-vibration

---

[†] For molecules with very low barriers, the question "planar or nonplanar" must be treated carefully. Lide [806] has discussed this problem in detail.

interaction taking place. By measuring the relative intensities of the satellite lines with respect to the ground state transitions, the vibrational energy separations can be estimated from the Boltzmann factor and any necessary statistical weight considerations. The relative intensities of the satellite lines are governed by nuclear statistics for the rotational and vibrational levels. Figure 7-15 illustrates the ground state transition and one of its satellites

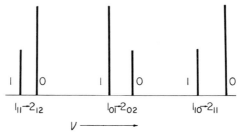

FIG. 7-15. $J = 1 \rightarrow 2$ transitions in cyanamide, H_2NCN. Integers represent the quantum number of the out-of-plane vibration. $v = 0$ for the ground state and $v = 1$ for the first excited state [807]. The relative intensities are governed by the nuclear statistics for the amine hydrogens.

for the three $J = 1 \rightarrow 2$ transitions in cyanamide. The statistics of the amine hydrogens for the inversion motion are similar to those in methylamine [807]. For hydrogen, the symmetric to antisymmetric weight ratio in the ground state is $1:3$ (for deuterium atoms it is $2:1$). Thus, in the ground vibrational state, the $K = 1$ transition is stronger than the $K = 0$ transition and for $v = 1$ the statistics are reversed. It is apparent that nuclear statistics may cause a rotational transition in the $v = 1$ state to be more intense than the same line in the ground vibrational state.

Symmetry statistics of this type do not apply to molecules whose inversion levels are effectively degenerate. Because the pairs of rotational transitions coalesce, the statistical weights of adjacent symmetric and antisymmetric levels add to make any intensity alternation indistinguishable.

7-12d. Stark Effect

If an inversion barrier is present in a near-planar molecule, its presence may be indicated by the existence of a transition moment (Chapter 8). Although the out-of-plane component may be too small to produce a readily observable set of transitions, it may affect the Stark splittings in another series of transitions, particularly if appropriate near-degeneracies exist. An estimate of the magnitude of the out-of-plane transition moment may then be helpful in estimating the degree of nonplanarity. If the proper near degeneracies are present, the Stark perturbation may also allow an estimate of the inversion doubling [820].

7-12e. Far Infrared Spectrum

A direct observation of the out-of-plane bending fundamental, i.e., the $v = 0 \to 1$ transition and its associated "hot bands" $1 \to 2, 2 \to 3, \ldots$ can lead to an assignment of the spacing of the inversion levels. To confirm this assignment, the frequencies of these transitions may sometimes be verified by relative intensity measurements on the satellite lines in the rotational spectrum [822a].

As illustrated by the case of trimethylene oxide, an unambiguous assignment of the complete series of Q branches in the far infrared region can be very difficult to achieve. It has been observed that although the unusual variation of the rotational constants with v discussed in Section 7-12f requires the presence of a small barrier in trimethylene oxide, the far infrared data can be successfully reproduced merely by adjusting the quartic potential constant. For this reason, the complementary infrared and microwave information should lead to complete agreement before a far infrared assignment and potential function for the inversion are accepted.

For a very low barrier on the order of tens of cm^{-1}, the spacing of the vibrational levels does provide a measure of the degree of anharmonicity associated with the out-of-plane vibration. A divergence of the splittings between adjacent vibrational states indicates a steeper potential than that of a harmonic oscillator; convergence of these splittings would indicate a potential which is not as steep as the harmonic parabola. When the barrier is relatively high so that the lower vibrational levels are below the top of the barrier, the far infrared spectrum becomes very difficult to assign with no regular progression of Q branch transitions. In these cases, the combination of microwave and infrared data is very useful and often necessary.

7-12f. Variation of Rotational Constants with Vibrational State

The rotational constants of a molecule are functions of the vibrational quantum numbers as expressed in (3-4). In the absence of any strong vibration-rotation perturbations (see Section 7-13), the rotational constants for a near-planar molecule may be expanded in terms of the vibrational normal coordinates X_j. By including the effects of other vibrational modes in either the rigid rotor terms or the expansion coefficients, the expansion can be given explicitly for the inversion coordinate X. Replacing the instantaneous coordinate values with the quantum-mechanical expectation values and recognizing that the odd vibrational averages vanish because the potential function is symmetric about $X = 0$,

$$\langle v|B_{gg}|v \rangle = B_{gg}^0 + \beta_2 \langle v|X^2|v \rangle + \beta_4 \langle v|X^4|v \rangle + \cdots \qquad (7\text{-}114)$$

B represents one of the rotational constants identified by the principal axis subscripts gg. B_{gg}^0 is the rotational constant for the molecule in its planar configuration. The coefficients β_k are defined by the Taylor series expansion. Here it has been assumed that the potential and kinetic energies of the out-of-plane vibration are separable from the rest of the Hamiltonian.

An interesting characteristic of molecules with low potential barriers is observed when the rotational constants are plotted as a function of the vibrational state. For levels in the vicinity of the barrier, the experimental values form a zigzag curve (Fig. 7-16); the rotational constants are functions

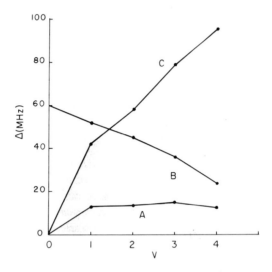

FIG. 7-16. Variation of the rotational constants A, B, and C of normal trimethylene oxide with the out-of-plane vibrational mode [798]. The relative change in rotational constant Δ is the difference between the excited state constant and the ground state constant, e.g., $A_v - A_0$ for the A constant.

of the average square amplitude of the out-of-plane vibration which is enhanced by the barrier. The zigzag character of the plots is produced solely by the effective barrier term. Because the odd vibrational wave functions have nodes at the planar configuration, the even levels tend to be more highly perturbed by the barrier than the odd levels, causing the zigzag feature. Usually some curvature is also observed and is associated with the presence of additional anharmonic terms. These features differ from the expected linear relationship expressed by the first two terms in (3-4); however, the expansions become equivalent if a sufficient number of higher terms in v are added to (3-4), although convergence of the latter is slower than of (7-114) for highly anharmonic potentials.

7-13. Vibration-Rotation Interactions

Important near degeneracies may occur as a result of inversion in asymmetric rotors, whenever the inversion splitting or vibrational energy level spacing and the rotational energy spacings are of the same order of magnitude. These interactions have been observed in several near-planar molecules such as trimethylene sulfide [822b], methylene cyclobutane and cyclopentene [820].

Lide [806] has discussed this type of perturbation using a Hamiltonian of the form

$$H = H_r + Gp^2 + V(x) + 2FpP_i \qquad (7\text{-}115)$$

where P_i is the component of rotational angular momentum involved in the interaction. The term involving $P_jP_k + P_kP_j$ has been eliminated from the Hamiltonian by using the instantaneous principal axis system. As discussed by Harris $et\ al.$ [822b], this term can also be used to express the vibration-rotation dependence; however, when a single vibrational mode produces an internal angular momentum component along only one axis, the vibration-rotation coupling can be expressed in terms of pP_i alone, by forcing all of the rotational angular momentum crossterms to vanish.

In the absence of any near degeneracies, the vibrational states could be treated individually with the rotational levels in each state following a rigid rotor pattern rather closely. However, if a near degeneracy results from the close proximity of a rotational level of a vibrational state with harmonic oscillator quantum number n and one of $n \pm 1$ connected by a nonvanishing matrix element of P_i, these levels are displaced from their rigid rotor positions. It becomes impossible to find a transformation which will completely eliminate the vibrational angular momentum from the Hamiltonian. A near degeneracy of this type involving $v = 0$ and $v = 1$ states of an out-of-plane vibration is illustrated in Fig. 7-17.

The perturbation is strongest when the vibrational spacing is of the same order of magnitude as the rotational energy spacing. For very low barriers, the vibrational spacing is relatively large and the coupling term can be included as a second-order correction to the rotational constant; if the barrier becomes very large, the vibrational levels draw together in pairs causing the vibrational momentum matrix element to approach zero. Therefore, the interaction becomes relatively ineffective for high and low barriers.

In a symmetric rotor basis, the energy matrix contains the usual elements diagonal in v and K and diagonal in v but off-diagonal in K. It is assumed that the out-of-plane mode can be separated from the other vibrations in the molecule. Also present are terms connecting even and odd v levels. The energy matrix factors into two submatrices as shown in Fig. 7-18. To treat

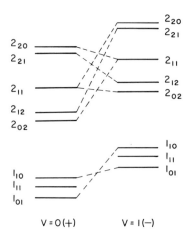

$$V = 0 (+) \qquad\qquad V = 1 (-)$$

FIG. 7-17. Perturbation connections (dashed lines) between the $J = 1, 2$ levels in the first two vibrational states of the ring-puckering mode in trimethylene sulfide [822b]. The inversion doubling is approximately 8232 MHz. Some of the perturbations exceed 100 MHz and, therefore, significantly distort the rigid rotor spectrum. Similar large perturbations have been observed in cyclopentene and methylenecyclobutane. The level spacings are not drawn to scale.

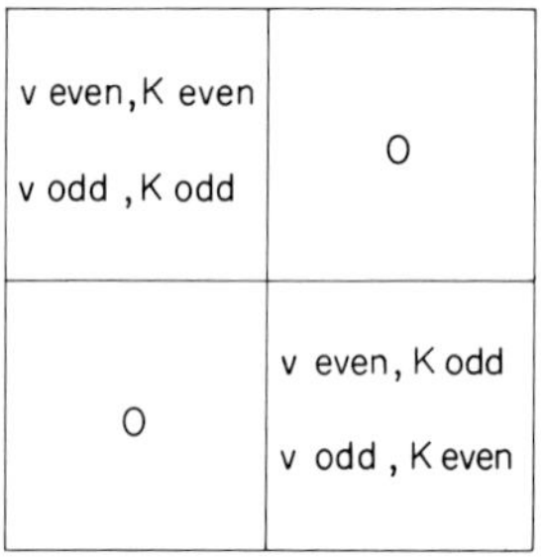

v even, K even v odd , K odd	0
0	v even, K odd v odd , K even

FIG. 7-18. Factoring of the energy matrix in a symmetric rotor basis prior to the application of a Van Vleck transformation.

this problem, the nearly degenerate levels are separated from the rest of the energy matrix by a Van Vleck transformation similar to that used in the internal rotation problem. The Van Vleck transformation allows the problem to be reduced to relatively small submatrices for each near degeneracy and these may be diagonalized individually to calculate the energy values.

If E_v is the vibrational energy for $Gp^2 + V(x)$ and E_r is the rotational energy, the energy to second order in an asymmetric rotor basis is

$$E = E_r + E_v + 4F^2 \sum_{v'}{}' \sum_{\tau'}{}' \frac{|\langle v|p|v'\rangle\langle J_\tau|P_i|J'_{\tau'}\rangle|^2}{E_v + E_{J_\tau} - (E_{v'} + E_{J'_{\tau'}})} \qquad (7\text{-}116)$$

F is assumed to be a constant independent of v. After separating those terms from the perturbation sum for which no important near degeneracy occurs, the approximate energy is [820]

$$E = E_r + E'_v + 4F^2 |\langle v|p|v'\rangle|^2 \sum_{\tau'}{}' \frac{|\langle J_\tau|P_i|J'_{\tau'}\rangle|^2}{E_v + E_{J_\tau} - (E_{v'} + E_{J_{\tau'}})} \qquad (7\text{-}117)$$

As a result of this perturbation, the rotational transitions in the vibrational states which are affected do not follow a rigid rotor pattern.

When the barrier is very low, on the order of a few cm^{-1} as in trimethylene oxide, the usual rigid rotor spectrum should be observed for all values of v. Neglecting the rotational contribution to the denominator in (7-117) the second-order correction then reduces to a constant correction for the rotational constant involved which can be absorbed by the first term in (7-114) [822].

CHAPTER 8 | STARK EFFECT

8-1. Introduction

One of the basic requirements for the existence of pure rotational transitions in a molecular spectrum is the presence of a permanent or induced dipole moment. The permanent dipole moment can be represented by a vector $\mathbf{\mu}$ whose magnitude is measured by the distribution of charge in the molecule and the distance between the centers of charge. Alternatively, it may be expressed as

$$\mathbf{\mu} = \sum_i e_i \mathbf{r}_i \qquad (8\text{-}1)$$

where e_i is the charge of the ith particle and $\mathbf{r}_i$ is the vector distance of that ith particle from the origin of a coordinate system fixed in the molecule. The summation is over all the nuclei and electrons in the molecule. The total dipole moment can be conveniently expressed in terms of the components along the three principal axes, since it is these components which are measured by a study of the rotational spectrum.

$$\mu^2 = \mu_a^2 + \mu_b^2 + \mu_c^2 \qquad (8\text{-}2)$$

Microwave spectroscopy provides one of the most accurate methods for the measurement of molecular dipole moments. Existence of a dipole moment causes an interaction between a rotating molecule and a static electric field. The rotational energy levels of the molecule are perturbed by the external electric field through this interaction, which is called the Stark effect. The high resolution available in the microwave region of the spectrum allows accurate measurements of the Stark perturbations and the associated dipole moment components. The moments are measured in the gas phase where solvent effects are not a factor. Measurements are also made in distinct vibrational and rotational states, instead of being averaged over a series of states. This allows a comparison of dipole moment changes caused by rotation-vibration interactions. Because it is a function of the rotational quantum numbers, the Stark effect also provides a method for identifying low J rotational transitions. The purity of the sample is no longer an important factor, as long as the proper spectrum can be identified and measured. Unstable molecules may also be studied even though they may be decomposing at a rapid rate. Because the Stark effect constitutes an external perturbation, it can be controlled by the spectroscopist and used to perturb the energy level structure over a relatively wide range.

8-2. General Properties of the Stark Effect

When a static electric field is imposed on a sample of molecules, it defines a preferred direction in space. The total rotational angular momentum vector $\mathbf{J}$ is constrained to $2J + 1$ possible orientations with respect to the static field direction. These orientations can be identified with the quantum number M, where $M = J, J - 1, \ldots, -J$. M is the projection of $\mathbf{J}$ in the ε direction, where ε represents the Stark field. In the absence of a perturbing field, the $2J + 1$ possible directions of $\mathbf{J}$ are energetically equivalent and the spatial M degeneracy is complete. The presence of an external field can partially or completely lift this degeneracy.

If the Stark effect perturbation is considerably smaller than the rotational energy level spacing, perturbation theory can be used to calculate the Stark splittings. The perturbation term H_ε is the interaction energy between the electric field ε and the molecular dipole moment $\boldsymbol{\mu}$. This interaction energy in vector notation is expressed as

$$H_\varepsilon = -\boldsymbol{\mu} \cdot \varepsilon \tag{8-3}$$

The effects of polarizability which are discussed in Section 8-9 have been neglected here. Both first- and second-order perturbations can be expressed in terms of H_ε averaged over the unperturbed states of the molecule represented by the wave functions $\psi_j^{(0)}$. $\boldsymbol{\mu}$ must be averaged over the rotational state to determine whether an average component of the dipole moment lies along the rotational angular momentum vector $\mathbf{J}$. If the molecule does not possess an average component of the dipole moment, the first-order Stark energy correction will be zero. The electric field may then induce a component of $\boldsymbol{\mu}$ in the $\mathbf{J}$ direction; this component then interacts with the field to produce a second-order energy correction. This second-order splitting is ordinarily much smaller than the first-order effect when the latter does not vanish.

It can be shown that the existence of an average directional component of the dipole moment in the absence of an external field requires the presence of an energy level degeneracy. This degeneracy is provided by the K degeneracy in symmetric tops but not by the M degeneracy which requires an external field for proper definition. Actually, a permanent dipole moment cannot exist in the absence of an external field or an effective energy level degeneracy.

If the first-order energy perturbation does not vanish, the results of first-order perturbation theory indicate that the energy correction will be proportional to the first power of the field. The M degeneracy is completely lifted and $2J + 1$ levels result for a given J. When the first-order energy vanishes, the second-order correction, which is proportional to ε^2, causes the Stark splitting. Because the ε^2 contributions to the energy are degenerate in $\pm\varepsilon$, only $J + 1$ resolvable Stark levels result. All levels for $M \neq 0$ are doubly degenerate in $\pm M$. Higher order effects can be considered in special cases when greater accuracy is necessary.

8-3. Matrix Elements of H_ε

From the scalar product (8-3), H_ε can be expressed in terms of the direction cosine between $\boldsymbol{\mu}$ and $\boldsymbol{\varepsilon}$.

$$H_\varepsilon = -\mu\varepsilon \cos\theta \qquad (8\text{-}4)$$

The matrix elements in a symmetric rotor representation can be constructed by using the direction cosine elements discussed in Chapter 2 and Table 2-11. The matrix elements diagonal in K and M are

$$\langle JKM|H_\varepsilon|JKM\rangle = -\mu\varepsilon\langle JKM|\cos\theta|JKM\rangle$$

$$= -\mu\varepsilon\langle J|\phi_{Fg}|J\rangle\langle JK|\phi_{Fz}|JK\rangle\langle JM|\phi_{Zg}|JM\rangle$$

$$= -\frac{\mu\varepsilon KM}{J(J + 1)} \qquad (8\text{-}5)$$

$$\langle JKM|H_\varepsilon|J + 1, KM\rangle = -\mu\varepsilon\langle J|\phi_{Fg}|J + 1\rangle\langle JK|\phi_{Fz}|J + 1, K\rangle$$

$$\times \langle JM|\phi_{Zg}|JM\rangle$$

$$= \frac{-\mu\varepsilon}{J + 1}\left[\frac{[(J + 1)^2 - K^2][(J + 1)^2 - M^2]}{(2J + 1)(2J + 3)}\right]^{1/2} \qquad (8\text{-}6)$$

Except for the presence of ε, these matrix elements are identical with (2-165) and (2-166).

The matrix elements of H_ε are pictured in Fig. 8-1. While the energy matrix is still diagonal in M, the Stark perturbation introduces elements off-diagonal in J. Strictly speaking, J is no longer a good quantum number and the convenient factoring produced by the Wang transformation is partially destroyed. For an asymmetric rotor, (8-43), (8-44), and (8-45) give the proper matrix elements of H_ε in terms of the transition strengths ${}^g S_{J_\tau J'_{\tau'}}$ after replacing m_J with M and multiplying by ε^2.

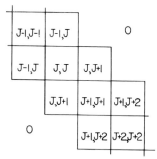

FIG. 8-1. Matrix elements for the Stark effect in a symmetric rotor representation. A block labeled $J, J + 1$ contains the element $\langle JKM|H_\varepsilon|J + 1, KM\rangle$ given in (8-6).

8-4. First-Order Stark Effect

The first-order energy is given by the perturbation result

$$E_j^{(1)} = \int \psi_j^{(0)} H_\varepsilon \psi_j^{(0)} \, d\tau \tag{8-7}$$

Therefore, the first-order energy correction to the rigid rotor energy levels consists of only the diagonal elements of H_ε; the off-diagonal elements connecting the $J, J + 1$ blocks enter in the second-order treatment. In the symmetric rotor basis (8-5) gives the first-order Stark energy as

$$E^{(1)} = \frac{-\mu\varepsilon KM}{J(J + 1)} = \mu\varepsilon D(JKM) \tag{8-8}$$

For a rigid linear molecule which is a special form of symmetric top only the case $K = 0$ is realized and the first-order energy vanishes. Equation (8-8) is nonvanishing for symmetric rotors when $K \neq 0$; the first-order correction vanishes for the $K = 0$ levels. For an asymmetric rotor, μ_J, the time-average component of $\boldsymbol{\mu}$ along $\mathbf{J}$, averages to zero over the molecular rotations and the first-order energy vanishes. However, should an important near degeneracy occur between two levels connected by the Stark perturbation, second-order perturbation theory becomes inadequate and a Stark effect which is essentially first-order in ε can result. An equivalent effect can be produced by near degeneracies in the excited states of linear molecules, e.g., in the l-type doublets of OCS.

8-5. Second-Order Stark Effect

The second-order energy correction for the Stark effect can be calculated with the standard perturbation result

$$E_i^{(2)} = \sum_{j \neq i}{}' \frac{|\langle \psi_i^{(0)}|H_\varepsilon|\psi_j^{(0)}\rangle \langle \psi_j^{(0)}|H_\varepsilon|\psi_i^{(0)}\rangle|}{E_i^{(0)} - E_j^{(0)}} \tag{8-9}$$

subject to the usual restrictions under which a perturbation treatment is valid. For an asymmetric rotor H_ε can be conveniently expressed in terms of the direction cosine ϕ_{Zg} and the component of the dipole moment along the gth principal axis.

$$H_\varepsilon = -\varepsilon \sum_g \phi_{Zg} \mu_g \tag{8-10}$$

ϕ_{Zg} represents the direction cosine between the space-fixed Z axis, defined by the field direction, and a principal axis. Appropriate basis functions for the perturbation treatment are the asymmetric rotor functions of (2-94). The form of the resulting perturbation matrix is pictured in Fig. 8-2.

	A	B_Z	B_Y	B_X
A		Z Z	Y Y	X X
B_Z	Z Z		X X	Y Y
B_Y	Y Y	X X		Z Z
B_X	X X	Y Y	Z Z	

FIG. 8-2. Structure of the perturbation matrix H_ε for the symmetry species of the asymmetric rotor four group V(xyz). The elements of each block are identified by the notation YY $\equiv \mu_y \phi_{Zy}$. V(xyz) can be correlated with V(abc) by using the appropriate representation in Table 2-5. This matrix follows directly from the selection rules of Table 2-7.

Because the Z components of the direction cosines have matrix elements which are diagonal in M, and the asymmetric rotor functions may be written as Wang linear combinations of the symmetric rotor functions with identical J and M, the direction cosine matrix elements of the Z components are also diagonal in M in the asymmetric rotor basis and each M value may be dealt with separately. However, in the symmetric rotor basis, the direction cosine elements in Table 2-11 introduce terms off-diagonal in J and K which prevent a convenient factoring of the energy matrix. The perturbation matrix of Fig. 8-2 is obtained by forcing the dipole matrix element (2-140) to belong to the totally symmetric irreducible representation A of the rotation group V (causing the diagonal terms to vanish). For a system with no near degeneracies, the lack of diagonal elements in the matrix results in the absence of any linear correction terms. The lack of any diagonal terms in H_ε in the asymmetric rotor basis may be demonstrated by applying the Wang transformation to the direction cosine matrix ϕ_{Fg} [840]. From Table 2-11, it is observed that the direction cosine factor which is diagonal in J and K is an odd function of K. Applying the Wang transformation causes the diagonal elements of $\mathbf{X}'\boldsymbol{\phi}_{F_g}\mathbf{X}$ to vanish. The remaining factors which are diagonal in J connect the levels $\langle K|K \pm 1\rangle$. The perturbation elements in Fig. 8-1 fall outside the unperturbed asymmetric rotor factors $\mathbf{E}^\pm$ and $\mathbf{O}^\pm$ and connect these submatrices with elements of the form $\langle J|J\rangle$ and $\langle J|J \pm 1\rangle$.

Combining (8-9) and (8-10)

$$E_i^{(2)} = \sum_g \mu_g^2 \varepsilon^2 \sum_{j \neq i}' \frac{|\langle \psi_i^{(0)}|\phi_{Zg}|\psi_j^{(0)}\rangle|^2}{E_i^{(0)} - E_j^{(0)}} \tag{8-11}$$

The matrix elements of ϕ_{Zg} transformed to an asymmetric rotor basis can be expressed in terms of the tabulated values of ${}^g S_{J_\tau J'_{\tau'}}$.

$$E_{J_\tau M}^{(2)} = \sum_g \frac{\mu_g^2 \varepsilon^2}{2J+1} \sum_{\tau'}' \left[\frac{J^2 - M^2}{J(2J-1)} \frac{{}^g S_{J_\tau J-1_{\tau'}}}{E_{J_\tau}^{(0)} - E_{J-1_{\tau'}}^{(0)}} + \frac{M^2}{J(J+1)} \frac{{}^g S_{J_\tau J_{\tau'}}}{E_{J_\tau}^{(0)} - E_{J_{\tau'}}^{(0)}} \right.$$
$$\left. + \frac{(J+1)^2 - M^2}{(J+1)(2J+3)} \frac{{}^g S_{J_\tau, J+1_{\tau'}}}{E_{J_\tau}^{(0)} - E_{J+1_{\tau'}}^{(0)}} \right] \tag{8-12}$$

This expression is commonly used for asymmetric top molecules and can be simplified to treat a linear or symmetric top (for $K = 0$). Employing the selection rule $\Delta J = \pm 1$ for the latter cases, only the two neighboring J states are summed in (8-11), and

$$E_{JM}^{(2)} = \frac{-\mu^2 \varepsilon^2}{2hB} \left[\frac{3M^2 - J(J+1)}{J(J+1)(2J-1)(2J+3)} \right] \tag{8-13}$$

If $J = 0$, (8-13) becomes

$$E_{0M}^{(2)} = \frac{-\mu^2 \varepsilon^2}{6hB} \tag{8-14}$$

For a symmetric top with $K \neq 0$,

$$E^{(2)} = \frac{\mu^2 \varepsilon^2}{2hB} \left[\frac{(J^2 - K^2)(J^2 - M^2)}{J^3(2J-1)(2J+1)} - \frac{[(J+1)^2 - K^2][(J+1)^2 - M^2]}{(J+1)^3(2J+1)(2J+3)} \right] \tag{8-15}$$

This reduces to (8-13) for $K = 0$. Again, only adjacent states are allowed in the summation in (8-11).

In each case it should be emphasized that the Stark perturbation results in a repulsion between the interacting levels. The net energy change is then a summation of the repulsions produced by those energy levels which are connected through the Stark perturbation. Thus, in (8-11) all the interacting levels must be included.

For an asymmetric rotor, it is convenient to write the second-order correction as a sum of two terms.

$$E^{(2)} = (A_{J_\tau} + B_{J_\tau}M^2)\varepsilon^2\mu_g^2 \tag{8-16}$$

Although the coefficients are usually evaluated exactly in a Stark effect analysis, functions proportional to A_{J_τ} and B_{J_τ} have been tabulated [840, 847] as a function of the rotational constants and asymmetry parameter κ.

8-6. High Field Stark Effect and Higher-Order Perturbation Terms

In order to obtain accurate dipole moment values, it is often necessary to extend Stark effect measurements to very high field strengths. Under these conditions the first correction to the energy may be inadequate and calculations must be extended to include higher-order corrections. For a first-order Stark effect, it is usually sufficient to include the second-order correction term.

$$E(\varepsilon) \approx E^{(1)} + E^{(2)} \tag{8-17}$$

When the first-order energy is zero, the second-order term can be supplemented by including the fourth-order energy correction. The third-order term vanishes in this case. As shown in Appendix 10, when the energy levels lack the K degeneracy necessary to produce a first-order Stark effect, all of the higher odd-order terms also vanish.

$$E(\varepsilon) \approx E^{(2)} + E^{(4)} \tag{8-18}$$

It must be remembered that the use of modern high speed digital computers can extend and simplify Stark calculations by easily allowing the inclusion of many higher order correction terms. The energy matrix can be constructed in a symmetric rotor basis using the known rigid rotor matrix elements in Chapter 2 and the Stark matrix elements of (8-5) and (8-6). The resulting matrix can then be diagonalized numerically without requiring the calculation of individual perturbation corrections. Some of the more appropriate approximate approaches are reviewed below.

Brouwer [827] and Hughes [833, 845] have written the Stark energy for a rigid linear molecule as an expansion in even powers of the parameter λ.

$$\lambda = \mu\varepsilon/hB \tag{8-19}$$

In terms of the field strength ε, this expansion to fourth order is

$$E = E^{(0)} - \frac{\mu^2\varepsilon^2}{2hB}F(J, M) + \frac{\mu^4\varepsilon^4}{h^3B^3}K(J, M) + \cdots \tag{8-20}$$

$E^{(0)}$ is the zero-field energy. $F(J, M)$ is given by the term in brackets in (8-13).

$$F(J, M) = \left[\frac{3M^2 - J(J + 1)}{J(J + 1)(2J - 1)(2J + 3)} \right] \tag{8-21}$$

$K(J, M)^\dagger$ has been given by Hughes [833, 845] up to $J = 2$, $M = \pm 2$ and by Marshall and Weber [862]. Kusch and Hughes [29a] extended these values through $J = 4$. The accuracy of (8-20) can be determined from a comparison with the continued fraction solution of Lamb [833].

$$E = hBM(M + 1)$$

$$-hB \left[\cfrac{A(M, M^2)\lambda^2}{(M + 1)(M + 2) - \cfrac{E}{hB} - \cfrac{A^2(M + 1, M)\lambda^2}{(M + 2)(M + 3) - E/hB - \cdots}} \right] \tag{8-22}$$

$$A(R, p^2) = \frac{[(R + 1)^2 - p^2]}{(2R + 1)(2R + 3)} \tag{8-23}$$

The expansion in (8-20) is convenient for molecular beam electric resonance studies where strong external fields may be used. If fourth-order effects can be detected, it is possible to determine both the dipole moment μ and the rotational constant B from measurements at different field strengths. The behavior of the rotational levels J, M up to $J = 2$ for a rigid linear molecule is shown in Fig. 8-3. Equation (8-20) is adequate for low values of λ up to the order of one (converges for $\lambda < J$). For higher values of λ, i.e., when the Stark energy is greater than the rotational energy, Peter and Strandberg [864] have derived a power series in $\lambda^{-1/2}$ that converges for large λ for E/hB of a linear rigid rotor.

$$\frac{E}{hB} = -\lambda + 2^{1/2}[2J - |M| + 1]\lambda^{1/2} + \tfrac{1}{4}[M^2 + 2|M|J - 2J^2 + |M| - 2J - 2]$$

$$+ 2^{1/2}/64[-4|M^3| + 6M^2J + 6|M|J^2 - 4J^3 + 3M^2 + 6|M|J - 6J^2$$

$$+ 3|M| - 6J - 2]\lambda^{-1/2} + \cdots \tag{8-24}$$

Figure 8-4 gives a plot of E/hB up to a λ value of 100 and for J values up to 4. An asymptotic expression also appropriate for $\mu\varepsilon > E$ has been discussed by Barriol [849]. The continued fraction approach of Lamb has been extended to symmetric top molecules by Shirley [890] up through $J = 4$.

In all of the discussions to this point, the presence of any induced component of the dipole moment has been neglected. There are situations in

---

† Some of the published values of $K(J, M)$ are in error. See Appendix 14.

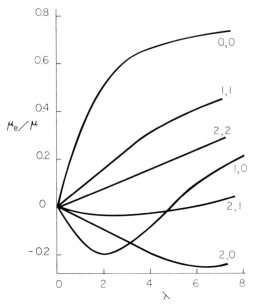

FIG. 8-3. The effective dipole moment of a linear molecule as a function of electric field strength (λ) through $J = 2$ [833]. The effective moment μ_e is defined as $-(\partial E/\partial \varepsilon)$. The curves are identified by the notation $J, |M|$.

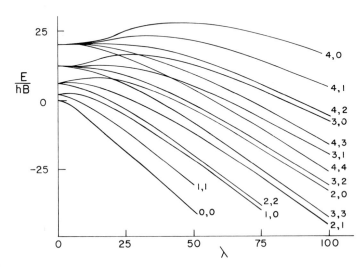

FIG. 8-4. The reduced energy of a rigid linear rotor for the levels $J, |M|$ up to $J = 4$ as a function of λ for high Stark fields.

which the induced moment is not negligible. In particular, polarizability effects may become very important for a small permanent dipole moment component in a very strong electric field.

8-7. Stark Effect for Near Degeneracies

As indicated in (8-12), the Stark effect connects the level of energy E_{J_τ} with adjoining levels of energies $E_{J-1_{\tau'}}$, $E_{J_{\tau'}}$, and $E_{J+1_{\tau'}}$. Should any of the energy differences $E_{J_\tau}^{(0)} - E_{J_{\tau'}'}^{(0)}$ in the denominators become small relative to the square of the perturbation matrix element of H_ε due to a near degeneracy, the perturbation approach breaks down and a secular equation must be solved. Near degeneracies may occur accidentally in asymmetric tops or naturally in near-symmetric rotors. In the latter case, as $|\kappa| \to 1$, the K doubling becomes very small, producing the required near degeneracies.

The possibility of near degeneracies and their effects on Stark splittings were first discussed by Penney [828] and extended by Golden and Wilson [840]. In the absence of Stark perturbation, the energy matrix in the asymmetric rotor basis factors into the usual submatrices $\mathbf{E}^\pm$ and $\mathbf{O}^\pm$ for each J. The Stark effect spoils this factoring by producing elements which connect the Wang submatrices. In order to separate the nearby degenerate levels from the nondegenerate levels, the Van Vleck transformation [1028] used in treating internal rotation problems can be applied to the energy matrix, thereby reducing the off-diagonal connecting elements to second order (fourth order in the energy). When only two levels need to be considered, the submatrix to be diagonalized results in a second degree secular equation having the structure

$$\begin{vmatrix} H_{11} - E & H_{12} \\ H_{12} & H_{22} - E \end{vmatrix} = 0 \qquad (8\text{-}25)$$

The H_{ii} are diagonal elements which contain correction terms from the Van Vleck transformation.

$$H_{ii} = E_{ii}^{(0)} + E_{ii}^{(2)} \qquad (8\text{-}26)$$

$E_{ii}^{(2)}$ is identical with the second-order perturbation term in (8-11). H_{12} consists of the connecting Stark perturbation term and Van Vleck correction terms $E_{12}^{(2)}$

$$H_{12} = \langle \psi_1^{(0)} | H_\varepsilon | \psi_2^{(0)} \rangle + E_{12}^{(2)} \qquad (8\text{-}27)$$

The off-diagonal correction terms $E_{12}^{(2)}$ have been discussed by Golden and Wilson [840] for different types of near degeneracies. Explicit evaluation of H_{12} depends on the selection rules for J and on the symmetries of the unperturbed states.

The solution of the secular equation for two nearly degenerate levels is

$$2E = H_{11} + H_{22} \pm \{(H_{11} - H_{22})^2 + 4H_{12}^2\}^{1/2} \qquad (8\text{-}28)$$

The dependence of the energy on the electric field strength is a function of the relative difference between the unperturbed energy levels compared to the size of the off-diagonal elements H_{12}. It is clear from (8-28) that if $|H_{12}| \gg |H_{11} - H_{22}|$,

$$E = \tfrac{1}{2}(H_{11} + H_{22}) \pm H_{12} + \cdots \qquad (8\text{-}29)$$

H_{12} is essentially first order in the electric field strength. Therefore, the near degeneracy introduces some first-order Stark dependence into the energy. This is reasonable because a first-order Stark effect is expected in the case of degenerate levels. If $H_{11} - H_{22}$ is allowed to vanish entirely, the problem reduces to that for a symmetric top.

The general first-order expression for a near degeneracy in an asymmetry doublet is then

$$E^{(1)} = C_g M \mu_g \varepsilon \qquad (8\text{-}30)$$

C_g is the first-order Stark coefficient and can be expressed as a function of the tabulated transition strength.

$$C_g = \pm \frac{{}^g S_{J_\tau J_{\tau'}}}{[J(J + 1)(2J + 1)]^{1/2}} \qquad (8\text{-}31)$$

When $|H_{11} - H_{22}| \gg |H_{12}|$, the expected quadratic field dependence dominates. For $H_{11} > H_{22}$,

$$E = \tfrac{1}{2}(H_{11} \pm H_{11}) + \tfrac{1}{2}(H_{22} \mp H_{22}) + \cdots \qquad (8\text{-}32)$$

This is just the solution in the absence of any near degeneracy.

The wave functions for the unperturbed energy levels are mixed by the electric field, and the mixing coefficients are functions of the electric field strength ε. The amount of mixing is determined by the relative size of H_{12}. Mixing is small when the separation of the two unperturbed levels is much larger than the Stark term; it reaches a maximum when the two levels are degenerate. The situation is analogous to the treatment of Fermi resonance in Chapter 3.

8-8a. Stark Effect and Quadrupole Hyperfine Structure

Because a large percentage of the molecules investigated in the microwave region possess quadrupole nuclei, it is important to analyze the interaction between the Stark effect and nuclear quadrupole coupling. By constructing appropriate vector diagrams, a simplified picture of this interaction can be obtained. The particular situations of interest can be classified with respect to the set of valid quantum numbers. Figure 8-5 illustrates three important cases for molecules with a single quadrupole nucleus. (a) shows the case of no quadrupole coupling; M_J is the projection of $\mathbf{J}$ along the field direction. When the spin angular momentum $\mathbf{I}$ of the quadrupole nucleus is introduced,[†] $\mathbf{I}$ and $\mathbf{J}$ couple to form a resultant angular momentum $\mathbf{F}$. In the limit of a weak field, $\mathbf{F}$ is a good quantum number and its projection along the field direction is M_F. M_F takes $2F + 1$ values from $-F$ to $+F$. $\mathbf{F}$ may be visualized as precessing about the field direction in a manner similar to the precession of $\mathbf{J}$ about the field direction in Fig. 8-5(a). J is still a good quantum number, but its projection M_J is no longer a constant of the motion.

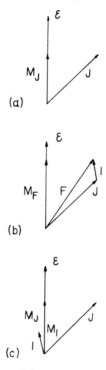

FIG. 8-5. Static vector coupling models used to treat the Stark effect in the presence of a single quadrupole nucleus: (a) no quadrupole coupling, (b) quadrupole coupling in a weak Stark field, and (c) quadrupole coupling in a strong Stark field.

The weak field assumption governing Fig. 8-5(b) requires the Stark energy to be much smaller than the quadrupole interaction energy, and the Stark effect appears as a perturbation on the hyperfine splitting. As the Stark field is increased, a situation is reached where the two energies are of comparable

---

[†] As noted in Chapter 5, a nuclear spin of $\frac{1}{2}\hbar$ does not produce a quadrupole interaction.

size. This is termed the intermediate case and is the most complex case to treat because considerable mixing of the wave functions occurs. Further increase in electric field strength produces an uncoupling of $\mathbf{I}$ and $\mathbf{J}$ as indicated in Fig. 8-5(c). The hyperfine splitting appears as a perturbation on the Stark levels, and the Stark effect can be treated approximately by neglecting the presence of the quadrupole interaction. In the strong field case M_J is reestablished as a good quantum number, and the projection of $\mathbf{I}$ on the field direction defines a new projection quantum number M_I. If the Stark energy is increased to a point where it is large compared with the rotational energy, J is eliminated as a practical quantum number.

Fano [838] discussed the case of a linear molecule. Low and Townes [848] and Coester [850] have treated the weak, intermediate, and strong field cases for a symmetric top. Extension to an asymmetric top whose coupled rotational states have a separation large with respect to the hyperfine structure was provided by Mizushima [857]. The strong field case has been discussed by Howe and Flygare [886].

The Hamiltonian may be written as

$$H = H_0 + H_\varepsilon + H_Q \tag{8-33}$$

H_0 is the Hamiltonian for the unperturbed molecule, H_ε represents the Stark energy and H_Q is the quadrupole energy. Energy expressions for H_0 are given in (2-41), (2-48–49), and (2-83) for linear, symmetric, and asymmetric tops, respectively. Equation (5-13) gives the general form of H_Q and (5-45), (5-48), and (5-55) give the necessary expressions for specific symmetries.

8-8b. Weak Field with a Single Quadrupole Nucleus ($\mu\varepsilon \ll eqQ$)

In the weak field case H_ε is treated as a perturbation. The appropriate basis functions diagonalize H_Q and H_0.

$$(H_0 + H_Q)\psi(IJFM_F) = (E_0 + E_Q)\psi(IJFM_F) \tag{8-34}$$

These basis functions may be expanded in terms of the rotational wave functions and nuclear spin functions. For a symmetric top

$$\psi(IJFM_F) = \sum_{m_J} C(IJFM_Fm_J)\psi(JKm_J)\Phi(I, m_I) \tag{8-35}$$

The lower case m indicates that m_I and m_J are not good quantum numbers for this model. $\psi(JKm_J)$ is the rotational wave function and $\Phi(Im_I)$ is the nuclear spin function. From (8-7) and (8-35), the first-order energy correction is

$$E^{(1)} = \langle IJFM_F|H_\varepsilon|IJFM_F\rangle = -\frac{\mu\varepsilon K}{J(J+1)}\sum_{m_J}|C(IJFM_Fm_J)|^2 m_J \tag{8-36}$$

The summation in (8-36) performs an averaging on m_J such that [848]

$$\sum_{m_J} |C(IJFM_Fm_J)|^2 m_J = \frac{M_F \mathbf{F} \cdot \mathbf{J}}{F(F+1)} = \frac{M_F[F(F+1) + J(J+1) - I(I+1)]}{2F(F+1)}$$

(8-37)

The $C(IJFM_Fm_J)$ are discussed by Condon and Shortley [1]. The first-order energy correction is

$$E^{(1)} = \frac{-\mu\varepsilon K M_F[F(F+1) + J(J+1) - I(I+1)]}{2J(J+1)F(F+1)}$$

(8-38)

This expression is used for symmetric top molecules when $K \neq 0$. As expected, $E^{(1)}$ vanishes for linear molecules and symmetric tops when $K = 0$. When $M_F = F$, (8-38) reduces to

$$E^{(1)} = -\mu\varepsilon K/(J+1)$$

(8-39)

which is independent of F and I and, therefore, of any quadrupole effects. From (8-8), this case is identical to that for $M_J = J$ with no nuclear quadrupole coupling.

For linear molecules, symmetric top molecules with $K = 0$, and asymmetric top molecules, the second-order energy correction must be evaluated.

$$E^{(2)} = \sideset{}{'}\sum_{F'} \sideset{}{'}\sum_{J'} \frac{|\langle IJ'F'M|H_\varepsilon|IJFM\rangle \langle IJFM|H_\varepsilon|IJ'F'M\rangle|}{E_{IJFM} - E_{IJ'F'M}}$$

(8-40)

The prime on the summation indicates that the term $F = F'$, $J = J'$ is omitted during the summing operation. The rotational wave function in (8-40) is the appropriate wave function for a linear, symmetric, or asymmetric top molecule.

The direction cosine matrix element needed for the second-order term can be obtained by Racah's method [496] (see also Mizushima [857]).

$$|\langle IJF\tau M|\phi_{Zg}|IJ'F'\tau'M\rangle|^2 = (2F+1)(2F'+1)[\langle J\tau\|\phi_{Zg}\|J'\tau'\rangle$$

$$\times W(JFJ'F'; I1)V(FF'1; -MM0)]^2$$

(8-41)

The coefficients W and V have been defined by Racah (see Chapter 5 and Appendix 6). The special matrix notation is

$$\langle J\tau\|\phi_{Zg}\|J'\tau'\rangle = [\langle J\tau m_J|\phi_{Zg}|J'\tau'm_J\rangle/V(JJ'1; -m_Jm_J0)]$$

(8-42)

$$|\langle J\tau m_J|\phi_{Zg}|J\tau'm_J\rangle|^2 = \frac{m_J^2 \, {}^gS_{J\tau J\tau'}}{J(J+1)(2J+1)}$$

(8-43)

$$|\langle J\tau m_J|\phi_{zg}|J-1,\tau'm_J\rangle|^2 = \frac{(J^2 - m_J^2)^g S_{J_\tau J-1_{\tau'}}}{J(4J^2 - 1)} \tag{8-44}$$

$$|\langle J\tau m_J|\phi_{zg}|J+1,\tau'm_J\rangle|^2 = \frac{[(J+1)^2 - m_J^2]^g S_{J_\tau J+1_{\tau'}}}{(J+1)(2J+1)(2J+3)} \tag{8-45}$$

By evaluating the Racah coefficients W and V, the second-order correction becomes

$$E^{(2)} = \sum_{g=a,b,c} \mu_g^2 \varepsilon^2 \left[f_1(JIFM) \sum_{\tau'} \frac{{}^g S_{J_\tau J+1_{\tau'}}}{E_{J_\tau F} - E_{J+1_{\tau'}F}} \right.$$

$$+ f_2(JIFM) \sum_{\tau'} \frac{{}^g S_{J_\tau J+1_{\tau'}}}{E_{J_\tau F} - E_{J+1_{\tau'}F+1}} + f_3(JIFM) \sum_{\tau'} \frac{{}^g S_{J_\tau J+1_{\tau'}}}{E_{J_\tau F} - E_{J+1_{\tau'}F-1}}$$

$$+ f_4(JIFM) \sum_{\tau'} \frac{{}^g S_{J_\tau J_{\tau'}}}{E_{J_\tau F} - E_{J_{\tau'}F+1}} + f_5(JIFM) \sum_{\tau'}' \frac{{}^g S_{J_\tau J_{\tau'}}}{E_{J_\tau F} - E_{J_{\tau'}F}}$$

$$+ f_4(JI, F-1, M) \sum_{\tau'} \frac{{}^g S_{J_\tau J_{\tau'}}}{E_{J_\tau F} - E_{J_{\tau'}F-1}}$$

$$+ f_1(J-1, IFM \sum_{\tau'} \frac{{}^g S_{J_\tau J-1_{\tau'}}}{E_{J_\tau F} - E_{J-1_{\tau'}F}}$$

$$+ f_2(J-1, I, F-1, M) \sum_{\tau'} \frac{{}^g S_{J_\tau J-1_{\tau'}}}{E_{J_\tau F} - E_{J-1_{\tau'}F-1}}$$

$$+ f_3(J-1, I, F+1, M) \sum_{\tau'} \frac{{}^g S_{J_\tau J-1_{\tau'}}}{E_{J_\tau F} - E_{J-1_{\tau'}F+1}} \right] \tag{8-46}$$

The coefficients $f_i(JIFM)$ have been evaluated by Mizushima [857] and are listed in Table 8-1.

It is possible to reduce (8-46) to a simpler form in cases where the approximation

$$E_{J_\tau F} - E_{J'_{\tau'}F} \approx E_{J_\tau} - E_{J'_{\tau'}} \tag{8-47}$$

can be used. This leads to an equation similar to the second-order expression without hyperfine structure if the average value of m_J^2 is substituted for M^2.

$$\langle m_J^2 \rangle = \langle JIFM|m_J^2|JIFM\rangle$$

$$= \frac{[3M^2 - F(F+1)][3D(D-1) - 4J(J+1)F(F+1)]}{6F(F+1)(2F-1)(2F+3)} + \frac{J(J+1)}{3} \tag{8-48}$$

where

$$D = (F+1) + J(J+1) - I(I+1) \tag{8-49}$$

TABLE 8-1

$$f_1(JIFM) = \frac{M^2(J+I+F+2)(I+F-J)(I+J-F+1)(F+J-I+1)}{4F^2(F+1)^2(2J+3)(2J+1)(J+1)}$$

$$f_2(JIFM) = \frac{(J+I+F+3)(J+I+F+2)(J-I+F+2)(J-I+F+1)[(F+1)^2-M^2]}{4(F+1)^2(2F+3)(2F+1)(2J+3)(2J+1)(J+1)}$$

$$f_3(JIFM) = \frac{(I+F-J)(I+F-J-1)(I+J-F+2)(I+J-F+1)(F^2-M^2)}{4F^2(2F-1)(2F+1)(2J+3)(2J+1)(J+1)}$$

$$f_4(JIFM) = \frac{(I+J+F+2)(I+J-F)(I+F-J+1)(J+F-I+1)[(F+1)^2-M^2]}{4J(J+1)(2J+1)(F+1)^2(2F+3)(2F+1)}$$

$$f_5(JIFM) = \frac{M^2[J(J+1)+F(F+1)-I(I+1)]^2}{4J(J+1)(2J+1)F^2(F+1)^2}$$

[a] From Ref. [857].

This gives

$$E^{(2)} = [A_{J_\tau} + B_{J_\tau}\langle m_J^2\rangle]\varepsilon^2 \tag{8-50}$$

From the direction cosine factors in Table 2-11, the second-order correction for a symmetric rotor may be obtained. The appropriate matrix elements are

$$|\langle JKm_J|\phi_{Zg}|J-1,Km_J\rangle|^2 = \frac{(J^2-K^2)(J^2-m_J^2)}{J^2(4J^2-1)} \tag{8-51}$$

$$|\langle JKm_J|\phi_{Zg}|JKm_J\rangle|^2 = \left[\frac{Km_J}{J(J+1)}\right]^2 \tag{8-52}$$

$$|\langle JKm_J|\phi_{Zg}|J+1,Km_J\rangle|^2 = \frac{[(J+1)^2-K^2][(J+1)^2-m_J^2]}{J^2(4J^2-1)} \tag{8-53}$$

$E^{(2)}$ for the symmetric rotor can be taken from (8-46) by making the substitutions

$$\sum_{\tau'}\frac{{}^gS_{J_\tau J+1_{\tau'}}}{E_{J_\tau F}-E_{J+1_{\tau'}F'}} \rightarrow \frac{(J+1)^2-K^2}{(J+1)(E_{JKF}-E_{J+1,KF'})} \tag{8-54}$$

$$\sum_{\tau'}\frac{{}^gS_{J_\tau J_{\tau'}}}{E_{J_\tau}-E_{J_{\tau'}F'}} \rightarrow \frac{(2J+1)K^2}{J(J+1)(E_{JKF}-E_{JKF'})} \tag{8-55}$$

$$\sum_{\tau'}\frac{{}^gS_{J_\tau J-1_{\tau'}}}{E_{J_\tau F}-E_{J_{\tau'}F'}} \rightarrow \frac{(J^2-K^2)}{J(E_{JKF}-E_{J-1,KF'})} \tag{8-56}$$

and neglecting the term whose coefficient is f_5, because this term reduces to a first-order contribution in the symmetric rotor case. A simpler expression is obtained by utilizing the approximations (8-54)–(8-56) and (8-48).

$$E^{(2)} = \frac{\mu^2\varepsilon^2}{hB}\left[\frac{\langle m_J^2\rangle K^2[(2J+3)(J+1)^3 - J^3(2J-1)] - 3J^2(J+1)^2(2J+1)}{2(2J-1)(2J+1)J^3(J+1)^3(2J+3)}\right.$$
$$\left. - \frac{3\langle m_J^2\rangle - J(J+1)}{2J(J+1)(2J+3)(2J-1)}\right] \tag{8-57}$$

For $K = 0$, the result for a linear molecule (or symmetric top with $K = 0$) is obtained [848].

$$E^{(2)} = \frac{\mu^2\varepsilon^2[J(J+1) - 3\langle m_J^2\rangle]}{2hBJ(J+1)(2J+3)(2J-1)} \tag{8-58}$$

8-8c. Strong Field with a Single Quadrupole Nucleus ($\mu\varepsilon \gg eqQ$)

In the strong-field case, the quadrupole interaction terms are treated as a small perturbation. The first-order correction for a symmetric rotor is given by

$$E^{(1)} = \langle JKm_Jm_I|H_Q|JKm_Jm_I\rangle \tag{8-59}$$

Using the operator corresponding to (5-13) for $|m_J| \neq 1$

$$E^{(1)} = \frac{\chi_{zz}}{4I(2I-1)(2J-1)(2J+3)}\left[\frac{3K^2}{J(J+1)} - 1\right][3m_I^2$$
$$- I(I+1)][3m_J^2 - J(J+1)] \tag{8-60}$$

A special case can arise for $|m_J| = 1$ and $K = 0$. The degenerate $|m_J| = 1$ levels are connected by an off-diagonal element produced by the quadrupole interaction. For this case, $M = m_I + m_J$ is a good quantum number. Because the quadrupole interaction connects only states with $\Delta m_J = \pm 2$, no other sets of degenerate levels can interact. This coupling for $|m_J| = 1$ requires the solution of a quadratic secular equation.

$$\begin{vmatrix} E(IJK) + \langle 1JK|H_Q|1JK\rangle - E & \langle 1JK|H_Q| - 1JK\rangle \\ \langle -1JK|H_Q|1JK\rangle & E(IJK) + \langle -1JK|H_Q| - 1JK\rangle - E \end{vmatrix} = 0 \tag{8-61}$$

For $M = I$ or $I + 1$, the state $m_J = -1$ cannot exist, and no interaction between the states $m_J = \pm 1$ can occur. $E^{(1)}$ is still given by (8-60) and no degenerate levels are connected by the quadrupole perturbation.

For an asymmetric rotor, Mizushima [857] gives the secular equation as

$$|\langle IJm_Im_J|H_Q|IJm_I'm_J'\rangle + (E_{J_\tau I=0m_J} - E)\delta_{m_Jm_J'}\delta_{m_Im_I'}| = 0 \qquad (8\text{-}62)$$

$E_{J_\tau I=0m_J}$ is found by letting $M = m_J$ in (8-12). δ is the Kronecker delta symbol. The factor $3(\mathbf{I}\cdot\mathbf{J})^2 + \frac{3}{2}(\mathbf{I}\cdot\mathbf{J}) - \mathbf{I}^2\mathbf{J}^2$ in H_Q has off-diagonal matrix elements connecting different states labeled by $\Delta m_J = \pm 1$, $\Delta m_I = \mp 1$ and $\Delta m_J = \pm 2$, $\Delta m_I = \mp 2$. These can be treated numerically or ignored in the strong-field case, because they do not occur in any off-diagonal terms common with H_ε. In any case, the secular equation factors into submatrices for each value of M because $\langle M|H_Q|M' \neq M\rangle$ vanishes.

Howe and Flygare [886] have discussed simplifications in strong field measurements on molecules containing two quadrupole nuclei. Once the strong field case is reached, the $M = 0$ components of $J = 0 \to 1$ transitions form a symmetrical triplet whose center component is not a function of the quadrupole interaction.

8-8d. Intermediate Case ($\mu\varepsilon \approx eqQ$)

When the Stark and quadrupole energies are of comparable size, a secular equation must be solved.

$$|\langle IJm_Fm_J|H_\varepsilon|IJm_Fm_{J'}\rangle - E\delta_{m_Jm_{J'}}| = 0 \qquad (8\text{-}63)$$

Low and Townes [848] show the structure of the determinant for a symmetric rotor in Fig. 8-6. The appendix of their paper gives a sample calculation for the intermediate field case. The largest submatrix to be diagonalized is of degree $2J + 1$ or $2I + 1$, depending on which of these two quantities is smaller.

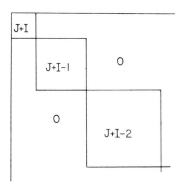

FIG. 8-6. Factoring of the energy matrix for Stark and quadrupole energies of approximately the same magnitude. Each block is labeled by the value of m_F.

8-8e. Near Degeneracies

Stark effect splittings in the presence of a nuclear quadrupole moment can be further complicated by the presence of a rotational near degeneracy. The terms $H_Q + H_\varepsilon$ of (8-33) may contain nonvanishing off-diagonal elements which connect the nearly degenerate rotational levels. The quadrupole elements of (5-36) and (5-37) connecting J with $J \pm 1$ and $J \pm 2$ and the Stark elements of (8-6) connecting J with $J \pm 1$ which normally enter as relatively weak second-order terms may produce strong interactions when the rotational, quadrupole, and Stark splittings are of the same magnitude.

Quadrupole terms connecting one of the nearly degenerate levels with another level may usually be neglected. Similar terms resulting from H_ε may be folded into the diagonal blocks by a Van Vleck transformation [1028]. Once the nearly-degenerate block has been separated from the remainder of the energy matrix, it can be diagonalized separately. The maximum size of this submatrix for two interacting rotational levels is $2(2I + 1)$, where I is the spin of the quadrupole nucleus. A detailed discussion of this problem has been given by Eagle et al. [896].

With a near-symmetric rotor, it is also possible that the asymmetry splitting may be small compared to $\mu\varepsilon$ which, in turn, is small compared to the hyperfine splitting. The Stark energy is then given by (8-30) [894] where M is replaced by $\alpha_J M_F$ [850].

$$\alpha_J = \frac{F(F + 1) - I(I + 1) + J(J + 1)}{2F(F + 1)} \tag{8-64}$$

8-9. Polarizability

An additional contribution to the interaction between a molecule and an external electric field may be provided by the tendency of the electric field to polarize the molecule. This results in an induced component of the dipole moment which is usually much smaller than the permanent dipole moment. The process is similar to the second-order Stark effect in an asymmetric rotor. A dipole moment is induced by the first power of the electric field and this moment then interacts with the field to cause a second-order effect. The possibility of quantitative measurement of the polarizability may occur in molecules with very small permanent moments and with the presence of extremely large electric field strengths; the polarizability dominates the dipole moment in HCCD [892].

The induced moment $\boldsymbol{\mu}_P$ is related to the electric field and polarizability by

$$\boldsymbol{\mu}_P = \boldsymbol{\alpha}\varepsilon \tag{8-65}$$

where $\boldsymbol{\alpha}$ is a second-rank tensor. The classical interaction energy is then given by the scalar product of μ_P and the electric field vector.

$$H_P = -\tfrac{1}{2}\varepsilon^+\alpha\varepsilon \tag{8-66}$$

In terms of the direction cosines between the field axes and the principal axes

$$E_P = -\tfrac{1}{2}\varepsilon^2 \sum_{g,h} \phi_{Zg}\phi_{Zh}\alpha_{gh} \tag{8-67}$$

α_{gh} is a component of the polarizability tensor α and g and h refer to the principal axes.

For a linear molecule, the polarizability tensor is simplified by molecular symmetry because $\alpha_{xx} = \alpha_{yy}$ and the off-diagonal elements vanish.

$$H_P = -\frac{\varepsilon^2}{2}[(\alpha_{zz} - \alpha_{xx})\cos^2\theta + \alpha_{xx}] \tag{8-68}$$

θ is the angle between the field direction and the figure axis. The first-order energy correction does not vanish and is proportional to the second power of the field.

$$E_P = \langle JM|H_P|JM\rangle$$

$$= -\frac{\varepsilon^2}{2}\alpha_A\left[\frac{J^2 - M^2}{(2J + 1)(2J - 1)} + \frac{(J + 1)^2 - M^2}{(2J + 1)(2J + 3)}\right] - \frac{\varepsilon^2}{2}\alpha_{xx} \tag{8-69}$$

The polarizability anisotropy α_A is defined as $\alpha_{zz} - \alpha_{xx}$. Because the last term in (8-69) is not a function of the rotational quantum numbers, it may be omitted. For an isotropic linear molecule, $\alpha_A = 0$ and the polarizability interaction vanishes.

From (8-13) and (8-69) it is apparent that the second-order dipole moment perturbation decreases at a faster rate with J than does the polarizability interaction. This situation causes polarizability effects to contribute a larger percentage of the Stark shift in higher J transitions. To extend measurements to higher field strengths, perturbation corrections resulting from the fourth power of the electric field are given in Appendix 14.

The dipole matrix element connects only those states which differ in J by two, i.e., the selection rule is $\Delta J = \pm 2$ for induced dipole transitions.

$$\nu = 2B(2J + 3) \tag{8-70}$$

The possibility of observing rotational transitions resulting from polarization by large electric fields in nonpolar molecules has been discussed by Townes and Schawlow [20].

This treatment is easily extended to symmetric and asymmetric-top molecules through the proper choice of direction-cosine matrix elements. For an asymmetric top, the tabulated transition strengths ${}^gS_{J_\tau J'_{\tau'}}$ are useful.

$$E_P = \tfrac{1}{2} \sum_g \alpha_{gg} \varepsilon^2 \left[\frac{J^2 - M^2}{J(4J^2 - 1)} \sum_{\tau'} {}^gS_{J_\tau J - 1_{\tau'}} + \frac{M^2}{J(J + 1)(2J + 1)} \right.$$

$$\left. \times \sum_{\tau'} {}^gS_{J_\tau J_{\tau'}} + \frac{(J + 1)^2 - M^2}{(J + 1)(2J + 1)(2J + 3)} \sum_{\tau'} {}^gS_{J_\tau J + 1_{\tau'}} \right] \qquad (8\text{-}71)$$

The polarizability correction can also be written in a form similar to (8-16).

$$E_P = \tfrac{1}{2} \alpha_{gg} [C_{J_\tau} + D_{J_\tau} M^2] \varepsilon^2 \qquad (8\text{-}72)$$

Although the polarizability interaction does contribute to the Stark effect in molecules containing a permanent dipole moment, it is often several orders of magnitude smaller and can usually be neglected.

8-10a. Stark Splittings and Relative Intensities

Once the Stark components of a microwave transition are resolved, valuable information can be obtained if the number of components, their spacing, and their relative intensities are known. With a knowledge of the selection rules, J and M values may be estimated to aid the assignment. Once an assignment has been made, the Stark displacements are utilized in the dipole determination.

Selection rules for M are governed by the relative orientation of the microwave radiation and the Stark field. If the microwave radiation field is parallel to the applied electric field (parallel electric vectors), the selection rule is $\Delta M = 0$. The selection rule $\Delta M = \pm 1$ holds when the microwave field is perpendicular to the Stark field. These $\Delta M = 0$ transitions present a spectrum which is easier to interpret than the spectrum of the $\Delta M = \pm 1$ transitions.

8-10b. $\Delta M = 0$ Transitions

The M dependence of the dipole matrix elements for the field-free case is given in Table 2-11. The actual intensities are proportional to the square of the dipole matrix elements in the representation which diagonalizes the energy when the field is present. For no near degeneracies, the intensities are very weak functions of the field, and the appropriate relative intensities can be taken from Table 2-11. Therefore, for $\Delta M = 0$ [840]

$$I(\Delta J = 0) \propto M^2 \qquad (8\text{-}73)$$

$$I(|\Delta J| = 1) \propto J^{*2} - M^2 \qquad (8\text{-}74)$$

J^* represents the larger of the two J values. From these expressions, estimates of the M values may be made through relative intensity measurements.

When a degeneracy exists for $\pm M$, a factor of $\frac{1}{2}$ must be included when $M = 0$. For Q-branch transitions in an asymmetric rotor, only J Stark components are observed because the $M = 0$ transition vanishes. Therefore, the maximum value of M is equal in magnitude to the J value of the transition. For R-branch transitions, the number of possible Stark components equals the upper J value. Because the value of M can be no larger than the J value of the lower transition, the magnitude of M_{max} is the value of the lower J.

The frequency shift is given by the difference of two terms of the form of (8-16).

$$\Delta v_M = (A' + B'M^2)\varepsilon^2\mu_g^2 \tag{8-75}$$

For a purely quadratic Stark effect, the signs of A' and B' determine in which direction (in frequency) the Stark components move for increasing field strength. When A' and B' are of the same sign, the component with the largest M value suffers the largest displacement from the unperturbed line.

Estimates of the value of M may be made either from frequency displacements or from relative intensities [840]. Using (8-75)

$$\Delta v_M - \Delta v_{M\pm 1} = \mp B'\varepsilon^2(2M \pm 1) \tag{8-76}$$

From frequency displacements for three consecutive resolved components

$$|M| = \left| \frac{3r - 1}{2 - 2r} \right| \tag{8-77}$$

where

$$r = \frac{\Delta v_M - \Delta v_{M\pm 1}}{\Delta v_{M\pm 1} - \Delta v_{M\pm 2}} = \frac{2M \pm 1}{2M \pm 3} \tag{8-78}$$

Using relative intensities for $\Delta J = 0$

$$|M| = \left| \frac{(I_M/I_{M\pm 1})^{1/2}}{1 - (I_M/I_{M\pm 1})^{1/2}} \right| \tag{8-79}$$

I_M represents the relative intensity of the M component. The functional dependence of the intensities on M gives the largest intensity to the component with the largest value of M. For R-branch lines

$$|M| = \left| \frac{3t - 1}{2 - 2t} \right| \tag{8-80}$$

$$t = \left(\frac{I_M - I_{M\pm 1}}{I_{M\pm 1} - I_{M\pm 2}} \right) \tag{8-81}$$

In this case the larger intensities belong to the lower M values. Experimental errors determine how close these equations come to the true value of M.

8-10c. $\Delta M = \pm 1$ Transitions

Intensity relations can again be obtained from Table 2-11. Using the notation of Golden and Wilson, the intensities for $\Delta J = 0$ are

$$I_M^{(+)} \propto (J - |M|)(J + |M| - 1) \tag{8-82}$$

$$I_M^{(-)} \propto (J + |M|)(J - |M| - 1) \tag{8-83}$$

Here the superscript $(+)$ corresponds to the transitions $|M| \to |M| + 1$ and $(-)$ corresponds to $|M| \to |M| - 1$. For an R-branch transition with $\Delta J = +1$,

$$I_M^{(+)} \propto (J + |M| + 1)(J + |M| + 2) \tag{8-84}$$

$$I_M^{(-)} \propto (J - |M| + 1)(J - |M| + 2) \tag{8-85}$$

Again, J refers to the lower value. Placing the selection rule $\Delta M = \pm 1$ in (8-16), the frequency displacements become

$$\Delta v_M^{(+)} = [A'' + B''M^2 + C''|M|]\varepsilon^2 \mu_g^2 \tag{8-86}$$

$$\Delta v_M^{(-)} = [A'' + B''M^2 - C''|M|]\varepsilon^2 \mu_g^2 \tag{8-87}$$

Figure 8-7 compares the allowed R-branch transitions for an asymmetric rotor under both sets of selection rules for M.

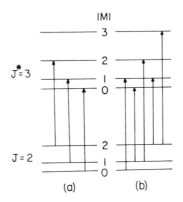

FIG. 8-7. Allowed transitions between Stark levels for a $J = 2 \to 3$ transition under (a) $\Delta M = 0$ and (b) $\Delta M = \pm 1$ selection rules.

8-10d. Intensities in the Presence of Hyperfine Structure

In the presence of quadrupole hyperfine structure, the intensities of the Stark components can be determined by a consideration of the weak and strong field limiting cases. Only the parallel selection rules $\Delta M = 0$ are considered here. In the limiting weak-field case Fig. 8-5(b) shows that the FM_F representation is valid. The relative intensities of the $\Delta F = 0$ transitions are given by a revision of (8-73).

$$I(\Delta F = 0) \propto M_F^2 \tag{8-88}$$

Similarly, from (8-74)

$$I(|\Delta F| = 1) \propto F^{*2} - M_F^2 \tag{8-89}$$

where F^* is the larger of the two F values. In the strong-field limit, the representation JM_J of Fig. 8-5(c) holds and equations (8-73) and (8-74) are appropriate. Relative intensities in the intermediate case where the Stark and quadrupole perturbations are of similar magnitudes are more difficult to obtain. It is possible to find an approximate solution by interpolating between the weak field and strong field intensities. The exact intensities for the intermediate field case are proportional to the square of the dipole matrix elements in the representation which diagonalizes the energy. However, the vector models of Fig. 8-5 cannot be used and a secular equation must be solved. The intermediate field causes a mixing of the original set of wave functions and produces a new set of functions for the perturbed levels.

8-11a. Stark Effect in a Linear Molecule—OCS

Carbonyl sulfide is a suitable linear molecule for Stark effect studies, because its spectrum is relatively simple and lacks quadrupole hyperfine structure. Its low J transitions fall throughout the centimeter and millimeter wave regions and the ground state transitions which are extremely strong exhibit an easily measured quadratic Stark effect. For these reasons, it has been the calibration standard for microwave dipole moment determinations. Marshall and Weber [862] measured the dipole moment in the ground vibrational state. Another interesting feature is the presence of l-type doublets in the excited bending vibrational state whose Stark effect is characteristic of near degeneracies. In addition, several transitions are observed which are forbidden in the absence of a perturbing field.

The ground state $J = 1 \rightarrow 2$ transition of $O^{16}C^{12}S^{32}$ occurs at 24325.921 MHz. For $\Delta M = 0$ selection rules, the $M = 0$ transition moves to low frequency and the $M = \pm 1$ transition moves to high frequency as the field strength increases. From careful measurements on these two Stark components, Marshall and Weber arrived at a dipole moment of 0.7124 ± 0.0002 Debye units. As indicated in Fig. 8-8, the weaker $M = 0$ lobe suffers a greater displacement for a given field strength than does the $|M| = 1$ lobe. When Δv is plotted against the square of the electric field strength, the resulting straight lines indicate an almost purely quadratic Stark effect. The

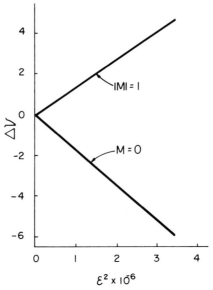

FIG. 8-8. Stark displacements Δv (MHz) for the $M = 0, \pm 1$ components of the $J = 1 \rightarrow 2$ transition of $O^{16}C^{12}S^{32}$ as a function of ε^2 (volts^2 cm^{-2}) [1110].

formula for the frequency displacement Δv is [852, 862]

$$\Delta v(J \rightarrow J + 1, \Delta M = 0) = \frac{[3M^2(16J^2 + 32J + 10) - 8J(J + 1)^2(J + 2)]\mu^2\varepsilon^2}{J(J + 2)(2J - 1)(2J + 1)(2J + 3)(2J + 5)h^2 v_0}$$

(8-90)

v_0 is the unperturbed transition frequency. The polarizability can be included by considering the classical energy expression (8-67). The perturbation energy including the polarizability term and fourth-order Stark correction is

$$H_\varepsilon = \frac{-\mu^2\varepsilon^2}{2hB}F(J, M) - \frac{1}{2}\alpha_A\varepsilon^2 G(J, M) + \frac{\mu^4\varepsilon^4}{h^3B^3}K(J, M) \qquad (8-91)$$

$F(J, M)$, $G(J, M)$, and $K(J, M)$ are the factors containing the quantum numbers in (8-13), (8-69), and (8-20). For a linear molecule, the relationship between the effective dipole moment μ_e and μ^2 is

$$\mu_e^2 = \mu^2 + h(\alpha_{zz} - \alpha_{xx})B\left[\frac{G(J, M) - G(J + 1, M)}{F(J, M) - F(J + 1, M)}\right] - \frac{2\mu^4\varepsilon^2}{h^2B^2}$$

$$\times \left[\frac{K(J, M) - K(J + 1, M)}{F(J, M) - F(J + 1, M)}\right]$$

(8-92)

μ^2 and $\alpha_{zz} - \alpha_{xx}$ can then be determined by graphing μ_e^2 versus ε^2 and extrapolating to $\varepsilon = 0$ for two values of M. μ_e is defined in Section 8-13.

8-11b. Stark Effect for an *l*-Type Doublet

A linear triatomic molecule in the degenerate bending mode v_2 has an effective structure which is nonlinear and the molecule behaves as a slightly asymmetric top. The inherent near-degeneracy results in a characteristic Stark effect approaching first-order behavior. For the most important case in which $|l| = 1$, let $\Delta v'$ be the frequency difference between the two *l*-doublet transitions at zero field. The matrix element connecting the two energy levels of an *l* doublet has been given in (3-27) and the calculated splitting is shown in (3-31). The Stark effect for the *l* doublet in $OCSe^{80}$ [1109] is illustrated in Fig. 8-9. For a weak field, H_ε is much smaller than the energy level spacing and the Stark effect has the second-order dependence characteristic of an asymmetric top. As the Stark perturbation increases, the splitting becomes first order due to the near degeneracy.

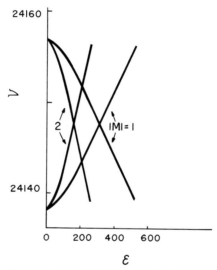

FIG. 8-9. Stark shifts of the $|M| = 1, 2$ components of the $J = 2 \rightarrow 3$ *l*-type doublet transitions in $O^{16}C^{12}Se^{80}$ [1109]. v is given in MHz and ε is given in volts cm^{-1}.

The Stark components of the lower frequency transition of the *l* doublet move to high frequency and those of the upper component move to low frequency. The dipole moment can be determined from $\Delta v'$ and from the field strength at which Stark components of the same M value coincide in frequency. For a $J \rightarrow J + 1$ transition,

$$\mu = \frac{J(J + 1)(J + 2)(J + 3)h\,\Delta v'}{4M\varepsilon} \tag{8-93}$$

In Fig. 8-9, the regions of first- and second-order behavior are easily recognized. The off-diagonal element H_{12} in (8-27) has been given by Penney [828].

$$H_{12} = \frac{\mu l M \varepsilon}{J(J + 1)} \tag{8-94}$$

The electric field has an interesting effect on the wave functions for the energy levels of an l doublet or for any set of nearly degenerate levels connected by the Stark effect. Figure 8-10 shows a schematic energy level

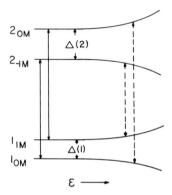

FIG. 8-10. Appearance of forbidden transitions (dashed lines) between l-doublet levels of OCS in the presence of an electric field.

diagram for two l doublets. In each case, the modified asymmetric rotor notation $J_{\tau M}$ [852] has been used to label the levels. In the zero-field limit, only the transitions represented by the solid lines are allowed. However, mixing of the wave functions produced by the Stark perturbation, which connects the nearly degenerate levels, allows previously forbidden transitions to occur (indicated by the dashed lines in Fig. 8-10). These transitions pass through a maximum intensity when H_{12} approaches the doublet separation and return toward zero intensity for large ε.

The intensities are affected because the zeroth-order wave functions, under the influence of an electric field, are mixed to form new functions of the general form

$$\psi(\varepsilon) = a(\varepsilon)\psi_1^{(0)} \pm b(\varepsilon)\psi_2^{(0)} \tag{8-95}$$

Because the wave functions are field dependent, the intensities become field dependent through the dipole matrix element. Figure 8-11 shows the first order dependence of the frequency separation Δv as a result of the near degeneracy in OCS. From (3-31), the l-doublet energy separations for a

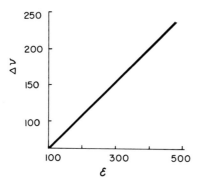

FIG. 8-11. Frequency separation Δv (MHz) of forbidden transitions between the $J = 1, 2$ l doublets of OCS as a function of electric field strength ε (volts cm^{-1}) [852].

$J \to J + 1$ transition are

$$\Delta(J) = 2qJ(J + 1) \tag{8-96}$$

$$\Delta(J + 1) = 2q(J + 1)(J + 2) \tag{8-97}$$

In the zero-field limit, assuming q is independent of J, the allowed transitions are separated by $\Delta(J + 1) - \Delta(J)$. The forbidden lines are separated by $\Delta(J + 1) + \Delta(J)$.

Using the results of Section 8-7, the field dependence of the frequency difference of the forbidden transitions is given as [852]

$$\Delta v'' = \left[(E_{20}^{(0)} - E_{2-1}^{(0)})^2 + \frac{\mu^2 \varepsilon^2}{9} \right]^{1/2} + [(E_{11}^{(0)} + E_{10}^{(0)})^2 + \mu^2 \varepsilon^2]^{1/2} \tag{8-98}$$

for the $J = 1 \to 2$ transition. An expansion similar to (8-29) reveals the first-order dependence for sufficiently large ε.

In the absence of a near degeneracy, the intensities of Stark components are still functions of the electric field strength. However, these effects are second order and not easily noticed because of the large uncertainty inherent in intensity measurements.

8-11c. Stark Effect in a Symmetric Top Molecule—CH$_3$F

The absence of a quadrupole nucleus makes methyl fluoride an excellent subject for Stark effect measurements. Larkin and Gordy [889] have studied first- and second-order effects in the $J = 1 \to 2$ transition for both $\Delta M = 0$ and $\Delta M = \pm 1$ selection rules. A first-order Stark effect is observed only for the $|K| = 1$ components of the transition. For $\Delta M = 0$, three transitions occur. From (8-8), the $M = 0 \to 0$ component is undisplaced from the zero field line and the $M = 1 \to 1$ and $-1 \to -1$ transitions are symmetrically spaced about v_0 (Fig. 8-12).

$$v(|M| = 1) = v_0 \pm \frac{\mu\varepsilon}{3h} \tag{8-99}$$

Figure 8-12 also shows the allowed transitions for $\Delta M = \pm 1$ selection rules. When only first-order effects are significant, it can be seen that four Stark

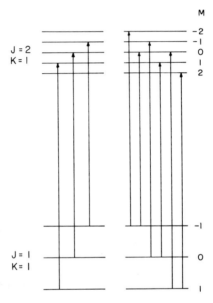

FIG. 8-12. First-order Stark splittings and allowed transitions for the $J = 1$, $K = 1$ and $J = 2$, $K = 1$ levels in a symmetric rotor. $\Delta M = 0$ transitions are shown on the left and $\Delta M = \pm 1$ transitions are shown on the right. The transitions are not drawn to scale for CH_3F.

components are resolvable for $\Delta M = \pm 1$. This results from a coincidence of the transitions $M = 0 \to 1$, $-1 \to -2$, and $M = 1 \to 2$, $0 \to -1$. The appropriate frequency displacements are

$$v = v_0 \pm (\mu\varepsilon/6h) \tag{8-100}$$

$$v = v_0 \pm (\mu\varepsilon/2h) \tag{8-101}$$

At high fields, for which the second-order corrections to the $|K| = 1$ levels become significant, this coincidental degeneracy is lifted. Second-order effects are best observed in the $K = 0$ transitions because the first-order correction vanishes.

8-11d. Stark Effect in an Asymmetric Rotor—CH$_3$CHF$_2$

The Stark effects of the $J = 1 \to 2$ transitions of the near-symmetric top CH$_3$CHF$_2$ exhibit a variety of interesting features [880]. The $M = 0$ lines show the quadratic Stark splitting characteristic of an asymmetric rotor and the $M = 1$ transitions, whose frequency displacements as a function of field strength are plotted in Fig. 8-13, suggest the presence of a near degeneracy. The $1_{10} \to 2_{11}$ component appears quadratic and the $1_{11} \to 2_{12}$ component appears linear in ε dependence. It has been pointed out that the behavior of the $1_{01} \to 2_{02}$ member approximately corresponds to the difference between the first two components.

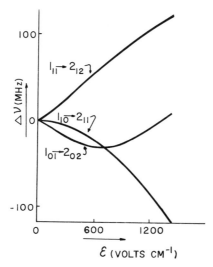

FIG. 8-13. Frequency displacements of the $M = 1$ components of the $J = 1 \to 2$ transitions in CH$_3$CHF$_2$ [880].

In the near degenerate treatment of Section 8-7, the Van Vleck transformation was applied to partially diagonalize the energy matrix so that strongly interacting levels could be separated from the rest of the problem. In the majority of cases, two levels are nearly degenerate and the calculation reduces to the solution of a 2×2 matrix block. For CH$_3$CHF$_2$, two components of the dipole moment contribute large perturbations, and the Van Vleck procedure may only be used to separate submatrices of different J resulting in a 3×3 submatrix for the $J = 1$ levels and a 5×5 block for the $J = 2$ levels. The structure of these matrices is such that the secular equations may be conveniently expanded in a continued fraction.

8-11e. Stark Effect in a Π Electronic State—NO

Most molecules possess ground electronic states with no resultant electronic angular momentum. However, in a few cases such as NO, a Π ground state results from an unpaired electron. In the diatomic molecule NO, the electronic angular momentum Ω is directed along the axis and has a magnitude of $\hbar/2$. The two possible orientations of Ω give rise to Λ-type doubling of the rotational energy levels. The presence of an angular momentum along the axis likens NO to a symmetric rotor.

The theory of the Stark effect for NO has been given by Mizushima [868]. In the presence of the N^{14} quadrupole nucleus, the weak and strong-field cases must be considered separately. In the weak-field case, the $IJFM_F$ representation is valid and a second-order effect occurs.

$$E^{(2)} = \frac{-\mu^2\varepsilon^2}{16J^2(J+1)^2}\left[\frac{M_F^2[J(J+1)+F(F+1)-2]^2}{(E_{dJF}^{(0)}-E_{cJF}^{(0)})F^2(F+1)^2}\right.$$

$$+\frac{(F^2-M_F^2)(F+J+2)(J-F+2)(F-J+1)(J+F-1)}{(E_{dJ,F-1}^{(0)}-E_{cJF}^{(0)})F^2(2F+1)(2F-1)}$$

$$\left.+[(F+1)^2-M_F^2]\frac{(F+J+3)(J-F+1)(F-J+2)(J+F)}{(E_{dJ,F+1}^{(0)}-E_{cJF}^{(0)})(F+1)^2(2F+3)(2F+1)}\right]$$

$$(8\text{-}102)$$

Here c and d refer to the lower and upper members of the Λ doublet. Matrix elements off-diagonal in J have been neglected. In the strong field case, the Stark energy is larger than the Λ doubling and the Stark effect becomes first order.

$$E = \tfrac{1}{2}(E_{cJ}^{(0)}+E_{dJ}^{(0)})\pm \mu\varepsilon M/2J(J+1)\cdots \qquad (8\text{-}103)$$

8-12. Stark Effect and Hindered Internal Motions

Internal molecular motions such as inversion and internal rotation often produce interesting Stark effects. First-order Stark effects may be observed when internal degeneracies are present, and, in some cases, can lead to independent determinations of hindering potentials. For molecules exhibiting internal rotation, the Stark effect is a function of the barrier height and molecular asymmetry. In the low barrier case of hindered internal rotation, the internal energy levels are labeled by the free rotation quantum number m. Except when $m = 0$, the levels are all doubly degenerate in $\pm m$ for free rotation. This degeneracy leads to a first-order Stark effect as long as $m \neq 0$ and K and M are not zero. Provided there is no near degeneracy, the $m = 0$ lines show the usual second-order effect. The introduction of a low sixfold barrier removes the m degeneracy only for those levels where m is a multiple of three, although the splitting is most pronounced for $m = \pm 3$. The Van Vleck transformation, used to remove the elements off-diagonal in m, also removes the first-order Stark terms which were diagonal in m and leaves only the second-order off-diagonal elements of H_ε. Thus the Stark effect is characteristically second-order, although for a small splitting of the $|m| = 3$ levels, an approach similar to that for near degeneracies in an asymmetric top must be used. The degeneracies of the remaining levels whose m values are not a multiple of three are unaltered by the barrier. Transitions involving these levels give first-order Stark effects as long as K and M are not zero.

For high barriers, the IAM or PAM formulations are convenient and the nondegenerate A torsional levels present a pseudorigid rotor spectrum and a quadratic Stark effect. The linear K terms characteristic of the E levels in a near symmetric top can contribute a linear term to the Stark energy. In the notation of the IAM for a parallel dipole component μ_g [676, 793]

$$E_E^{(1)} = \frac{2KM\delta_K\mu_g\varepsilon}{\Delta\omega_{JK}J(J+1)} \tag{8-104}$$

$\Delta\omega_{JK}$ is the K-type splitting of an asymmetric rotor, and δ_K is the barrier dependent term given in (6-209).

In the PAM, the first-order term $-2\xi_v\mathscr{P}$ in the perturbation expansion (6-103) can connect the internal barrier with the Stark perturbation. Figure

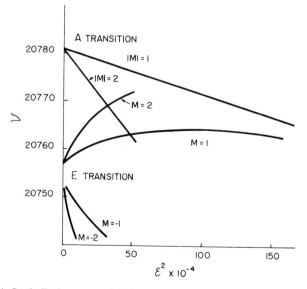

FIG. 8-14. Stark displacements of the internal rotation components of the $2_{11} \rightarrow 3_{12}$ transition in cis-1-chloropropylene [1632].

8-14 shows the Stark effect of the $2_{11} \rightarrow 3_{12}$ transition in cis-1-chloropropylene [1632]. The near degeneracy of the $K = \pm 1$ levels provides the coupling. The important matrix elements in a prolate symmetric rotor representation take the form

$$\langle JKM|H|JKM \rangle = E_s + DK + E_\varepsilon^{(1)} \qquad (8\text{-}105)$$

$$\langle JKM|H|J, K \pm 2, M \rangle = E_a \qquad (8\text{-}106)$$

E_s is the symmetric rotor energy in (2-72), $E_\varepsilon^{(1)}$ is given by (8-8), D is the coefficient of the linear momentum term which provides a linear K dependence, and E_a is given by (2-73). By solving the 2×2 determinant for the $K = \pm 1$ levels and obtaining dipole moment components from the quadratic Stark splitting of an A transition, an accurate value of the barrier height can be calculated from D and from the Stark splitting of the $\pm M$ lobes.

Nonquadratic Stark effects may also result from near degeneracies between inversion levels having connecting dipole matrix elements. From these effects, information concerning the barrier height and inversion splitting, particularly for low barriers in near planar molecules, may be obtained. Molecules which are slightly nonplanar and possess a small out-of-plane component of the dipole moment† usually exhibit a very large inversion doubling. Although this moment may not be directly detectable in the spectrum, its influence may be felt in the Stark effect of transitions from larger dipole components. An upper limit can often be placed on the magnitude of the out-of-plane transition moment. An example of a near-degeneracy of inversion levels is illustrated in Fig. 8-15 for trimethylene oxide. The out-of-plane component μ_c connects nearly-degenerate levels, while the observed transitions result from μ_a. The Stark effect of only one of the transitions $(- \leftrightarrow -)$ is expected to have some first-order character. The mixing of wave functions which occurs for a near degeneracy may also produce otherwise forbidden transitions.

8-13. Dipole Moment Measurement Techniques

The Stark effect provides a very convenient method for determining the magnitudes of molecular dipole moments. Once the quantum numbers of a transition are known, measurement of the frequency displacement of an appropriate Stark component as a function of the electric field strength results in a relationship between Δv and ε. This expression contains the constant μ. If the molecule possesses more than one nonzero dipole moment component, an equivalent number of transitions must be studied.

---

† This is actually a transition moment connecting two vibrational levels, e.g., $\langle 0|\mu_c|1 \rangle$.

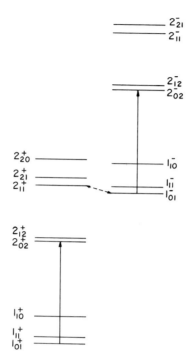

FIG. 8-15. $1_{01} \to 2_{02}$ transition in trimethylene oxide [798]. These a-type transitions connect inversion levels of the same symmetry ($\pm \to \pm$) through the a component of the dipole moment. The c-type connection which would be produced by a nonvanishing out-of-plane moment $\langle 0|\mu_c|1\rangle$ is identified by the dashed line ($1_{01}^- \to 2_{11}^+$). If the inversion splittings of the 1_{01} and 2_{02} levels are identical, the two a-type components will occur at the same frequency; the presence of a strong Stark perturbation produced by a near degeneracy can cause the Stark effect of one of the transitions to differ from that of the other transition resulting in a splitting of the observed Stark components. No splitting was observed in trimethylene oxide, indicating a small or vanishing out-of-plane transition moment and a planar or nearly planar molecule.

With the high resolution available in the microwave region, the frequency displacements Δv are relatively easy to measure to a high degree of accuracy provided the molecule has a sufficiently large dipole moment and a relatively low J transition can be found which has a resolvable Stark effect. However, the electric field strength is not as easy to determine to the same degree of accuracy. The electric field strength depends on the voltage applied to the cell as well as on the electrode spacing. The possible error sources encountered in the determination of the field strength have been discussed by Shulman and Townes [852] and Tobler et al. [194] for an X-band waveguide Stark cell. These errors include inaccuracies in the measurement of applied voltages, electric field inhomogeneities, and distortions introduced by the Stark electrode and its insulators. An improved value of ε may be obtained by using a parallel-plate cell. This cell configuration provides a more uniform Stark field through the use of evenly spaced flat electrodes. Using a cell of this type, Marshall and Weber [862] have provided a very accurate value of 0.7124 ± 0.0002 Debye units for the ground state dipole moment in OCS. With this value, it is possible to conduct dipole moment determinations in standard waveguide Stark cells by calibrating the guide against OCS before and after measuring the Stark displacements of the molecules being studied. Using the known value of the dipole moment, the measured frequency displacements, and the quantum numbers of the OCS transition, the calibration measurements allow the effective electric field strength to be determined. In this way, all microwave dipole moment measurements can be based on the standard value for OCS.

As an alternative method for dipole moment determinations, Lindfors and Cornwell [894] observed that under conditions of weak, zero-based, square-wave modulation, the rotational line shapes resemble first or second derivatives of the zero-field line. Dipole moment information may be obtained by peak-to-peak intensity measurements. This method can be used to advantage when low J transitions are not available in the frequency range being studied or when the Stark components are difficult to resolve. Also, quadrupole hyperfine structure and Stark components from nearby lines present fewer problems.

A convenient method for treating Stark effect data in linear and symmetric top molecules was mentioned briefly in Section 8-11a. It consists of defining an effective dipole moment μ_e. For a first-order Stark effect where the second-order correction is included, the effective moment may be defined as

$$\mu_e = \frac{h\,\Delta\nu}{\varepsilon[D(J+1, KM) - D(JKM)]} \tag{8-107}$$

and it follows that

$$\mu_e = \mu + \frac{\mu^2\varepsilon}{2hB}\left[\frac{F(J+1, KM) - F(JKM)}{D(J+1, KM) - D(JKM)}\right] \tag{8-108}$$

By plotting μ_e against ε, the $\varepsilon = 0$ intercept gives the dipole moment μ directly. For a second-order Stark effect with a fourth-order correction included,

$$\mu_e = \frac{2h^2\,\Delta\nu B}{\varepsilon^2[F(J+1, KM) - F(JKM)]} \tag{8-109}$$

and

$$\mu_e^2 = \mu^2 + \frac{2\mu^4\varepsilon^2}{h^2B^2}\left[\frac{K(J+1, KM) - K(JKM)}{F(J+1, KM) - F(JKM)}\right] \tag{8-110}$$

In the latter case μ_e^2 is plotted against ε^2 to obtain μ^2.

A similar treatment may be applied to asymmetric rotor molecules. Rewriting (8-12) as

$$E_g^{(2)} = \mu_g^2 \varepsilon^2 H(J\tau M) \tag{8-111}$$

the effective moment may be defined by

$$\mu_e^2 = \frac{h\,\Delta\nu}{\varepsilon^2[H(J'\tau'M') - H(J\tau M)]} \tag{8-112}$$

Then,

$$\mu_e^2 = \mu^2 + h\mu^4\varepsilon^2\left[\frac{I(J'\tau'M') - I(J\tau M)}{H(J'\tau'M') - H(J\tau M)}\right] \tag{8-113}$$

The $I(J\tau M)$ are the fourth-order Stark coefficients which are not available in a closed form. However, these coefficients are not really necessary because they determine only the slope of the μ_e^2 versus ε^2 plot and not the $\varepsilon = 0$ intercept which defines μ^2 [892]. Therefore, this method allows the Stark effect data to be treated to two orders of approximation without the necessity of an explicit knowledge of the Stark coefficients for the second correction term.

8-14. Stark Effects in Rapidly Varying Fields

The Stark effects which have been studied to this point can be called static because during the time when the applied electric field is present it assumes a constant value ε. If a sinusoidally varying ε field is used and its frequency is increased to the point where it is comparable to the line width or to certain closely spaced energy level differences, some interesting phenomena may be observed in the microwave spectrum. The exact behavior of the Stark effect must then be determined by solving the time-dependent wave equation [836].

Let the varying field be of the form $E_0 \cos 2\pi\nu_0 t$. When ν_0 is considerably less than the linewidth, e.g., 1 kHz, each Stark component follows the field. The absorption is then effectively spread over a frequency range from the undisplaced line to the position the Stark component in a static field E_0. When ν_0 is comparable to the line width, e.g., 100 kHz, each Stark component is resolved into a set of lines whose spacing depends on ν_0. The relative intensities are determined by the ratio of ν_0 to the magnitude of the Stark displacement. As ν_0 becomes larger than the linewidth, one of these components dominates in intensity. It gives the appearance of a single Stark component which is displaced an amount equivalent to its average displacement if it were able to follow the field. The resulting spectrum resembles that for the static field case [20].

A more interesting effect from the viewpoint of molecular spectroscopy is the resonant case. The frequency of the rapidly varying field can be resonant with an allowed transition between closely spaced energy levels. The treatment has been developed by Autler and Townes [858]. An example of this type of system is the *l*-type doublets of the $J = 1 \rightarrow 2$ transition in OCS. When the strong r.f. field approaches either of the small doublet splittings, 12.78 MHz for $J = 1$ or 38.28 MHz for $J = 2$, the modulation produced by the field splits the observed transitions into two components which are equal in intensity only at the resonant frequency. By varying the frequency until the observed intensities are equal, the transition frequencies between closely spaced levels can be measured. A detailed treatment of the problem again requires the solution of a time-dependent wave equation.

8-15. Variation of μ with Isotopic Substitution and with Vibrational State

It has long been recognized that the dipole moment of a molecule may change with isotopic substitution [829, 867]. This has been emphasized by the observation of a small permanent dipole moment in $H-C\equiv C-D$ [892]. This effect has been ascribed to the anharmonicity of vibrations involving the substituted atom and to the lack of a linear relationship between the dipole moment and the internuclear distance or displacement. The latter is essentially electrical anharmonicity. Because the largest percentage mass changes during isotopic substitution occur for hydrogen, it is convenient to consider the change in dipole moment of a linear diatomic molecule $H-X$ when it is substituted to $D-X$. The change in dipole moment can be expressed as a Taylor series expansion in the change of the average internuclear distance $\langle r_D \rangle - \langle r_H \rangle$ in a particular vibrational state.

$$\mu_D - \mu_H = \left(\frac{\partial \mu}{\partial r}\right)_0 (\langle r_D \rangle - \langle r_H \rangle) + \cdots \qquad (8\text{-}114)$$

This is equivalent to stating that the dipole moment of $H-X$ becomes equal to the dipole moment of $D-X$ when the average $H-X$ bond length $\langle r_H \rangle$ is changed to the value $\langle r_D \rangle$. Higher derivatives may be of some importance for polyatomic molecules.

The dipole derivative $(\partial \mu/\partial r)$ is evaluated at the equilibrium position in the actual expansion. Evaluation of the sign and magnitude of this derivative is valuable because they can be compared with $(\partial \mu/\partial Q_i)$ data from quantitative infrared intensity studies. Q_i is the appropriate normal coordinate (assumed to be primarily a pure bond stretch or a pure angle bend). This data takes on added importance when it is remembered that the sign of the dipole derivative is not obtained from the intensity studies.

In Chapter 4 it is generalized that the $H-X$ bond length is reduced by 0.003–0.005 Å for a deuterium substitution. $\mu_D - \mu_H$ has been found to be positive for the representative pairs HCl—DCl [829] and $(CH_3)_3CH$—$(CH_3)_3CD$ [881]. Within the scope of the assumptions leading to this answer, it may be concluded that the dipole moment decreases for increasing internuclear distance in H—X near the equilibrium position. X is either a single atom or a symmetric group of atoms. In the latter case, the symmetrical stretching vibration is assumed to have the greatest effect on the dipole moment. However, negative $\mu_D - \mu_H$ values for the methylacetylene pairs CH_3CCH—CH_3CCD and CD_3CCH—CD_3CCD have been reported [892]. From this data it is apparent that the use of (8-114) in polyatomic systems requires a knowledge of the molecular charge distribution, normal vibrations and anharmonicity, and structure.

A variation of dipole moment with vibrational state is intuitively reasonable, since the molecular structure and charge distribution differ from those in the ground vibrational state. This conclusion has been verified by Stark effect measurements in excited states of molecules like OCS [852] and OCSe [1109]. The moment variation can be treated approximately by considering the change of effective bond length with vibrational quantum number.

CHAPTER 9 | INSTRUMENTATION

9-1. Spectroscopy in the Microwave Region

Before 1945, very little was known about the rotational spectra of any but the lightest molecules. Although a low resolution study of the inversion transitions of ammonia in the microwave region had been accomplished in 1934 [1008], the invention and subsequent development of the klystron tube and other continuous microwave oscillators were required to open a new region of the electromagnetic spectrum to the spectroscopist. Using the microwave techniques developed in connection with radar, working microwave spectrometers were constructed from which many variations have appeared.

A microwave spectrometer has the essential features of any absorption spectrometer (Fig. 9-1); namely, a source of monochromatic radiation with the proper frequency range, a sample cell, a detection system, and a method for spectrum presentation. However, the basic components differ significantly from the corresponding systems used in other spectral regions. The optimum spectrometer configuration and characteristics for the study of any particular aspect of the spectrum will depend on the nature of the sample and the required sensitivity and resolution.

Fig. 9-1. Essential features of an absorption spectrometer. Radiation control devices (mirrors or waveguides), dispersive elements, and external perturbations, e.g., electric or magnetic fields, may also be present.

Some interesting comparisons can be made with infrared and optical spectrometers. Low power microwave sources are readily available in the centimeter and longer millimeter wavelength regions. Unlike a conventional thermal source for the infrared which produces a continuous output spectrum governed by the black body distribution curve, microwave oscillators are essentially monochromatic and do not require a dispersive prism or grating. At normal temperatures for a thermal source ($\sim 1500°K$), the radiation density peaks in the vicinity of 3.5 microns ($\sim 3000\,cm^{-1}$) and decreases rapidly with increasing wavelength. At microwave frequencies, the intensity is so low that an electronic source must be used. However, due to transit-time effects, conventional electronic oscillator techniques are not successful at these frequencies and special vacuum tubes such as klystrons, backward-wave oscillators, and traveling-wave tubes have been developed.

The electromagnetic radiation produced by the source is transmitted through a conducting metal tube called a waveguide to the sample cell and detector. Each waveguide has a low-frequency cutoff below which no energy will propagate; all frequencies above cutoff are transmitted with certain field configurations or modes which increase in number with increasing frequency. The mode forms are governed by boundary conditions specified at the waveguide walls. Sample cells must also act as waveguides, while at the same time performing other special functions including the application of external electric or magnetic fields to the sample and amplitude-modulation to the microwave signal. Modulation of the signal is somewhat analogous to the low-frequency mechanical chopping characteristic of infrared spectrometers.

Detection and amplification may be achieved with either wide-band or narrow-band systems using varying degrees of frequency or amplitude-modulation, and in conjunction with radiofrequency techniques, frequencies can be measured to a high degree of accuracy. Crystal detectors have preference over the thermal and photoconductive detectors used at higher frequencies. The absorption lines are displayed either on an oscilloscope or on a chart recorder along with a set of frequency markers produced by mixing a sample of the microwave radiation with a known reference frequency.

9-2. General Qualities of the Spectrometer

High resolution and high sensitivity are the most desirable characteristics of any spectrometer. The former allows detailed investigations of hyperfine splittings; the latter enables the investigator to observe weak transitions, particularly those from isotopic species in low natural abundance and those arising from molecules in excited vibrational states. The ability to resolve microwave transitions is limited mainly by the properties of the molecular sample, while sensitivity is a strong function of the operating characteristics of the spectrometer. However, resolution and sensitivity are not independent; they are functions of both the spectrometer and the sample. High resolution can be obtained only at some expense to the sensitivity; an increase in sensitivity may adversely affect the resolution.

TABLE 9-1

BROADENING MECHANISMS LIMITING RESOLUTION AND SENSITIVITY

	Line broadening	Mechanism	Approximate magnitude
Natural line width	$\dfrac{32\pi^3 v^3 |\langle i|\mathbf{\mu}|j\rangle|^2}{3hc^3}$	Zero-point vibrations of electromagnetic radiation	$\sim 10^{-4}$ Hz
Pressure broadening	Proportional to pressure and usually dominant over range from 10^{-3} to 10^2 Torr	Collisions between molecules	>25 kHz
Saturation broadening	Increased by a factor of $$\left[1 + \frac{16\pi^2 |\langle i|\mathbf{\mu}|j\rangle|^2 vIt}{3ch\,\Delta v_0}\right]^{1/2}$$ for an unsaturated line width of Δv_0, a collisional transition probability t, and a radiation intensity I	Excess radiation field density	For low pressures saturation can be prominant at μ-watt power levels

Doppler broadening	$3.581 \times 10^{-7} \nu \left(\dfrac{T}{M}\right)^{1/2}$ for a molecular weight M and temperature T	Relative motion parallel to direction of propagation of radiation. Reduced by beam techniques.	~ 40 kHz
Modulation broadening	Increased by a factor of $\left[1 + \dfrac{1}{4}\left(\dfrac{\nu_{mod}}{\Delta\nu_0}\right)^2\right]$ over the unmodulated line width $\Delta\nu_0$	Inability of transitions to follow modulation field	Slightly greater than square-wave modulation frequency, $\nu_{mod} \leq 100$ kHz
Source instability	Short-term drift essentially eliminated by frequency or phase stabilization	Thermal drift, mechanical shock	≥ 200 Hz at ~ 20 GHz
Wall collision broadening	$\dfrac{A}{2\pi V}\left(\dfrac{RT}{2\pi M}\right)^{1/2}$ for a surface area A and a volume V	Collisions with physical dimensions of sample cell	10–15 kHz

Maximum resolution is specified by the minimum detectable absorption line half-width at half intensity. The line-broadening interactions which limit the effective resolution of a microwave spectrometer are listed in Table 9-1. Depending on the experimental conditions, one of these mechanisms will govern the minimum linewidth.

As a result of the uncertainty principle, every transition possesses a natural line width of the order of 10^{-4} Hz, caused by the interaction of the zero-point energy of electromagnetic radiation with the molecular sample. This width is negligible when compared with broadening effects produced by molecular collisions in the sample, collisions of the sample with the container walls, source instabilities, and Doppler, saturation, and modulation broadening. Neglecting source instabilities and noise contributions from the spectrometer, pressure and saturation effects usually are dominant in low resolution work. Under optimum conditions where line widths are very narrow, Doppler broadening becomes the limiting factor.

Most microwave transitions are studied at sample pressures from 10^{-3} to 10^{-1} Torr (mm Hg) where intermolecular collisions are usually the most important line broadening factor (pressure broadening). When these conditions hold for a transition, the half width is a linear function of pressure and the maximum intensity is relatively independent of the pressure.

If the pressure is lowered to reduce pressure broadening effects, saturation of the transition can occur if the power level of the incident radiation exceeds a limit set by the molecular sample. A large radiation density will alter the equilibrium Boltzmann distribution, forcing the populations of these two levels to be nearly equal. This situation results in a broadening of the line and causes an effective decrease in the peak absorption as shown in Fig. 9-2 because the populations of the levels cannot relax toward equilibrium at an adequate rate. For the low pressures used in most microwave studies, saturation is easily achieved, often with only a few microwatts of incident power. Independent of other considerations, saturation can be prevented by reducing the incident power level, increasing the sample volume, or increasing the sample pressure.

Once the line width is reduced to the order of 100 kHz or less, Doppler and modulation broadening become important. Modulation is discussed in Section 9-3e and can result in the appearance of sidebands on the absorption line unless the modulation frequency is less than the line width, i.e., less than the intermolecular collision frequency. Doppler broadening effects are introduced by motions of the molecules relative to the direction of propagation of the incident radiation. Although modulation broadening can be reduced by lowering the modulation frequency, crystal noise effects which are inversely proportional to the modulation frequency become very important at frequencies below about 20 kHz. If high frequency modulation

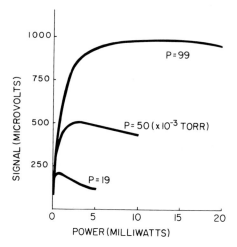

FIG. 9-2. Pressure dependence of the spectrometer signal for the $1_{01} \rightarrow 1_{10}$ transition of ethylene oxide at 11,385.93 MHz as a function of microwave power [186]. The effects of power saturation are apparent.

is abandoned and a special technique is employed to study only the group of molecules moving normal to the radiation field, modulation broadening effects are removed and Doppler broadening may be reduced to the order of 10 kHz.

The maximum sensitivity of a microwave spectrometer is measured by the weakest detectable absorption line for which the signal-to-noise ratio is one. It follows that the total noise introduced during absorption, detection, and amplification is the limiting factor which places the maximum sensitivity of present spectrometer systems in the range from 10^{-9} to 10^{-10} cm^{-1}. An absorption coefficient of 10^{-10} cm^{-1} corresponds to a change in the detector power level of $10^{-6} \%$ for a cell 1 meter long.

Maximum sensitivity is obtained by using high sample pressures and high power levels, although saturation must be avoided. The pressure is increased in order to give the peak absorption coefficient its maximum value. At this pressure, collisions provide the dominant line-broadening mechanism and a further increase in pressure will not produce a corresponding increase in line intensity. Sensitivity may also be improved through a proper considera-tion of temperature. If a ground state transition is being studied, a lowering of the temperature will increase the population of the lower energy levels. It is then advantageous to do microwave studies at low temperatures, provided the sample has sufficient vapor pressure.

The length of the absorption cell can often be increased to enhance the sensitivity. An increase in path length allows more molecules to be in the radiation field for a given pressure. However, after an optimum distance which depends on the construction and transmission characteristics of the cell, further increases in length reduce the effective sensitivity [20].

Data is obtained from the microwave spectrum of a molecule through measurements of the frequencies and relative intensities of pure rotational transitions. Frequency measurements are generally more important to the study of rotational spectra than are relative or absolute intensity measurements; however, the latter are indispensable for identifying transitions and hyperfine components, determining low energy vibrational frequencies, and measuring barriers to internal rotation where other schemes fail. The ability to measure rotational transition frequencies with accuracies greater than 10 kHz results in excellent values for the rotational constants and moments of inertia, although the accuracy of measurements depends strongly on the line width and intensity. Intensity measurements are inherently much less accurate due to the large number of variables which must be controlled [169]. With an adequate microwave spectrometer, a frequency region can be searched for possible rotational transitions, and once found, these transitions may be measured and then identified by studying characteristic Stark effects or hyperfine splittings.

9-3a. Characteristics of Microwave Spectrometers

Because most microwave spectrometers have been designed and built in the laboratory, each spectrometer has many unique characteristics which are functions of the component parts used in its construction and operation. Although radiation sources, sample cells, and methods of presentation are quite diverse, it is the detection scheme which primarily identifies each instrument. In a video spectrometer, the detected signal is amplified by a wide-band system which suffers the limiting effects of detector noise. To avoid this problem, modulation is applied either to the source or to the cell, and the detected signal is amplified by a relatively narrow-band system.

A majority of measurements on rotational transitions in the microwave region have been performed with Stark-modulation spectrometers in which the modulation is applied directly to the sample cell [51, 67, 70]. In addition to improved operating characteristics, this spectrometer allows simultaneous detection of the unperturbed absorption line and its components in the presence of an electric field. A typical laboratory configuration is shown as a block diagram in Fig. 9-3. The basic concepts utilized in this spectrometer are the generation of monochromatic radiation at centimeter or millimeter wavelengths, modulation of this energy through the modulation of molecular energy levels, amplification and detection by a narrow-band system whose detection circuit is synchronized with the modulation, and display on an oscilloscope or recorder.

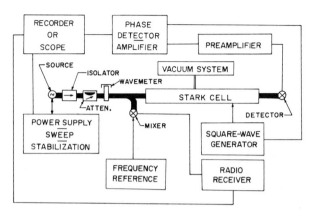

FIG. 9-3. Block diagram of one of the possible configurations for a Stark-modulated micro-wave spectrometer.

9-3b. Radiation Sources

For spectroscopic purposes, the microwave power is usually supplied by a reflex klystron which is essentially a tunable monochromatic microwave oscillator. The klystron can be mechanically tuned over a range of several GHz by changing its cavity size. Finer tuning can be managed electrically over a range of the order of 25 MHz. Other tube-type sources such as backward-wave oscillators and traveling-wave oscillators are used less frequently, although they possess some special advantages inherent in their operation, e.g., wider electronic tuning ranges and high frequency operation. Solid-state sources such as the Gunn effect oscillator and avalanche transit-time devices (Read diodes) also may become competitive [196h].

The klystrons used in microwave spectroscopy are low power sources capable of generating milliwatts of power through most of the centimeter and millimeter regions, although maximum power is rarely needed for spectroscopy at the lower frequencies. A simplified diagram of one form of tube is illustrated in Fig. 9-4. It contains a cathode assembly which produces a beam of electrons by thermal emission. This beam of electrons is focused to pass through a single resonant cavity which acts as an anode, since it is positive relative to the cathode. Instead of striking the anode as electrons would in a normal vacuum tube, the electrons pass through a hole in the anode. The beam then comes under the influence of a negative voltage which has been impressed on the reflector electrode (sometimes called the repeller) and is forced back through the anode cavity before it has reached the reflector.

Under the proper values of beam, anode, and reflector voltages, oscillations occur in the resonant cavity. The dominant frequency of this oscillation is determined by the resonant frequency of the cavity. Once oscillation has

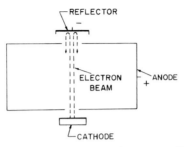

Fɪɢ. 9-4. Simplified diagram of a reflex klystron microwave oscillator. The tube is operated under a high vacuum.

begun, power is transferred to the output when the oscillations are sustained by the electron beam. An r.f. field appears across the gap in the anode through which the electrons pass. Once the electrons reach this gap, they are velocity modulated by the field. The phase of the r.f. field determines whether the electrons of the beam are accelerated or decelerated. The effect of this modulation is to bunch the electrons of the beam. The electron beam is then reversed in direction by the reflector and passes back through the gap. The position of the r.f. phase during which the groups of electrons reenter the gap determines whether they add energy to the cavity and sustain the oscillations or take energy from the field. If the r.f. field slows the bunched electrons, thereby removing energy from them, the cavity will continue to oscillate. The microwave energy which is released passes through a window into the waveguide system.

The frequency of radiation emitted by the klystron can be varied by fine tuning the cavity size or the reflector voltage. The size of the cavity and its resonant frequency can be changed by a mechanical tuning stub. This type of tuning allows large changes in frequency and determines the frequency range of the tube.

Klystron tubes operate in several modes which are determined by the effective cavity size and the reflector voltage; these modes of operation are limited by the boundary conditions which the cavity places on the frequency of oscillation. The frequency of oscillation on a given mode can be varied slightly by changing the reflector voltage in small increments. Increasing the magnitude of the negative reflector voltage decreases the time it takes the electron beam to traverse the cavity. This change produces a corresponding increase in the frequency of oscillation.

Beam voltages between 500 and 3000 volts are normally required for tubes operating at centimeter and millimeter wavelengths. The higher voltage values are associated with the higher frequencies. As higher frequencies are reached, the physical size of the cavity restricts the frequencies which can be attained by conventional reflex klystrons.

9-3c. Source Stabilization

The sensitivity of a microwave spectrometer is limited by the noise power which appears in the output spectrum containing the molecular absorption lines. An effective method of minimizing this noise is to reduce the effective band-width of the detection system, i.e., increase the time constant which characterizes the detector. However, to permit a faithful reproduction of the absorption line shape, the rate at which the source frequency is swept through the absorption line also must be decreased (Section 9-3e). As the sweep rate is lowered, source instabilities place a limit on how slowly the spectrum may be searched. A free-running reflex klystron or other microwave oscillator normally suffers from incoherent low-frequency fluctuations; major causes of this frequency instability include temperature changes, mechanical disturbances, control element voltage variations, stray external fields, variations in the load admittance, and noise generated in the electron beam [70a]. All except the last of these noise sources may be reduced by stabilizing the microwave oscillator. Stability is commonly achieved by comparing the frequency of the source with an external standard such as a crystal-controlled oscillator, a high Q resonant cavity, a narrow absorption line, or another stabilized source. The error voltage which is generated then is utilized to correct the source.

A number of stabilization systems have been designed. Frequency stabilization schemes have been presented by Pound [52], Dayhoff [72], and Rideout [54], while closely related phase stabilization methods have been described by Peter and Strandberg [104], Narath and Gwinn [165], Poynter and Steffensen [175], and others [154, 170]. Because these systems may assume many configurations and show a wide range of operating characteristics, Table 9-2 presents only a representative list of operating conditions for several types of stabilization schemes.

TABLE 9-2

REPRESENTATIVE COMPARISON OF MICROWAVE SOURCE STABILIZATION METHODS[a,b]

	Stability[c]	Approximate tuning range[c]
Cavity with a.f.c. circuit	$\sim 1:2 \times 10^6$	$\sim 1\% (200\,\text{MHz})$
Crystal harmonics with a.f.c. circuit	$\sim 1:5 \times 10^6$	$\sim 0.1\% (20\,\text{MHz})$
Crystal · harmonics with a phase-stabilized system	$\sim 1:10^7$	$\sim 0.5\% (100\,\text{MHz})$
Crystal harmonics with an extremely stable phase-stabilized system	$\sim 1:10^9$	$\sim 0.01\% (2\,\text{MHz})$

[a] From Ref. [174].

[b] Characteristics of individual systems may differ widely from those stated here.

[c] For a source frequency of approximately 20 GHz.

Frequency stabilization generally requires the use of a discriminator circuit to produce the correcting voltage. A harmonic of the low-frequency crystal-controlled oscillator is mixed with the source signal to produce an intermediate frequency. The discriminator then compares the actual i.f. with a reference signal and generates a small voltage difference which is used to correct the source frequency. Phase-lock stabilization schemes employ a phase-sensitive detection circuit to compare the i.f. with a standard reference signal. Phase variations in the microwave oscillator are detected in the phase-sensitive circuit, forming a correction voltage which is a function of the phase difference between the two signals.

Frequency stabilization is achieved with a relatively simple experimental configuration but does not allow the exact transfer of stability from a low frequency reference to the microwave source which is characteristic of phase stabilization. If a high Q resonant cavity is to be used in a frequency stabilization network, it must be maintained at a constant temperature to prevent frequency drift and should tune smoothly over a wide frequency range. The relatively high power consumption and sensitive coupling conditions characteristic of a cavity sometimes prove to be disadvantageous.

Figure 9-5 depicts a block diagram of a phase-lock system similar to that proposed by Narath and Gwinn. Initially, a low-frequency microwave oscillator, e.g., a 4–8 GHz klystron, is phase-locked to a low-frequency

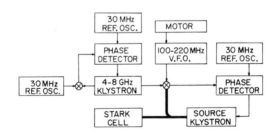

FIG. 9-5. Block diagram of a phase stabilization system.

crystal-controlled oscillator. This is accomplished by mixing the proper harmonic of the stable crystal oscillator with the klystron frequency to produce an intermediate frequency which is typically 30 MHz. The i.f. enters a phase detection circuit which compares it to a 30 MHz reference signal obtained from a reference oscillator. The phase detector detects any phase difference between the two signals and sends a correcting voltage to the reflector of the klystron to restore a fixed phase relationship between the two signals. By choosing a low frequency klystron which has an octave tuning range, a series of overlapping harmonics is provided to allow continuous operation over the spectrum up to the highest usable harmonic.

With the low-frequency klystron stabilized, its signal can be used to phase-lock the source klystron of the spectrometer. This is done by using a second phase-detection circuit and a 30 MHz reference oscillator. However, at this point the signal from a variable frequency oscillator (v.f.o.) is mixed with a harmonic of the low-frequency stabilized klystron and the source klystron frequency to produce the i.f. which is fed into the phase detector. The source klystron is then locked to a v.f.o. sideband of a harmonic of the low-frequency klystron. The v.f.o. frequency can be varied slowly by a servo-system. Because the phase detector continually corrects the klystron, the change of v.f.o. frequency sweeps the klystron over a frequency range equal to the range covered by the v.f.o. Typical frequency ranges for the components are shown in Fig. 9-5. Figure 9-6 illustrates an absorption line recorded in conjunction with a phase-stabilized source. To take advantage of the improved sensitivity and resolution provided by narrow-bandwidth, slow-sweep operation, sweep rates on the order of 1 MHz per hour have been used in conjunction with detection system time constants of ∼50 seconds [165].

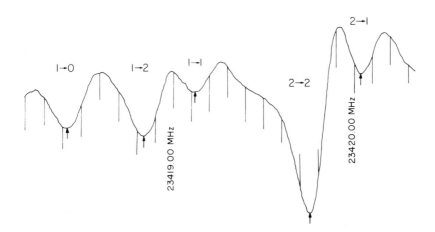

FIG. 9-6. Trace of a phase-lock measurement of five quadrupole components belonging to an internal rotation component of the $1_{01} \rightarrow 1_{11}$ transition in an excited torsional state of $(CH_3)_2N^{14}H$. The $F = 0 \rightarrow 1$ component occurs at a higher frequency and is now shown. The transitions were swept at a rate of 0.5 MHz per minute using a one second time constant. The markers occur every 0.1 MHz. The zero-field transitions (down) are partially obscured by the Stark components (up) which move to high frequency.

9-3d. Waveguide Stark Cell

The microwave radiation passes through a series of waveguide sections into the absorption cell which holds the sample. The radiation is linearly polarized and generally used in the dominant waveguide mode TE_{10} (the mode for which the lowest frequency of propagation is possible) for a rectangular guide. This TE or transverse electric wave is characterized by a transverse electric field component with no axial electric field. The electric field vector is normally oriented parallel to the short side of the waveguide; however, electromagnetic theory requires that the field strength approach zero at the guide walls if they are considered as perfect conductors. This places the maximum electric field strength at the center of the waveguide. As required, the magnetic field forms closed loops whose planes are parallel to the wide side of the waveguide.

To prevent saturation effects, an attenuator can be used to adjust the power level entering the cell. The cell is directly connected to a vacuum system and is sealed from the atmosphere by transmitting windows. The rectangular waveguide used for the Stark cell is usually X or K band[†] depending on the frequency region being studied. For centimeter wavelengths, the cell is normally three to five meters in length, although slightly longer cells may be employed for greater sensitivity. A thin metal septum, insulated from the waveguide and parallel to the wider edge, runs almost the entire length of the cell. Insulation can be provided by machined strips of teflon which also extend the length of the waveguide. A slot of appropriate thickness is machined into the insulator to rigidly hold the septum at the center of the cell. Figure 9-7a shows a simplified cross section of a Stark cell. The septum and insulator strips are tapered near the ends of the cell to reduce unwanted reflections.

An improved Stark cell based on the approach of Strandberg [124] has been constructed by Tobler et al. [195]. The Stark electrode is placed in grooves machined inside the waveguide and is insulated from the guide with folded teflon inserts. Most of the dielectric has been effectively removed from the waveguide to reduce the Stark field inhomogeneity, and the cell exhibits improved electrical and mechanical characteristics.

The function of the septum is to introduce modulation onto the microwave energy passing through the cell. When the vapor is exposed to an electric field, a splitting of the energy levels (Stark effect) occurs. The Stark effect leads to the measurement of dipole moments and serves as a means for identifying rotational transitions. Stark cells which do not contain a septum may also be constructed. For example [187], the waveguide may be split and

---

[†] Appendix 2 lists some common microwave nomenclature.

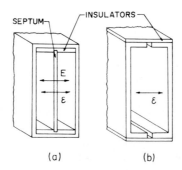

Fig. 9-7. Simplified end views of two Stark cells. Connections with the external electric field have been omitted. In (a) the Stark field ε is carried by a metal septum which is rigidly fixed and centered parallel to the broad side of the waveguide by two insulating teflon strips. The microwave radiation is transmitted in the dominant TE_{10} mode; the microwave electric field vector E and the Stark field are parallel. In (b) the waveguide is split along the zero-current line and expanded; the Stark field is applied between the two halves of the waveguide. To obtain a uniform Stark field, a length-to-width ratio of about 4:1 is necessary [195].

expanded in the dimension parallel to the microwave electric field; the Stark modulation is then applied between the two halves of the guide. This arrangement, which is shown in Fig. 9-7b, has advantages at high frequencies [184] and in high temperature applications [192].

Tobler *et al.* [194] have quantitatively investigated the effects of an inhomogeneous electric field in a waveguide Stark cell. A double-width X-band waveguide was shown to provide much better Stark effect performance characteristics than a normal X-band cell. In effect, the double-width cell very closely approximates a parallel plate cell (Section 9-4b) and allows much improved dipole moment measurements. Theoretically, for a line half-width of 0.1 MHz this configuration would allow Stark displacements of 1000 MHz to be studied as conveniently as displacements of 6 MHz in a conventional X-band Stark cell.

9-3e. Modulation, Detection, and Display

Zero-based square-wave Stark modulation is convenient for the study of rotational spectra, because this technique allows the absorption line as well as its Stark components to be observed simultaneously. When the electric field is absent, the unperturbed absorption line is detected; when the electric field is present, Stark components of the transition are observed. The two sets of lines can be presented with opposite phases, allowing the Stark components to be easily distinguished from the zero-field lines. Figure 9-8 illustrates the Stark component and zero-field line for a $1_{01} \rightarrow 1_{11}$ transition.

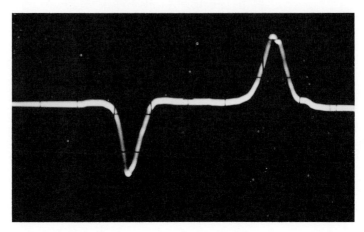

FIG. 9-8. Oscilloscope trace of the $1_{01}^{+} \rightarrow 1_{11}^{-}$ transition of $(CH_3)_2N^{15}H$ under conditions of low resolution and sensitivity to illustrate the Stark displacement. The frequency separation is about 7 MHz. The zero-field line is down and frequency increases to the right.

Introduction of modulation increases the sensitivity of the spectrometer with respect to video operation by allowing relatively narrow-band amplification and phase-sensitive detection. Modulation is usually performed by a square-wave signal with a frequency in the range from 5 to 100 kHz and a voltage which is continuously variable from zero to several thousand volts. Sine-wave modulation can also be employed, but the resulting spectrum is more difficult to interpret [67].

Except for low J transitions with no hyperfine structure, it is difficult to resolve all of the individual Stark components. Transitions with predominantly second-order Stark effects require relatively large electric field strengths to produce the necessary frequency shifts, and as the Stark field is increased, inhomogeneous portions of the field cause extensive broadening of the Stark components. However, this is not a major problem because transition frequencies can be measured even if the Stark structure is not completely resolved and because dipole moment studies are normally performed on Stark components with the greatest frequency shift.

Stark modulation has several advantages over straight detection and amplification. As an example, detection and amplification at 100 kHz selectively avoids the low frequency region where crystal and source noise are a problem. High quality narrow-band amplifiers are available to selectively amplify the modulated signal. At higher frequencies, the effective impedance of the waveguide system decreases, and it is difficult to produce high-amplitude square-wave modulation. Modulation broadening becomes important at frequencies above 100 kHz because side bands are present above and below the absorption line at intervals approximately equal to the modulation frequency. A lower radiofrequency (for example, 5 kHz) can be used to decrease the effects of modulation broadening, although the sensitivity is somewhat reduced and crystal noise becomes a factor.

The amplitude-modulated signal which reaches the detector is rectified, amplified by a tuned amplifier system, and phase detected. The detector is usually a silicon (semiconductor) crystal in contact with a small metal whisker; this combination is then placed in a protective cartridge. A major factor limiting the sensitivity of a video (wideband) spectrometer is the noise characteristic of a crystal rectifier. The crystal noise generated in the effective bandwidth Δv of the detection system can be attributed to two sources: thermal noise which is a function of the temperature T and crystal noise[†] which is a function of the rectification process. The noise power generated in the crystal is

$$ P = \left(kT + \frac{CI^2}{v} \right) \Delta v \tag{9-1} $$

where v is the modulation frequency, C is a constant, I is the rectified crystal current, and k is Boltzmann's constant. Modulation in a video spectrometer is supplied by a low-frequency sawtooth sweep applied to the reflector electrode which frequency modulates the klystron. Because crystal noise is inversely proportional to the frequency and directly proportional to the bandwidth, the second term in (9-1) is the limiting noise factor for the spectrometer, whenever the crystal current is sufficiently high. This condition is easily fulfilled in the centimeter region where milliwatts of power are usually available; however, for very low power levels (a few microwatts) the low frequency noise is no longer the dominant term. Equation (9-1) indicates that the noise level can be reduced by reducing the bandwidth and by increasing the modulation frequency. High frequency modulation can increase v to the order of 100 kHz and allows Δv to be decreased well below 100 Hz. However, bandwidth reduction must also be accompanied by a reduced sweep rate to prevent rejection of high frequency information and subsequent distortion of absorption line shapes. When a stabilized source is used in conjunction with a slow sweep rate, the bandwidth can be made very narrow to the order of 1 Hz, thereby reducing contributions from both thermal and rectification noise.

[†] This contribution is usually referred to as "$1/f$" noise.

The efficiency of the rectification process is specified as the conversion gain, the ratio of the change in output power to the change in input power at the detector. This factor is usually much less than one. If the crystal is acting as a perfect square-law detector, the output power is proportional to the square of the input power, i.e., the output power and rectification noise depend on the crystal current in the same manner. This condition implies that an increase in crystal current in the square-law region does not cause a deterioration of the signal-to-noise ratio. However, if the input power level drops much below 100 microwatts, the conversion gain decreases rapidly, thereby reducing the signal-to-noise ratio and the sensitivity [81].

The large conversion loss characteristic of low incident power levels at the crystal detector can be reduced by using superheterodyne detection. This is accomplished by detecting at an intermediate frequency produced when a local oscillator signal is mixed with the source signal. A constant i.f. is maintained with an automatic frequency control (a.f.c.) circuit, which forces the local oscillator to follow the source frequency. Detecting at a heterodyne frequency on the order of 30 MHz allows the crystal to be operated in a region of high conversion gain and low crystal noise. These characteristics remove the modulation requirement and attendant broadening effects, although low frequency modulation can still be included if the Stark effect is to be studied.

To avoid saturation of the i.f. amplifier by the increased signal level, heterodyne detection can be used in conjunction with a balanced bridge configuration as shown in Fig. 9-9. The input radiation is divided equally between the reference and sample arms of the bridge; after passing through the bridge, the signals are recombined to produce an output which is the difference of the two signals. This is accomplished by making the two arms

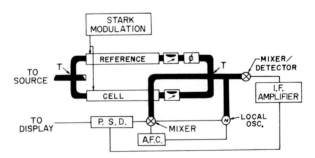

FIG. 9-9. Basic components of a bridge spectrometer employing a superheterodyne detector circuit. Low frequency Stark modulation may or may not be used. P.S.D. denotes the phase-sensitive detector, A.F.C. identifies the automatic frequency control circuit, and ϕ is a phase shifter. T identifies a hybrid junction or magic tee which is used to couple the sample and reference arms of the bridge.

of the bridge as identical as possible and by providing attenuation and phase adjustments in the reference arm. The resulting signal level can be adjusted to attain optimum sensitivity. The bridge technique allows noise contributions from the source oscillator to be balanced out; however, the tuning requirements of the bridge and superheterodyne detector restrict its use to high resolution studies over relatively small frequency intervals.

The phase-sensitive detector circuit is referenced to the modulation frequency and allows only those signal components which are phase-coherent with the reference voltage to reach the output. In the absence of a stabilized source, the output signal is applied to the vertical plates of a dual-beam oscilloscope. A sawtooth voltage which provides the horizontal sweep in the oscilloscope is applied to the reflector of the klystron. This voltage sweeps the klystron over a finite frequency range on the order of a few MHz, allowing this portion of the spectrum to be observed on the oscilloscope. Higher sensitivity is obtained with a stabilized source and with slow sweep rates. The resulting spectrum is then displayed on a recorder.

In one phase-sensitive detection scheme the amplified signal is split into two components and applied to the control grids of two matched pentodes. At the same time, a high level reference signal from the square-wave modulation source is placed on the two suppressor grids. By time-averaging to zero all signals which are not phase-coherent with the reference signal, the detector allows only the square-wave modulated information to pass.

It is also possible to modulate the source directly by applying the high frequency signal to the reflector electrode of the klystron [60]; instead of periodically shifting the absorption line with an electric field, the source frequency is shifted relative to the transition. A narrow-band detection system tuned to the modulation frequency can still be utilized to overcome detector noise characteristics. For square-wave frequency modulation, the absorption line appears twice as the klystron is swept across the transition; in conjunction with phase-sensitive detection, the two components are displayed with opposite phases. If the Stark effect is to be studied, a static electric field can be applied to the cell to resolve the Stark components; however, the zero-field line would then be absent, making the spectrum more difficult to interpret. In addition to complicating searching procedures, the source-modulation technique is susceptible to frequency-dependent reflections which may appear to be absorption lines.

Modulation has been implemented by shifting the energy levels with an external electric field as well as by rapidly varying the source frequency relative to the absorption line; it may also be useful to modulate the energy level population distribution with a discontinuous radiation source. This second radiation source should have sufficient power to disturb the equilibrium population distribution during its operating period. Switching can

then be accomplished with a high speed diode switch. It has also been proposed [1707] that this modulation technique be extended to infrared frequencies using variable speed mechanical chopping. Population modulation
could be very useful in situations where Stark modulation is difficult to
apply and has been used successfully to measure rotational relaxation times
in gases.

9-3f. Frequency Measurements

Frequency measurements may be accomplished on two levels. An approximate frequency can be obtained by using an absorption-type wavemeter
which is placed in the waveguide system ahead of the Stark cell. This wavemeter is a high Q resonant cavity which absorbs energy from the waveguide
system whenever the microwave signal frequency falls within the resonant
absorption curve of the cavity. The resonance frequency of the wavemeter
usually can be varied over an entire microwave band. At higher frequencies,
direct absorption wavemeters are not as common and harmonics of a low
frequency source such as an S-band klystron are mixed with the source
radiation to produce sum and difference sidebands which are observed using
a radio receiver. Wavemeter measurements depend on prior calibration and
are usually good to within 25 MHz at the lower microwave frequencies.
The harmonic method requires proper identification of the harmonic being
used; an error in reading the fundamental frequency will be increased by the
order of the observed harmonic.

While these approximate methods are useful when searching a spectrum,
the more precise techniques for measuring frequency require a stable
frequency reference and a calibrated radio receiver (Fig. 9-10). A reference
signal with a typical frequency of 5 MHz and stable to at least one part in
10^7 can be easily obtained from a crystal-controlled oscillator. This frequency
is then raised by about two orders of magnitude in a multiplier chain which
consists of a series of radiofrequency multiplication stages. For high frequency
measurements it may be necessary to raise the reference signal directly into
the microwave region with a varactor multiplier. The reference output of the
multiplier chain is an exact multiple of the basic reference frequency. This
signal then is applied to a crystal diode whose nonlinear response results in
the generation of harmonics of the input frequency. In most cases the same
crystal also acts as a microwave mixer to beat the reference harmonics with
a sample of source radiation. If all of the multiplier stages have a broad-band
response, the output will contain some power in all the harmonics of the
basic reference signal, but by making the first few multiplications with
narrow-band stages, the strongest harmonic components in the output will
be more widely spaced. The frequency of the heterodyned r.f. signals leaving
the mixer correspond to differences between the known reference harmonic

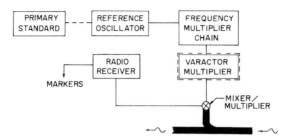

FIG. 9-10. Block diagram of a frequency measurement scheme. The reference oscillator usually operates at a frequency on the order of 5 MHz which can be checked by comparison with standard transmissions (WWV) or a primary laboratory standard. In the absence of a high frequency multiplier, the output frequency v_m of the last stage of the multiplier chain is on the order of 500 MHz; the receiver then detects the signal $\pm nv_m \mp v_s$ produced in the crystal by mixing the nth harmonic of v_m with the microwave frequency v_s. Because v_s is usually swept over a range of several MHz when a free-running source is used, these beat frequencies are observed as sum and difference markers on the oscilloscope trace. Harmonic generation and mixing can be accomplished in the same crystal. For high frequency measurements involving signals well into the millimeter region, it may be advantageous to multiply the known reference directly to the microwave region by using a varactor multiplier or other suitable method.

frequency and the unknown microwave frequency. The harmonic frequency is easily identified with a wavemeter. As the microwave source is swept over a range of several MHz, its beat frequency with any particular reference harmonic changes continuously and is amplified by the receiver only when the beat frequency and the receiver setting are identical. The receiver must have an adequate tuning range to respond to the beat frequencies, and the reference source must provide sufficient harmonic power.

Using conventional multiplier chains, adequate harmonic power usually can be produced at frequencies well over 30 GHz, and the reference harmonics are normally spaced at 50 MHz intervals in conjunction with a 30 MHz tuning range for the receiver. The amplified heterodyne signals appear as spikes on the oscilloscope trace. These markers are aligned with the absorption lines and measured on the receiver. If a recorder is being used with a stabilized source, the frequency markers can be placed directly on the chart paper. Relative frequencies of centimeter transitions whose line-shapes are not excessively broadened usually can be measured to the nearest 10 kHz or one part in 10^6 at 10 GHz.

9-3g. Millimeter and Submillimeter Techniques

The generation of millimeter and submillimeter radiation by reflex oscillators becomes more difficult as the dimensions of the tubes are scaled down to prohibitively small sizes. These cavity devices may be supplanted by traveling-wave structures which are capable of operation at higher frequencies with relatively large tuning ranges or by tubes using a distributed interaction process such as a Laddertron [196e]. Although primary sources for frequencies above 100 GHz are becoming available, harmonics from centimeter and millimeter wave oscillators have been the most successful radiation source. From the infrared limit, neither the thermal black body nor the maser find general use as spectroscopic sources in the millimeter region. The former provides a continuous output spectrum which is too weak at millimeter wavelengths except at unreasonably high operating temperatures and the latter produces radiation at relatively fixed frequencies. One such stimulated emission source at 0.337 mm (337 μ) uses molecular gases containing C and N [184a, 192a]; stimulated emission has also been detected in the H_2O system at several frequencies in the submillimeter region [196a, 196d]. Excitation is achieved by an electric discharge through the flowing gas.

The harmonic generators used in microwave spectroscopy usually consist of point-contact rectifier crystals suitably mounted in waveguide structures as illustrated in Fig. 9-11 [136, 190, 196b]. The nonlinear point contact

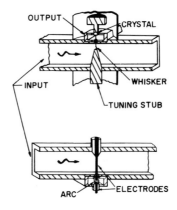

FIG. 9-11. Simplified illustrations of a point-contact crystal harmonic generator (upper) and a Froome harmonic generator (lower). Both devices are shown in the crossguide configuration which is generally more efficient than other waveguide designs.

occurs at the junction formed by the crystal and a metal whisker of tungsten or phosphor bronze. In the cross-waveguide structure which has been the most efficient, the crystal is mounted in the smaller waveguide to reduce capacitive losses associated with the whisker. These diodes exhibit a non-linear response to the fundamental radiation composed of the fundamental frequency combined with its harmonic components.

Other specialized methods include the use of magnetron harmonics and the output of a Froome harmonic generator [84, 196g]. In the Froome generator (Fig. 9-11), a microscopic arc discharge struck between two electrodes in the output of a crossguide structure serves as the nonlinear circuit element. With this arrangement watts of fundamental power can be used; the harmonic power is proportional to $\sim n^{-4}$ where n is the harmonic number.

Several advantages are inherent in the use of harmonic power. The frequency range which can be covered by a single oscillator is increased to the order of the harmonic being employed. For example, if sufficient third harmonic power is generated, a primary oscillator operating at 30–35 GHz can be used from 90–105 GHz. As the harmonic number is increased, the frequency ranges covered by adjacent harmonics will eventually overlap, allowing continuous coverage of the spectrum as long as sufficient harmonic power is available. In this case, the sixth and seventh harmonics are both operative at 210 GHz.

If an increased absolute error can be tolerated, the fundamental frequency can be measured by the usual techniques and multiplied by an integer to obtain the harmonic frequency. Any measurement error is also multiplied by the harmonic number and there also exists the possibility of incorrectly identifying the harmonic, although the latter problem is easily corrected by checking several frequencies.

The highest usable harmonic is a function of the fundamental frequency signal power and stability, the harmonic generator efficiency, and the detector efficiency at the harmonic frequency. Because harmonic power falls off rapidly with harmonic number, it is often necessary to drive the crystal with the maximum fundamental power available. However, excessive fundamental power may destroy the point contact or drive the diode beyond the strongly nonlinear portion of its voltage-current characteristic. In one instance, the twelfth harmonic of a 55–60 GHz klystron has been used to detect the $J = 5 \rightarrow 6$ transition of $C^{12}O^{16}$ at 691,472.6 MHz [1643]. By using superheterodyne detection, harmonics as high as the twentieth may be detected. Attempts have been made to phase-lock and generate harmonics from primary sources operating at frequencies as high as 300 GHz [184]. Crystal detectors are still used at these higher frequencies; however, they must usually be mounted directly in the waveguide and each crystal must be individually tested to determine its efficiency and bandwidth.

As the output signals from the crystal pass into the waveguide cell, the fundamental and lower harmonics are automatically filtered out if they are below the cutoff frequency of the guide. High-pass and band-pass filter sections can also be constructed to selectively eliminate unwanted frequencies.

The presence of a range of harmonics may be usefully employed for linear and symmetric top molecules. Because the transitions of these molecules are almost multiples of each other (differing only when nonrigid effects are present), a small sweep of the primary klystron through an absorption line will sweep each of the less intense higher harmonics through higher absorption lines. For rigid linear and symmetric molecules, all of the transitions would appear to coincide. Because of nonrigid effects, the transitions will be displaced from each other, allowing rapid measurement of all the transitions that can be detected and accurate estimates of important distortion parameters.

Observations of this kind are aided by a natural increase in the absorption coefficient with an increase of the frequency; however, as the dimensions of the waveguide are decreased, losses and reflections associated with a Stark septum reach intolerable levels. One alternative is to revert to the use of video or source-modulation configurations which do not require a Stark cell. If the millimeter wave power is very low, crystal noise effects which are troublesome in the centimeter region no longer completely dominate the noise power of (9-1), thereby partially removing one of the objections to the video spectrometer. Another choice which permits Stark-modulated operation is the use of a split-waveguide cell (Section 9-3d). Once the Stark septum is eliminated and sufficient harmonic power is available, the total waveguide length often may be reduced to the order of 50 centimeters or less.

Crystal detectors are still used in the shorter wavelength regions, although performance below about one centimeter is reduced as shunting effects of the point-contact capacity become important. In one form of point-contact detector design, the crystal and whisker are placed in pressure contact by a differential drive mechanism. To reduce the contact area, the whisker point can be electrolytically etched. Other possibilities include the pneumatic Golay cell, cooled and superconductive bolometers, and the photoconductive InSb Putley detector [175a]. Complex design, slow response, low temperature operation, or low sensitivity are often important negative factors. Superheterodyne detection has advantages at high frequencies; however, a stable, relatively high power local oscillator is required. In some cases, this requirement can be satisfied by superheterodyne harmonic mixing, where the local oscillator signal is produced by harmonic generation from a lower frequency source.

In addition to extending microwave techniques up into the submillimeter region, methods characteristic of optical and infrared spectroscopy can be modified for use at lower frequencies. Reflection gratings blazed for millimeter wavelengths may serve to separate harmonics. Absorption cells designed around interferometers can be used for Stark and Zeeman measurements and may be tuned over frequency intervals exceeding 50 GHz.

An interferometer provides a long effective path length and an increased radiation field strength. The equivalent path length is about $Q\lambda/2\pi$, where λ is the wavelength and Q is the resonator quality factor. Absorption of radiation by the sample reduces the Q of the interferometer, and the absorption line appears superimposed on the interferometer resonance. A semiconfocal type Fabry–Perot interferometer video spectrometer for use in the millimeter region has been described [174, 189]; this type of interferometer shown in Fig. 9-12 is easier to align and has reduced diffraction loss when

FIG. 9-12. A semiconfocal interferometer absorption cell. Q values on the order of 5×10^4 have been demonstrated in the millimeter region (courtesy J. J. Gallagher, The Martin Company, Orlando, Florida).

compared with a flat plate design. Waveguide input and output to the resonator are located on the flat plate with an iris for control of resonator loading. Figure 9-13 pictures an absorption line detected with this spectrometer.

9-4. Relative Intensity and Line Width Measurement

Accurate relative intensity measurements of microwave lines are difficult to achieve because there are many experimental factors to be controlled. When two transitions are tens or hundreds of megahertz apart, it is almost

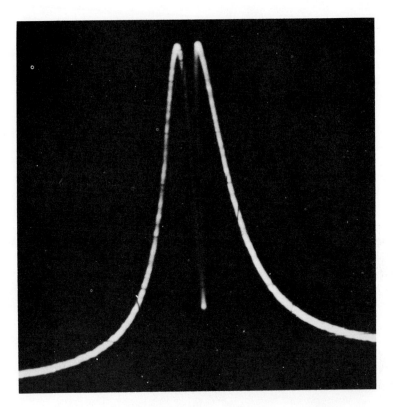

FIG. 9-13. The $2_{11} \rightarrow 2_{20}$ transition of H_2S^{32} observed at 216.710 GHz with a video spectrometer using a semiconfocal interferometer absorption cell (courtesy J. J. Gallagher, The Martin
Company, Orlando, Florida).

impossible to obtain identical experimental conditions for the two measurements. The most important sources of error in a waveguide spectrometer are
frequency-dependent reflections within the microwave transmission line and
nonlinearities in the detection system [169]. Multiple reflections can originate
at misaligned transitions between microwave components, at the Stark
electrode and its insulators, and at the crystal detector. Other factors which
may introduce errors into relative intensity measurements include the
presence of unresolved or interfering transitions and Stark components,
saturation of the transitions by excess microwave power, and, under some
conditions, changes of sample composition during the intensity measurements. Ferrite isolators can be used to reduce reflections at the source and
detector, while a matched calibrated attenuator placed between the pre-
amplifier and detector circuits allows both intensity measurements to be
performed on the same portion of the detector response curve. By attenuating

the stronger transition, both lines can be recorded at the same apparent intensity; a factor based on the response curve of the detector and on the attenuation gives the corrected intensity ratio. By optimizing the operation of a spectrometer, relative intensities accurate to within a few per cent are possible [169].

Relative intensity studies have been attempted with resonant cavities [127]. Although they give better results than the conventional waveguide configuration, these cells usually suffer from narrow-band operation, multiple tuning, and limited applicability.

A microwave spectrometer capable of absolute intensity coefficient measurements is pictured in Fig. 9-14. The microwave signal is supplied by a phase-locked, power-leveled, backward-wave oscillator (BWO) which allows a constant signal level input to the sample. Intensities are measured by simulating the molecular absorption in a signal calibrator system composed of precision attenuators, a modulator, and a phase shifter. A small amount of incident microwave signal is sampled and modulated at the Stark modulation frequency. The level and phase of this signal is adjusted so that it exactly matches the absorption of the sample, i.e., completely nulls the absorption. Then the intensity coefficient for the absorption line is the ratio of the simulated signal power to the incident power. It is possible to operate with a fixed power level at the detector, while the microwave power in the Stark cell changes. The changes in the spectrometer signal as a function of the power in the cell represent variations of the microwave field due to interactions with the sample only [822a].

Source modulation has been used to measure microwave line widths [158, 193]. By frequency modulating the reflector of the klystron with a low-amplitude r.f. voltage, and by detecting at the modulation frequency with a phase-sensitive system, the displayed signal is found to be the first derivative of the absorption curve (a dispersion curve). The frequency separation of the maximum and minimum of the dispersion curve is a function of the linewidth. This method can be improved by using a third modulation frequency which allows the dispersion curve to be superimposed on a flat baseline. The modulation can be supplied by the usual high-level Stark voltage applied to the septum. Without the Stark modulation, the detected signal produced by source modulation is the first derivative of the klystron mode, even in the absence of resonant absorption. With Stark modulation the output of the crystal detector is amplified, demodulated at the Stark frequency, and phase-detected at the r.f. source-modulation frequency.

In many instances all of the Stark components of a microwave transition may not be resolved from the zero-field line even at maximum electric field strength. By expanding the expression for the maximum intensity of a microwave line in a power series in the electric field strength [894], the ratio of the

FIG. 9-14. The X8400 *A* microwave spectrometer built by the Hewlett–Packard Company. (Courtesy H. Harrington, Hewlett–Packard, Palo Alto, California).

peak intensities of two lines can be calculated from the known values of the Stark coefficients, the quantum numbers of the transitions, and the half-widths of the lines.

9-5. Parallel Plate Spectrometers

One of the inherent disadvantages in the standard waveguide Stark cell is the broadening of Stark components by nonuniformities in the electric field. In some cases, it is advantageous to have a highly uniform Stark field whose intensity is well known. Such an arrangement is desirable for precision dipole moment determinations. The parallel plate transmission cell pictured in Fig. 9-15 allows a uniform Stark field to be created between two electrodes of metal or silvered, optically flat glass. The two plates can be evenly spaced by optically flat spacers; the electric field appears between the two inner faces of the plates.

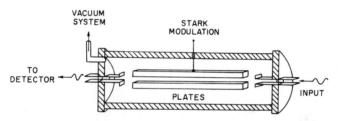

FIG. 9-15. Cross section of a parallel plate Stark cell. Spacers between the plates and plate supports have been omitted.

Microwave energy is exchanged with the cell through a set of electromagnetic horns. The horns allow a relatively smooth transition from the dimensions of the external microwave components to those of the metal or silvered glass plates. The entire sample area is evacuated by placing the transmission system in a cylindrical steel or pyrex vacuum chamber. Suitable flanges are placed at each end, and windows allow the radiation to pass through the evacuated cell.

The parallel plate spectrometer has several interesting features. When the microwave and Stark fields are parallel, the propagated TE mode has no low-frequency cutoff corresponding to the one which characterizes a rectangular waveguide. In the other configuration, where the two fields are orthogonal, the cutoff wavelength corresponds to twice the plate spacing. The uniformity of the field strength reduces Stark component broadening and allows measurements at higher fields than are possible with the standard Stark cell.

In dipole moment determinations, the Stark modulation usually is applied in a slightly different manner by placing a dc bias between the plates with a regulated dc voltage supply. This voltage, normally ranging from several hundred to several thousand volts, is then modulated by a low voltage square wave. Using phase-sensitive detection, each Stark transition appears as a doublet with the two components 180° out-of-phase. For large values of the dc bias, an average of the two component frequencies gives the position of the Stark component within experimental error.

9-6. High Temperature and Molecular Beam Spectroscopy

If a substance possesses a vapor pressure which is too low to allow its spectrum to be studied at room temperature, a cell capable of generating temperatures up to the order of 1000°C may be employed to produce a sufficient number of vapor phase molecules. The requirement of high temperature severely limits the type of materials used in the construction of the Stark cell; for example, fused quartz and certain ceramics are used as insulators. The split-waveguide Stark cell described in Section 9-3d is often preferred for this application because its simplified construction removes the need for a Stark septum [187]. Heating coils are usually wrapped around the waveguide and precautions are taken to assure that the sample does not condense on any cold spots within the cell, particularly on the windows.

For the most part, diatomic molecules with high melting points, e.g., the alkali halides, have been studied with high temperature spectrometers. Extension of these measurements to polyatomic systems introduces sensitivity problems associated with an increased number of low-lying vibrational states, an increased number of rotational states, and a general reduction in the magnitude of the largest component of the dipole moment.

High temperature spectroscopy also may be accomplished by heating the molecular sample to a temperature sufficient to produce a beam and observing changes in molecular trajectory as transitions are induced by r.f. or microwave fields. A schematic diagram of an electric-resonance molecular beam apparatus is shown in Fig. 9-16 [164, 833]. After the sample is vaporized

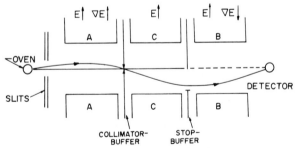

FIG. 9-16. Schematic diagram of a molecular beam electric resonance spectrometer. Field gradients of the *A* and *B* fields are arranged for a "flop-out" experiment. In addition to the dipole fields shown here, quadrupole focusing fields are often used.

in an oven and collimated into a beam by a set of slits, it passes through the influence of three main electric fields. The two outer fields A and B are inhomogeneous electric fields which select the rotational state to be studied by focusing molecules in that state onto the detector. The resultant forces on the molecular beam are caused by the gradients of the A and B fields. Mechanical stops are inserted to help remove molecules in other states and to reduce the background noise at the detector.

At the center is a homogeneous electric field C which provides the Stark effect and keeps the molecules in a definite quantum state in the absence of induced transitions. Buffer fields are also present to reduce electric field variations along the beam path which would otherwise cause Majorana (nonadiabatic) transitions. The ambient beam trajectory is a function of the effective dipole moment and the gradients of the A and B fields.

Transitions are produced by introducing a radiofrequency or microwave field perpendicular to the beam and to the homogeneous electric field. Usually, radiofrequency fields are used to induce $\Delta J = 0$ transitions between Stark levels split by the static electric field, whereas a higher-frequency microwave field is required for the observation of $\Delta J = \pm 1$ transitions. Depending on the orientation of the incident radiation, both $\Delta M = 0$ and $\Delta M = \pm 1$ transitions can be observed. When an appropriate transition is induced, molecules undergoing the transition are not refocused to the detector and a decrease in beam intensity is observed. This is called a "flop-out" experiment. If only those molecules undergoing a transition are refocused, the experiment is of the "flop-in" type. In both instances, the electric fields are oriented in the same direction; for a "flop-in" experiment, the electric field gradients have the same direction, while for a "flop-out" experiment, they assume opposite directions.

Molecular detection can be accomplished with a tungsten or oxidized tungsten hot-wire surface ionization detector, a mass spectrometer, and an electron multiplier. Rusk and Gordy [167] have applied a similar technique in the millimeter wave region but with direct absorption and detection of the microwave energy; increased absorption coefficients at these higher frequencies allow this method to be used successfully. Molecular beam studies generally have been limited to diatomic and simple triatomic molecules. In optimum cases, several vibrational states can be detected and accurate values of the dipole moment, rotational constant, and vibrational frequency can be obtained. Possible applications as a millimeter frequency standard have also been discussed [191d].

Using molecular beams, very narrow linewidths can be achieved by an inherent reduction in Doppler broadening. With the beam directed perpendicular to the direction of propagation of the radiation, only a selected group of molecules whose velocity spread is much smaller than the average thermal velocity is studied. Instead of using the single interaction zone provided by the C-field region, further reduction of the Doppler width can be achieved by passing the beam through two separate cavities separated by a distance d. If the radiation fields in the two cavities have the same phase, the Doppler width is $\sim v/d$, where v is the molecular velocity. Interferometers have been used successfully in this application [191c].

9-7. Applications of Double-Resonance and Beam-Maser Spectrometers

Several types of double-resonance experiments have been conducted in the microwave region. The sample is irradiated simultaneously at two separate frequencies; one microwave signal is used to saturate a transition (pump frequency), while the second source is operated below saturation on a related transition (signal frequency). A system composed of three levels is pictured in Fig. 9-17. In one type of experiment [141], the $1 \rightarrow 2$ line has been

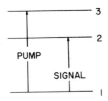

Fig. 9-17.
A three level system used to illustrate maser spectroscopy.

assigned, and the $1 \rightarrow 3$ transition is to be identified. The sample is irradiated at the signal frequency $1 \rightarrow 2$, and the Stark-modulated absorption is monitored on an oscilloscope. The pump frequency is swept through the portion of the spectrum which contains the $1 \rightarrow 3$ transition. When this frequency is reached, the $1 \rightarrow 3$ transition is saturated, decreasing the absorption coefficient of the $1 \rightarrow 2$ line. In this way, the assignment of the $1 \rightarrow 3$ transition may be confirmed. Alternatively, the pump frequency can be fixed and the signal frequency swept through the $1 \rightarrow 2$ line.

Double-resonance effects in three level systems have been discussed by Javan [1385] and observed in OCS [155, 191a], HCOOH [1539a] and HDCO [153], as well as in more complicated molecules [191a, 1697]. The technique displays its greatest usefulness whenever an important transition is inaccessible or its Stark effect cannot be used for identification. Low-frequency transitions which are difficult to observe directly, e.g., direct transitions between K-type and l-type doublets as well as direct hyperfine transitions, can be studied by indirect double resonance methods.

Using double resonance techniques, Oka [1705] has observed the normally forbidden $\Delta J = 3$ transition $0_{00} \rightarrow 3_{03}$ in ethyl iodide which is weakly allowed as a result of the strong quadrupole interaction. In this case the allowed $3_{03} \rightarrow 4_{04}$ transition was monitored and observed to increase in intensity when the 3_{03} level was populated by pumping at the $0_{00} \rightarrow 3_{03}$ frequency. In another form of double resonance experiment [1706] collisional transitions from $J = 2 \rightarrow 3$ in ethylene oxide appear to be preferred for levels connected by nonvanishing dipole matrix elements.

Selective distortion of the population distribution of molecular rotational levels by intense pumping radiation can also allow the estimation of rotational relaxation times in the gas phase. Unland and Flygare [1707] have applied a balanced bridge spectrometer with wideband superheterodyne detection to the measurement of relaxation times in OCS and have discussed a variety of double resonance techniques for studying rotational and vibrational relaxation.

Maser action can be used to aid microwave studies of rotational spectra. The word maser implies the inversion of a population distribution between two levels through a pumping mechanism and the subsequent amplification of a signal frequency by means of stimulated emission. Line-widths observed in maser spectrometers can be reduced by using a molecular beam to overcome Doppler broadening effects which limit resolution to about 50 kHz in the centimeter region. Low-frequency transitions could be studied because the Doppler width decreases with decreasing frequency; however, the line intensity is reduced in proportion to the third power of the frequency and only strong low-frequency transitions can be observed.

The reduction in Doppler width is supplemented by a focusing technique which increases the population difference for a set of energy levels. A simplified diagram of a beam-maser spectrometer is shown in Fig. 9-18. The

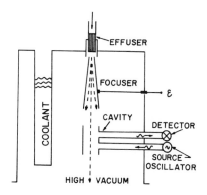

FIG. 9-18. Diagram of a beam-maser spectrometer. The molecular effuser usually consists of a number of small diameter parallel tubes which form the beam, while the focuser is a cage of parallel electrodes carrying large alternate potentials. Lower state molecules are conveniently defocused by being attracted toward the electrodes; upper state molecules remain axial and enter the cavity.

molecular effuser produces a beam of molecules which passes through an electrostatic focuser. In the focuser, the molecular beam is exposed to a high intensity inhomogeneous electric field, and the Stark effect generally forces a repulsion between two levels which possess a nonvanishing dipole matrix element. This repulsion allows the focuser to separate molecules in the upper energy state from those in the lower energy state. The former then pass into a high Q cavity. Emission transitions are stimulated in the inverted population and detected with a microwave receiver. For low-frequency transitions occurring in the radiofrequency region, the cavity is replaced by a parallel plate capacitor which is part of a resonant circuit.

Strongly polar linear and symmetric top molecules, as well as asymmetric top molecules of low molecular weight which possess closely spaced pairs of levels, are best suited to beam-maser techniques. Gordon *et al.* [101] were able to study the hyperfine interactions in NH_3. The reduced sensitivity of the beam-maser spectrometer may be circumvented by large dipole moments in the linear and symmetric top molecules and by the combination of relatively large rotational constants in the asymmetric rotors. These conditions produce a favorable distribution of molecules in the levels which lie in the microwave region. In favorable cases, the narrow line-widths (on the order of 5 kHz) produced in beam-maser spectrometers allow the observation of small quadrupole splittings, interactions of nuclear magnetic moments with small internal molecular magnetic fields in $^1\Sigma$ electronic ground states, and direct magnetic dipole-dipole interactions.

9-8. Study of Free Radicals and Unstable Species

The short lifetimes and low concentrations of most unstable species, particularly free radicals, make observation of their microwave spectra difficult. Special cells with reaction flow systems must be used to produce the radicals and pass them into the microwave field. The radicals are most easily formed either directly by an r.f. electric discharge or by reacting the atomic species formed in the discharge with a stable sample. In the latter case, the atomic species can be produced by discharges through hydrogen or oxygen. Alternative methods of radical production such as flash photolysis or pyrolysis do not yield a continuous supply of the unstable species.

The reactive nature of most free radicals requires the use of specially designed absorption cells containing as little metal surface as possible. Waveguide cells similar to that described by Lide [187] can be coated with a low-loss inert film to reduce reaction of the species at the cell wall. Because of the large volume-to-surface area ratio and relative inertness of glass, a pyrex "free space" absorption cell with teflon or polystyrene microwave lenses is particularly suited to studies of reactive species [115]. A cell design which makes use of dielectric rod propagation has also been described [114],

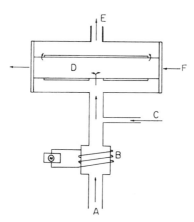

FIG. 9-19. Schematic diagram of a free-radical Stark cell [989]. The gas at A enters the discharge cell B. Atomic species produced by the discharge react with the stable sample entering at C, the reaction products pass into the cell D, and they are pumped out at E. Microwave radiation enters the cell at F.

and unstable species have been observed using a modified millimeter-wave interferometer [191d].

A representation of the system used by Powell and Lide [989] is shown in Fig. 9-19. Atomic species are produced in the water-cooled discharge cell by a high-frequency power oscillator. These reactive products flow into the waveguide and react with a suitable gas. Radicals also may be formed by reacting the discharge flow with a solid which is deposited on the walls just before the entrance to the waveguide. The newly formed radicals are subjected to the microwave and Stark fields and then removed from the cell by the pumping system. Flow rates must be adjusted to fit the particular reaction and free radical species.

In addition to stable paramagnetic molecules like O_2 and NO, transitions in the unstable free radical species OH, OD, and SO and the unstable molecular species CS have been observed. The OH and OD spectra consist of transitions between Λ-doublet components, while the microwave transitions of O_2 occur between states of a Σ triplet.

9-9. Zeeman Effect Spectrometers

Although the spatial M degeneracy can be lifted by an external magnetic field as well as by an external electric field, the Zeeman effect is not as generally useful in rotational spectroscopy. However, a number of microwave Zeeman studies have been attempted, particularly on paramagnetic molecules where the interaction is relatively large. Appendix 13 gives a brief introduction to the Zeeman effect; Section XI of Appendix 1 should be consulted for more detailed treatments of magnetic interactions in molecules with $^1\Sigma$ and paramagnetic ground electronic states.

A variety of spectrometer designs have been used to measure the magnetic perturbations of rotational transitions. The sample cell may be a resonant cavity [904], a coiled waveguide [17], or a normal or slotted waveguide surrounded by a solenoid which applies the magnetic field. When a resonant cavity is used, the absorption line is superimposed on the resonance of the cavity, and the relatively small size of a cavity makes it convenient for the application of the magnetic field. The size of a straight waveguide can be reduced by coiling the guide. Coiling enables it to fit between the pole faces of the magnet; however, this arrangement is not suitable for the application of a simultaneous Stark field. Excellent discussions of Zeeman effect spectrometers have been given by Zimmerer [154], Eshbach and Strandberg [79], Shimoda and Nishikawa [78] and others [17, 20, 907].

The Zeeman effect in molecular spectroscopy separates into two categories; large splittings for paramagnetic molecules and very small splittings for diamagnetic molecules. While it is easy to produce a sizable splitting in molecules like O_2 and NO, it is sometimes difficult to obtain magnetic fields large enough to cause resolution of all the Zeeman components for a molecule in a $^1\Sigma$ ground state. For this reason, Zeeman studies of paramagnetic molecules have been pursued to a greater extent. To solve the search and detection problem in pure Zeeman studies, the magnetic field may be applied in conjunction with a Stark field. The combined Stark-Zeeman splittings are usually complicated [850], but their analysis can be avoided by observing the pure Zeeman splittings of the zero Stark-field line. To simplify the

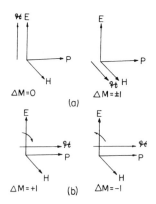

FIG. 9-20. Vector models for Zeeman transitions with (a) linearly polarized and (b) circularly polarized radiation. **P** represents the direction of propagation and $\mathcal{H}$ is the external magnetic field.

identification of the Zeeman components, a strong Stark field can be used to move the Stark-Zeeman components well away from the zero-field line.

The two types of commonly observed Zeeman transitions correspond to the selection rules, $\Delta M = 0$ (π transitions) and $\Delta M = \pm 1$ (σ transitions). For π transitions, the static magnetic field is parallel to the microwave electric field. These fields must be orthogonal to produce σ transitions. The Zeeman effect has been studied in the microwave region with both linearly polarized radiation and circularly polarized radiation. Use of circularly polarized radiation can selectively cause either $\Delta M = +1$ or $\Delta M = -1$ transitions, leading to information on the absolute sign of the molecular g factor. For these transitions to occur, the magnetic field must be parallel to the direction of propagation of the microwave radiation, while for linearly polarized radiation the field must always be normal to the direction of propagation. The $\Delta M = +1$ transition is produced by right-circular polarization and the $\Delta M = -1$ transition by left-circular polarization. Simplified vector representations for these possible transitions are shown in Fig. 9-20. A waveguide circular polarizer analogous to that described by Eshbach and Strandberg [79] or Strauch et al. [189] can be used to produce predominantly right- or left-handed circular polarization from a linearly polarized source. Alternatively, the Faraday effect [932] may be used to obtain sign information.

APPENDIX 1 REFERENCES

The references listed in this bibliography include a majority of the important papers and books that are related to the development of microwave spectroscopy. General references relating to the basic concepts of rotational and, in a limited way, vibrational spectroscopy, are also included. Titles of dissertations, reports which have not been published in the open literature, and abstracts of papers presented at spectroscopy symposia generally are not given. Rather than a pure chronological listing, the references have been placed under specific topic headings whenever possible. A chronological order under these headings is maintained. Since a unique classification of each article is impossible, references which do not fall directly under one of the specific topics are listed in Section 12.

Several other bibliographies are available. Townes and Schawlow [20] compiled a complete listing up through 1954. In addition, Favero [35] has compiled a bibliography covering 1954 through 1962, and Starck [39] has completed one for 1945 through 1962. The latter is very useful because it is indexed by compound. This bibliography appears in a recent book [46a] by Sugden and Kenney. The bibliography listed here was previously published as U.S. Army Missile Command Report No. RD-TM-65-14, August 1965. It includes a majority of the references concerning microwave spectroscopy through 1965 and a number of references from early 1966.

I. General and Review Articles

1. E. U. Condon and G. H. Shortley, "The Theory of Atomic Spectra." McGraw-Hill, New York, 1935.
2. G. Herzberg, "Infrared and Raman Spectra." Van Nostrand, Princeton, New Jersey, 1945.
3. W. Gordy, Microwave spectroscopy, *Rev. Mod. Phys.* **20**, 668–717 (1948).
4. B. P. Dailey, Microwave spectra and chemical analysis, *Anal. Chem.* **21**, 540–544 (1949).
5. H. B. G. Casimir, The influence of magnetic and electrical properties of atomic nuclei on the energy levels of atoms and molecules, *Ned. Tijdschr. Natuurk.* **16**, 198–206 (1950).
6. B. L. Crawford, Jr. and D. E. Mann, Spectroscopy, *Ann. Rev. Phys. Chem.* **1**, 151–169 (1950).

7. G. Herzberg, "Spectra of Diatomic Molecules." Van Nostrand, Princeton, New Jersey, 1950.

8. P. Kisliuk and C. H. Townes, Molecular microwave spectra tables, *J. Res. Natl. Bur. Std.* **44**, 611–641 (1950).

9. D. H. Whiffen, Rotation spectra, *Quart. Rev.* (*London*) **4**, 131–152 (1950).

10. E. B. Wilson, Jr., Microwave spectroscopy of gases, *Ann. Rev. Phys. Chem.* **2**, 151–176 (1951).

11. B. Bak, A microwave spectroscope and a review of microwave spectroscopy, *Trans. Instr. Meas. Conf. 1952* **8**, 8–14, Stockholm, 1952.

12. P. Kisliuk and C. H. Townes, Molecular microwave spectra tables, *Natl. Bur. Std. Circ.* **518**, 1–127 (1952).

13. A. H. Nethercot, J. A. Klein, J. H. N. Loubser, and C. H. Townes, Spectroscopy near the boundary between the microwave and infrared regions, *Nuovo Cimento* **9**, 358–363 (1952).

14. C. H. Townes, The present status of microwave spectroscopy, *Ann. N.Y. Acad. Sci.* **55**, 745–750 (1952).

15. E. B. Wilson, Jr., The significance of the results of microwave spectroscopy to chemical valence theory, *Ann. N.Y. Acad. Sci.* **55**, 943–954 (1952).

16. B. P. Dailey, Microwaves and nuclear resonance, *Ann. Rev. Phys. Chem.* **4**, 425–444 (1953).

17. W. Gordy, W. V. Smith, and R. F. Trambarulo, "Microwave Spectroscopy." Wiley, New York, 1953.

18. R. J. Myers and W. D. Gwinn, The microwave spectra of gases, *Ann. Rev. Phys. Chem.* **5**, 385–394 (1954).

19. M. W. P. Strandberg, "Microwave Spectroscopy." Methuen, London, 1954.

20. C. H. Townes and A. L. Schawlow, "Microwave Spectroscopy." McGraw-Hill, New York, 1955.

21. E. B. Wilson, Jr., J. C. Decius, and P. C. Cross, "Molecular Vibrations." McGraw-Hill, New York, 1955.

22. E. B. Wilson, Jr. and D. R. Lide, Jr., Microwave spectroscopy *in* "Determination of Organic Structures by Physical Methods (E. A. Braude and F. C. Nachod, ed.), Vol. 1, Chapter 12. Academic Press, New York, 1955.

23. B. P. Dailey, Microwave spectroscopy *in* "Physical Methods in Chemical Analysis" (W. G. Beel, ed.), Vol. 3, pp. 281–301, Academic Press, New York, 1956.

24. D. J. E. Ingram, "Spectroscopy at Radio and Microwave Frequencies." Philosophical Library, New York, 1956.

25. E. Roubine, Microwave spectroscopy of gases, *Chim. Anal.* (*Paris*), **38**, 402–409, 428–431 (1956).

26. J. H. N. Loubser, Chemical analysis by microwave spectroscopy, *Tydskr. Wetenskap Kuns* **17**, 166–174 (1957).

27. J. Sheridan, Recent progress in the microwave spectroscopy of gases, *Boll. Sci. Fac. Chim. Ind. Bologna* **16**, 71–79 (1958).

28. J. Sheridan, Some contributions of microwave spectroscopy to chemistry, *Ric. Sci. Suppl.* **28**, 1801–1816 (1958).

29. L. A. Biyumenfeld and V. V. Voevodskii, Radiospectroscopy and its application in chemistry, *Vestn. Akad. Nauk. SSSR* **29**, 16–21 (1959).

29a. P. Kusch and V. W. Hughes, Atomic and molecular beam spectroscopy, *in* "Handbuch der Physik," **Vol. 37/1**, p. 141. Springer, Berlin, 1959.

30. W. Zeil, Possible uses of microwave spectroscopy for qualitative and quantitative analysis, *Z. Anal. Chem.* **170**, 19–29 (1959).

31. D. Ingram, Spectra in the microwave region, *Discovery* **23**, 29–35 (1962).

32. W. Maier, Microwave spectroscopy, *Pure Appl. Chem.* **4**, 157–174 (1962).

33. E. B. Wilson, Jr., Vibrational-rotational spectra, *Pure Appl. Chem.* **4**, 1–13 (1962).

34. H. C. Allen, Jr. and P. C. Cross, "Molecular Vib-Rotors. Wiley, New York, 1963.

35. P. G. Favero, "Microwave Gas Spectroscopy Bibliography, 1954–1962." Istituto di Chim. Fis. Dell' Univ. di Padova, Padova, Italy, 1963.

36. L. Kellner, Microwave spectroscopy, *Scientia* (*Milan*) **98**, 51–56 (1963).

37. W. Maier, Applications of microwave spectroscopy in physical chemistry, *Ber. Bunsenges. Phys. Chem.* **67**, 539–553 (1963).

38. D. J. Millen, Developments in microwave spectroscopy, *Chem. & Ind.* (*London*) **1963**, 1472–1482 (1963).

39. B. Starck, "Bibliography of Research in the Microwave Spectra of Molecules During the Years 1945–1962." Physikalisches Institut der Universität Freiburg i. Br., Germany. 1963.

40. E. B. Wilson, Jr., Recent results of chemical interest from microwave spectroscopy, *Pure Appl. Chem.* **7**, 23–31 (1963).

41. G. W. King, "Spectroscopy and Molecular Structure." Holt, New York, 1964.

42. D. R. Lide, Jr., Microwave spectroscopy, *Ann. Rev. Phys. Chem.* **15**, 225–250 (1964).

43. J. Sheridan, Microwave spectroscopy of gases, *Ann. Rept. Progr. Chem.* (*Chem. Soc. London*) **60**, 160–176 (1964).

44. K. Shimoda, Beam maser spectroscopy and applications, *Quantum Electronics Conf., Paris, 1963*, pp. 349–355. Columbia Univ. Press, New York, 1964.

45. P. F. Wacker, M. Mizushima, J. D. Petersen, and J. R. Ballard, Microwave spectral tables. Diatomic molecules, *Natl. Bur. Std.* (*U.S.*) *Monograph* **70**, (1964).

46. D. J. Millen, Microwave spectroscopy and its applications, *Lab. Pract.* **14**, 820–825 (1965).

46a. T. M. Sugden and C. N. Kenney, "Microwave Spectroscopy of Gases." Van Nostrand, Princeton, New Jersey, 1965.

II. Instrumentation

47. R. V. Pound, Electronic frequency stabilization of microwave oscillators, *Rev. Sci. Instr.* **17**, 490–505 (1946).

48. A. Roberts, Y. Beers, and A. G. Hill, The measurement of nuclear spin, magnetic moment, and hyperfine structure separation by a microwave frequency modulation method, *Phys. Rev.* **70**, 112 (1946).

49. R. L. Carter and W. V. Smith, Microwave spectrum frequency markers, *Phys. Rev.* **72**, 1265–1266 (1947).

50. W. Gordy and M. Kessler, A new electronic system for detecting microwave spectra, *Phys. Rev.* **72**, 644 (1947).

51. R. H. Hughes and E. B. Wilson, Jr., A microwave spectrograph, *Phys. Rev.* **71**, 562–563 (1947).

52. R. V. Pound, Frequency stabilization of microwave oscillators, *Proc. IRE* **35**, 1405–1415 (1947).

53. R. V. Pound, "Techniques of Microwave Measurements" (C. G. Montgomery, ed.), pp. 58–78. McGraw-Hill, New York, 1947.

54. V. C. Rideout, Automatic frequency control of microwave oscillators, *Proc. IRE* **35**, 767–771 (1947).

55. W. V. Smith, J. L. G. De Quevedo, R. L. Carter, and W. S. Bennett, Frequency stabilization of microwave oscillators by spectrum lines, *J. Appl. Phys.* **18**, 1112–1115 (1947).

56. R. J. Watts and D. Williams, A double modulation detection method for microwave spectra, *Phys. Rev.* **72**, 1122–1123 (1947).

57. R. J. Watts and D. Williams, A modified Stark-effect modulation spectrograph for micro-waves, *Phys. Rev.* **72**, 980–981 (1947).
58. W. D. Herschberger, Minimum detectable absorption in microwave spectroscopy and an analysis of the Stark modulation method, *J. Appl. Phys.* **19**, 411–419 (1948).
59. C. K. Jen, A method for measuring the complex dielectric constant of gases at microwave frequencies by using a resonant cavity, *J. Appl. Phys.* **19**, 649–653 (1948).
60. R. Karplus, Frequency modulation in microwave spectroscopy, *Phys. Rev.* **73**, 1027–1034 (1948).
61. R. Karplus and J. Schwinger, A note on saturation in microwave spectroscopy, *Phys. Rev.* **73**, 1020–1026 (1948).
62. J. L. G. De Quevedo and W. V. Smith, Frequency stabilization of microwave oscillators by spectrum lines. II, *J. Appl. Phys.* **19**, 831–836 (1948).
63. C. H. Townes and S. Geschwind, Limiting sensitivity of a microwave spectrometer, *J. Appl. Phys.* **19**, 795–796 (1948).
64. W. G. Tuller, W. C. Galloway, and F. P. Zaffarano, Recent developments in frequency stabilization of microwave oscillators, *Proc. IRE* **36**, 794–800 (1948).
65. R. Unterberger and W. V. Smith, A microwave secondary frequency standard, *Rev. Sci. Instr.* **19**, 580–585 (1948).
66. L. C. Hedrick, A flexible high voltage square-wave generator, *Rev. Sci. Instr.* **20**, 781–783 (1949).
67. K. B. McAfee, Jr., R. H. Hughes, and E. B. Wilson, Jr., A Stark-effect microwave spectro-graph of high sensitivity, *Rev. Sci. Instr.* **20**, 821–826 (1949).
68. D. H. Baird, R. M. Fristrom, and M. H. Sirvetz, Stark effect absorption cells for microwave spectroscopy, *Rev. Sci. Instr.* **21**, 881 (1950).
69. T. R. Hartz and A. Van der Ziel, A square-wave modulation method for microwave spectra, *Phys. Rev.* **78**, 473 (1950).
70. A. H. Sharbaugh, The design and construction of a Stark-modulation microwave spectro-graph, *Rev. Sci. Instr.* **21**, 120–135 (1950).
70a. J. C. Slater, "Microwave Electronics." Van Nostrand, Princeton, New Jersey, 1950.
71. I. Takahashi, A. Okaya, T. Ogawa, and T. Hashi, 1.5 cm wavelength microwave spectro-scope, *Mem. Coll. Sci. Univ. Kyoto Ser. A* **26**, 113–121 (1950).
72. E. S. Dayhoff, A frequency controller for reflex klystrons, *Rev. Sci. Instr.* **22**, 1025–1026 (1951).
73. R. Freymann, Remark on the rotational method and the method of perturbations in the ultra-Hertzian region. Apparatus for measuring the absorption of vapors for frequencies near 10 000 Mc, *Physica* **17**, 328–332 (1951).
74. L. C. Hedrick, Synchronizer for 100 kc square-wave generator, *Rev. Sci. Instr.* **22**, 537 (1951).
75. G. Newell and R. H. Dicke, A method for reducing the Doppler breadth of microwave absorption lines, *Phys. Rev.* **83**, 1064–1065 (1951).
76. E. Roubine, Realization of a spectroscope for millimeter waves, *Rev. Tech. C.F.T.H.* **16**, 21–44 (1951).
77. L. J. Rueger, H. Lyons, and R. G. Nuckolls, A high temperature broad-band Stark cell for microwave spectroscopy, *Rev. Sci. Instr.* **22**, 428 (1951).
78. K. Shimoda and T. Nishikawa, A Zeeman modulation microwave spectrograph of high sensitivity, *J. Phys. Soc. Japan* **6**, 516–520 (1951).
79. J. R. Eshbach and M. W. P. Strandberg, Apparatus for Zeeman effect measurements on microwave spectra, *Rev. Sci. Instr.* **23**, 623–628 (1952).
80. S. Geschwind, High-resolution microwave spectroscopy, *Ann. N.Y. Acad. Sci.* **55**, 751–773 (1952).

81. W. Gordy, Microwave spectroscopy above 60 kMc, *Ann. N.Y. Acad. Sci.* **55**, 774–788 (1952).

82. R. H. Hughes, Chemical analysis with the microwave spectrograph, *Ann. N.Y. Acad. Sci.* **55**, 872–890 (1952).

83. H. R. Johnson, Resolution and sensitivity of microwave spectrographs, *Phys. Rev.* **85**, 764 (1952).

84. J. A. Klein, J. H. N. Loubser, A. H. Nethercot, and C. H. Townes, Magnetron harmonics at millimeter wavelengths, *Rev. Sci. Instr.* **23**, 78–82 (1952).

85. H. Lyons, Spectral lines as frequency standards, *Ann. N.Y. Acad. Sci.* **55**, 831–871 (1952).

86. L. Essen, A highly stable microwave oscillator and its application to the measurement of the spatial variations of refractive index in the atmosphere, *Proc. Inst. Elec. Engrs.* (*London*), *Pt. C*, **100**, 19–24 (1953).

87. D. H. Baird and G. R. Bird, A method for the estimation of the relative intensities of microwave absorption lines, *Rev. Sci. Instr.* **25**, 319–323 (1954).

88. G. R. Bird, Note on the estimation of absolute absorption intensities with a Stark-modulated microwave spectrograph, *Rev. Sci. Instr.* **25**, 324–326 (1954).

89. R. J. Collier, Variable-frequency microwave cavity spectrometer, *Rev. Sci. Instr.* **25**, 1205–1207 (1954).

90. W. A. Hardy, P. Fletcher, and V. Suarez, A microwave absorption cell for reactive molecules, *Rev. Sci. Instr.* **25**, 1135 (1954).

91. C. M. Johnson, D. M. Slager, and D. D. King, Millimeter waves from harmonic generators, *Rev. Sci. Instr.* **25**, 213–217 (1954).

92. W. C. King and W. Gordy, One-to-two millimeter wave spectroscopy IV. Experimental methods and results for OCS, CH_3F, and H_2O, *Phys. Rev.* **93**, 407–412 (1954).

93. T. M. Sanders, Jr., A. L. Schawlow, G. C. Dousmanis, and C. H. Townes, Examination of methods for detecting OH, *J. Chem. Phys.* **22**, 245–246 (1954).

94. M. L. Stitch, A. Honig, and C. H. Townes, A high-temperature microwave spectrometer, *Rev. Sci. Instr.* **25**, 759–764 (1954).

95. M. W. P. Strandberg and H. Dreicer, Doppler line-width reduction, *Phys. Rev.* **94**, 1393–1394 (1954).

96. M. W. P. Strandberg, H. R. Johnson, and J. R. Eshbach, Apparatus for microwave spectroscopy, *Rev. Sci. Instr.* **25**, 776–792 (1954).

97. P. A. Tate and M. W. P. Strandberg, A simple high-temperature microwave spectrograph, *Rev. Sci. Instr.* **25**, 956–958 (1954).

98. R. H. Dicke and R. H. Romer, Pulse techniques in microwave spectroscopy, *Rev. Sci. Instr.* **26**, 915–928 (1955).

99. G. Erlandsson, A microwave spectrometer and its applications to some organic molecules, *Arkiv Fysik* **9**, 399–343 (1955).

100. J. P. Gordon, Hyperfine structure in the inversion spectrum of $N^{14}H_3$ by a new high-resolution microwave spectrometer, *Phys. Rev.* **99**, 1253–1263 (1955).

101. J. P. Gordon, H. J. Zeiger, and C. H. Townes, The maser—new type of microwave amplifier, frequency standard, and spectrometer, *Phys. Rev.* **99**, 1264–1274 (1955).

102. A. Okaya, Some devices for Stark modulation millimeter-wave spectrograph, *Rev. Sci. Instr.* **26**, 1024–1028 (1955).

103. M. Peter and M. W. P. Strandberg, Molecular-beam microwave absorption spectroscope, *Phys. Rev.* **99**, 667 (1955).

104. M. Peter and M. W. P. Strandberg, Phase stabilization of microwave oscillators, *Proc. IRE.* **43**, 869–873 (1955).

105. K. Shimoda and T. C. Wang, New method for the observation of hyperfine structure in NH_3 in a "maser" oscillator, *Rev. Sci. Instr.* **26**, 1148–1149 (1955).

106. M. W. P. Strandberg and M. Peter, Precision of microwave spectrographs, *Phys. Rev.* **133**, 963 (1955).

107. J. Bonanomi and J. Herrmann, Ammonia frequency standard, *Helv. Phys. Acta* **29**, 224–226 (1956).

108. C. A. Burrus, Jr. and W. Gordy, Millimeter and submillimeter wave spectroscopy, *Phys. Rev.* **101**, 599–602 (1956).

109. M. Cowan and W. Gordy, Further extension of microwave spectroscopy in the submillimeter region, *Phys. Rev.* **104**, 551–552 (1956).

110. G. Erlandsson and H. Selen, Frequency measurements in microwave spectroscopy, *Arkiv. Fysik* **11**, 391–393 (1956).

111. J. Herrmann and J. Bonanomi, Special arrangement for microwave spectroscopy in a cavity resonator, *Helv. Phys. Acta* **29**, 448–451 (1956).

112. W. R. Hoisington, C. Kellner, and M. J. Pentz, High-resolution microwave Zeeman spectrometer, *Nature* **178**, 1111–1112 (1956).

113. J. Bonanomi, J. De Prins, J. Herrmann, and P. Kartaschoff, Microwave spectrograph of high resolution, *Helv. Phys. Acta* **30**, 290–292 (1957).

114. E. B. Brackett, P. H. Kasai, and R. J. Myers, Dielectric rod wave guide cells for microwave spectroscopy, *Rev. Sci. Instr.* **28**, 699–702 (1957).

115. C. C. Costain, A "free space" absorption cell for microwave spectroscopy, *Can. J. Phys.* **35**, 241–247 (1957).

116. E. F. Davis, External Publ. No. 380, Univ. California Jet Propulsion Lab., Pasadena, California, (June, 1957).

117. A. K. Garrison and W. Gordy, High temperature molecular beam microwave spectrometer, *Phys. Rev.* **108**, 899–900 (1957).

118. S. A. Marshall and J. Weber, Plane parallel plate transmission line Stark microwave spectrograph, *Rev. Sci. Instr.* **28**, 134–137 (1957).

119. M. Peter and M. W. P. Strandberg, Theoretical and experimental study of molecular-beam microwave spectroscopy. Mass. Inst. Technol. Res. Lab. Electron. Cambridge, Massachusetts, Tech. Rept. 336 (1957).

120. M. C. Thompson and J. V. Cateora, High-order harmonics for X-band oscillator stabilization, *Rev. Sci. Instr.* **28**, 656 (1957).

121. I. R. Hurle and T. M. Sugden, Microwave spectrometer for the study of free radicals, *J. Sci. Instr.* **35**, 319–323 (1958).

122. R. D. Mattuck and M. W. P. Strandberg, Micromodulator. A device for measuring the intensities of microwave absorption lines, *Rev. Sci. Instr.* **29**, 717–721 (1958).

123. J. M. Richardson, Experimental evaluation of the oxygen microwave absorption as a possible atomic frequency standard, *J. Appl. Phys.* **29**, 137–145 (1958).

124. M. W. P. Strandberg, Microwave spectroscopy wave-guide Stark cell with high performance capabilities, *Rev. Sci. Instr.* **29**, 656–657 (1958).

125. M. C. Thompson, M. J. Vetter, and D. M. Waters, SHF frequency standard uses double conversion, *Electronics* **31**, 100–101 (1958).

126. P. H. Verdier, Stark effect resonant cavity microwave spectrograph, *Rev. Sci. Instr.* **29**, 646–647 (1958).

127. P. H. Verdier and E. B. Wilson, Jr., Relative intensities of microwave absorption lines, *J. Chem. Phys.* **29**, 340–347 (1958).

128. Y. Beers, Theory of the cavity microwave spectrometer and molecular frequency standard, *Rev. Sci. Instr.* **30**, 9–16 (1959).

129. F. Bruin and D. Van Ladesteyn, Frequency stabilization of a reflex klystron oscillator, *Physica* **25**, 1–8 (1959).

130. H. E. Bussy and G. Birnbaum, Cavity resonators for spectroscopy of compressed gases, *Rev. Sci. Instr.* **30**, 800–804 (1959).

131. J. H. Corn, Microwave measurement, *Electronics* **32**, 74 (1959).
132. A. Dymanus, Intensity measurements in microwave spectroscopy. The "antimodulation" method, *Physica* **25**, 859–888 (1959).
133. A. Dymanus, High-Q Stark cavity absorption cell for microwave spectrometers, *Rev. Sci. Instr.* **30**, 191–195 (1959).
134. J. J. Gallagher and J. B. Newman, A gas laser at millimeter wavelengths, *Spectrochim. Acta* **15**, 769 (1959).
135. L. Genzel, H. Happ, and R. Weber, A grating spectrometer for the region of the far infrared and short microwaves, *Z. Physik* **154**, 1–12 (1959).
136. W. Gordy, Millimeter and submillimeter waves in physics, *Proc. Symp. Millimeter Waves, New York, March, 1959*, pp. 1–23. Polytechnic Press, Brooklyn, New York, 1959, distributed by Wiley (Interscience), New York.
137. J. Herve, J. Pescia, and M. Sauzade, Frequency stabilization of a high power carcinotron, *Compt. Rend.* **249**, 1486–1488 (1959).
138. D. Ilias, A recording microwave spectrometer for gas study, *J. Phys. Radium* **20**, 653–655 (1959).
139. M. W. Long, Sensitivity of microwave spectrometers and hyperfine spectra of $CFCl_3$. *U.S. Dept. Comm., Office Tech. Serv., PB Rept.* 147,451 (1959).
140. R. S. Ohl, P. P. Budenstein, and C. A. Burrus, Improved diode for the harmonic generation of millimeter and submillimeter waves, *Rev. Sci. Instr.* **30**, 765–774 (1959).
141. K. Shimoda, Radiofrequency spectroscopy using three-level maser action, *J. Phys. Soc. Japan* **14**, 954–959 (1959).
142. R. W. Zimmer, Transistor phase detector for phase-lock stabilization of a 30,000 Mc klystron, *Rev. Sci. Instr.* **30**, 1052–1053 (1959).
143. A. Dymanus and A. Bouwknegt, Measurements on power-conversion gain and noise ratio of the 1N26 crystal rectifiers, *Physica* **26**, 115–126 (1960).
144. A. Dymanus, H. A. Dijkerman, and G. R. D. Zijderveld, New method for the measurement of microwave integrated line intensities and line widths, *J. Chem. Phys.* **32**, 717–723 (1960).
145. G. Erlandsson and A. Rachman, Microwave spectrophotometer with Stark modulation, *Ciencia Invest. (Buenos Aires)* **16**, 166–176 (1960).
146. J. A. Giordmaine and T. C. Wang, Molecular beam formation by long parallel tubes, *J. Appl. Phys.* **31**, 463–471 (1960).
147. J. P. Gordon, Molecular beam masers, *Quantum Electronics Conf., Bloomingburg, New York, September, 1959*, pp. 3–16. Columbia Univ. Press, New York, 1960.
148. M. W. Long, Detectors for microwave spectrometers, *Rev. Sci. Instr.* **31**, 1286–1289 (1960).
149. E. A. Rinehart, H. Kleen, and C. C. Lin, Measurement of the widths of microwave spectral lines, *J. Mol. Spectry.* **5**, 458–473 (1960).
150. H. D. Rudolph, H. Dreizler, and W. Maier, Microwave spectrum of methanol between 9 and 16×10^3 Mc by using the carcinotron as radiation source, *Z. Naturforsch.* **15A**, 274–275 (1960).
151. K. Shimoda, H. Takuma, and T. Shimizu, Beam-type masers for radiofrequency spectroscopy, *J. Phys. Soc. Japan* **15**, 2036–2041 (1960).
152. P. Thaddeus, J. Loubser, A. Javan, L. Krisher, and H. Lecar, Use of some new molecules in a beam-type maser for spectroscopy and frequency standards, *Quantum Electronics Conf., Bloomingburg, New York, September 1959*, pp. 46–56. Columbia Univ. Press, New York, 1960.
153. T. Yajima and K. Shimoda, The three level gas maser as a microwave spectrometer, *J. Phys. Soc. Japan* **15**, 1668–1675 (1960).
154. R. W. Zimmerer, Precision Zeeman modulation spectrometer, *Rev. Sci. Instr.* **31**, 106–111 (1960).

155. A. Battaglia, A. Gozzini, and E. Polacco, A new method for modulation of molecular absorption in microwave spectroscopy. Study of the transition $J = 0 \to 1$ of OCS, *Arch. Sci. (Geneva)* **13**, 171–177 (1961).

156. Y. Beers, Comparison of the sensitivity of the beam maser and cavity absorption spectrometers, *Rev. Sci. Instr.* **32**, 23–27 (1961).

157. A. Dymanus and H. A. Dijkerman, The σ-Stark effect of rotational transitions I. Experimental aspects, *Physica* **27**, 593–602 (1961).

158. E. A. Rinehart and C. C. Lin, Sensitive triple modulation method for measuring widths of microwave spectral lines, *Rev. Sci. Instr.* **32**, 562–563 (1961).

159. H. D. Rudolph, Stark effect microwave spectrograph with high resolving power, *Z. Angew. Phys.* **13**, 401–409 (1961).

160. P. Thaddeus and L. C. Krisher, A beam maser spectrometer, *Rev. Sci. Instr.* **32**, 1083–1089 (1961).

161. H. W. de Wijn, High voltage square wave generator, *Rev. Sci. Instr.* **32**, 735–736 (1961).

162. Y. Beers and G. L. Strine, The measurement of voltage by the use of the Stark effect, *IRE Trans. Instr.* **11**, 171–176 (1962).

163. J. J. Gallagher, J. W. Dees, R. G. Strauch, and R. E. Cupp, Excitation and detection techniques for millimeter wave transitions. Martin Co. 1st Quart. Progress Rept. 1962.

164. A. J. Hebert, A molecular-beam electric-resonance spectrometer and the radio-frequency spectra of lithium fluoride, Lawrence Radiation Laboratory, Berkeley, California, UCRL-10482 (1962).

165. A. Narath and W. D. Gwinn, Phase-stabilized klystron system and its application to microwave spectroscopy and microwave frequency standards, *Rev. Sci. Instr.* **33**, 79–82 (1962).

166. T. Nishikawa, Developments in the millimeter and submillimeter wave technique and its application in chemistry, *Kagaku No Ryoiki* **16**, 657–664 (1962).

167. J. R. Rusk and W. Gordy, Millimeter wave molecular beam spectroscopy-alkali bromides and iodides, *Phys. Rev.* **127**, 817–830 (1962).

168. J. Sheridan, A. P. Cox, and J. K. Tyler, Microwave spectroscopy. *U.S. Dept. Comm., Office Tech. Serv.* AD 273,614 (1962).

169. A. S. Esbitt and E. B. Wilson, Jr., Relative intensity measurements in microwave spectroscopy, *Rev. Sci. Instr.* **34**, 901–907 (1963).

170. J. J. Gallagher and R. G. Strauch, Excitation and detection techniques for millimeter wave transitions. Martin Co. 2nd Quart. Progr. Rept. 1963.

171. J. J. Gallagher, R. G. Strauch, and R. E. Cupp, Excitation and detection techniques for millimeter wave transitions. Martin Co. 3rd Quart. Progr. Rept. 1963.

172. J. J. Gallagher, R. G. Strauch, and R. E. Cupp, Excitation and detection techniques for millimeter wave transitions. Martin Co. 4th Quart. Progr. Rept. 1963.

173. J. J. Gallagher, R. G. Strauch, and R. E. Cupp, Excitation and detection techniques for millimeter wave transitions. Martin Co. 5th Quart. Progr. Rept. 1963.

174. M. Lichtenstein, J. J. Gallagher, and R. E. Cupp, Millimeter spectrometer using a Fabry–Perot interferometer, *Rev. Sci. Instr.* **34**, 843–846 (1963).

175. R. L. Poynter and G. R. Steffensen, Tunable, high stability, microwave oscillator, *Rev. Sci. Instr.* **34**, 77–82 (1963).

175a. E. H. Putley, The detection of sub-mm radiation, *Proc. IEEE* **51**, 1412–1423 (1963).

176. "The Microwave Engineers Handbook and Buyers Guide—1964." Horizon House, Microwave Inc., Dedham, Massachusetts, 1963.

177. R. W. Zimmerer, M. V. Anderson, G. L. Strine, and Y. Beers, Millimeter wavelength resonant structures, *IEEE Trans. Microwave Theory Tech.* **11**, 142–149 (1963).

178. A. Benjaminson, Phase-locked microwave oscillator systems with 0.1 cps stability, *Microwave J.* **7**(12), 65–69 (1964).

179. F. W. Breivogel, Jr., The radiofrequency and microwave spectra of LiBr and LiI, Lawrence Radiation Laboratory, Berkeley, California, UCRL-11665 (1964).

180. P. L. Clouser and W. Gordy, Millimeter-wave molecular beam spectroscopy-alkali chlorides, *Phys. Rev.* **134**, 863–870 (1964).

181. J. J. Gallagher, R. G. Strauch, and R. E. Cupp, Excitation and detection techniques for millimeter wave transitions, Martin Co. 6th Quart. Progr. Rept. 1964.

182. J. J. Gallagher, R. G. Strauch, and R. E. Cupp, Excitation and detection techniques for millimeter wave transitions, Martin Co. 7th Quart. Progr. Rept. 1964.

183. J. J. Gallagher, R. G. Strauch, and R. E. Cupp, Excitation and detection techniques for millimeter wave transitions, Martin Co. 8th Quart. Progr. Rept. 1964.

184. J. J. Gallagher, R. G. Strauch, and R. E. Cupp, Excitation and detection techniques for millimeter wave transitions, Martin Co. 9th Quart. Progr. Rept. 1964.

184a. H. A. Gebbie, N. W. B. Stone, and F. D. Findlay, A stimulated emission source at 0.34 millimeter wave-length, *Nature* **202**, 685 (1964).

185. Y. Hanyu, Construction of a Stark-modulated microwave spectrometer and the spectrum of a hydrogen-bonded system of acetic acid and Trifluoroacetic acid, *Nippon Kagaku Zasshi* **85**, 5–8 (1964).

186. H. W. Harrington and R. H. Bauhaus, Absolute intensity coefficient measurements in microwave spectroscopy, *Mol. Spectry. Symp.* Ohio State Univ., Columbus, Ohio, 1964.

187. D. R. Lide, Jr., Versatile Stark waveguide for microwave spectroscopy, *Rev. Sci. Instr.* **35**, 1226 (1964).

188. Y. Morino and E. Hirota, Microwave spectrometer for analytical use and its application to the analysis of deuterated propylene, *Nippon Kagaku Zasshi* **85**, 535–538 (1964).

189. R. G. Strauch, R. E. Cupp, M. Lichtenstein, and J. J. Gallagher, Quasi-optical techniques in millimeter spectroscopy, *Proc. Symp. on Quasi-Optics, New York, June 1964.* Polytechnic Press, Brooklyn, New York, 1964, distributed by Wiley (Interscience), New York.

190. F. L. Wentworth, J. W. Dozier, and J. D. Rodgers, Millimeter wave harmonic generators, mixers and detectors, *Microwave J.* **7**, 69–75 (1964).

191. F. W. Breivogel, Jr., A. J. Hebert, and K. Street, Jr., Radiofrequency and microwave spectra of Li^6I^{127} by the molecular-beam electric-resonance method, *J. Chem. Phys.* **42**, 1555–1558 (1965).

191a. A. P. Cox, G. W. Flynn, and E. B. Wilson, Jr., Microwave double resonance experiments, *J. Chem. Phys.* **42**, 3094–3105 (1965).

191b. J. J. Gallagher, R. G. Strauch, and R. E. Cupp, Excitation and detection techniques for millimeter wave transitions, Martin Co. 10th Quart. Progr. Rept. 1965.

191c. J. J. Gallagher, R. G. Strauch, and R. E. Cupp, Excitation and detection techniques for millimeter wave transitions, Martin Co. 11th Quart. Progr. Rept. 1965.

191d. J. J. Gallagher, R. G. Strauch, and R. E. Cupp, Excitation and detection techniques for millimeter wave transitions, Martin Co. 12th Quart. Progr. Rept. 1965.

192. D. R. Lide, Jr., High-temperature microwave spectroscopy: AlF and AlCl, *J. Chem. Phys.* **42**, 1013–1018 (1965).

192a. L. E. Mathias, A. Crocker, and M. S. Wills, Laser oscillations at submillimeter wave-lengths from pulsed gas discharges in compounds of hydrogen, carbon, and nitrogen, *Electron. Letters* **1**, 45–46 (1965).

193. E. A. Rinehart, R. L. Legan, and C. C. Lin, Microwave spectrograph for linewidth measurements, *Rev. Sci. Instr.* **36**, 511–517 (1965).

194. H. J. Tobler, A. Bauder, and Hs. H. Guenthard, Distortion of line shapes in Stark-modulated microwave spectrometers, *J. Sci. Instr.* **42**, 236–239 (1965).

195. H. J. Tobler, H. U. Wenger, A. Bauder, and Hs. H. Guenthard, Electrical and mechanical properties of an improved microwave Stark cell, *J. Sci. Instr.* **42**, 240–242 (1965).

196. S. E. Veazey and W. Gordy, Millimeter-wave molecular-beam spectroscopy: Alkali fluorides, *Phys. Rev.* **138**, 1303–1311 (1965).

196a. D. P. Akitt, W. Q. Jeffers, and P. D. Coleman, Water vapor gas laser operating at 118-microns wavelength, *Proc. IEEE* **54**, 547–551 (1966).

196b. R. J. Bauer, M. Cohn, J. M. Cotton, Jr., and R. F. Packard, Millimeter wave semiconductor diode detectors, mixers and frequency multipliers, *Proc. IEEE* **54**, 595–605 (1966).

196c. C. A. Burrus, Jr., Millimeter-wave point-contact and junction diodes, *Proc. IEEE* **54**, 575–587 (1966).

196d. G. T. Flesher and W. M. Muller, Submillimeter gas laser, *Proc. IEEE* **54**, 543–546 (1966).

196e. D. C. Forster, High power sources at millimeter wavelengths, *Proc. IEEE* **54**, 532–539 (1966).

196f. J. Gilbert and R. M. Vaillancourt, A saturation effect spectrometer, *Proc. IEEE* **54**, 514–519 (1966).

196g. P. H. Knapp and D. H. Martin, Submillimeter spectroscopy using a Froome harmonic generator (metal-plasma junction), *Proc. IEEE* **54**, 528–531 (1966).

196h. W. G. Matthei, Recent developments in solid state microwave devices, *Microwave J.* **9**, 39–46 (1966).

196i. R. G. Strauch, R. E. Cupp, V. E. Derr, and J. J. Gallagher, Millimeter electric resonance spectroscopy, *Proc. IEEE* **54**, 506–513 (1966).

196j. E. P. Valkenburg and V. E. Derr, A high-Q Fabry–Perot interferometer for water vapor absorption measurements in the 100–300 Gc/s frequency range, *Proc. IEEE* **54**, 493–498 (1966).

III. Line Shape and Line Broadening

197. H. A. Lorentz, Absorption and emission lines of gases, *Proc. Acad. Sci. Amsterdam* **8**, 591–611 (1906).

198. V. F. Weisskopf, Width of spectral lines in gases, *Physik. Z.* **34**, 1–24 (1933).

199. H. Kuhn, Pressure shift and broadening of spectral lines, *Phil. Mag.* **18**, 987–1003 (1934).

200. H. Kuhn and F. London, Limitation of the potential theory of broadening of spectral lines, *Phil. Mag.* **18**, 983–987 (1934).

201. H. Margenau and D. T. Warren, Long range interactions between dipole molecules, *Phys. Rev.* **51**, 748–753 (1937).

202. L. Spitzer, Jr., Impact broadening of spectral lines, *Phys. Rev.* **58**, 348–357 (1940).

203. A. Jablonski, General theory of pressure broadening of spectral lines, *Phys. Rev.* **68**, 78–93 (1945). Errata—*Phys. Rev.* **69**, 31 (1946).

204. J. H. Van Vleck and V. F. Weisskopf, On the shape of collision-broadened lines, *Rev. Mod. Phys.* **17**, 227–236 (1945).

205. H. M. Foley, The pressure broadening of spectral lines, *Phys. Rev.* **69**, 616–628 (1946).

206. H. Frohlich, Shape of collision-broadened spectral lines, *Nature* **157**, 478 (1946).

207. A. Jablonski, Pressure broadening of spectral lines, *Physicas Grav.* **7**, 541–551 (1946).

208. E. Lindholm, Pressure broadening of spectral lines, *Arkiv. Mat. Astron. Fysik* **32A**, Paper 17 (1946).

209. C. H. Townes, The ammonia spectrum and line shapes near 1.25 cm wavelength, *Phys. Rev.* **70**, 665–671 (1946).

210. B. Bleaney and R. P. Penrose, Collision broadening of the inversion spectrum of ammonia at centimeter wavelengths I. Self-broadening at high pressure, *Proc. Phys. Soc. (London)* **59**, 418–428 (1947).

211. T. A. Pond and W. F. Cannon, Saturation effect in microwave spectrum of ammonia, *Phys. Rev.* **72**, 1121–1122 (1947).

212. B. Bleaney and J. H. N. Loubser, Collision broadening of the ammonia inversion spectrum at high pressures, *Nature* **161**, 522–523 (1948).

213. B. Bleaney and R. P. Penrose, Collision broadening of the inversion spectrum of ammonia III. The collision cross sections for self-broadening and for mixtures with nonpolar gases, *Proc. Phys. Soc. (London)* **60**, 540–549 (1948).

214. H. M. Foley, The theory of the pressure broadening of spectral lines: A reply, *Phys. Rev.* **73**, 259 (1948).

215. A. Jablonski, On the phase shift approximation in the theory of pressure broadening of spectral lines, *Phys. Rev.* **73**, 258–259 (1948).

216. D. F. Smith, Pressure broadening in ammonia at centimeter wavelengths, *Phys. Rev.* **74**, 506–507 (1948).

217. P. W. Anderson, On the anomalous line-shapes in the ammonia inversion spectrum at high pressures, *Phys. Rev.* **75**, 1450 (1949).

218. P. W. Anderson, Pressure broadening in the microwave and infrared regions, *Phys. Rev.* **76**, 647–661 (1949).

219. H. Margenau, Pressure broadening in the inversion spectrum of ammonia, *Phys. Rev.* **76**, 121–124 (1949).

220. H. Margenau, Inversion frequency of ammonia and molecular interaction, *Phys. Rev.* **76**, 1423–1429 (1949).

221. J. H. Van Vleck and H. Margenau, Collision theories of pressure broadening of spectral lines, *Phys. Rev.* **76**, 1211–1214 (1949).

222. P. W. Anderson, Pressure broadening of the ammonia inversion line by foreign gases. Quadrupole-induced dipole interactions, *Phys. Rev.* **80**, 511–513 (1950).

223. T. Holstein, Pressure broadening of spectral lines, *Phys. Rev.* **79**, 744 (1950).

224. R. R. Howard and W. V. Smith, Temperature dependence of microwave line widths, *Phys. Rev.* **77**, 840–841 (1950).

225. L. C. Jones, Pressure broadening and the line shift in microwave spectra, *Phys. Rev.* **77**, 741 (1950).

226. H. Margenau and S. Bloom, Pressure broadening of spectral lines and frequency modulation, *Phys. Rev.* **79**, 213 (1950).

227. W. V. Smith and R. R. Howard, Microwave collision diameters II. Theory and correlation with molecular quadrupole moments, *Phys. Rev.* **79**, 132–136 (1950).

228. B. V. Gokhale and M. W. P. Strandberg, Line breadths in the 5-mm microwave absorption of oxygen, *Phys. Rev.* **84**, 844 (1951).

229. R. M. Hill and W. V. Smith, Microwave collision diameters and associated quadrupole moments, *Phys. Rev.* **82**, 451 (1951).

230. D. C. M. Leslie, Collision broadening of microwave frequencies, *Phil. Mag.* **42**, 37–55 (1951).

231. H. Margenau, Statistical theory of pressure broadening, *Phys. Rev.* **82**, 156–158 (1951).

232. M. Mizushima, The theory of pressure broadening and its application to microwave spectra, *Phys. Rev.* **83**, 94–103 (1951). Errata—*Phys. Rev.* **84**, 363 (1951).

233. C. A. Potter, A. V. Bushkovitch, and A. G. Rouse, Pressure broadening in the microwave spectrum of ammonia, *Phys. Rev.* **83**, 987–989 (1951).

234. R. S. Anderson, W. V. Smith, and W. Gordy, Line-breadths of the microwave spectrum of oxygen, *Phys. Rev.* **87**, 561–568 (1952).

235. W. V. Smith, Pressure broadening, *Ann. N.Y. Acad. Sci.* **55**, 891–903 (1952).

236. R. S. Anderson, Variation of line width with rotational state and temperature in the microwave spectrum of OCS, *Phys. Rev.* **97**, 1654–1660 (1955).

237. E. P. Gross, Shape of collision-broadened spectral lines, *Phys. Rev.* **97**, 395–403 (1955).
238. C. S. G. Phillips, Line broadening and dielectric relaxation in compressed gases, *J. Chem. Phys.* **23**, 2388–2394 (1955).
239. W. V. Smith, H. A. Lackner, and A. B. Volkov, Pressure broadening (of microwave lines) of linear molecules. II. Theory. *J. Chem. Phys.* **23**, 389–396 (1955). Errata—*J. Chem. Phys.* **23**, 1559 (1955).
240. M. Tinkham and M. W. P. Strandberg, Line breadths in the microwave magnetic resonance spectrum of oxygen, *Phys. Rev.* **99**, 537–539 (1955).
241. A. A. Kolosov and L. L. Myasnikov, The half-widths of the absorption microradiowave lines of ammonia, *Opt. i Spektroskopiya* **1**, 374–377 (1956).
242. W. V. Smith, Evaluation of molecular quadrupole moments from microwave spectral line widths I. Theoretical, *J. Chem. Phys.* **25**, 510–515 (1956).
243. V. M. Fain, Natural line widths of microwaves, *Soviet Phys. JETP* (*English Transl.*) **5**, 501–503 (1957).
244. H. Feeny, W. Madigosky, and B. Winters, Evaluation of molecular quadrupole moments from microwave line breadths II. Experimental, *J. Chem. Phys.* **27**, 898–900 (1957).
245. Krishnaji and G. P. Srivastava, Temperature variation of microwave absorption co-efficient in ethyl chloride, *Proc. Phys. Soc.* (*London*) **70B**, 621–622 (1957).
246. K. Matsuura, Y. Sugiura, and G. M. Hatoyama, Frequency shift in ammonia absorption due to self-broadening, *J. Phys. Soc. Japan* **12**, 314 (1957).
247. K. Matsuura, Y. Sugiura, and G. M. Hatoyama, Frequency shift in the absorption line of ammonia in the microwave region, *Denki Shikensho Iho* **21**, 612–621 (1957).
248. I. Takahashi, T. Ogawa, M. Yamano, and A. Hirai, Shift of center frequency of an ammonia inversion spectrum, *Phys. Rev.* **106**, 606 (1957).
249. K. Tomita, Pressure shift of the inversion frequency of ammonia, *Progr. Theoret. Phys.* (Kyoto) **18**, 316–318 (1957).
250. L. J. Kieffer and A. V. Bushkovitch, Critical analysis and application of a quasi-resonant theory of pressure broadening of linear molecules, *J. Mol. Spectry.* **2**, 558–565 (1958).
251. A. Battaglia, A. Gozzini, and E. Polacco, Some phenomena related to the saturation of rotational resonances in the microwave spectrum of COS, *Nuovo Cimento* **14**, 1076–1081 (1959).
252. W. S. Benedict and C. D. Kaplan, Calculation of line widths in H_2O–N_2 collisions, *J. Chem. Phys.* **30**, 388–399 (1959).
253. A. Dymanus, Power saturation of the $J = 1 \rightarrow 2$ rotational transition of OCS, *Phys. Rev.* **116**, 351–355 (1959).
254. J. E. Boggs, A. P. Deam, and J. M. King, Temperature variation of the linewidth in nonresonant microwave absorption, *J. Chem. Phys.* **33**, 1852–1855 (1960).
255. J. A. Fulford, Line breadths in the ammonia spectrum, *Nature* **188**, 1097–1098 (1960).
256. R. G. Breene, Jr., "The Shift and Shape of Spectral Lines." Pergamon Press, Oxford, 1961.
257. G. Birnbaum and A. A. Maryott, Collision-induced microwave absorption in compressed gases II. Molecular electric quadrupole moments, *J. Chem. Phys.* **36**, 2032–2036 (1962).
258. A. A. Maryott and G. Birnbaum, Collision-induced microwave absorption in compressed gases I. Dependence on density, temperature and frequency in CO_2, *J. Chem. Phys.* **36**, 2026–2032 (1962).
259. M. L. Sage, Pressure broadening and the electric quadrupole moment of OCS. *U.S. Dept. Comm. Office Tech. Serv.*, AD 284,174 (1962).
260. L. Galatry, Theory of spectral line shape in the microwave region, *J. Phys. Radium* **24**, 265–272 (1963).
261. Krishnaji and S. Chandra, Molecular interaction and linewidth of asymmetric molecule SO_2 I. SO_2–N_2 collisions, *J. Chem. Phys.* **38**, 232–236 (1963).

262. Krishnaji and S. Chandra, Molecular interaction and line width of asymmetric molecule SO$_2$ III. SO$_2$–CH$_3$Br and SO$_2$–SO$_2$ collisions, *J. Chem. Phys.* **38**, 2690–2692 (1963).
263. G. Birnbaum, "Optical Masers." Academic Press, New York, 1964.
264. G. Birnbaum and A. A. Maryott, Nonresonant absorption and collision diameters in the foreign-gas broadening of symmetric top molecules, *J. Chem. Phys.* **41**, 154–157 (1964).
265. Krishnaji and S. L. Srivastava, Quadrupole moment of OCS, *J. Chem. Phys.* **41**, 2201 (1964).
266. Krishnaji and S. L. Srivastava, First-order London dispersion forces and microwave spectral linewidth, *J. Chem. Phys.* **41**, 2266–2270 (1964).
267. A. DiGiacomo, Shape of Zeeman and Stark components of spectral lines in the microwave region at low pressure and high temperature, *Nuovo Cimento* **36**, 916–934 (1965).
268. R. L. Legan, J. A. Roberts, E. A. Rinehart, and C. C. Lin, Linewidths of the microwave inversion spectrum of ammonia, *J. Chem. Phys.* **43**, 4337–4345 (1965).
268a. W. Parsons and J. A. Roberts, The Doppler contribution to microwave line widths, *J. Mol. Spectry.* **18**, 412–417 (1965).
269. S. L. Srivastava and V. Prakash, Molecular quadrupole moment of BrCN from microwave spectral line width, *J. Chem. Phys.* **42**, 3738–3739 (1965).
270. H. W. de Wijn, Collision broadening of microwave spectral lines of linear rotators, *Physica* **31**, 1215–1223 (1965).

IV. The Rigid Rotor

271. F. Reiche and H. Rademacher, Quantization of a symmetrical top according to Schrödinger's undulation mechanics, *Z. Physik* **39**, 444–464 (1926).
272. R. L. Kronig and I. I. Rabi, The symmetrical top in the undulatory mechanics, *Phys. Rev.* **29**, 262–269 (1927).
273. H. Rademacher and F. Reiche, Quantization of the symmetrical top according to Schrödinger's undulation mechanics, *Z. Physik* **41**, 453–492 (1927).
274. E. E. Witmer, The quantization of the rotational motion of the polyatomic molecule by the new wave mechanics, *Proc. Nat. Acad. Sci. U.S.* **13**, 60–65 (1927).
275. H. A. Kramers and G. P. Ittman, On the quantization of the asymmetric top, *Z. Physik* **53**, 553–565 (1929).
276. S. C. Wang, On the asymmetrical top in quantum mechanics, *Phys. Rev.* **34**, 243–252 (1929).
277. H. B. G. Casimir, "Rotation of a Rigid Body in Quantum Mechanics." Wolters, The Hague, 1931.
278. B. S. Ray, Eigenvalues of an asymmetrical rotator, *Z. Physik* **78**, 74–91 (1932).
279. G. W. King, R. M. Hainer, and P. C. Cross, The asymmetric rotor I. Calculation and symmetry classification of energy levels, *J. Chem. Phys.* **11**, 27–42 (1943).
280. P. C. Cross, R. M. Hainer, and G. W. King, The asymmetric rotor II. Calculation of dipole intensities and line classification, *J. Chem. Phys.* **12**, 210–225 (1944).
281. G. W. King, The asymmetric rotor VI. Calculation of higher levels by means of the correspondence principle, *J. Chem. Phys.* **15**, 820–830 (1947).
282. S. Golden, An asymptotic expression for the energy levels of the rigid rotor, *J. Chem. Phys.* **16**, 78–86 (1948).
283. R. Karplus, Note on the energy of a rotating molecule, *J. Chem. Phys.* **16**, 1170–1171 (1948).

284. E. E. Witmer, An explicit solution of the problem of the asymmetric rotator according to quantum mechanics, *Phys. Rev.* **74**, 1247 (1948).
285. E. E. Witmer, An explicit formula for the energy levels of the asymmetric rotor according to quantum mechanics, *Phys. Rev.* **74**, 1250 (1948).
286. S. Golden and J. K. Bragg, An asymptotic expression for the energy levels of the asymmetric rotor III. Approximation for the essentially degenerate levels of the rigid rotor, *J. Chem. Phys.* **17**, 439–441 (1949).
287. R. M. Hainer, P. C. Cross, and G. W. King, The asymmetric rotor VII. Extension of the calculation of energy levels, *J. Chem. Phys.* **17**, 826–836 (1949).
288. D. R. Lide, Jr., A note on rotational line strengths in slightly asymmetric rotors, *J. Chem. Phys.* **20**, 1761–1763 (1952).
289. B. L. Hicks, T. E. Turner, and W. W. Widule, Applications of large digital computers to calculations of microwave spectroscopy, *J. Chem. Phys.* **21**, 564 (1953).
290. D. Kivelson, A (K + 2)nd order formula for asymmetry doublets in rotational spectra, *J. Chem. Phys.* **21**, 536–538 (1953).
291. C. Van Winter, The asymmetric rotator in quantum mechanics, *Physica* **20**, 274–292 (1954).
292. G. Erlandsson, Extended energy level tables for the rigid asymmetric rotor, *Arkiv Fysik* **10**, 65–88 (1956).
293. D. W. Posener, Asymmetric rotor. Convergence in the continued fraction expansion of the reduced energies, *J. Chem. Phys.* **24**, 546–547 (1956).
294. W. Givens, The characteristic value-vector problem, *J. Assoc. Computing Machinery* **4**, 298–307 (1957).
295. S. R. Polo, Energy levels of slightly asymmetric top molecules, *Can. J. Phys.* **35**, 880–885 (1957).
296. R. H. Schwendeman, Table of coefficients for the energy levels of a near symmetric top, *J. Chem. Phys.* **27**, 986 (1957).
297. R. H. Schwendeman, "A Table of Coefficients for the Energy Levels of a Near Symmetric Top." Dept. of Chem., Harvard Univ. Cambridge, Massachusetts, 1957.
298. W. H. Shaffer, Operational derivation of wave functions for a symmetrical rigid rotator, *J. Mol. Spectry.* **1**, 69–80 (1957).
299. D. G. Burkhard, Factorization and wave functions for the symmetric rigid rotator, *J. Mol. Spectry.* **2**, 187–202 (1958).
300. E. K. Gora, Simplified methods for the computation of asymmetric rotor energy levels and line strengths, *J. Mol. Spectry.* **2**, 259–272 (1958).
301. F. Kneubuhl, T. Gaumann, T. Ginsburg, and Hs. H. Gunthard, Calculation program for evaluation of the rotational spectrum of rigid molecules, *Helv. Phys. Acta* **31**, 276–277 (1958).
302. R. H. Schwendeman and V. W. Laurie, "Tables of Line Strengths." Pergamon Press, Oxford, 1958.
303. L. C. Brown and P. M. Parker, "Tables of Asymmetry Parameter Function." Departmental Publ., Ohio State Univ., Columbus, Ohio, 1959.
304. C. T. Fike, Energy levels of an asymmetric rotor, *J. Chem. Phys.* **31**, 568–569 (1959).
305. F. Kneubuhl, T. Gaumann, and Hs. H. Gunthard, A program for automatic digital computation of transition frequencies and analysis of microwave rotational spectra of rigid asymmetric tops, *J. Mol. Spectry.* **3**, 349–362 (1959).
306. P. M. Parker and L. C. Brown, Computation of rigid asymmetric rotator constants from energy moments II, *J. Chem. Phys.* **30**, 909–912 (1959).
307. P. M. Parker and L. C. Brown, Energy moment method in quantum mechanics, *Am. J. Phys.* **27**, 509–514 (1959).

308. W. H. Shaffer and J. D. Louck, Operational procedure for the determination of the matrix elements of the direction cosines for a rigid symmetrical rotator, *J. Mol. Spectry.* **3**, 123–131 (1959).

309. E. D. Trifonov, A new method of calculating the statistical weights of the rotational energy levels of polyatomic molecules, *Dokl. Akad. Nauk SSSR* **129**, 74–76 (1959).

310. J. M. Bennett, I. G. Ross, and E. J. Wells, Asymmetric rotor energy levels—An improved computational procedure, *J. Mol. Spectry.* **4**, 342–348 (1960).

311. N. Jannuzzi and S. P. S. Porto, Table of energy levels of a slightly asymmetrical top rotor, *J. Mol. Spectry.* **4**, 459–467 (1960).

312. J. A. Norris and V. W. Laurie, Energy levels of a slightly asymmetric top, *J. Chem. Phys.* **32**, 1591 (1960). Erratum—*J. Chem. Phys.* **33**, 1256 (1960). Comments and Errata— J. E. Beam and H. L. Davis, *J. Chem. Phys.* **33**, 1255 (1960).

♦313. L. Pierce, Calculation of the eigenvalues of a tridiagonal Hermitian matrix, *J. Math. Phys.* **2**, 740–741 (1961).

314. R. H. Schwendeman, The matrix elements of the direction cosines in the Wang symmetric rotator basis, *J. Mol. Spectry.* **7**, 280–286 (1961).

♦ 315. J. D. Swalen and L. Pierce, Remarks on the continued fractions calculation of eigenvalues and eigenvectors, *J. Math. Phys.* **2**, 736–739 (1961).

316. B. G. West and M. Mizushima, Table of rotational transitions strengths for asymmetric rotators, University of Colorado, Boulder, Colorado, Quart. Prog. Rept. DA-36-039- SC-87277 (Dec. 1961).

317. J. W. Blaker, M. Sidran, and A. Kaercher, Rotational energy levels of asymmetric top molecules, Pt. I. Discussion of the theory. Grumman Res. Rept. RE-155 (March, 1962).

§ 318. J. W. Blaker, M. Sidran, and A. Kaercher, Rotational energy levels of asymmetric top molecules, Pt. II. Table of reduced energies. Grumman Res. Rept. RE-155 (March 1962).

319. J. D. Louck, Trace formulas for a rigid asymmetric rotator type Hamiltonian, *J. Mol. Spectry.* **10**, 263–277 (1963).

320. M. Sidran, F. Nolan, and J. W. Blaker, Rotational energy levels of asymmetric top molecules, Pt. III. Table of reduced energies for $J = 6$ to 9. Grumman Res. Rept. RE-155 (June 1963).

321. F. J. Nolan, M. Sidran, and J. W. Blaker, Rotational energy levels of asymmetric top molecules, Table of reduced energies (Pt. IV. $J = 10$ to 13). Grumman Res. Rept. RE-172 (March 1964).

322. F. J. Nolan, M. Sidran, and J. W. Blaker, Rotational energy levels of asymmetric top molecules, table of reduced energies (Pt. V. $J = 14$ to 16). Grumman Res. Rept. RE-178 (June 1964).

323. R. H. Schwendeman, A table of $\langle P_z^2 \rangle$ and $\langle P_z^4 \rangle$ for asymmetric rotator molecules, Dept. of Chem., Michigan State Univ., East Lansing, Michigan (1964).

324. M. Sidran, F. Nolan, and J. W. Blaker, Rotational energy levels of asymmetric top molecules, table of reduced energies (Pt. VI. $J = 17$ to 18). Grumman Res. Rept. RE-189 (October 1964).

325. M. Sidran, F. Nolan, and J. W. Blaker, Rotational energy levels of asymmetric top molecules, table of reduced energies (Pt. VII. $J = 19$ to 20). Grumman Res. Rept. RE-196 (December 1964).

326. P. F. Wacker and M. R. Pratto, Microwave spectra tables. Line strengths of asymmetric rotors, *Natl. Bur. Std.* (*U.S.*) *Monograph* **70**, Pt. 2 (1964).

327. D. G. Burkhard and W. E. Brittin, The asymmetric top—an analytical treatment, *J. Mol. Spectry.* **18**, 87–109 (1965).

328. V. Dobyns, Tables for the asymmetric rotor, *J. Chem. Phys.* **43**, 4534–4535 (1965).
329. J. D. Louck, Eigenvectors of a slightly asymmetric rotator, *J. Mol. Spectry.* **15**, 83–99 (1965).
330. S. C. Wait, Jr., and C. A. Pinkham, Asymmetric rotor line strengths, *J. Mol. Spectry.* **19**, 34–44 (1966).

Va. General Vibration-Rotation Interaction

331. J. L. Dunham, The energy levels of a rotating vibrator, *Phys. Rev.* **41**, 721–731 (1932).
332. D. M. Dennison and M. Johnston, The interaction between vibration and rotation for symmetrical molecules, *Phys. Rev.* **47**, 93–94 (1935).
333. M. Johnston and D. M. Dennison, The interaction between vibration and rotation for symmetrical molecules, *Phys. Rev.* **48**, 868–883 (1935).
334. E. B. Wilson, Jr., The vibration-rotation energy levels of polyatomic molecules II. Perturbations due to nearby vibrational states, *J. Chem. Phys.* **4**, 313–316 (1936).
335. E. B. Wilson, Jr. and J. B. Howard, The vibration-rotation energy levels of polyatomic molecules I. Mathematical theory of semirigid asymmetric top molecules, *J. Chem. Phys.* **4**, 260–268 (1936).
336. H. H. Nielsen, The vibration-rotation energies of polyatomic molecules, *Phys. Rev.* **60**, 794–810 (1941).
337. W. H. Shaffer, Infra-red spectra of axially symmetric XY_3Z molecules I. Vibration-rotation energies, *J. Chem. Phys.* **10**, 1–9 (1942).
338. S. Silver, Vibration-rotation energies of planar ZXY_2 molecules. Pt. II. The quantum-mechanical Hamiltonian and the energy values, *J. Chem. Phys.* **10**, 565–574 (1942).
339. S. Silver and E. S. Ebers, Vibration-rotation energies of planar ZXY_2 molecules. Pt. I. The vibrational modes and frequencies, *J. Chem. Phys.* **10**, 559–564 (1942).
340. A. H. Nielsen, The vibration-rotation energies of the linear XYZ type molecule, *J. Chem. Phys.* **11**, 160–163 (1943).
341. H. H. Nielsen, The quantum mechanical Hamiltonian for the linear polyatomic molecule treated as a limiting case of the nonlinear polyatomic molecule, *Phys. Rev.* **66**, 282–287 (1944).
342. H. H. Nielsen, The energies of polyatomic molecules, *J. Opt. Soc. Am.* **34**, 521–528 (1944).
343. W. H. Shaffer and R. P. Schuman, The infra-red spectra of bent XYZ molecules. Pt. I. Vibration-rotation energies, *J. Chem. Phys.* **12**, 504–513 (1944).
344. H. H. Nielsen, The vibration-rotation energies of polyatomic molecules. Pt. II. Accidental degeneracies, *Phys. Rev.* **68**, 181–191 (1945).
345. W. H. Shaffer and R. C. Herman, The tetrahedral X_2YZ_2 molecular model. Pt. II. Rotation-vibration energies, *J. Chem. Phys.* **13**, 83–88 (1945).
346. R. C. Herman and W. H. Shaffer, The calculation of perturbation energies in vibrating rotating polyatomic molecules, *J. Chem. Phys.* **16**, 453–465 (1948).
347. H. H. Nielsen, Anomalies in the microwave spectrum of methyl cyanide and methyl isocyanide, *Phys. Rev.* **75**, 1961 (1949).
348. R. C. Herman and W. H. Shaffer, The vibration-rotation energies of the plane symmetrical $X_2Y_2X_2$ molecular model, *J. Chem. Phys.* **18**, 1207–1211 (1950).
349. W. Low and C. H. Townes, Effect of Fermi resonance on rotation-vibration interaction in OCS and OCSe, *Phys. Rev.* **79**, 224 (1950).
350. H. H. Nielsen, Anomalies in the microwave spectra of symmetric molecules, *Physica* **17**, 432–439 (1951).
351. H. H. Nielsen, The vibration-rotation energies of molecules, *Rev. Mod. Phys.* **23**, 90–136 (1951).

352. S. M. Ferigle and A. Weber, The Eckart conditions for a polyatomic molecule, *Am. J. Phys.* **21**, 102–107 (1953).

353. W. Low, Fermi resonance in the microwave spectrum of linear XYZ molecules, *Phys. Rev.* **97**, 1664–1667 (1955).

354. M. Goldsmith, G. Amat, and H. H. Nielsen, Higher order rotation-vibration energies of polyatomic molecules I, *J. Chem. Phys.* **24**, 1178–1182 (1956).

355. G. Amat, M. Goldsmith, and H. H. Nielsen, Higher order rotation-vibration energies of polyatomic molecules II, *J. Chem. Phys.* **27**, 838–844 (1957).

356. G. Amat and H. H. Nielsen, Influence of rotational distortions on the vibration-rotation spectrum of linear molecules, *Compt. Rend.* **244**, 2302–2304 (1957).

357. G. Amat and H. H. Nielsen, Higher order rotation-vibration energies of polyatomic molecules III, *J. Chem. Phys.* **27**, 845–850 (1957).

358. P. R. Swan, Jr. and M. W. P. Strandberg, Vibration-internal rotation interactions in molecules containing a symmetric top group, *J. Mol. Spectry.* **1**, 333–378 (1957).

359. G. Amat and H. H. Nielsen, Higher order rotation-vibration energies of polyatomic molecules IV, *J. Chem. Phys.* **29**, 665–672 (1958).

360. G. Amat and L. Henry, Resonances and K-type doubling in molecules having axial symmetry, *J. Phys. Radium* **21**, 728–730 (1960).

361. T. Oka and Y. Morino, Microwave spectrum of formaldehyde III. Vibration-rotation interaction, *J. Phys. Soc. Japan* **16**, 1235–1242 (1961).

362. G. Amat and H. H. Nielsen, Higher order rotation-vibration energies of polyatomic molecules V, *J. Chem. Phys.* **36**, 1859–1865 (1962).

363. M. L. Grenier-Besson and G. Amat, Rotational spectrum of molecules with C_{3v} symmetry in an excited vibrational state, $v_t = 1$, *J. Mol. Spectry.* **8**, 22–29 (1962).

364. M. L. Grenier-Besson, G. Amat, and H. H. Nielsen, Higher order rotation-vibration energies of polyatomic molecules VI, *J. Chem. Phys.* **36**, 3454–3459 (1962).

365. D. R. Herschbach and V. W. Laurie, Influence of vibrations on molecular structure determinations I. General formulation of vibration-rotation interactions, *J. Chem. Phys.* **37**, 1668–1686 (1962).

366. S. Maes, Some third order corrections to the rotation-vibration energies of polyatomic molecules, *J. Mol. Spectry.* **9**, 204–215 (1962).

367. K. T. Chung and P. M. Parker, Asymmetric-top vibration-rotation Hamiltonians, *J. Chem. Phys.* **38**, 8–17 (1963). Errata—*J. Chem. Phys.* **39**, 240 (1963).

368. N. Jacobi and J. H. Jaffe, Influence of vibration-rotation interaction on spectral line intensities of linear molecules, *J. Mol. Spectry.* **10**, 1–11 (1963).

369. W. B. Olsen and H. C. Allen, Jr., On the fourth-order Hamiltonian of an asymmetric rotor molecule of orthorhombic symmetry, *J. Res. Natl. Bur. Std.* **A67**, 359–362 (1963).

370. F. Dorman and C. C. Lin, Determination of the cubic anharmonic potential constants from the vibration-rotation interaction constants of the OCS and N_2O molecules, *J. Mol. Spectry.* **12**, 119–128 (1964).

371. J. W. C. Johns, K-type doubling of linear molecules in $^1\Pi$ electronic states, *J. Mol. Spectry.* **15**, 473–482 (1965).

Vb. Centrifugal Distortion

372. E. L. Hill and J. H. Van Vleck, On the quantum mechanics of the rotational distortion of multiplets in molecular spectra, *Phys. Rev.* **32**, 250–272 (1928).

373. E. B. Wilson, Jr., The effect of rotational distortion on the thermodynamic properties of water and other polyatomic molecules, *J. Chem. Phys.* **4**, 526–528 (1936).

374. E. B. Wilson, Jr., The vibration-rotation energy levels of polyatomic molecules II. Effect of centrifugal distortion, *J. Chem. Phys.* **5**, 617–620 (1937).

375. Z. I. Slawsky and D. M. Dennison, The centrifugal distortion of axial molecules, *J. Chem. Phys.* **7**, 509–521 (1939).

376. S. Golden, An asymptotic expression for the energy levels of the asymmetric rotor II. Centrifugal distortion correction, *J. Chem. Phys.* **16**, 250–253 (1948). Errata—*J. Chem. Phys.* **17**, 586 (1948).

377. W. S. Benedict, Centrifugal stretching in H_2O and D_2O, *Phys. Rev.* **75**, 1317 (1949).

378. H. H. Nielsen, A Note on the centrifugal stretching in axially symmetric molecules, *Phys. Rev.* **78**, 415–416 (1950).

379. J. W. Simmons and W. E. Anderson, Microwave determination of the centrifugal distortion constants of CH_3Cl, CH_3Br, CH_3I, BrCN, and ICN, *Phys. Rev.* **80**, 338–342 (1950).

380. R. E. Hillger and M. W. P. Strandberg, Centrifugal distortion in asymmetric molecules II. HDS, *Phys. Rev.* **83**, 575–581 (1951).

381. R. B. Lawrence and M. W. P. Strandberg, Centrifugal distortion in asymmetric top molecules I. Ordinary formaldehyde, $H_2C^{12}O$, *Phys. Rev.* **83**, 363–369 (1951).

382. D. Kivelson and E. B. Wilson, Jr., Approximate treatment of the effect of centrifugal distortion on the rotational energy levels of asymmetric-rotor molecules, *J. Chem. Phys.* **20**, 1575–1579 (1952).

383. M. W. P. Strandberg, Centrifugal distortion, *Ann. N.Y. Acad. Sci.* **55**, 808–813 (1952).

384. F. D. Bedard, J. J. Gallagher, and C. M. Johnson, Microwave measurement of D_0 for CO, *Phys. Rev.* **92**, 1440 (1953).

385. T. S. Chang and D. M. Dennison, Centrifugal distortion effects in methyl chloride, *J. Chem. Phys.* **21**, 1293 (1953).

386. D. Kivelson and E. B. Wilson, Jr., Theory of centrifugal distortion constants of polyatomic rotor molecules. *J. Chem. Phys.* **21**, 1229–1236 (1953).

387. J. Cox, W. J. O. Thomas, and W. Gordy, Centrifugal distortion in the methyl halides, *Phys. Rev.* **95**, 299 (1954).

388. D. Kivelson, The determination of the potential constants of SO_2 from centrifugal distortion effects, *J. Chem. Phys.* **22**, 904–908 (1954).

389. D. W. Posener and M. W. P. Strandberg, Centrifugal distortion in asymmetric top molecules III. H_2O, D_2O, and HDO, *Phys. Rev.* **95**, 374–384 (1954).

390. W. J. O. Thomas, J. T. Cox, and W. Gordy, Millimeter wave spectra and centrifugal stretching constants of the methylhalides, *J. Chem. Phys.* **22**, 1718–1722 (1954).

391. G. Amat, M. Goldsmith, and H. H. Nielsen, Influence of Fermi resonance on the centrifugal stretching constant of a linear molecule, *J. Chem. Phys.* **24**, 44–47 (1956).

392. L. Pierce, Determination of the potential constants of ozone from centrifugal distortion effects, *J. Chem. Phys.* **24**, 139–142 (1956).

393. J. M. Dowling, R. Gold, and A. G. Meister, Calculation of rotational distortion constants for some axially symmetric ZX_3Y molecules, *J. Mol. Spectry.* **1**, 265–269 (1957).

394. H. H. Nielsen, G. Amat, and M. Goldsmith, Anomalous centrifugal distortion coefficients in linear polyatomic molecules, *J. Chem. Phys.* **26**, 1060–1066 (1957).

395. E. B. Wilson, Jr., Centrifugal distortion in symmetric rotor molecules, *J. Chem. Phys.* **27**, 986–987 (1957).

396. J. M. Dowling, R. Gold, and A. G. Meister, A note on the calculation of rotational distortion constants for axially symmetric ZX_3Y molecules, *J. Mol. Spectry.* **2**, 411–412 (1958).

397. G. Erlandsson, Computer program for centrifugal distortion in asymmetric top rotational spectra, *Arkiv Fysik* **16**, 181–184 (1959).

398. P. M. Parker and L. C. Brown, Computation of asymmetric rotator constants from energy moments III. First-order centrifugal stretching effects, *J. Chem. Phys.* **31**, 1227–1230 (1959).

399. P. Favero, A. Mirri, and J. G. Baker, Centrifugal effects in millimeter wave spectra-formyl fluoride, *Nuovo Cimento* **17**, 740–748 (1960).

400. M. W. Long, Centrifugal distortion in symmetric top molecules, *J. Chem. Phys.* **32**, 948 (1960).

401. J. M. Dowling, Centrifugal distortion in planar molecules, *J. Mol. Spectry.* **6**, 550–553 (1961).

402. H. C. Allen, Jr. and W. B. Olsen, Sum rules for vibrational-rotational energy levels including centrifugal distortion, *J. Chem. Phys.* **37**, 212–214 (1962).

403. R. A. Hill and T. H. Edwards, First-order centrifugal distortion in planar asymmetric molecules, *J. Mol. Spectry.* **9**, 494–497 (1962).

404. R. C. Johnson, Q. Williams, and T. L. Weatherly, Centrifugal stretching of $CClF_3$ and some other symmetric tops, *J. Chem. Phys.* **36**, 1588–1590 (1962).

405. P. M. Parker, Symmetry properties of the asymmetric-rotator centrifugal distortion constants, *J. Chem. Phys.* **37**, 1596–1599 (1962).

406. M. G. K. Pillai and R. F. Curl, Jr., Microwave spectrum of chloride dioxide IV. Determination of centrifugal distortion effects and potential constants, *J. Chem. Phys.* **37**, 2921–2926 (1962).

407. H. D. Rudolph, The centrifugal correction in rotational spectra of molecules with internal rotation such as $(CH_3)_2S$, *Z. Naturforsch.* **17A**, 288–297 (1962).

408. P. G. Favero and A. M. Mirri, Millimeter wave spectra and centrifugal distortion constants of $CHCl_3$ and $CFCl_3$, *Nuovo Cimento* **30**, 502–506 (1963).

409. R. A. Hill and T. H. Edwards, Sum rules for planar asymmetric molecules, *J. Mol. Spectry.* **11**, 433–439 (1963).

410. L. Pierce, N. DiCianni, and R. H. Jackson, Centrifugal distortion effects in asymmetric rotor molecules I. Quadratic potential constants and average structure of oxygen difluoride from the ground state rotational spectrum, *J. Chem. Phys.* **38**, 730–739 (1963).

411. A. Bauer, J. Bellet, P. Pouzet, and A. Remy, Determination of the rotational and centrifugal distortion constants of $S^{32}O_2$ in the v_2 excited state, *Compt. Rend.* **259**, 761–764 (1964).

412. H. Dreizler and R. Peter, "Tables for the Analysis of Rotational Spectra with Centrifugal Distortion and Torsional Fine Structure." Physikalisches Institut der Universität Freiburg i. Br., Germany, 1964.

413. M. Winnewisser and R. L. Cook, Centrifugal distortion effects and structure of hydrazoic acid from the millimeter wave rotational spectra, *J. Chem. Phys.* **41**, 999–1004 (1964).

414. K. T. Chung and P. M. Parker, Higher-order centrifugal-distortion effects in asymmetric rotors, *J. Chem. Phys.* **43**, 3865–3868 (1965).

415. K. T. Chung and P. M. Parker, Centrifugal distortion coefficients of the nonlinear XYX molecule, *J. Chem. Phys.* **43**, 3869–3874 (1965).

Vc. Coriolis Coupling

416. H. A. Jahn, New Coriolis perturbation in the methane spectrum. Pt. I. Vibrational-rotational Hamiltonian and wave functions. Part II. Energy levels, *Proc. Roy. Soc.* **A168**, 469–518 (1938).

417. H. A. Jahn, Note on Coriolis coupling terms in polyatomic molecules, *Phys. Rev.* **56**, 680–683 (1939).

418. H. H. Nielsen, A Note concerning the Coriolis contribution to the energy of a symmetric polyatomic molecule, *Phys. Rev.* **70**, 184–186 (1946).

419. D. R. J. Boyd and H. C. Longuet-Higgins, Coriolis interaction between vibration and rotation in symmetric top molecules, *Proc. Roy. Soc.*, **A213**, 55–73 (1952).

420. R. C. Lord and R. E. Merrifield, Evaluation of the zeta sums for rotation-vibration interaction in axially symmetrical molecules, *J. Chem. Phys.* **20**, 1348–1350 (1952).

421. J. H. Meal and S. R. Polo, Vibration-rotation interaction in polyatomic molecules I. The zeta matrices, *J. Chem. Phys.* **24**, 1119–1125 (1956).

422. J. H. Meal and S. R. Polo, Vibration-rotation interaction in polyatomic molecules II. The determination of Coriolis coupling coefficients, *J. Chem. Phys.* **24**, 1126–1133 (1956).

423. V. W. Laurie and D. T. Pence, Microwave spectrum of F_2CO excited vibrational states and Coriolis coupling, *J. Mol. Spectry.* **10**, 155–160 (1963).

Vd. *l*-Type Doubling

424. G. Herzberg, *l*-type doubling in linear polyatomic molecules, *Rev. Mod. Phys.* **14**, 219–223 (1942).

425. H. H. Nielsen and W. H. Shaffer, A note concerning *l*-type doubling in linear polyatomic molecules, *J. Chem. Phys.* **11**, 140–144 (1943). Errata—*Phys. Rev.* **75**, 1961 (1949).

426. H. H. Nielsen, *l*-type doubling in polyatomic molecules and its application to the microwave spectrum of methyl cyanide and methyl isocyanide, *Phys. Rev.* **77**, 130–135 (1950).

427. H. H. Nielsen, *l*-type doubling in OCS and HCN, *Phys. Rev.* **78**, 296 (1950).

428. R. G. Shulman and C. H. Townes, New types of microwave transitions involving *l*-type doubling in OCS and HCN, *Phys. Rev.* **77**, 421–422 (1950).

429. J. De Heer, A Note concerning *l*-type doubling in axially symmetric molecules, in particular with reference to molecules belonging to the symmetry groups C_{4v} and V_d, *Phys. Rev.* **83**, 741–745 (1951).

430. J. De Heer and H. H. Nielsen, *l*-type doubling in energy levels of carbon dioxide coupled by Fermi resonance, *J. Chem. Phys.* **20**, 101–104 (1952).

431. T. L. Weatherly and D. Williams, *l*-type doubling transitions in HCN and DCN, *Phys. Rev.* **87**, 517–518 (1952).

432. R. J. Collier, Direct *l*-doublet transition of HCN in the 10-centimeter wavelength region, *Phys. Rev.* **95**, 1200–1202 (1954).

433. J. F. Westerkamp, Variation of the *l*-type doubling constant in HCN, *Phys. Rev.* **93**, 716 (1954).

434. A. Miyahara, H. Hirakawa, and K. Shimoda, *l*-type doubling spectra of HCN and DCN in the superhigh frequency region, *J. Phys. Soc. Japan* **11**, 335 (1956).

435. G. Amat, M. L. Grenier-Besson, and H. Z. Cummins, Sign of the constant *q* of *l*-type doubling, *Compt. Rend.* **244**, 2380–2381 (1957).

436. L. Yarmus, Direct *l*-type doubling transitions in ClCN, *Phys. Rev.* **105**, 928–929 (1957).

437. G. Amat and H. H. Nielsen, Vibrational *l*-type doubling and *l*-type resonance in linear polyatomic molecules, *J. Mol. Spectry.* **2**, 152–162 (1958).

438. G. Amat and H. H. Nielsen, Rotational distortion in linear molecules arising from *l*-type resonance, *J. Mol. Spectry.* **2**, 163–172 (1958).

439. T. S. Jaseja, The microwave spectrum of methyl cyanide and *l*-type doubling in CH_3CN, CH_3NC, CH_3CCH, and CF_3CCH, *Proc. Indian Acad. Sci.* **50A**, 108–128 (1959).

440. M. L. Grenier-Besson, Rotational *l*-type doubling and resonance in molecules having axial symmetry, *J. Phys. Radium* **21**, 555–565 (1960).

441. T. Torring, *l*-type doublets of the isotopic HCN molecules, *Z. Physik* **161**, 179–189 (1961).

442. P. Venkateswarlu, J. G. Baker, and W. Gordy, The millimeter wave spectrum of methyl cyanide and the *l*-type doubling, *J. Mol. Spectry.* **6**, 215–228 (1961).
443. G. G. Weber, On the *l*-type doubling and *l*-type resonance of molecules in the microwave region, *J. Mol. Spectry.* **10**, 321–347 (1963).
444. Y. Morino and T. Nakagawa, Vibrational dependence of the *l*-type doubling constants of linear XYZ molecules, *J. Chem. Phys.* **44**, 841–842 (1966).

VI. Molecular Structure

445. W. Gordy, Dependence of bond order and of bond energy upon bond length, *J. Chem. Phys.* **15**, 305–310 (1947).
446. W. Gordy, A re-evaluation of the covalent radii of some of the elements, *J. Chem. Phys.* **15**, 81–84 (1947).
447. R. Freymann, Centimeter waves and molecular structure, *Onde Élec.* **30**, 416–424 (1950).
448. E. B. Wilson, Jr., Determination of molecular structure with microwave spectroscopy, *Discussions Faraday Soc.* **9**, 108–114 (1950).
449. J. N. Shoolery, R. G. Shulman, W. F. Sheehan, Jr., V. Schomaker, and D. M. Yost, The structure of trifluoromethyl acetylene from the microwave spectrum and electron diffraction pattern, *J. Chem. Phys.* **19**, 1364–1369 (1951).
450. D. Kivelson and E. B. Wilson, Jr., An aid in the determination of internal parameters from rotational constants for polyatomic molecules, *J. Chem. Phys.* **21**, 1236 (1953).
451. J. Kraitchman, Determination of molecular structure from microwave spectroscopic data, *Am. J. Phys.* **21**, 17–24 (1953).
452. L. M. Sverdlov, Relations between moments of inertia and rotation frequencies of isotopic molecules, *Dokl. Akad. Nauk SSSR* **88**, 249–252 (1953).
453. W. D. Gwinn, Information pertaining to molecular structure as obtained from the microwave spectra of molecules of the asymmetric rotor type, *Discussions Faraday Soc.* **19**, 43–51 (1955).
454. A. Almenningen and O. Bastiansen, Accuracy of the electron diffraction method for the determination of structural parameters in the gaseous state, *Res. Correspondence* [Suppl. with *Research* (London)] **9**, 35–36 (1956).
455. T. E. Turner and J. A. Howe, Determination of molecular structures from rotational spectra measurements, *J. Chem. Phys.* **24**, 924–925 (1956).
456. L. F. Thomas, J. S. Heeks, and J. Sheridan, Studies of conjugation and hyperconjugation in several molecules by microwave spectroscopy, *Arch. Sci.* (Geneva) **10**, 180–183 (1957).
457. W. Zeil and J. F. Perommer, Microwave spectroscopic measurements concerning the knowledge of the C—C distance in the C—CN group of nitriles, *Z. Elektrochem.* **61**, 938–940 (1957).
458. C. C. Costain, Determination of molecular structures from ground state rotational constants, *J. Chem. Phys.* **29**, 864–874 (1958).
459. V. W. Laurie, Note on the determination of molecular structure from spectroscopic data, *J. Chem. Phys.* **28**, 704–706 (1958).
460. D. R. Lide, Jr. and D. E. Mann, Molecular structure studies of hydrocarbons by microwave spectroscopy, *Am. Chem. Soc. Div. Petrol Chem. Gen. Papers* **3**, 49–50 (1958).
461. C. C. Costain and B. P. Stoicheff, Microwave spectrum, molecular structure of vinyl cyanide, and a summary of carbon-carbon, carbon-hydrogen bond lengths in simple molecules, *J. Chem. Phys.* **30**, 777–782 (1959).
462. V. W. Laurie, Comments on the structure of 1,1,1-trifluoro-2-butyne, *J. Chem. Phys.* **30**, 1101–1102 (1959).

463. T. Nishikawa, Studies of molecular structure by microwave method, *Kagaku No Ryoiki* **13**, 385–395 (1959).

464. L. Pierce, Note on the use of ground-state rotational constants in the determination of molecular structure, *J. Mol. Spectry.* **3**, 575–580 (1959).

465. P. H. Verdier and E. B. Wilson, Jr., Force constant calculations in linear triatomic molecules from infrared and microwave data, *J. Chem. Phys.* **30**, 1372–1373 (1959).

466. L. C. Krisher and L. Pierce, Second differences of moments of inertia in structural calculations-application to methyl fluorosilane molecules, *J. Chem. Phys.* **32**, 1619–1625 (1960).

467. J. K. Brown and A. P. Cox, Near-equilibrium bond distances in simple molecules, *Spectrochim. Acta* **17**, 1230–1239 (1961).

468. D. R. Herschbach and V. W. Laurie, Anharmonic potential constants and their dependence upon bond length, *J. Chem. Phys.* **35**, 458–463 (1961).

469. D. R. Lide, Jr. and D. Christensen, Molecular structure of propylene, *J. Chem. Phys.* **35**, 1374–1378 (1961).

470. D. R. Lide, Jr. and D. Christensen, An improved structure determination for vinyl fluoride, *Spectrochim. Acta* **17**, 665–668 (1961).

471. T. Oka and Y. Morino, Calculation of inertia defect Pt. I. General formulation, *J. Mol. Spectry.* **6**, 472–482 (1961).

472. B. Bak, D. Christensen, W. B. Dixon, L. Hansen-Nygaard, and J. Rastrup-Andersen, Benzene ring distortion by one substituent. Microwave determination of the complete structure of benzonitrile, *J. Chem. Phys.* **37**, 2027–2031 (1962).

473. B. Bak, D. Christensen, W. B. Dixon, L. Hansen-Nygaard, J. Rastrup-Andersen, and M. Schottlander, The complete structure of furan, *J. Mol. Spectry.* **9**, 124–129 (1962).

474. B. Bak, D. Christensen, L. Hansen-Nygaard, and J. Rastrup-Andersen, Analysis of the microwave spectrum of 2-fluoro-naphthalene with a discussion of structure determination possibilities, *Spectrochim. Acta* **18**, 229–233 (1962).

475. M. Jen and D. R. Lide, Jr., Molecular structure of chloroform, *J. Chem. Phys.* **36**, 2525–2526 (1962).

476. V. W. Laurie and D. R. Herschbach, Influence of vibrations on molecular structure determinations II. Average structures derived from spectroscopic data, *J. Chem. Phys.* **37**, 1687–1692 (1962).

477. Y. Morino, K. Kuchitsu, and T. Oka, Internuclear distance parameters, *J. Chem. Phys.* **36**, 1108–1109 (1962).

478. T. Oka and Y. Morino, Calculation of inertia defect Pt. II. Nonlinear symmetric XY_2 molecules, *J. Mol. Spectry.* **8**, 9–21 (1962).

479. L. S. Bartell, Calculation of mean atomic positions in vibrating polyatomic molecules, *J. Chem. Phys.* **38**, 1827–1833 (1963).

480. U. Blukis, P. H. Kasai, and R. J. Myers, Microwave spectra and structure of dimethyl ether, *J. Chem. Phys.* **38**, 2753–2760 (1963).

481. D. R. Herschbach and V. W. Laurie, Influence of vibrations on molecular structure determinations III. Inertial defects, Lawrence Radiation Laboratory, Berkeley, California, UCRL-11208 (1963).

482. D. R. Lide, Jr., and M. Jen, Microwave spectrum of tertiary butyl chloride. A comparison of tertiary butyl structures, *J. Chem. Phys.* **38**, 1504–1507 (1963).

483. T. Oka and Y. Morino, Inertia defect Pt. III. Inertia defect and planarity of four-atomic molecules, *J. Mol. Spectry.* **11**, 349–367 (1963).

484. A. Chutjian, Determination of structure by isotopic substitution in molecules with symmetrically equivalent atoms, *J. Mol. Spectry.* **14**, 361–370 (1964).

485. M. Toyama, T. Oka, and Y. Morino, Effect of vibration and rotation on the internuclear distance, *J. Mol. Spectry.* **13**, 193–213 (1964).

486. K. Kuchitsu, T. Oka, and Y. Morino, Calculation of inertia defect. Pt. IV. Ethylene-type molecules, *J. Mol. Spectry.* **15**, 51–67 (1965).
487. L. H. Scharpen and V. W. Laurie, Structure of cyclopentadiene, *J. Chem. Phys.* **43**, 2765–2766 (1965).
488. R. H. Schwendeman and J. D. Kelly, Carbon-halogen distances in deuterated methyl chloride and methyl bromide, *J. Chem. Phys.* **42**, 1132–1134 (1965).

VII. Nuclear Quadrupole Coupling

489. E. L. Hill, Relative intensities in nuclear spin multiplets, *Proc. Natl. Acad. Sci. U.S.* **15**, 779–784 (1929).
490. L. Pauling and S. Goudsmit, "The Structure of Line Spectra." McGraw-Hill, New York, 1930.
491. H. E. White, "Introduction to Atomic Spectra." McGraw-Hill, New York, 1934.
492. H. B. G. Casimir, "On the Interaction Between Atomic Nuclei and Electrons." Teylers Tweede Genootschap, Bohn, Haarlem, 1936.
493. J. M. B. Kellogg, I. I. Rabi, N. F. Ramsey, and H. R. Zacharias, An electrical quadrupole moment of the deuteron. The radiofrequency spectra of HD and D_2 molecules in a magnetic field, *Phys. Rev.* **57**, 677–695 (1940).
494. A. Nordsieck, On the value of the electric quadrupole moment of the deuteron, *Phys. Rev.* **58**, 310–315 (1940).
495. G. Racah, Theory of complex spectra. I, *Phys. Rev.* **61**, 186–197 (1942).
496. G. Racah, Theory of complex spectra. II, *Phys. Rev.* **62**, 438–462 (1942).
497. G. Racah, Theory of complex spectra. III, *Phys. Rev.* **63**, 367–382 (1943).
498. B. T. Feld and W. E. Lamb, Jr., Effect of nuclear quadrupole moment on the energy levels of a diatomic molecule in a magnetic field. Pt. I. Heteronuclear molecules, *Phys. Rev.* **67**, 15–33 (1945).
499. B. P. Dailey, R. L. Kyhl, M. W. P. Strandberg, J. H. Van Vleck, and E. B. Wilson, Jr., The hyperfine structure of the microwave spectrum of ammonia and the existence of a quadrupole moment in N^{14}, *Phys. Rev.* **70**, 984 (1946).
500. B. T. Feld, On the nuclear electric quadrupole interaction in molecular spectra, *Phys. Rev.* **72**, 1116–1117 (1947).
501. H. M. Foley, Note on the nuclear electric quadrupole spectrum of a homonuclear diatomic molecule in a magnetic field, *Phys. Rev.* **71**, 747–751 (1947).
502. C. H. Townes, Electrostatic field strengths in molecules and nuclear quadrupole moments, *Phys. Rev.* **71**, 909–910 (1947).
503. C. H. Townes, A. N. Holden, J. Bardeen, and F. R. Merritt, The quadrupole moments and spins of Br, Cl, and N nuclei, *Phys. Rev.* **71**, 644–645 (1947). Errata—*Phys. Rev.* **71**, 829 (1947).
504. J. H. Van Vleck, Formula for the coupling of nuclear quadrupole moments in symmetrical polyatomic molecules, *Phys. Rev.* **71**, 468–469 (1947).
505. R. J. Watts and D. Williams, Nuclear quadrupole moment effects in the inversion spectrum of ammonia, *Phys. Rev.* **72**, 263–265 (1947).
506. R. J. Watts and D. Williams, Nuclear quadrupole moment effects in the microwave spectrum of ammonia, *Phys. Rev.* **71**, 639 (1947).
507. J. Bardeen and C. H. Townes, Calculation of nuclear quadrupole effects in molecules, *Phys. Rev.* **73**, 97–105 (1948).
508. J. Bardeen and C. H. Townes, Second-order corrections to quadrupole effects in molecules, *Phys. Rev.* **73**, 627–629 (1948). Errata—*Phys. Rev.* **73**, 1204 (1948).
509. J. K. Bragg, The interaction of nuclear electric quadrupole moments with molecular rotation in asymmetric-top molecules. I, *Phys. Rev.* **74**, 533–538 (1948).

510. W. Gordy, H. Ring, and A. B. Burg, Nuclear spins and quadrupole moments of B^{10} and B^{11}, *Phys. Rev.* **74**, 1191 (1948).

511. G. Knight and B. T. Feld, Interaction of nuclear quadrupole moments with molecular rotation in slightly asymmetric rotor molecules, *Phys. Rev.* **74**, 354 (1948).

512. A. G. Smith, H. Ring, W. V. Smith, and W. Gordy, Nuclear quadrupole coupling of nitrogen in ICN and N_2O, *Phys. Rev.* **73**, 633 (1948).

513. C. H. Townes and S. Geschwind, Spin and quadrupole moment of S^{33}, *Phys. Rev.* **74**, 626–627 (1948).

514. J. W. Trischka, Nuclear quadrupole interaction in CsF, *Phys. Rev.* **74**, 718–727 (1948).

515. R. T. Weidner, Nuclear quadrupole interaction in the ICl spectrum, *Phys. Rev.* **73**, 254 (1948).

516. J. K. Bragg and S. Golden, The interaction of nuclear electric quadrupole moments with molecular rotation in asymmetric top molecules II. Approximate methods for first-order coupling, *Phys. Rev.* **75**, 735–738 (1949).

517. V. W. Cohen, W. S. Koski, and T. Wentink, Nuclear spin and quadrupole coupling of S^{35}, *Phys. Rev.* **76**, 703–704 (1949).

518. J. H. Goldstein and J. K. Bragg, Nuclear quadrupole effects in the microwave spectrum of the asymmetric top molecule, vinyl chloride, *Phys. Rev.* **75**, 1453–1454 (1949).

519. P. Kusch, On the nuclear quadrupole moment of Li^6, *Phys. Rev.* **75**, 887–888 (1949).

520. R. Livingston, O. R. Gilliam, and W. Gordy, The nuclear spin and quadrupole moment of I^{129}, *Phys. Rev.* **76**, 149–150 (1949).

521. C. H. Townes and L. C. Aamodt, Nuclear spin and quadrupole moment of Cl^{36}, *Phys. Rev.* **76**, 691–692 (1949).

522. C. H. Townes and B. P. Dailey, Determination of electronic structure of molecules from nuclear quadrupole effects, *J. Chem. Phys.* **17**, 782–796 (1949).

523. C. H. Townes, H. M. Foley, and W. Low, Nuclear quadrupole moments and nuclear shell structure, *Phys. Rev.* **76**, 1415–1416 (1949).

524. C. H. Townes, J. M. Mays, and B. P. Dailey, Evidence on nuclear moments of stable Ge and Si isotopes from microwave spectra, *Phys. Rev.* **76**, 700 (1949).

525. R. Bersohn, Quadrupole coupling of three nuclei in a rotating molecule, *J. Chem. Phys.* **18**, 1124–1125 (1950).

526. J. H. Goldstein and J. K. Bragg, Determination of double bond character from the microwave spectrum of planar asymmetric top molecules with a quadrupole nucleus, *Phys. Rev.* **78**, 347 (1950).

527. J. Rainwater, Nuclear energy level argument for a spheroidal nuclear model, *Phys. Rev.* **79**, 432–434 (1950).

528. N. F. Ramsey, Quadrupole moment of the electron distribution in hydrogen molecules, *Phys. Rev.* **78**, 221–222 (1950).

529. R. Sternheimer, On nuclear quadrupole moments, *Phys. Rev.* **80**, 102–103 (1950).

530. C. H. Townes and B. P. Dailey, Nuclear quadrupole coupling and ionic character of molecules, *Phys. Rev.* **78**, 346–347 (1950).

531. M. T. Weiss, M. W. P. Strandberg, R. B. Lawrence, and C. C. Loomis, On the nuclear spin of B^{10}, *Phys. Rev.* **78**, 202–204 (1950).

532. S. Geschwind, R. Gunther-Mohr, and C. H. Townes, Ratio of quadrupole moments of Cl^{35} and Cl^{37}, *Phys. Rev.* **81**, 288–289 (1951).

533. W. Gordy, Interpretation of nuclear quadrupole couplings in molecules, *J. Chem. Phys.* **19**, 792–793 (1951).

534. C. M. Johnson, W. Gordy, and R. Livingston, On the spin and quadrupole moment of Cl^{36}, *Phys. Rev.* **83**, 1249 (1951).

535. J. M. Mays and C. H. Townes, The nuclear spins and quadrupole moments of stable germanium isotopes, *Phys. Rev.* **81**, 940–941 (1951).

536. M. Mizushima and T. Ito, On the hyperfine structure of the rotational spectra of XYZ_3-type molecule, where nuclei Z have electric quadrupole moments, *J. Chem. Phys.* **19**, 739–744 (1951).

537. C. H. Townes, Determination of nuclear properties by microwave spectroscopy, *Physica* **17**, 354–377 (1951).

538. L. C. Biedenharn, J. M. Blatt, and M. E. Rose, Some properties of the Racah and associated coefficients, *Rev. Mod. Phys.* **24**, 249–257 (1952).

539. J. Duchesne, Nuclear quadrupole coupling constants and molecular vibrations, *J. Chem. Phys.* **20**, 1804–1805 (1952).

540. S. Geschwind, G. R. Gunther-Mohr, and G. Silvey, The spin and quadrupole moment of O^{17}, *Phys. Rev.* **85**, 474–477 (1952).

541. D. A. Gilbert, The nuclear spin of Cl^{36} from the microwave spectrum of $C^{12}H_3Cl^{36}$, *Phys. Rev.* **85**, 716 (1952).

542. W. A. Hardy, G. Silvey, and C. H. Townes, The spin and quadrupole moment of Se^{79}, *Phys. Rev.* **85**, 494–495 (1952).

543. A. Javan and C. H. Townes, Anomalies in the hyperfine structure of ICN, *Phys. Rev.* **86**, 608 (1952).

544. R. A. Logan, R. E. Cote, and P. Kusch, The sign of the quadrupole interaction energy in diatomic molecules, *Phys. Rev.* **86**, 280–287 (1952).

545. R. J. Myers and W. D. Gwinn, The microwave spectra, dipole moment, and chlorine nuclear quadrupole coupling constants of methylene chloride, *J. Chem. Phys.* **20**, 1420–1427 (1952).

546. J. D. Rogers and D. Williams, Nuclear quadrupole interactions in the microwave spectrum of hydrogen azide, *Phys. Rev.* **86**, 654 (1952).

547. C. H. Townes and B. P. Dailey, Nuclear quadrupole effects and electronic structure of molecules in the solid state, *J. Chem. Phys.* **20**, 35–40 (1952).

548. T. C. Wang, C. H. Townes, A. L. Schawlow, and A. N. Holden, Quadrupole coupling ratio of the chlorine isotopes, *Phys. Rev.* **86**, 809–810 (1952).

549. H. G. Dehmelt, Nuclear quadrupole resonance in rhombic sulfur and the quadrupole moments of S^{33} and S^{35}, *Phys. Rev.* **91**, 313–314 (1953).

550. I. I. Goldman, On the spectroscopic determination of the quadrupole moments of nuclei, *Dokl. Akad. Nauk SSSR* **88**, 241–243 (1953).

551. W. A. Hardy, G. Silvey, C. H. Townes, B. F. Burke, M. W. P. Strandberg, G. W. Parker, and V. W. Cohen, The nuclear moment of Se^{79}, *Phys. Rev.* **92**, 1532–1537 (1953).

552. A. Javan, G. Silvey, C. H. Townes, and A. V. Grosse, On the quadrupole moments of Mn^{35}, Re^{185}, and Re^{187}, *Phys. Rev.* **91**, 222–223 (1953).

553. P. Kusch, Sign of the quadrupole interaction of Li^6 and LiCl, *Phys. Rev.* **92**, 268–270 (1953).

554. R. Livingston, B. M. Benjamin, J. T. Cox, and W. Gordy, The nuclear spin and quadrupole moment of I^{131}, *Phys. Rev.* **92**, 1271–1272 (1953).

555. S.-Y. Obi, T. Ishidzu, H. Horie, S. Yanagawa, Y. Tanabe, and M. Sato, Tables of the Racah coefficients W(abcd, ef). I. Coefficients having all their variables integral, *Ann. Tokyo Astron. Obs.* **3**, 89–142 (1953).

556. N. F. Ramsey, Pseudo-quadrupole effect for nuclei in molecules, *Phys. Rev.* **89**, 527 (1953).

557. G. W. Robinson and C. D. Cornwell, The interaction with molecular rotation of the nuclear electric quadrupole moments of two nuclei having spins 3/2, *J. Chem. Phys.* **21**, 1436–1442 (1953).

558. R. L. White, Quadrupole coupling of the deuteron in DCCCl and DCN, *Phys. Rev.* **91**, 1014 (1953).

559. R. L. White and C. H. Townes, The spin of Si^{29} and mass ratios of the stable Si isotopes, *Phys. Rev.* **92**, 1256–1257 (1953).

560. L. C. Aamodt, P. C. Fletcher, G. Silvey, and C. H. Townes, The spin and quadrupole moment of Se[75], *Phys. Rev.* **94**, 789 (1954).

561. G. R. Bird and C. H. Townes, Sulfur bonds and the quadrupole moments of O, S, and Se isotopes, *Phys. Rev.* **94**, 1203–1208 (1954).

562. H. M. Foley, R. M. Sternheimer, and D. Tycko, Nuclear quadrupole coupling in polar molecules, *Phys. Rev.* **93**, 734–742 (1954).

563. W. Gordy, Relation of nuclear quadrupole couplings to the chemical bond, *J. Chem. Phys.* **22**, 1470–1471 (1954).

564. J. A. Kraitchman and B. P. Dailey, Variation in the quadrupole coupling constant with vibrational state in the methyl halides, *J. Chem. Phys.* **22**, 1477–1481 (1954).

565. H. W. Morgan and J. H. Goldstein, Second-order quadrupole effects in asymmetric tops. The microwave spectrum of vinyl iodide, *J. Chem. Phys.* **22**, 1427–1429 (1954).

566. N. F. Ramsey, "Nuclear Moments." Wiley, New York 1954.

567. P. N. Schatz, Deductions about hybridization from nuclear quadrupole coupling constants, *J. Chem. Phys.* **22**, 755 (1954).

568. R. M. Sternheimer, Effect of the atomic core on the nuclear quadrupole coupling, *Phys. Rev.* **95**, 736–750 (1954).

569. F. Sterzer and Y. Beers, Pure quadrupole spectrum of methyl iodide vapor, *Phys. Rev.* **94**, 1410 (1954).

570. L. C. Aamodt and P. C. Fletcher, Spin, quadrupole moment, and mass of selenium-75, *Phys. Rev.* **98**, 1224–1229 (1955).

571. B. P. Dailey, The interpretation of quadrupole spectra, *Discussions Faraday Soc.* **19**, 255–259 (1955).

572. B. P. Dailey and C. H. Townes, The ionic character of diatomic molecules, *J. Chem. Phys.* **23**, 118–123 (1955).

573. W. Gordy, Quadrupole couplings, dipole moments, and the chemical bond, *Discussions Faraday Soc.* **19**, 14–29 (1955).

574. A. Javan, Effects of the bending mode of vibration on the hyperfine structure of ICN, *Phys. Rev.* **99**, 1302–1306 (1955).

575. F. Sterzer and Y. Beers, Pure quadrupole spectra of CH_3I and CF_3I vapors, *Phys. Rev.* **100**, 1174–1180 (1955).

576. R. L. White, Nuclear quadrupole interaction in HCN and DCN in the bending vibrational mode, *J. Chem. Phys.* **23**, 249–252 (1955).

577. R. L. White, Quadrupole coupling of the deuteron in DCCCl and DCN, *J. Chem. Phys.* **23**, 253–255 (1955).

578. J. H. Goldstein, Quadrupole coupling and bond character in the vinyl halides, *J. Chem. Phys.* **24**, 106–109 (1956).

579. D. R. Lide, Jr., Nuclear quadrupole interactions in the microwave spectra of internally rotating molecules, *Bull. Am. Phys. Soc.* [2] **1**, 13 (1956).

580. R. M. Sternheimer, Nuclear quadrupole coupling in polar molecules, *Phys. Rev.* **102**, 731 (1956).

581. T. Oka and H. Hirakawa, Microwave spectrum of BrCN and dependence of quadrupole coupling constant on the vibrational state, *J. Phys. Soc. Japan* **12**, 820–823 (1957).

582. D. W. Posener, Hyperfine structure in the microwave spectrum of water I. Quadrupole coupling in deuterated water, *Australian J. Phys.* **10**, 376–385 (1957).

583. M. E. Rose, "Elementary Theory of Angular Momentum." Wiley, New York, 1957.

584. B. Rosenblum and A. H. Nethercot, Jr., Quadrupole coupling constant and molecular structure of carbon monoxide O^{17}, *J. Chem. Phys.* **27**, 828–829 (1957).

585. M. J. Stevenson and C. H. Townes, Quadrupole moment of oxygen-17, *Phys. Rev.* **107**, 716–723 (1957).

586. T. P. Das and E. L. Hahn, "Nuclear Quadrupole Resonance Spectroscopy." Academic Press, New York, 1958.

587. P. C. Fletcher and E. Amble, Spin and quadrupole moment of iodine-125 and magnetic moment of iodine-131, *Phys. Rev.* **110**, 536–543 (1958).

588. R. H. Jackson and D. J. Millen, Microwave spectrum and nuclear quadrupole coupling coefficients for chlorine monoxide, *Proc. Chem. Soc.* **1959**, 10 (1959).

589. Y. Kikuchi, E. Hirota, and Y. Morino, Second order quadrupole effect in the microwave spectrum of propargyl bromide, *J. Chem. Phys.* **31**, 1139–1140 (1959).

590. J. K. Wilmshurst, Empirical expression for ionic character and the determination of *s* hybridization from nuclear quadrupole coupling constants, *J. Chem. Phys.* **30**, 561–565 (1959).

591. J. A. Howe, Microwave spectrum of *cis*-1-chloro-2 fluoroethylene, *J. Chem. Phys.* **34**, 1247–1249 (1961).

592. Y. Kikuchi, E. Hirota, and Y. Morino, Microwave spectra of propargyl halides II. Molecular structure and second-order quadrupole effect of propargyl bromide, *Bull. Chem. Soc. Japan* **34**, 348–353 (1961).

593. W. H. Flygare and W. D. Gwinn, Electron distribution in the C—Cl bonds of CH_2Cl_2 and derivation of matrix elements off-diagonal in *J* for two quadrupolar nuclei in an asymmetric rotor, *J. Chem. Phys.* **36**, 787–794 (1962).

594. W. H. Flygare and J. A. Howe, Microwave spectrum and quadrupole interaction in *cis*-1,2-dichloroethylene, *J. Chem. Phys.* **36**, 440–443 (1962).

595. W. H. Flygare, A. Narath, and W. D. Gwinn, Microwave spectrum, structure, quadrupole interaction, dipole moment, and bent C—Cl bonds in 1,1-dichlorocyclopropane, *J. Chem. Phys.* **36**, 200–208 (1962).

596. C. T. Okonski, Nuclear quadrupole resonance spectroscopy, *in* "Determination of Organic Structures by Physical Methods," Vol. II. Chapter 11. Academic Press, New York, 1962.

597. R. A. Furman and D. R. Lide, Jr., Quadrupole coupling constants from the microwave spectrum of hydrazoic acid, *J. Chem. Phys.* **39**, 1133–1134 (1963).

598. W. H. Flygare, The microwave spectrum, partial structure, and quadrupole coupling constants in 1,1-dichloroethane, *J. Mol. Spectry.* **14**, 145–155 (1964).

599. W. H. Flygare, Experimental determinations of the field gradient at the deuteron in formaldehyde, *J. Chem. Phys.* **41**, 206–214 (1964).

600. J. T. Lowe and W. H. Flygare, Calculation of the field gradient at the deuterium in formaldehyde, *J. Chem. Phys.* **41**, 2153–2158 (1964).

601. E. Rosenthal and B. P. Dailey, Microwave spectrum of bromobenzene, its structure, quadrupole coupling constants and carbon-bromine bond, *J. Chem. Phys.* **43**, 2093–2110 (1965).

602. R. H. Schwendeman, Matrix elements of some products of direction cosines and second-order quadrupole coupling calculations, *J. Mol. Spectry.* **15**, 451–461 (1965).

603. H. W. de Wijn, Effect of quenching of polarizations in polar diatomic molecules on nuclear-quadrupole coupling, its vibrational dependence, and molecular dipole moments, *J. Chem. Phys.* **44**, 810–815 (1966).

VIII. Internal Rotation

604. H. H. Nielsen, The torsional oscillator-rotator in the quantum mechanics, *Phys. Rev.* **40**, 445–456 (1932).

605. J. B. Howard, The rotation-vibration spectrum of C_2H_6 and the question of free internal rotation, *J. Chem. Phys.* **5**, 451–459 (1937).

606. E. Gorin, J. Walter, and H. Eyring, Internal rotation and resonance in hydrocarbons, *J. Am. Chem. Soc.* **61**, 1876–1886 (1939).

607. B. L. Crawford, The partition functions and energy levels of molecules with internal torsional motions, *J.Chem. Phys.* **8**, 273–281 (1940).

608. J. S. Koehler and D. M. Dennison, Hindered rotation in methyl alcohol, *Phys. Rev.* **57**, 1006–1021 (1940).

609. D. Price, The partition functions of molecules with internal torsion I. Single asymmetric top attached to rigid framework, *J. Chem. Phys.* **9**, 807–815 (1941). Erratum—*J. Chem. Phys.* **10**, 80 (1942).

610. K. S. Pitzer and W. D. Gwinn, Energy levels and thermodynamic functions for molecules with internal rotation I. Rigid frame with attached tops, *J. Chem. Phys.* **10**, 428–440 (1942).

611. J. G. Aston, S. Isserow, G. J. Szasz, and R. M. Kennedy, An empirical correlation and method of calculation of barriers hindering internal rotation, *J. Chem. Phys.* **12**, 336–344 (1944).

612. F. A. French and R. S. Rasmussen, A relation between internuclear distances and potential barriers of methyl groups, *J. Chem. Phys.* **14**, 389–394 (1946).

613. K. S. Pitzer, Energy levels and thermodynamic functions for molecules with internal rotation II. Unsymmetrical tops attached to a rigid frame, *J. Chem. Phys.* **14**, 239–243 (1946).

614. E. N. Lasettre and L. B. Dean, Origin of the potential barrier hindering rotation in ethane and related substances, *J. Chem. Phys.* **16**, 151–152 (1948).

615. B. P. Dailey, H. Minden, and R. G. Shulman, Torsion vibrational states of CH_3CF_3, *Phys. Rev.* **75**, 1319 (1949).

616. J. E. Kilpatrick and K. S. Pitzer, Energy levels and thermodynamic functions for molecules with internal rotation III. Compound rotation, *J. Chem. Phys.* **17**, 1064–1075 (1949).

617. E. N. Lassettre and L. B. Dean, An electrostatic theory of the potential barriers hindering rotation around single bonds, *J. Chem. Phys.* **17**, 317–332 (1949).

618. J. O. Halford, Energy levels and thermodynamic properties of the internal rotator, *J. Chem. Phys.* **18**, 444–448 (1950).

619. D. R. Lide, Jr. and D. K. Coles, Microwave spectroscopic evidence for internal rotation in methyl silane, *Phys. Rev.* **80**, 911 (1950).

620. P. Torkington, The moments of inertia of molecules with internal rotation, *J. Chem. Phys.* **18**, 407–413 (1950).

621. H. T. Minden and B. P. Dailey, Hindered rotation in CH_3CF_3 and CH_3SiF_3, *Phys. Rev.* **82**, 338 (1951).

622. L. J. Oosterhoff, Restricted rotation in ethane, *Discussions Faraday Soc.* **10**, 79–87 (1951).

623. K. S. Pitzer, Potential energies for rotation about single bonds, *Discussions Faraday Soc.* **10**, 66–73 (1951).

624. "Tables Relating to Mathieu Functions." Columbia Univ. Press, New York, 1951. See also [641].

625. B. P. Dailey, Hindered rotation and microwave spectroscopy, *Ann. N.Y. Acad. Sci.* **55**, 915–927 (1952).

626. H. T. Minden, The complete symmetry group for internal rotation in CH_3CF_3 and like molecules, *J. Chem. Phys.* **20**, 1964–1965 (1952).

627. S. Mizushima, Y. Morino, and T. Shimanouchi, Some problems of internal rotation, *Phys. Chem.* **56**, 324–326 (1952).

628. J. Van Dranen, Born repulsion and restricted free rotation, *J. Chem. Phys.* **20**, 1982–1983 (1952).

629. F. A. Andersen, B. Bak, and J. Rastrup-Andersen, Microwave investigation of tertiary butyl fluoride, *Acta Chem. Scand.* **7**, 463 (1953).

630. B. Bak, L. Hansen, and J. Rastrup-Andersen, Experimental evidence of restricted rotation in CH_3CCCF_3, *J. Chem. Phys.* **21**, 1612–1613 (1953).

631. D. G. Burkhard, Hindered rotation involving two asymmetric groups, *J. Chem. Phys.* **21**, 1541–1549 (1953).

632. N. W. Luft, Asymmetric internal rotational barriers about single bonds, *J. Chem. Phys.* **21**, 179 (1953).

633. N. W. Luft, Internal potential barriers in saturated hydrocarbons, *Trans. Faraday Soc.* **49**, 118–121 (1953).

634. D. Kivelson, Theory of the interaction of hindered internal rotation with over-all rotations. I. Symmetric rotors-methyl silane, *J. Chem. Phys.* **22**, 1733–1739 (1954). Errata—*J. Chem. Phys.* **27**, 980 (1957).

635. D. R. Lide, Jr., Effects of internal motion in the microwave spectrum of methyl amine, *J. Chem. Phys.* **22**, 1613–1614 (1954).

636. N. W. Luft, Assignment of torsional frequencies in some halogenated ethanes, *J. Chem. Phys.* **22**, 155–156 (1954).

637. N. W. Luft, Magnitudes of barriers in intramolecular rotation, *J. Chem. Phys.* **22**, 1814–1820 (1954).

638. M. Mizushima, "Structure of Molecules and Internal Rotation." Academic Press, New York, 1954.

639. A-C. Tang, Internal rotation in molecules, *Sci. Sinica (Peking)* **3**, 279–299 (1954).

640. E. Tannenbaum, R. D. Johnson, R. J. Myers, and W. D. Gwinn, Microwave spectrum and barrier to internal rotation of nitromethane, *J. Chem. Phys.* **22**, 949 (1954).

641. G. Blanch and I. Rhodes, Table of characteristic values of Mathieu's equation for large values of the parameter, *J. Wash. Acad. Sci.* **45**, 166–196 (1955).

642. D. G. Burkhard and J. C. Irwin, Solution of the wave equation for internal rotation of two completely asymmetric molecules, *J. Chem. Phys.* **23**, 1405–1414 (1955). Erratum—*J. Chem. Phys.* **23**, 2469 (1955).

643. E. V. Ivash, J. C. M. Li, and K. S. Pitzer, Thermodynamic properties of ideal gaseous methanol, *J. Chem. Phys.* **23**, 1814–1818 (1955).

644. R. W. Kilb, Internal barrier height of methyl mercaptan, *J. Chem. Phys.* **23**, 1736–1737 (1955).

645. D. Kivelson, Theory of internal over-all rotational interactions II. Hamiltonian for the non-rigid internal rotor, *J. Chem. Phys.* **23**, 2230–2235 (1955).

646. D. Kivelson, Theory of internal overall rotational interactions III. Nonrigid asymmetric rotors, *J. Chem. Phys.* **23**, 2236–2243 (1955). Addendum—*J. Chem. Phys.* **27**, 980 (1957).

647. D. R. Lide, Jr., and D. Kivelson, Internal rotation in methyl-trifluoromethyl acetylene, *J. Chem. Phys.* **23**, 2191 (1955).

648. N. W. Luft, Intra-molecular torsional vibrations, *Z. Elektrochem.* **59**, 46–55 (1955).

649. E. A. Mason and M. M. Kreevoy, A simple model for barriers to internal rotation, *J. Am. Chem. Soc.* **77**, 5808–5814 (1955).

650. J. T. Massey and R. W. Hart, Effect of a high *cis*-barrier on the microwave spectrum of hydrogen peroxide, *J. Chem. Phys.* **23**, 942–946 (1955).

651. H. T. Minden, Molecular distortion caused by hindered rotation, *Phys. Rev.* **98**, 1160 (1955).

652. J. D. Swalen, Structure and potential barrier to hindered rotation in methyl alcohol, *J. Chem. Phys.* **23**, 1739–1740 (1955).

653. P. R. Swan and M. W. P. Strandberg, Excited torsional states in asymmetric hindered rotors, *Phys. Rev.* **99**, 667 (1955).

654. R. S. Wagner and B. P. Dailey, Proof of the staggered configuration of ethyl chloride, *J. Chem. Phys.* **23**, 1355 (1955).

655. E. B. Wilson, Jr., C. C. Lin, and D. R. Lide, Jr., Calculation of energy levels for internal torsion and overall rotation I. CH_3BF_2 type molecules, *J. Chem. Phys.* **23**, 136–142 (1955).

656. B. Bak, Calculation of potential barriers for ethane-like symmetric tops, *J. Chem. Phys.* **24**, 918–919 (1956).

657. D. G. Burkhard, Hindered rotation in symmetric-asymmetric molecules, *Trans. Faraday Soc.* **52**, 1–6 (1956).

658. T. P. Das, Tunneling through high periodic barriers I, *J. Chem. Phys.* **25**, 896–903 (1956).

659. D. R. Herschbach, Internal barrier in CH_3CH_2F and CH_3CHF_2 from torsional satellites, *J. Chem. Phys.* **25**, 358–359 (1956).

660. R. W. Kilb, "Tables of Mathieu Eigenvalues and Mathieu Eigenfunctions for Special Boundary Conditions." Dept. of Chem., Harvard Univ., Cambridge, Massachusetts, 1956.

661. J. C. M. Li and K. S. Pitzer, Energy levels and thermodynamic functions for molecules with internal rotation. IV. Extended tables for molecules with small moments of inertia, *J. Phys. Chem.* **60**, 466–474 (1956).

662. C. C. Lin and R. W. Kilb, Microwave spectrum and internal barrier of acetaldehyde, *J. Chem. Phys.* **24**, 631 (1956).

663. T. Nishikawa, Fine structure of $J = 1$–0 transition due to internal rotation in methyl alcohol, *J. Phys. Soc. Japan* **11**, 781–786 (1956).

664. J. D. Swalen, Calculation of energy levels in molecules with internal torsion, *J. Chem. Phys.* **24**, 1072–1074 (1956).

665. E. Tannenbaum, R. J. Myers, and W. D. Gwinn, Microwave spectra, dipole moment, and barrier to internal rotation of CH_3NO_2 and CD_3NO_2, *J. Chem. Phys.* **25**, 42–47 (1956).

666. T. Das, Tunneling through high periodic barriers. II. Application to nuclear magnetic resonance in solids, *J. Chem. Phys.* **27**, 763–781 (1957).

667. J. O. Halford, Partition function for internal rotation in methanol and similar molecular models, *J. Chem. Phys.* **26**, 851–855 (1957).

668. K. T. Hecht and D. M. Dennison, Hindered rotation in molecules with relatively high potential barriers, *J. Chem. Phys.* **26**, 31–47 (1957).

669. K. T. Hecht and D. M. Dennison, Vibration-hindered rotation interactions in methyl alcohol. The $J = 0$–1 transition, *J. Chem. Phys.* **26**, 48–69 (1957).

670. D. R. Herschbach, "Tables for the Internal Rotation Problem." Dept. of Chem., Harvard Univ., Cambridge, Massachusetts, (1957).

671. D. R. Herschbach, Tables of Mathieu integrals for the internal rotation problem, *J. Chem. Phys.* **27**, 975 (1957).

672. D. R. Herschbach, Comments on the internal rotation problem, *J. Chem. Phys.* **27**, 1420–1421 (1957).

673. R. W. Kilb, C. C. Lin, and E. B. Wilson, Jr., Calculation of energy levels for internal torsion and overall rotation II. Acetaldehyde-type molecules-acetaldehyde spectra, *J. Chem. Phys.* **26**, 1695–1703 (1957).

674. R. W. Kilb and L. Pierce, Microwave spectrum, structure, and internal barrier of methyl silane, *J. Chem. Phys.* **27**, 108–112 (1957).

675. M. M. Kreevoy and E. A. Mason, A simple model for barriers to internal rotation II. Rotational isomers, *J. Am. Chem. Soc.* **79**, 4851–4854 (1957).

676. D. R. Lide, Jr. and D. E. Mann, Microwave spectra of molecules exhibiting internal rotation I. Propylene, *J. Chem. Phys.* **27**, 868–873 (1957).

677. D. R. Lide, Jr. and D. E. Mann, Microwave spectra of molecules exhibiting internal rotation II. Methylallene, *J. Chem. Phys.* **27**, 874–877 (1957).

678. Y. Mashiko, Potential energy surface for torsional oscillations in dimethyl ether, *Nippon Kagaku Zasshi* **78**, 1131–1139 (1957).

679. R. W. Naylor, Jr. and E. B. Wilson, Jr., Microwave spectrum and barrier to internal rotation in CH_3BF_2, *J. Chem. Phys.* **26**, 1057–1060 (1957).

680. T. Nishikawa, Microwave studies of the internal motion and structure of methylamine, *J. Phys. Soc. Japan* **12**, 668–680 (1957).

681. S. Siegel, Microwave spectrum and barrier to internal rotation for *trans*-fluoropropylene, *J. Chem. Phys.* **27**, 989–990 (1957).

682. J. D. Swalen and D. R. Herschbach, Internal barrier of propylene oxide from the microwave spectrum I, *J. Chem. Phys.* **27**, 100–108 (1957).

683. W. J. Tabor, Microwave spectrum and barrier to internal rotation of acetic acid, *J. Chem. Phys.* **27**, 974–975 (1957).

684. E. B. Wilson, Jr., On the origin of potential barriers to internal rotation in molecules, *Proc. Natl. Acad. Sci. U.S.* **43**, 816–820 (1957).

685. H. Eyring, G. H. Stewart, and R. P. Smith, Principle of minimum bending of localized and delocalized orbitals-ethane barrier and related effects, *Proc. Natl. Acad. Sci. U.S.* **44**, 259–260 (1958).

686. S. Golden, Evaluation of the partition function for restricted internal rotation, *J. Phys. Chem.* **62**, 74–75 (1958).

687. D. R. Herschbach and L. C. Krishner, Microwave spectrum of $CH_2DCH=CH_2$; equilibrium conformation of propylene, *J. Chem. Phys.* **28**, 728–729 (1958).

688. D. R. Herschbach and J. D. Swalen, Internal barrier of propylene oxide from the microwave spectrum II, *J. Chem. Phys.* **29**, 761–776 (1958).

689. D. R. Lide, Jr., Internal barrier in ethane, *J. Chem. Phys.* **29**, 1426–1427 (1958).

690. D. R. Lide, Jr. and D. E. Mann, Microwave spectra of molecules exhibiting internal rotation III. Trimethylamine, *J. Chem. Phys.* **28**, 572–576 (1958).

691. D. R. Lide, Jr. and D. E. Mann, Microwave spectra of molecules exhibiting internal rotation IV. Isobutane, tertiary butyl fluoride, and trimethyl phosphine, *J. Chem. Phys.* **29**, 914–920 (1958).

692. C. C. Lin, On the classical mechanics of the internal rotation of molecules, *Am. J. Phys.* **26**, 319–323 (1958).

693. L. Pauling, The nature of bond orbitals and the origin of potential barriers to internal rotation in molecules, *Proc. Natl. Acad. Sci. U.S.* **44**, 211–216 (1958).

694. D. G. Burkhard and D. M. Dennison, Rotation spectrum of methyl alcohol, *J. Mol. Spectry.* **3**, 299–334 (1959).

695. W. B. Dixon, Internal rotation barrier and dipole moment of methyl nitrate, *Spectrochim. Acta* **15**, 767 (1959).

696. A. A. Evett, Comparison of exact and approximate energy levels for a hindered rotor, *J. Chem. Phys.* **31**, 1419–1420 (1959).

697. G. M. Harris and F. E. Harris, Valence bond calculation of the barrier to internal rotation in molecules, *J. Chem. Phys.* **31**, 1450–1453 (1959).

698. D. R. Herschbach, Calculation of energy levels for internal torsion and overall rotation III, *J. Chem. Phys.* **31**, 91–108 (1959).

699. P. H. Kasai and R. J. Myers, Microwave spectrum, structure, and internal rotation of dimethyl ether, *J. Chem. Phys.* **30**, 1096–1097 (1959).

700. V. W. Laurie, Microwave spectrum and internal rotation of ethyl cyanide, *J. Chem. Phys.* **31**, 1500–1505 (1959).

701. V. W. Laurie and D. R. Lide, Jr., Microwave spectrum and internal rotation of 1-chloro-2-butyne, *J. Chem. Phys.* **31**, 939–943 (1959).

702. D. R. Lide, Jr., Microwave spectra of molecules exhibiting internal rotation V. Barrier height in ethyl chloride and ethyl bromide, *J. Chem. Phys.* **30**, 37–39 (1959).

703. C. C. Lin and J. D. Swalen, Internal rotation and microwave spectroscopy, *Rev. Mod. Phys.* **31**, 841–892 (1959).

704. L. Pierce, Internal rotation in double internal rotor molecules—The microwave spectrum of dimethylsilane, *J. Chem. Phys.* **31**, 547–548 (1959).

705. J. D. Swalen and C. C. Costain, Internal rotation in molecules with two internal rotors—microwave spectrum of acetone, *J. Chem. Phys.* **31**, 1562–1574 (1959).

706. W. Weltner, Polytypism and the origin of the potential barrier hindering internal rotation in molecules, *J. Chem. Phys.* **31**, 264–265 (1959).

707. E. B. Wilson Jr., The problem of barriers to internal rotation in molecules, *Advan. Chem. Phys.* **2**, 367–393 (1959).

708. D. G. Burkhard, Internal angular momentum in hindered rotation, *J. Opt. Soc. Am.* **50**, 1214–1227 (1960).

709. W. L. Clinton, Note on the internal rotation problem, *J. Chem. Phys.* **33**, 632–633 (1960).

710. M. Karplus, Note on the internal-rotation barrier in ethanic compounds, *J. Chem. Phys.* **33**, 316–317 (1960).

711. T. Kojima, Potential barrier of phenol from its microwave spectrum, *J. Phys. Soc. Japan* **15**, 284–287 (1960).

712. R. J. Myers and E. B. Wilson, Jr., Application of symmetry principles to the rotation-internal torsion levels of molecules with two equivalent methyl groups, *J. Chem. Phys.* **33**, 186–191 (1960).

713. H. D. Rudolph, H. Dreizler, and W. Maier, Microwave spectrum, structure, and hinderance potential of $(CH_3)_2S$, *Z. Naturforsch.* **15A**, 742 (1960).

714. H. Dreizler, Group theoretical considerations of the microwave spectrum of molecules containing two methyl groups with hindered rotation and with different carbon isotopes, *Z. Naturforsch.* **16A**, 477–484 (1961).

715. H. Dreizler, Group theoretical analysis of the microwave spectra of molecules with two rotation-hindered trigonally symmetric molecule groups, *Z. Naturforsch.* **16A**, 1354–1367 (1961).

716. H. Dreizler and H. D. Rudolph, The torsion fine structure in the rotational spectrum of dimethylsulfide and the internal hinderance potential, *Z. Naturforsch.* **17A**, 712–732 (1961).

717. W. G. Fateley and F. A. Miller, Torsional frequencies in the far infrared-I. Molecules with a single methyl rotor, *Spectrochim. Acta* **17**, 857–868 (1961).

718. M. Hayashi and L. Pierce, Tables for the internal rotation problem, *J. Chem. Phys.* **35**, 1148–1149 (1961).

719. T. Kojima, E. L. Breig, and C. C. Lin, Microwave spectrum and internal barrier of methyl phosphine, *J. Chem. Phys.* **35**, 2139–2144 (1961).

720. W. F. Libby, Isotope size effect in van Der Waals radii and the barrier to rotation around the carbon-carbon single bond, *J. Chem. Phys.* **35**, 1527 (1961).

721. L. Pierce, Energy levels for internal and overall rotation of two top molecules I. Microwave spectrum of dimethyl silane, *J. Chem. Phys.* **34**, 498–506 (1961).

722. L. Pierce and M. Hayashi, Microwave spectrum, dipole moment, structure, and internal rotation of dimethyl sulfide, *J. Chem. Phys.* **35**, 479–485 (1961).

723. M. L. Sage, Internal rotation of *cis* 2,3-epoxybutane from the microwave spectrum, *J. Chem. Phys.* **35**, 142–148 (1961).

724. W. G. Fateley and F. A. Miller, Torsional frequencies in the far infrared II. Molecules with two or three methyl rotors, *Spectrochim. Acta* **18**, 977–993 (1962).

725. E. Hirota, Rotational isomerism and microwave spectroscopy I. The microwave spectrum of normal propyl fluoride, *J. Chem. Phys.* **37**, 283–291 (1962).

726. E. Hirota, Rotational isomerism and microwave spectroscopy II. The microwave spectrum of butyronitrile, *J. Chem. Phys.* **37**, 2918–2920 (1962).

727. B. Kirtman, Interactions between ordinary vibrations and hindered internal rotation I. Rotational energies, *J. Chem. Phys.* **37**, 2516–2539 (1962).

728. V. Magnasco, An empirical method for calculating barriers to internal rotation in simple molecules, *Nuovo Cimento* **24**, 425–441 (1962).

729. K. D. Moller and H. G. Andresen, Theory of torsion vibrations of $(CH_3)_2X$-type molecules, *J. Chem. Phys.* **37**, 1800–1807 (1962).

730. Y. A. Pentin and V. M. Tatevskii, Investigation of internal rotation and *cis-trans* isomerism of molecular structure by spectroscopic methods, *Izv. Akad. Nauk SSSR, Ser. Fiz.* **26**, 1241–1246 (1962).

731. C. R. Quade, "Tables of Integrals for Application to the Internal Rotation of Certain Asymmetric Internal Rotors," Dept. of Phys., Univ. of Oklahoma, Norman, Oklahoma, 1962.

732. R. L. Redington, W. B. Olsen, and P. C. Cross, Studies of hydrogen peroxide—The infrared spectrum and the internal rotation problem, *J. Chem. Phys.* **36**, 1311–1326 (1962).

733. R. A. Beaudet, Microwave spectrum, barrier to internal rotation, and dipole moment of *cis*-crotononitrile, *J. Chem. Phys.* **38**, 2548–2552 (1963).

734. H. Dreizler and R. Peter, Tables for the Analysis of rotational spectra containing centrifugal distortion and torsional splitting, *J. Chem. Phys.* **39**, 1132 (1963).

735. H. Dreizler, H. G. Schirdewahn, and B. Stark, Numerical values of some disturbance sums for the analysis of the torsion fine structure of rotation spectra, *Z. Naturforsch.* **18A**, 670–671 (1963).

736. W. G. Fateley and F. A. Miller, Torsional frequencies in the far infrared III. The form of the potential curve for hindered internal rotation of a methyl group, *Spectrochim. Acta* **19**, 611–628 (1963).

737. D. R. Herschbach, Bibliography for hindered internal rotation and microwave spectroscopy, Lawrence Radiation Laboratory, Berkeley, California, UCRL-10404 (1963).

738. K. D. Moller and H. G. Andresen, On the theory of torsional vibrations of $(CH_3)_3X$ type molecules, *J. Chem. Phys.* **38**, 17–22 (1963).

739. C. R. Quade and C. C. Lin, Internal rotation in completely asymmetric molecules I. A general theory and analysis of the microwave rotational spectrum of CH_2DCOH, CD_2HCOH, and $CHOOCH_2D$, *J. Chem. Phys.* **38**, 540–550 (1963).

740. O. L. Stiefvater and J. Sheridan, Microwave spectrum and barrier to internal rotation in acetyl acetylene, *Proc. Chem. Soc.* **1963**, 368 (1963).

741. B. Kirtman, Interactions between ordinary vibrations and hindered internal rotation II. Theory of internal rotation fine structure in some perpendicular bands of ethane-type molecules, *J. Chem. Phys.* **41**, 775–788 (1964).

742. B. Kirtman, Electron distributions involved in barriers to internal rotation, *J. Chem. Phys.* **41**, 3262 (1964).

743. V. W. Laurie, Internal rotation and Coriolis coupling in symmetric top molecules, *J. Mol. Spectry.* **13**, 283–287 (1964).

743a. J. Michielsen-Effinger, Microwave spectrum and internal rotation of ethyl alcohol, *Bull. Classe Sci. Acad. Roy. Belg.* **50**, 645–657 (1964).

744. I. A. Mukhtarov, Determination of the frequency of torsional vibration for trifluoroethylene from the microwave spectrum, *Opt. i Spektroskopiya* **16**, 910 (1964).

744a. R. I. Mukhtarov., Rotational transitions in molecules consisting of two asymmetric rotors with hindered internal rotation, *Tr. Komis. po Spektroskopii, Akad. Nauk SSSR* **3**, 240–247 (1964).

745. S. Nakagawa, T. Kojima, S. Takahashi, and C. C. Lin, Microwave spectrum and internal barrier of methylthiocyanate, *J. Mol. Spectry.* **14**, 201 (1964).

746. D. Stelman, Denominator correction to the Van Vleck transformation—Internal rotation problem, *J. Chem. Phys.* **41**, 2111–2115 (1964).
747. J. T. Yardley, J. Hinze, and R. F. Curl, Jr., Equilibrium conformation of *N*-methylene-methylamine from microwave data, *J. Chem. Phys.* **41**, 2562–2563 (1964).
748. R. C. Woods, III., A computer calculation of internal rotation splittings applied to the microwave spectrum of fluoral, *Mol. Spectry. Symp. Columbus, Ohio, June 1964*, Navy Publications and Printing Office, 1965. (Also see [1708].)
749. R. W. Wyatt and R. G. Parr, Origin of the barrier hindering internal rotation in ethane, *J. Chem. Phys.* **41**, 3262–3263 (1964).
750. E. Hirota, Rotational isomerism and microwave spectroscopy III. The microwave spectrum of 3-fluoropropene, *J. Chem. Phys.* **42**, 2071–2089 (1965).
751. R. H. Hunt, R. A. Leacock, C. W. Peters, and K. T. Hecht, Internal-rotation in hydrogen peroxide. The far-infrared spectrum and the determination of the hindering potential, *J. Chem. Phys.* **42**, 1931–1946 (1965).
752. W. H. Kirchoff and D. R. Lide, Jr., Microwave spectrum and barrier to internal rotation in methylsilylacetylene, *J. Chem. Phys.* **43**, 2203–2212 (1965).
753. J. P. Lowe and R. G. Parr, Internal rotation in hydrogen peroxide and methyl alcohol: a simple electrostatic model, *J. Chem. Phys.* **43**, 2565–2566 (1965).
754. S. Nakagawa, S. Takahashi, T. Kojima, and C. C. Lin, Microwave spectrum and internal rotation of methylthiocyanate, *J. Chem. Phys.* **43**, 3583–3585 (1965).
755. R. Nelson and L. Pierce, Microwave spectrum, structure, and barrier to internal rotation of acetone, *J. Mol. Spectry.* **18**, 344–352 (1965).
755a. H. D. Rudolph and H. Seiler, Microwave spectrum, hinderance potential of the internal rotation and dipole moment of *p*-fluorotoluene, *Z. Naturforsch.* **20A**, 1682–1686 (1965).
755b. L. H. Scharpen and V. W. Laurie, Microwave spectrum of excited torsional states of propane: barrier to internal rotation, *Mol. Spectry. Symp., Columbus, Ohio, June 1964*, Navy Publications and Printing Office, 1965.
756. R. A. Scott and H. A. Scheraga, Method for calculating internal rotation barriers, *J. Chem. Phys.* **42**, 2209–2215 (1965).
756a. D. Sutter, H. Dreizler, and H. D. Rudolph, Microwave spectrum, structure, dipole moment, and internal rotation potential of dimethyldisulfide, *Z. Naturforsch.* **20A**, 1676–1681 (1965).
757. W. M. Tolles, E. T. Handelman, and W. D. Gwinn, Microwave spectrum and barrier to internal rotation in trifluoronitromethane, *J. Chem. Phys.* **43**, 3019–3024 (1965).
758. M. L. Unland, V. Weiss, and W. H. Flygare, Barrier studies in the halopropenes I. The microwave spectrum, barrier to internal rotation, quadrupole coupling constants, and microwave double-resonance spectra of 2-chloropropene, *J. Chem. Phys.* **42**, 2138–2149 (1965).
758a. J. P. Lowe and R. G. Parr, Semiempirical treatment of hindered rotation in simple hydrides and halosubstituted ethane like molecules, *J. Chem. Phys.* **44**, 3001–3009 (1966).
758b. C. R. Quade, Internal rotation in completely asymmetric molecules II. Interactions between vibration and internal rotation, *J. Chem. Phys.* **44**, 2512–2523 (1966).
758c. O. J. Sovers and M. Karplus, Distortional effects on the ethane internal rotation barrier, *J. Chem. Phys.* **44**, 3033–3037 (1966).

IX. Inversion

759. F. Hund, Significance of molecular spectra. Pt. III. Notes on the oscillation and rotation spectra of molecules with more than two nuclei, *Z. Physik* **43**, 805–826 (1927).

760. P. M. Morse and E. C. G. Stuckelberg, Solution of the eigenvalue problem for a potential field with two minima, *Helv. Phys. Acta* **4**, 337–354 (1931).

761. D. M. Dennison and G. E. Uhlenbeck, The two-minima problem and the ammonia molecule, *Phys. Rev.* **41**, 313–321 (1932).

762. N. Rosen and P. M. Morse, On the vibrations of polyatomic molecules, *Phys. Rev.* **42**, 210–217 (1932).

763. M. F. Manning, Energy levels of a symmetrical double minima problem with applications to the NH_3 and ND_3 molecules, *J. Chem. Phys.* **3**, 136–138 (1935).

764. F. T. Wall and G. Glocker, The double minimum problem applied to the ammonia molecules, *J. Chem. Phys.* **5**, 314–315 (1937).

765. H.-Y. Sheng, E. F. Barker, and D. M. Dennison, Further resolution of two parallel bands of ammonia and the interaction between vibration and rotation, *Phys. Rev.* **60**, 786–794 (1941).

766. B. Bleaney and R. P. Penrose, The inversion spectrum of ammonia, *Phys. Rev.* **70**, 775–776 (1946).

767. W. E. Good, The inversion spectrum of ammonia, *Phys. Rev.* **70**, 213–218 (1946).

768. B. Bleaney and R. P. Penrose, The inversion spectrum of ammonia at centimeter wavelengths, *Proc. Roy. Soc.* **A189**, 358–371 (1947).

769. H. H. Nielsen and D. M. Dennison, Anomalous values of certain of the fine structure lines in the ammonia microwave spectrum, *Phys. Rev.* **72**, 1101–1108 (1947).

770. M. W. P. Strandberg, R. Kyhl, T. Wentink, and R. E. Hillger, Inversion spectrum of ammonia. *Phys. Rev.* **71**, 326 (1947). Errata—*Phys. Rev.* **71**, 639 (1947).

771. R. R. Newton and L. H. Thomas, Internal molecular motions of large amplitude illustrated by the symmetrical vibration of ammonia, *J. Chem. Phys.* **16**, 310–323 (1948).

772. J. W. Simmons and W. Gordy, Structure of the inversion spectrum of ammonia, *Phys. Rev.* **73**, 713–718 (1948).

773. N. Carrara, P. Lombardini, R. Cini, and L. Sacconi, Microwave spectroscopy. The inversion spectrum of ammonia, *Nuovo Cimento* **6**, 552–558 (1949).

774. A. H. Sharbaugh, T. C. Madison, and J. K. Bragg, Inversion spectrum of ammonia, *Phys. Rev.* **76**, 1529 (1949).

775. M. Tomassini, The inversion spectrum of ammonia, *Nuovo Cimento* **7**, 1–11 (1950).

776. C. C. Costain, An empirical formula for the microwave spectrum of ammonia, *Phys. Rev.* **82**, 108 (1951).

777. R. G. Nuckolls, L. J. Rueger, and H. Lyons, Measurement of the microwave inversion spectrum of ND_3, *Phys. Rev.* **83**, 880–881 (1951).

778. M. T. Weiss and M. W. P. Strandberg, The microwave spectra of the deutero-ammonias, *Phys. Rev.* **83**, 567–575 (1951).

779. C. C. Costain and G. B. B. M. Sutherland, A method of determining the potential barriers restricting inversion in ammonia, phosphine, and arsine from vibrational force constants, *Phys. Chem.* **56**, 321–324 (1952).

780. T. Nishikawa and K. Shimoda, New lines of the inversion spectrum of ammonia, *J. Phys. Soc. Japan* **8**, 426 (1953).

781. G. W. Rathjens, Jr., N. K. Freeman, W. D. Gwinn, and K. S. Pitzer, Infrared absorption spectra, structure and thermodynamic properties of cyclobutane, *J. Am. Chem. Soc.* **75**, 5634–5642 (1953).

782. K. Shimoda, T. Nishikawa, and T. Itoh, Microwave investigation of hindered rotation and inversion of methylamine, *J. Chem. Phys.* **22**, 1456 (1954).

783. J. Fernandez, R. J. Myers, and W. D. Gwinn, Microwave spectrum and planarity of the ring of trimethylene oxide, *J. Chem. Phys.* **23**, 758–759 (1955).

784. D. Kivelson and D. R. Lide, Jr., Internal motion in methylamine, *Phys. Rev.* **99**, 667 (1955).

785. T. Nishikawa and K. Shimoda, Inversion spectrum of ammonia, *J. Phys. Soc. Japan* **10**, 89–92 (1955).

786. K. Shimoda, T. Nishikawa, and T. Itoh, Microwave spectrum of methylamine, *Phys. Rev.* **98**, 1160 (1955).

787. W. S. Benedict and E. K. Plyler, Interaction of stretching vibrations and inversion in ammonia, *J. Chem. Phys.* **24**, 904 (1956).

788. J. Bonanomi and J. Herrmann, Determination of the inversion frequency of ammonia, *Helv. Phys. Acta* **29**, 451–452 (1956).

789. T. Itoh, Molecular structure of methylamine, *J. Phys. Soc. Japan* **11**, 264–271 (1956).

790. G. Erlandsson and W. Gordy, Submillimeter wave spectroscopy, rotation-inversion transitions in ND_3, *Phys. Rev.* **106**, 513–515 (1957).

791. H. G. Fitzky, R. Honerjager, and W. Wilke, Inversion spectrum of ammonia, *Z. Physik* **149**, 471–479 (1957).

792. D. Kivelson and D. R. Lide, Jr., Theory of internal motions and application to CD_3ND_2, *J. Chem. Phys.* **27**, 353–360 (1957).

793. D. R. Lide, Jr., Structure of the methyl amine molecule I. Microwave spectrum of CD_3ND_2, *J. Chem. Phys.* **27**, 343–352 (1957).

794. G. Herrmann, Ground state inversion spectrum of $N^{14}D_3$, *J. Chem. Phys.* **29**, 875–879 (1958).

795. E. Heilbronner, H. Rutishauser, and F. Gerson, Eigenvalues, eigenfunctions, and thermodynamic functions for the 6-fold potential of a linear oscillator, *Helv. Chim. Acta* **42**, 2304–2314 (1959).

796. J. K. Tyler, L. F. Thomas, and J. Sheridan, Microwave spectrum and structure of cyanamide, *Proc. Chem. Soc.* **1959**, 155–156 (1959).

797. A. A. Vuylsteke, Maser states in ammonia-inversion, *Am. J. Phys.* **27**, 554–565 (1959).

798. S. I. Chan, J. Zinn, J. Fernandez, and W. D. Gwinn, Trimethylene oxide I. Microwave spectrum, dipole moment, and double minimum vibration, *J. Chem. Phys.* **33**, 1643–1655 (1960).

799. S. I. Chan, J. Zinn, and W. D. Gwinn, Double minimum vibration in trimethylene oxide, *J. Chem. Phys.* **33**, 295–296 (1960).

800. C. C. Costain and J. M. Dowling, Microwave spectrum and molecular structure of formamide, *J. Chem. Phys.* **32**, 158–165 (1960).

801. A. Danti, W. J. Lafferty, and R. C. Lord, Far infrared spectrum of trimethylene oxide, *J. Chem. Phys.* **33**, 294–295 (1960).

802. S. I. Chan, J. Zinn, and W. D. Gwinn, Trimethylene oxide II. Structure, vibration-rotation interaction, and origin of potential function for ring puckering motion, *J. Chem. Phys.* **34**, 1319–1329 (1961).

803. F. Gerson, The one-dimensional oscillator 6-fold potential as a basis for a symmetrical double minimum problem, *Helv. Chim. Acta* **44**, 471–476 (1961).

804. G. P. Shipulo, Rotational spectrum of cyanamide, *Opt. Spectry.* **10**, 288 (1961).

805. T. Kasuya, Microwave studies of internal motions of hydrazine molecule, *Sci. Papers Inst. Phys. Chem. Res. (Tokyo)* **56**, 1–39 (1962).

806. D. R. Lide, Jr., Vibration-rotation interactions in cyanamide—The question of planarity of amides, *J. Mol. Spectry.* **8**, 142–152 (1962).

807. D. J. Millen, G. Topping, and D. R. Lide, Jr., Microwave spectrum and nonplanarity of cyanamide, *J. Mol. Spectry.* **8**, 153–163 (1962).

808. G. W. Rathjens, Microwave investigation of cyclopentene, *J. Chem. Phys.* **36**, 2401–2406 (1962).

809. R. L. Somorjai and D. F. Hornig, Double-minimum potentials in hydrogen-bonded solids, *J. Chem. Phys.* **36**, 1980–1987 (1962).

810. J. D. Swalen and J. A. Ibers, Potential function for the inversion of ammonia, *J. Chem. Phys.* **36**, 1914–1918 (1962).

811. W. T. Weeks, K. T. Hecht, and D. M. Dennison, Inversion-vibration and inversion-rotation interactions in the ammonia molecule, *J. Mol. Spectry.* **8**, 30–57 (1962).

812. S. I. Chan and D. Stelman, Some energy levels and matrix elements of the quartic oscillator, *J. Mol. Spectry.* **10**, 278–299 (1963).

813. S. I. Chan and D. Stelman, Oscillators perturbed by Gaussian barriers, *J. Chem. Phys.* **39**, 545–551 (1963).

814. W. H. Fletcher and F. B. Brown, Vibrational spectra and the inversion phenomenon in cyanamide and deuterated cyanamide, *J. Chem. Phys.* **39**, 2478–2490 (1963).

815. T. Kasuya and T. Kojima, Internal motions of hydrazine, *J. Phys. Soc. Japan* **18**, 364–368 (1963).

816. V. W. Laurie and J. Wollrab, Microwave spectrum and inversion of dimethylamine, *Bull. Am. Phys. Soc.* [2] **8**, 327 (1963).

816a. S. I. Chan, D. Stelman, and L. E. Thompson, Quartic oscillator as a basis for energy level calculations of some anharmonic oscillators, *J. Chem. Phys.* **41**, 2828–2835 (1964).

817. M. Lichtenstein, J. J. Gallagher, and V. E. Derr, Spectroscopic investigations of the deutero-ammonias in the millimeter region, *J. Mol. Spectry.* **12**, 87–97 (1964).

818. C. B. Moore and G. C. Pimentel, Out-of-plane CH_2 bending potential functions of diazomethane, ketene, and related molecules, *J. Chem. Phys.* **40**, 1529–1534 (1964).

819. C. F. Bunge and A. Bunge, Upper and lower limits to the eigenvalues of double-minimum potentials, *J. Chem. Phys.* **43**, S194–S198 (1965).

820. S. S. Butcher and C. C. Costain, Vibration-rotation interaction in the microwave spectrum of cyclopentene, *J. Mol. Spectry.* **15**, 40–50 (1965).

821. W. M. Tolles and W. D. Gwinn, Quadrupole coupling constants and lower limit to the barrier for inversion in ethylenimine, *J. Chem. Phys.* **42**, 2253–2254 (1965).

821a. M. S. White and E. L. Beeson, Jr., Microwave spectrum of trimethylene sulfide, *J. Chem. Phys.* **43**, 1839–1841 (1965).

822. S. I. Chan, T. R. Borgers, J. W. Russell, H. L. Strauss, and W. D. Gwinn, Trimethylene oxide III. Far infrared spectrum and double-minimum vibration, *J. Chem. Phys.* **44**, 1103–1111 (1966).

822a. H. W. Harrington, Out-of-plane bending frequencies in triethylene sulfide from microwave intensity measurements, *J. Chem. Phys.* **44**, 3481–3485 (1966).

822b. D. O. Harris, H. W. Harrington, A. C. Luntz, and W. D. Gwinn, Microwave spectrum, vibration-rotation interaction, and potential function for the ring-puckering vibration of trimethylene sulfide, *J. Chem. Phys.* **44**, 3467–3480 (1966).

823. H. Kim and W. D. Gwinn, Microwave spectra, dipole moments, structure, and ring puckering vibration of cyclobutyl chloride and cyclobutyl fluoride, *J. Chem. Phys.* **44**, 865–873 (1966).

X. Stark Effect

824. R. de L. Kronig, The dielectric constant of diatomic dipole-gases on the new quantum mechanics, *Proc. Natl. Acad. Sci. U.S.* **12**, 488–493 (1926).

825. R. de L. Kronig, The dielectric constant of symmetrical polyatomic dipole-gases on the new quantum mechanics, *Proc. Natl. Acad. Sci. U.S.* **12**, 608–612 (1926).

826. P. Debye, "Polar Molecules." Chem. Catalog Co., New York, 1929.

827. F. Brouwer, Dissertation, Univ. of Amsterdam. Amsterdam, 1930.

828. W. G. Penney, The Stark effect in band spectra, *Phil. Mag.* **11**, 602–609 (1931).

829. R. P. Bell and I. E. Coop, The dipole moments of hydrogen and deuterium chlorides, *Trans. Faraday Soc.* **34**, 1209–1214 (1938).

830. T. W. Dakin, W. E. Good, and D. K. Coles, Resolution of a rotational line of the OCS molecule and its Stark effect, *Phys. Rev.* **70**, 560 (1946).

831. D. K. Coles and W. E. Good, Stark and Zeeman effects in microwave spectroscopy, *Phys. Rev.* **72**, 157 (1947).

832. B. P. Dailey, First order Stark effect in the microwave spectrum of methyl alcohol, *Phys. Rev.* **72**, 84–85 (1947).

833. H. K. Hughes, The electric resonance method of radiofrequency spectroscopy. The moment of inertia and electric dipole moment of CsF, *Phys. Rev.* **72**, 614–623 (1947).

834. J. M. Jauch, The hyperfine structure and the Stark effect of the ammonia inversion spectrum, *Phys. Rev.* **72**, 715–723 (1947).

835. W. V. Smith, Determination of nuclear spin from the Stark effect of microwave rotational spectra, *Phys. Rev.* **71**, 126–127 (1947).

836. C. H. Townes and F. R. Merritt, Stark effect in high frequency fields, *Phys. Rev.* **72**, 1266–1267 (1947).

837. D. K. Coles, Microwave absorption line frequencies of methyl alcohol and their Stark effect, *Phys. Rev.* **74**, 1194–1195 (1948).

838. U. Fano, Electric quadrupole coupling of the nuclear spin with the rotation of a polar diatomic molecule in an external electric field, *J. Res. Natl. Bur. Std.* **40**, 215–223 (1948).

839. S. Golden, T. Wentink, R. Hillger, and M. W. P. Strandberg, Stark spectrum of H_2O, *Phys. Rev.* **73**, 92–93 (1948).

840. S. Golden and E. B. Wilson, Jr., The Stark effect for a rigid asymmetric rotor, *J. Chem. Phys.* **16**, 669–685 (1948).

841. W. A. Nierenberg, I. I. Rabi, and M. Slotnick, A note on the Stark effect in diatomic molecules, *Phys. Rev.* **73**, 1430–1433 (1948).

842. W. A. Nierenberg and M. Slotnick, A note on the Stark effect in diatomic molecules, *Phys. Rev.* **74**, 1246 (1948).

843. M. W. P. Strandberg, T. Wentink, R. E. Hillger, G. H. Wannier, and M. L. Deutsch, Stark spectrum of HDO, *Phys. Rev.* **73**, 188 (1948).

844. L. G. Wesson, "Tables of Electric Dipole Moments." Technology Press, Cambridge, Massachusetts, 1948.

845. H. K. Hughes, The rotational Stark spectrum of linear molecules, *Phys. Rev.* **76**, 1675–1677 (1949).

846. R. Karplus and A. H. Sharbaugh, Second-order Stark effect of methyl chloride, *Phys. Rev.* **75**, 889–890 (1949). Errata—*Phys. Rev.* **75**, 1449 (1949).

847. A. Lenard, "Tables for Calculation of Stark and Zeeman Effects." Dept. of Phys., Iowa State Univ., Ames, Iowa, 1949 (out of print).

848. W. Low and C. H. Townes, Molecular dipole moments and Stark effects I. Stark effects on symmetric top molecules with nuclear quadrupole coupling, *Phys. Rev.* **76**, 1295–1299 (1949).

849. J. Barriol, The study of the Stark effect for the case of a rotator possessing a permanent dipole, *J. Phys. Radium* **11**, 62–66 (1950).

850. F. Coester, Stark–Zeeman effects on symmetric top molecules with nuclear quadrupole coupling, *Phys. Rev.* **77**, 454–462 (1950).

851. R. G. Shulman, B. P. Dailey, and C. H. Townes, Molecular dipole moments and Stark effects III. Dipole moment determinations, *Phys. Rev.* **78**, 145–148 (1950).

852. R. G. Shulman and C. H. Townes, Molecular dipole moments and Stark effects II. Stark effects in OCS, *Phys. Rev.* **77**, 500–506 (1950).

853. D. K. Coles, W. E. Good, J. K. Bragg, and A. H. Sharbaugh, The Stark effect of the ammonia inversion spectrum, *Phys. Rev.* **82**, 877–878 (1951).

854. D. W. Magnuson, Determination of the two-dipole moment components in nitrosyl fluoride, *J. Chem. Phys.* **19**, 1071 (1951).

855. J. N. Shoolery and A. H. Sharbaugh, Some molecular dipole moments determined by microwave spectroscopy, *Phys. Rev.* **82**, 95 (1951).

856. S. N. Ghosh, R. Trambarulo, and W. Gordy, Electric dipole moments of several molecules from the Stark effect, *J. Chem. Phys.* **21**, 308–310 (1953).

857. M. Mizushima, Theory of the Stark effect of asymmetric rotator with hyperfine structure, *J. Chem. Phys.* **21**, 539–541 (1953).

858. S. H. Autler and C. H. Townes, Stark effect in rapidly varying fields, *Phys. Rev.* **100**, 703–722 (1955).

859. C. C. Lin, New method for the calculation of Stark effect in microwave spectra, *Bull. Am. Phys. Soc.* [2] **1**, 13 (1956).

860. G. Birnbaum, Nonresonant absorption of symmetric top molecules. Shape of the non-resonant spectra, *J. Chem. Phys.* **27**, 360–368 (1957). Errata—*J. Chem. Phys.* **28**, 992 (1958).

861. D. Kivelson, Theory of internal overall-rotational interactions IV. Stark effect in nonrigid internal rotors, *J. Chem. Phys.* **26**, 215–216 (1957).

862. S. A. Marshall and J. Weber, Microwave Stark effect measurement of the dipole moment and polarizability of carbonyl sulfide, *Phys. Rev.* **105**, 1502–1506 (1957).

863. A. A. Maryott and S. J. Kryder, Dipole moment of perchloryl fluoride, *J. Chem. Phys.* **27**, 1221–1222 (1957).

864. M. Peter and M. W. P. Strandberg, High field Stark effect in linear rotors, *J. Chem. Phys.* **26**, 1657–1659 (1957).

865. C. A. Burrus, Stark effect from 1.1 to 2.6 millimeters wavelength-PH$_3$, PD$_3$, DI, and CO, *J. Chem. Phys.* **28**, 427–429 (1958).

866. C. A. Burrus and J. D. Graybeal, Stark effect at 2.0 and 1.2 millimeters—nitric oxide, *Phys. Rev.* **109**, 1553–1556 (1958).

867. E. A. Halevi, Polarity differences between deuterated and normal molecules, *Trans. Faraday Soc.* **54**, 1441–1446 (1958).

868. M. Mizushima, Theory of the Stark effect of the NO molecule, *Phys. Rev.* **109**, 1557–1559 (1958).

869. E. L. Beeson, J. Q. Williams, and T. L. Weatherly, Stark effect for near-degenerate rotational levels of NOCl, *Bull. Am. Phys. Soc.* [2] **4**, 291 (1959).

870. C. A. Burrus, Stark effect at 0.93-, 1.18-, and 1.5-millimeter wavelength—DCl, DBr, and DI, *J. Chem. Phys.* **31**, 1270–1272 (1959).

871. H. Dreizler and H. D. Rudolph, Stark effect of the microwave absorption line of methanol at 19967.3 Mc, *Z. Naturforsch.* **14A**, 758 (1959).

872. D. F. Eagle, T. L. Weatherly, and J. Q. Williams, Theory of the Stark effect and hyperfine structure for near-degenerate energy levels of an asymmetric rotor, *Bull. Am. Phys. Soc.* [2] **4**, 291 (1959).

873. D. F. Eagle, T. L. Weatherly, and Q. Williams, Stark effect in the microwave spectrum of nitrosyl bromide, *J. Chem. Phys.* **30**, 603–604 (1959).

874. A. A. Maryott and S. J. Kryder, Nonresonant microwave absorption and electric dipole moment of NO in the gaseous state, *J. Chem. Phys.* **31**, 617–621 (1959).

875. E. B. Wilson, Jr., Conditions required for nonresonant absorption in asymmetric rotor molecules, *J. Phys. Chem.* **63**, 1339–1340 (1959).

876. B. N. Bhattacharya and W. Gordy, Observation of σ-Stark components in microwave spectroscopy-precision measurements on HCN, *Phys. Rev.* **119**, 144–149 (1960).

877. H. Dreizler and H. D. Rudolph, A special Stark effect of a K doublet in the microwave spectrum of methanol, *Z. Naturforsch.* **15A**, 1013–1014 (1960).

878. P. Favero and J. G. Baker, Anomalous Stark effects in the millimeter wave spectrum of formyl fluoride, *Nuovo Cimento* **17**, 734–739 (1960).
879. K. Kondo and T. Oka, Stark–Zeeman effect on asymmetric top molecules. HCHO, *J. Phys. Soc. Japan* **15**, 307–314 (1960).
880. G. H. Kwei and D. R. Herschbach, Stark effect and dipole moment of CH_3CHF_2, *J. Chem. Phys.* **32**, 1270–1271 (1960).
881. D. R. Lide, Jr., Structure of isobutane molecule-change of dipole moment on isotopic substitution, *J. Chem. Phys.* **33**, 1519–1522 (1960).
882. H. B. Thompson, The electric moments of molecules with symmetric rotational barriers, *J. Phys. Chem.* **64**, 280–281 (1960).
883. L. Wharton, L. P. Gold, and W. Klemperer, Dipole moment of lithium hydride, *J. Chem. Phys.* **33**, 1255 (1960).
884. R. T. Meyer and R. J. Myers, Dipole moment of the OH radical from the Stark effect of its microwave spectrum, *J. Chem. Phys.* **34**, 1074–1075 (1961).
885. H. A. Dijkerman and A. Dymanus, σ-Stark effect of rotational transitions II. Microwave spectrum of methyl alcohol, *Physica* **28**, 977–992 (1962).
886. J. A. Howe and W. H. Flygare, Strong field Stark effect, *J. Chem. Phys.* **36**, 650–652 (1962).
887. H. Kim, R. Keller, and W. D. Gwinn, Dipole moment of formic acid, HCOOH, HCOOD, *J. Chem. Phys.* **37**, 2748–2750 (1962).
888. W. M. Tolles, J. L. Kinsey, R. F. Curl, and R. F. Heidelberg, Microwave spectrum of chlorine dioxide V. Stark and Zeeman effects, *J. Chem. Phys.* **37**, 927–930 (1962).
889. D. M. Larkin and W. Gordy, Stark effect and dipole moment of methyl fluoride, *J. Chem. Phys.* **38**, 2329–2333 (1963).
890. J. H. Shirley, Stark energy levels of symmetric-top molecules, *J. Chem. Phys.* **38**, 2896–2913 (1963).
891. B. G. West and M. Mizushima, Strong-field Stark effect of asymmetric-top rotator, *J. Chem. Phys.* **38**, 251–252 (1963).
892. J. S. Muenter and V. W. Laurie, Isotope effects on molecular dipole moments. Microwave spectrum of monodeuteroacetylene. *Mol. Spectry. Symp., Columbus, Ohio, June 1964,* Navy Publications and Printing Office, 1965.
893. J. H. Choi and D. W. Smith, Lower bounds to energy eigenvalues for the Stark effect in a rigid rotor, *J. Chem. Phys.* **43**, S189–S193 (1965).
894. K. R. Lindfors and C. D. Cornwell, Rate-of-growth technique for the measurement of molecular dipole moments from microwave spectra at weak modulation fields, *J. Chem. Phys.* **42**, 149–155 (1965).
895. A. A. Maryott, S. J. Kryder, and R. R. Holmes, Dipole moment of PCl_4F from the non-resonant microwave absorption of the vapor, *J. Chem. Phys.* **43**, 2556–2557 (1965).
896. D. F. Eagle, T. L. Weatherly, and Q. Williams, Stark effect and hyperfine splitting for near-degenerate levels of an asymmetric rotor. Application to NO_2Cl and NOBr, *J. Chem. Phys.* **44**, 847–852 (1966).

XI. Electronic and Magnetic Effects (Zeeman Effect)

897. E. L. Hill, On the Zeeman effect in doublet band spectra, *Phys. Rev.* **34**, 1507–1516 (1929).
898. J. H. Van Vleck, On σ-type doubling and electron spin in the spectra of diatomic molecules, *Phys. Rev.* **33**, 467–506 (1929).
899. R. S. Mulliken and A. Christy, Λ-type doubling and electron configurations in diatomic molecules, *Phys. Rev.* **38**, 87–119 (1931).

900. F. H. Crawford, Zeeman effect in diatomic molecular spectra, *Rev. Mod. Phys.* **6**, 90–117 (1934).
901. R. Renner, Interaction of electronic and nuclear motions in triatomic rod-shaped molecules, *Z. Physik* **92**, 172–193 (1934).
902. R. Schmid, A. Budo, and J. Zemplen, Zeeman effect of atmospheric oxygen bands, *Z. Physik* **103**, 250–262 (1936).
903. H. M. Foley, Second-order magnetic perturbations in nuclear quadrupole spectra and the pseudo-quadrupole effect in diatomic molecules, *Phys. Rev.* **72**, 504–505 (1947).
904. C. K. Jen, Microwave spectra and Zeeman effect in a resonant cavity absorption cell, *Phys. Rev.* **72**, 986 (1947).
905. R. S. Henderson and J. H. Van Vleck, Coupling of electron spins in rotating polyatomic molecules, *Phys. Rev.* **74**, 106–107 (1948).
906. J. M. Jauch, Spin-orbit effect in the hyperfine structure of the ammonia inversion spectrum, *Phys. Rev.* **74**, 1262 (1948).
907. C. K. Jen, The Zeeman effect in microwave molecular spectra, *Phys. Rev.* **74**, 1396–1406 (1948).
908. G. C. Wick, On the magnetic field of a rotating molecule, *Phys. Rev.* **73**, 51–57 (1948).
909. R. Beringer and J. G. Castle, Jr., Microwave magnetic resonance absorption in oxygen, *Phys. Rev.* **75**, 1963 (1949).
910. R. Beringer and J. G. Castle, Jr., Microwave magnetic resonance absorption in nitric oxide, *Phys. Rev.* **76**, 868 (1949).
911. W. Gordy, O. R. Gilliam, and R. Livingston, Nuclear magnetic moments from microwave spectra—I^{127} and I^{129}, *Phys. Rev.* **76**, 443–444 (1949).
912. C. K. Jen, Rotational magnetic moments for H_2O and HDO, *Phys. Rev.* **76**, 471 (1949).
913. R. Beringer and J. G. Castle, Jr., Magnetic resonance absorption in nitric oxide, *Phys. Rev.* **78**, 581–586 (1950).
914. J. H. Burkhalter, R. S. Anderson, W. V. Smith, and W. Gordy, The fine structure of the microwave absorption spectrum of oxygen, *Phys. Rev.* **79**, 651–655 (1950).
915. J. G. Castle, Jr. and R. Beringer, Microwave magnetic resonance absorption in nitrogen dioxide, *Phys. Rev.* **80**, 114–115 (1950).
916. A. F. Henry, The Zeeman effect in oxygen, *Phys. Rev.* **80**, 396–401 (1950).
917. A. F. Henry, Hyperfine structure of Zeeman levels in nitric oxide, *Phys. Rev.* **80**, 549–552 (1950).
918. H. Margenau and A. Henry, Theory of magnetic resonance in nitric oxide, *Phys. Rev.* **78**, 587–592 (1950).
919. K. B. McAfee, Jr., Magnetic electron spin-nuclear spin interaction in the rotational spectrum of NO_2, *Phys. Rev.* **78**, 340 (1950).
920. N. F. Ramsey, Magnetic shielding of nuclei in molecules, *Phys. Rev.* **78**, 699–703 (1950).
921. R. S. Anderson, C. M. Johnson, and W. Gordy, Resonant absorption of oxygen at 2.5-millimeter wavelength, *Phys. Rev.* **83**, 1061–1062 (1951).
922. W. E. Good, D. K. Coles, G. R. Gunther-Mohr, A. L. Schawlow, and C. H. Townes, A new type of hyperfine structure in the NH_3 microwave spectrum, *Phys. Rev.* **83**, 880 (1951).
923. C. K. Jen, Rotational magnetic moments in polyatomic molecules, *Phys. Rev.* **81**, 197–203 (1951).
924. K. Shimoda and T. Nishikawa, The hyperfine structure of sodium by a microwave absorption method, *J. Phys. Soc. Japan* **6**, 512–516 (1951).
925. J. H. Van Vleck, Theory of the hyperfine splitting of the levels $K = 1$ in NH_3, *Phys. Rev.* **83**, 880 (1951).

926. J. H. Van Vleck, The coupling of angular momentum vectors in molecules, *Rev. Mod. Phys.* **23**, 213–227 (1951).

927. R. Beringer, Microwave resonance absorption in paramagnetic gases, *Ann. N.Y. Acad. Sci.* **55**, 814–821 (1952).

928. R. Beringer and E. B. Rawson, Lambda-doubling in a microwave spectrum of nitric oxide, *Phys. Rev.* **86**, 607 (1952).

929. J. R. Eshbach, R. E. Hillger, and M. W. P. Strandberg, The nuclear magnetic moment of S^{33} from microwave spectroscopy, *Phys. Rev.* **85**, 532–539 (1952).

930. J. R. Eshbach and M. W. P. Strandberg, Rotational magnetic moments of $^1\Sigma$ molecules, *Phys. Rev.* **85**, 24–34 (1952).

931. R. A. Frosch and H. M. Foley, Magnetic hyperfine structure in diatomic molecules, *Phys. Rev.* **88**, 1337–1349 (1952).

932. C. K. Jen, Molecular and nuclear magnetic moments, *Ann. N.Y. Acad. Sci.* **55**, 822–830 (1952).

933. C. K. Jen, J. W. B. Borghausen, and R. W. Stanley, Sign determination for molecular magnetic moments, *Phys. Rev.* **85**, 717 (1952).

934. R. Sternheimer, Effect of the atomic core on the magnetic hyperfine structure, *Phys. Rev.* **86**, 316–324 (1952).

935. B. F. Burke and M. W. P. Strandberg, Zeeman effect in rotational spectra of asymmetric rotor molecules, *Phys. Rev.* **90**, 303–308 (1953).

936. J. T. Cox, P. B. Peyton, Jr., and W. Gordy, Zeeman effect in the microwave spectra of methyl fluoride and methyl acetylene, *Phys. Rev.* **91**, 222 (1953).

937. S. L. Miller and C. H. Townes, The microwave absorption spectrum of O_2^{16} and $O^{16}O^{17}$, *Phys. Rev.* **90**, 537–541 (1953).

938. S. L. Miller, C. H. Townes, and M. Kotani, The electronic structure of O_2. *Phys. Rev.* **90**, 542–543 (1953).

939. N. F. Ramsey, Electron coupled interactions between nuclear spins in molecules, *Phys. Rev.* **91**, 303–307 (1953).

940. T. M. Sanders, A. L. Schawlow, G. C. Dousmanis, and C. H. Townes, A microwave spectrum of the free OH radical, *Phys. Rev.* **89**, 1158–1159 (1953).

941. J. O. Artman and J. P. Gordon, Absorption of microwaves by oxygen in the millimeter wavelength region, *Phys. Rev.* **96**, 1237–1245 (1954).

942. B. F. Burke, M. W. P. Strandberg, V. W. Cohen, and W. S. Koski, The nuclear magnetic moment of S^{35} by microwave spectroscopy, *Phys. Rev.* **93**, 193–194 (1954).

943. G. C. Dousmanis, Microwave spectrum of the free OD radical, *Phys. Rev.* **94**, 789 (1954).

944. J. P. Gordon, H. J. Zeiger, and C. H. Townes, Molecular microwave oscillator and new hyperfine structure in the microwave spectrum of NH_3, *Phys. Rev.* **95**, 282–284 (1954).

945. G. R. Gunther-Mohr, C. H. Townes, and J. H. Van Vleck, Hyperfine structure in the spectrum of $N^{14}H_3$ I. Theoretical Discussion, *Phys. Rev.* **94**, 1191–1203 (1954).

946. M. Mizushima, Theory of the hyperfine structure of NO molecule, *Phys. Rev.* **94**, 569–574 (1954).

947. M. Mizushima and R. M. Hill, Microwave spectrum of O_2, *Phys. Rev.* **93**, 745–748 (1954).

948. G. C. Dousmanis, T. M. Sanders, and C. H. Townes, Microwave spectra of the free radicals OH and OD, *Phys. Rev.* **100**, 1735–1754 (1955).

949. C. C. Lin, Theory of the fine structure of the microwave spectrum of NO_2, *Phys. Rev.* **99**, 666–667 (1955).

950. M. Mizushima, J. T. Cox, and W. Gordy, Zeeman effect in the rotational spectrum of nitric oxide, *Phys. Rev.* **98**, 1034–1038 (1955).

951. M. Tinkham and M. W. P. Strandberg, Theory of the fine structure of the molecular oxygen ground state, *Phys. Rev.* **97**, 937–951 (1955).

952. Y. Torizuka, Y. Kojima, T. Okamura, and K. Kamiryo, The Zeeman effect in ammonia microwave spectra, *J. Phys. Soc. Japan* **10**, 417–420 (1955).

953. R. L. White, Magnetic hyperfine structure due to rotation in $^1\Sigma$ molecules, *Rev. Mod. Phys.* **27**, 276–288 (1955).

954. J. T. Cox and W. Gordy, Zeeman effect of some linear and symmetric top molecules, *Phys. Rev.* **101**, 1298–1300 (1956).

955. J. J. Gallagher and C. M. Johnson, Uncoupling effects in the microwave spectrum of nitric oxide, *Phys. Rev.* **103**, 1727–1737 (1956).

956. A. Okaya, Theoretical analysis of the magnetic hyperfine structure of the microwave spectrum of C_{2v} molecules, *J. Phys. Soc. Japan* **11**, 249–258 (1956).

957. G. F. Hadley, Theoretical study of the hyperfine structure in inversion spectra of the deuteroammonias, *J. Chem. Phys.* **26**, 1482–1495 (1957).

958. G. F. Hadley, $J = 3$, $K = 2$ line in the inversion spectrum of $N^{14}H_3$, *Phys. Rev.* **108**, 291–293 (1957).

959. F. R. Innes, Microwave Zeeman effect and theory of complex spectra, *Phys. Rev.* **111**, 194–202 (1958).

960. D. W. Posener, Coupling of nuclear spins in molecules, *Australian J. Phys.* **11**, 1–17 (1958).

961. B. Rosenblum, A. H. Nethercot, Jr., and C. H. Townes, Isotopic mass ratios, magnetic moments, and the sign of the electric dipole moment in carbon monoxide, *Phys. Rev.* **109**, 400–412 (1958).

962. J. C. Baird and G. R. Bird, Magnetic hyperfine structure in the rotational spectrum of nitrogen dioxide, *Bull. Am. Phys. Soc.* [2] **4**, 68 (1959).

963. J. G. Baker, Hyperfine structure in the rotational spectra of free radicals, *Bull. Am. Phys. Soc.* [2] **4**, 290 (1959).

964. C. A. Burrus, Zeeman effect in the 1- to 3-millimeter wave region—Molecular g factors of several light molecules, *J. Chem. Phys.* **30**, 976–983 (1959).

965. G. Ehrenstein, C. H. Townes, and M. J. Stevenson, Ground state lambda doubling transitions of OH radical, *Phys. Rev. Letters* **3**, 40–41 (1959).

966. P. Favero, A. M. Mirri, and W. Gordy, Millimeter-wave rotational spectrum of nitric oxide in the $^2\Pi_{3/2}$ state, *Phys. Rev.* **114**, 1534–1537 (1959).

967. C. C. Lin, Theory of the fine structure of the microwave spectrum of nitrogen dioxide, *Phys. Rev.* **116**, 903–910 (1959).

968. D. W. Posener, Contributions of high-resolution microwave spectroscopy to the electronic structure of the water molecule, *Spectrochim. Acta* **15**, 783 (1959).

969. H. E. Radford and V. W. Hughes, Microwave Zeeman spectrum of atomic oxygen, *Phys. Rev.* **114**, 1274–1279 (1959).

970. H. Takuma, T. Shimizu, and K. Shimoda, Magnetic hyperfine spectrum of H_2CO by a maser, *J. Phys. Soc. Japan* **14**, 1595–1599 (1959).

971. P. Thaddeus and J. Loubser, Beam maser spectroscopy on HDO, *Nuovo Cimento* **13**, 1060–1064 (1959).

972. P. Thaddeus, J. Loubser, L. Krisher, and H. Lecar, Beam maser spectroscopy on formaldehyde, *J. Chem. Phys.* **31**, 1677–1678 (1959).

973. K. Kondo, H. Hirakawa, A. Miyahara, T. Oka, and K. Shimoda, Microwave Zeeman effect of HCHO, *J. Phys. Soc. Japan* **15**, 303–306 (1960).

974. B. D. Osipov, *I-J* interaction in the methyl iodide molecule, *Opt. i Spektroskopiya* **8**, 581–582 (1960).

975. D. W. Posener, Hyperfine structure in the microwave spectrum of water II. Effects of magnetic interactions, *Australian J. Phys.* **13**, 168–185 (1960).

976. M. S. Child and H. C. Longuet-Higgins, Studies of the Jahn–Teller effect III. The rotational and vibrational spectra of symmetric-top molecules in electronically degenerate states, *Phil. Trans. Roy. Soc. London Ser. A.* **254**, 259–294 (1961).

977. R. F. Curl, Jr. and J. L. Kinsey, Calculation of interaction matrix elements for asymmetric rotors with resultant electronic spin and nuclear spin, *J. Chem. Phys.* **35**, 1758–1765 (1961).

978. H. E. Radford, Microwave Zeeman effect of free hydroxyl radicals, *Phys. Rev.* **122**, 114–130 (1961).

979. H. Takuma, Magnetic hyperfine structure in the rotational spectrum of H_2CO, *J. Phys. Soc. Japan* **16**, 309–317 (1961).

980. A. Guarnieri, P. Favero, A. M. Mirri, and G. Semerano, The Zeeman effect of formyl fluoride in the millimeter waves region, *Boll. Sci. Fac. Chim. Ind. Bologna* **20**, 105–109 (1962).

981. H. E. Radford, Microwave Zeeman effect of free hydroxyl radicals, *Phys. Rev.* **126**, 1035–1045 (1962).

982. E. B. Treacy and Y. Beers, Hyperfine structure of the rotational spectrum of HDO, *J. Chem. Phys.* **36**, 1473–1480 (1962).

983. G. Ehrenstein, Hyperfine structure in $O^{17}H$ and the OH dipole moment, *Phys. Rev.* **130**, 669–674 (1963).

984. L. Pierce and N. DiCianni, Spin-rotational hyperfine structure in the microwave spectrum of oxygen difluoride, *J. Chem. Phys.* **38**, 2029–2030 (1963).

985. G. R. Bird, J. C. Baird, A. W. Jache, J. A. Hodgeson, R. F. Curl, Jr., A. C. Kunkle, J. W. Bransford, J. Rastrup-Andersen, and J. Rosenthal, Microwave spectrum of NO_2—Fine structure and magnetic coupling, *J. Chem. Phys.* **40**, 3378–3390 (1964).

986. S. I. Chan, D. Ikenberry, and T. P. Das, Remarks on the determination of electric dipole moments from rotational magnetic moments. The dipole moment of hydrogen fluoride, *J. Chem. Phys.* **41**, 2107–2110 (1964).

987. Y. Chiu, Rotation-electronic interaction in the Rydberg states of diatomic molecules, *J. Chem. Phys.* **41**, 3235–3249 (1964).

988. K. M. Evenson, J. L. Dunn, and H. P. Broida, Optical detection of microwave transitions between excited electronic states of CN and the identification of the transitions involved, *Phys. Rev.* **136**, 1566–1571 (1964).

989. F. X. Powell and D. R. Lide, Jr., Microwave spectrum of the SO radical, *J. Chem. Phys.* **41**, 1413–1419 (1964).

990. H. E. Radford, Hyperfine structure of the $B^2\Sigma^+$ state of CN, *Phys. Rev.* **136**, 1571–1575 (1964).

991. W. T. Raynes, Spin splittings and rotational structures of nonlinear molecules in doublet and triplet electronic states, *J. Chem. Phys.* **41**, 3020–3032 (1964).

992. P. Thaddeus, L. C. Krisher, and P. Cahill, Hyperfine structure in the microwave spectrum of NH_2D, *J. Chem. Phys.* **41**, 1542–1547 (1964).

993. P. Thaddeus, L. C. Krisher, and J. H. N. Loubser, Hyperfine structure in the microwave spectrum of HDO, HDS, CH_2C, and CHDO—Beam-maser spectroscopy on asymmetric-top molecules, *J. Chem. Phys.* **40**, 257–273 (1964).

XII. General Microwave Papers and Related Topics

994. H. A. Kramers, Wave mechanics and seminumerical quantization, *Z. Physik* **39**, 828–840 (1926).

995. M. Born and J. R. Oppenheimer, Quantum theory of molecules, *Ann. Physik* **4-84**, 457–484 (1927).

996. B. Podolsky, Quantum-mechanically correct form of Hamiltonian function for conservative systems, *Phys. Rev.* **32**, 812–816 (1928).

997. P. M. Morse, Diatomic molecules according to the wave mechanics II. Vibrational levels, *Phys. Rev.* **34**, 57–64 (1929).

998. C. Eckart, The application of group theory to the quantum dynamics of monatomic systems, *Rev. Mod. Phys.* **2**, 305–380 (1930).

999. R. S. Mulliken, The interpretation of band spectra Pts. I, IIA, IIB, *Rev. Mod. Phys.* **2**, 60–115 (1930).

1000. D. M. Dennison, The infrared spectra of polyatomic molecules. Pt. I, *Rev. Mod. Phys.* **3**, 280–345 (1931).

1001. E. Fermi, On the Raman effect in carbon dioxide, *Z. Physik* **71**, 250–259 (1931).

1002. R. S. Mulliken, The interpretation of band spectra. Pt. IIC. Empirical band types, *Rev. Mod. Phys.* **3**, 89–155 (1931).

1003. E. Wigner, "Group Theory and Its Application to the Quantum Mechanics of Atomic Spectra." Vieweg, Brunswick, Germany, 1931.

1004. H. Eyring, Steric hinderance and collision diameters, *J. Am. Chem. Soc.* **54**, 3191–3203 (1932).

1005. R. de L. Kronig, Note on the determination of isotopic masses from band spectra, *Physica* **1**, 617–622 (1933).

1006. G. Placzek and E. Teller, Rotation structure of the Raman bands of polyatomic molecules, *Z. Physik* **81**, 209–258 (1933).

1007. N. Wright and H. M. Randall, The far infrared absorption spectra of ammonia and phosphine gases under high resolving power, *Phys. Rev.* **44**, 391–398 (1933).

1008. C. E. Cleeton and N. H. Williams, Electromagnetic waves of 1.1 cm wavelength and the absorption spectrum of ammonia, *Phys. Rev.* **45**, 234–237 (1934).

1009. G. H. Dieke and G. B. Kistiakowsky, The structure of the ultraviolet absorption spectrum of formaldehyde I, *Phys. Rev.* **45**, 4–28 (1934).

1010. C. Eckart, The kinetic energy of polyatomic molecules, *Phys. Rev.* **46**, 383–387 (1934).

1011. G. Herzberg, F. Patat, and J. W. T. Spinks, Rotation vibration spectra of molecules containing deuterium. Pt. I. Spectrum of C_2HD and the $C—C$ and $C—H$ distances in acetylene, *Z. Physik* **92**, 87–99 (1934).

1012. O. M. Jordahl, The effect of crystalline electric fields on the paramagnetic susceptibility of cupric salts, *Phys. Rev.* **45**, 87–97 (1934).

1013. C. L. Pekeris, The rotation-vibration coupling in diatomic molecules, *Phys. Rev.* **45**, 98–103 (1934).

1014. P. F. Bartunek and E. F. Barker, The infrared absorption spectra of the linear molecules carbonyl sulfide and deuterium cyanide, *Phys. Rev.* **48**, 516–521 (1935).

1015. F. H. Crawford and T. Jorgensen, Jr., The band spectra of the hydrides of lithium. Pt. I. Li^7D, *Phys. Rev.* **47**, 358–366 (1935).

1016. F. H. Crawford and T. Jorgensen, Jr., The band spectra of the hydrides of lithium, *Phys. Rev.* **47**, 932–941 (1935).

1017. C. Eckart, Some studies concerning rotating axes and polyatomic molecules, *Phys. Rev.* **47**, 552–558 (1935).

1018. L. Pauling and E. B. Wilson, Jr., "Introduction to Quantum Mechanics." McGraw-Hill, New York, 1935.

1019. J. H. Van Vleck, The rotational energy of polyatomic molecules, *Phys. Rev.* **47**, 487–494 (1935).

1020. E. B. Wilson, Jr., The statistical weights of the rotational levels of polyatomic molecules, including methane, ammonia, benzene, cyclopropane, and ethylene, *J. Chem. Phys.* **3**, 276–285 (1935).

1021. E. B. Wilson, Jr., Symmetry considerations concerning the splitting of vibration-rotation levels in polyatomic molecules, *J. Chem. Phys.* **3**, 818–821 (1935).

1022. F. H. Crawford and T. Jorgensen, Jr., The band spectra of the hydrides of lithium. Pt. III. Potential curves and isotope relations, *Phys. Rev.* **49**, 745–752 (1936).

1023. C. Gilbert, The theory of the band spectra of PH and NH, *Phys. Rev.* **49**, 619–624 (1936).
1024. J. H. Van Vleck, On the isotope corrections in molecular spectra, *J. Chem. Phys.* **4**, 327–338 (1936).
1025. A. Budo, Rotational structure of $^4\Sigma \rightarrow {}^4\Pi$ bands, *Z. Physik* **105**, 73–80 (1937).
1026. B. L. Crawford and P. C. Cross, Elements of the factored secular equation for the semi-rigid water type rotator with application to the hydrogen sulfide band at 10,000 Å, *J. Chem. Phys.* **5**, 621–625 (1937).
1027. J. B. Howard, The normal vibrations and the vibrational spectrum of C_2H_6, *J. Chem. Phys.* **5**, 442–450 (1937).
1028. E. C. Kemble, "Fundamental Principles of Quantum Mechanics." McGraw-Hill, New York, 1937.
1029. T. E. Nevin, Rotational analysis of the visible O_2^+ bands, *Nature* **140**, 1101 (1937).
1030. T. E. Nevin, Rotational analysis of the first negative band spectrum of oxygen, *Phil. Trans. Roy. Soc. London Ser. A.* **237**, 471–507 (1938).
1031. E. B. Wilson, Jr., Nuclear spin and symmetry effects in the heat capacity of ethane gas, *J. Chem. Phys.* **6**, 740–745 (1938).
1032. H. Margenau, Van der Waals forces, *Rev. Mod. Phys.* **11**, 1–35 (1939).
1033. T. Y. Wu, "Vibrational Spectra and Structure of Polyatomic Molecules." National Univ. of Peking, Kun-Ming, China, 1939.
1034. B. T. Darling and D. M. Dennison, The water vapor molecule, *Phys. Rev.* **57**, 128–139 (1940).
1035. D. M. Dennison, Infra-red spectra of polyatomic molecules. Pt. II, *Rev. Mod. Phys.* **12**, 175–214 (1940).
1036. I. Sandeman, Energy levels of a rotating vibrator, *Proc. Roy. Soc. Edinburgh* **A60**, 210–233 (1940).
1037. E. B. Wilson, Jr., The present status of the statistical method of calculating thermodynamic functions, *Chem. Rev.* **27**, 17–38 (1940).
1038. H. M. Hulbert and J. O. Hirschfelder, Potential energy functions for diatomic molecules, *J. Chem. Phys.* **9**, 61–69 (1941).
1039. V. Schomaker and D. P. Stevenson, Some revisions of the covalent radii and the additivity rule for the lengths of partially ionic single covalent bonds, *J. Am. Chem. Soc.* **63**, 37–40 (1941).
1040. H. Eyring, J. Walter, and G. E. Kimball, "Quantum Chemistry." Wiley, New York, 1944.
1041. G. E. Becker and S. H. Autler, Water vapor absorption of electromagnetic radiation in the centimeter wavelength range, *Phys. Rev.* **70**, 300–307, (1946).
1042. R. Beringer, The absorption of one-half centimeter electromagnetic waves in oxygen, *Phys. Rev.* **70**, 53–57 (1946).
1043. B. Bleaney and R. P. Penrose, Ammonia spectrum in the 1 cm wavelength region, *Nature* **157**, 339–340 (1946).
1044. D. K. Coles and W. E. Good, Stark and Zeeman effects in the inversion spectrum of ammonia, *Phys. Rev.* **70**, 979 (1946).
1045. D. ter Haar, The vibrational levels of an anharmonic oscillator, *Phys. Rev.* **70**, 222–223 (1946).
1046. L. N. Hadley and D. M. Dennison, The microwave spectrum of ammonia, *Phys. Rev.* **70**, 780–781 (1946).
1047. W. D. Herschberger, The absorption of microwaves by gases, *J. Appl. Phys.* **17**, 495–500 (1946).
1048. C. I. Beard and B. P. Dailey, Microwave spectrum and structure of isothiocyanic acid, *J. Chem. Phys.* **15**, 762 (1947).

1049. D. K. Coles, E. S. Elyash, and J. G. Gorman, Microwave absorption spectra of N_2O, *Phys. Rev.* **72**, 973 (1947).

1050. B. P. Dailey, S. Golden, and E. B. Wilson, Jr., Preliminary analysis of the microwave spectrum of SO_2, *Phys. Rev.* **72**, 871–872 (1947).

1051. B. P. Dailey and E. B. Wilson, Jr., Microwave spectra of several polyatomic molecules, *Phys. Rev.* **72**, 522 (1947).

1052. T. W. Dakin, W. E. Good, and D. K. Coles, Bond distances in OCS from microwave absorption lines, *Phys. Rev.* **71**, 640–641 (1947).

1053. W. E. Good and D. K. Coles, Microwave absorption frequencies of $N^{14}H_3$ and $N^{15}H_3$, *Phys. Rev.* **71**, 383–384 (1947).

1054. W. E. Good and D. K. Coles, Precision frequency measurements of microwave absorption lines and their fine structure, *Phys. Rev.* **72**, 157 (1947).

1055. W. Gordy and M. Kessler, Microwave spectra—The hyperfine structure of ammonia, *Phys. Rev.* **71**, 640 (1947).

1056. W. Gordy, J. W. Simmons, and A. G. Smith, Nuclear and molecular constants from microwave spectra—methyl chloride and methyl bromide, *Phys. Rev.* **72**, 344–345 (1947).

1057. W. Gordy, A. G. Smith, and J. W. Simmons, Microwave spectra—methyl iodide, *Phys. Rev.* **71**, 917 (1947).

1058. W. Gordy, A. G. Smith, and J. W. Simmons, Analysis of the hyperfine structure in the microwave spectrum of the symmetric top molecule CH_3I, *Phys. Rev.* **72**, 249–250 (1947).

1059. W. Gordy, W. V. Smith, A. G. Smith, and H. Ring, Millimeter-wave spectra hyperfine structure of BrCN and ICN, *Phys. Rev.* **72**, 259–260 (1947).

1060. W. D. Herschberger and J. Turkevich, Absorption of methyl alcohol and methylamine for 1.25-cm waves, *Phys. Rev.* **71**, 554 (1947).

1061. R. E. Hillger, M. W. P. Strandberg, T. Wentink, and R. Kyhl, The microwave absorption spectrum of carbonyl sulfide, *Phys. Rev.* **72**, 157 (1947).

1062. G. W. King and R. M. Hainer, Interpretation of the microwave absorption of HDO at 1.3 centimeters, *Phys. Rev.* **71**, 135 (1947).

1063. G. W. King, R. M. Hainer, and P. C. Cross, Expected microwave absorption coefficients of water and related molecules, *Phys. Rev.* **71**, 433–443 (1947).

1064. H. Ring, H. Edwards, M. Kessler, and W. Gordy, Microwave spectra-methyl cyanide and methyl isocyanide, *Phys. Rev.* **72**, 1262–1263 (1947).

1065. W. V. Smith and R. L. Carter, Saturation effect in microwave spectrum of ammonia, *Phys. Rev.* **72**, 638–639 (1947).

1066. C. H. Townes, A. N. Holden, and F. R. Merritt, Rotational spectra of some linear molecules near 1-cm wavelength, *Phys. Rev.* **71**, 64 (1947).

1067. C. H. Townes, A. N. Holden, and F. R. Merritt, Microwave spectra of linear molecules, *Phys. Rev.* **72**, 513–514 (1947).

1068. R. T. Weidner, The microwave spectrum of iodine monochloride at 4.5 centimeters wavelength, *Phys. Rev.* **72**, 1268–1269 (1947).

1069. D. Williams, Further work on satellites in the microwave spectrum of ammonia, *Phys. Rev.* **72**, 974 (1947).

1070. G. L. Cunningham, W. I. LeVan, and W. D. Gwinn, The rotational spectrum of ethylene oxide, *Phys. Rev.* **74**, 1537 (1948).

1071. B. P. Dailey, K. Rusinow, R. G. Shulman, and C. H. Townes, Pure rotational spectrum of AsF_3, *Phys. Rev.* **74**, 1245–1246 (1948).

1072. W. F. Edgell and A. Roberts, The moment of inertia of CF_3CH_3, *J. Chem. Phys.* **16**, 1002 (1948).

1073. A. Fletcher, G. W. King punched card methods in analyzing infra-red spectra, *Math. Tables and Other Aids to Computation* **3**, 27–29 (1948).

1074. O. R. Gilliam, H. D. Edwards, and W. Gordy, Anomalies in the hyperfine structure of CH_3I and ICN, *Phys. Rev.* **73**, 635–636 (1948).

1075. W. Gordy, J. W. Simmons, and A. G. Smith, Microwave determination of the molecular structures and nuclear couplings of the methyl halides, *Phys. Rev.* **74**, 243–249 (1948).

1076. R. S. Henderson, On the fine structure in the inversion spectrum of ammonia, *Phys. Rev.* **74**, 107 (1948). Erratum—*Phys. Rev.* **74**, 626 (1948).

1077. M. Kessler and W. Gordy, Methods in microwave spectroscopy, *Phys. Rev.* **74**, 123 (1948).

1078. M. Mizushima, On the ammonia molecule, *Phys. Rev.* **74**, 705–706 (1948).

1079. A. Roberts, Rotational spectrum of $OC^{14}S$ and the nuclear spin of C^{14}, *Phys. Rev.* **73**, 1405 (1948).

1080. A. H. Sharbaugh, Microwave determination of the molecular structure of chlorosilane, *Phys. Rev.* **74**, 1870 (1948).

1081. R. G. Shulman, B. P. Dailey, and C. H. Townes, Preliminary analysis of the microwave spectrum of ethylene oxide, *Phys. Rev.* **74**, 846 (1948).

1082. H. A. Skinner, The geometry of CH_3X molecules, *J. Chem. Phys.* **16**, 553–554 (1948).

1083. A. G. Smith, H. Ring, W. V. Smith, and W. Gordy, Interatomic distances and nuclear quadrupole couplings in ClCN, BrCN, and ICN, *Phys. Rev.* **74**, 370–372 (1948).

1084. M. W. P. Strandberg, Microwave rotational absorption in D_2O, *Phys. Rev.* **74**, 1245 (1948).

1085. C. H. Townes, A. N. Holden, and F. R. Merritt, Microwave spectra of some linear XYZ molecules, *Phys. Rev.* **74**, 1113–1133 (1948).

1086. C. H. Townes, F. R. Merritt, and B. D. Wright, The pure rotational spectrum of ICl, *Phys. Rev.* **73**, 1334–1337 (1948).

1087. B. Bak, E. S. Knudsen, and E. Madsen, Microwave absorption of some organic vapors, *Phys. Rev.* **75**, 1622–1623 (1949).

1088. C. I. Beard and B. P. Dailey, The microwave spectra of CH_3NCS and CH_3SCN, *J. Am. Chem. Soc.* **71**, 929–936 (1949).

1089. D. Bianco, G. Matlack, and A. Roberts, Isotopic frequencies in the microwave spectra of OCS and CH_3Cl, *Phys. Rev.* **76**, 473 (1949).

1090. J. K. Bragg and A. H. Sharbaugh, Microwave spectrum of formaldehyde, *Phys. Rev.* **75**, 1774–1775 (1949).

1091. D. K. Coles and R. H. Hughes, Microwave spectra of nitrous oxide, *Phys. Rev.* **76**, 178 (1949).

1092. D. K. Coles and R. H. Hughes, Microwave spectrum of CF_3Cl, *Phys. Rev.* **76**, 858 (1949).

1093. G. L. Cunningham, A. W. Boyd, W. D. Gwinn, and W. I. LeVan, Structure of ethylene oxide, *J. Chem. Phys.* **17**, 211–212 (1949).

1094. B. P. Dailey, J. M. Mays, and C. H. Townes, Microwave rotational spectra and structures of GeH_3Cl, SiH_3Cl, and CH_3Cl, *Phys. Rev.* **76**, 136–137 (1949).

1095. H. D. Edwards, O. R. Gilliam, and W. Gordy, Microwave spectrum of methyl alcohol and of methyl amine, *Phys. Rev.* **76**, 196 (1949).

1096. D. A. Gilbert, A. Roberts, and P. A. Griswold, Nuclear and molecular information from the microwave spectrum of FCl, *Phys. Rev.* **76**, 1723 (1949).

1097. O. R. Gilliam, H. D. Edwards, and W. Gordy, Microwave investigations of methyl fluoride, fluoroform, and phosphorus tri-fluoride, *Phys. Rev.* **75**, 1014–1016 (1949).

1098. W. Low and C. H. Townes, O^{17} and S^{36} in the rotational spectrum of OCS, *Phys. Rev.* **75**, 529–530 (1949).

1099. M. Mizushima, On the ammonia molecule II, *J. Phys. Soc. Japan* **4**, 191–196 (1949).

1100. W. J. Pietenpol and J. D. Rogers, Microwave absorption spectrum of methylene bromide, *Phys. Rev.* **76**, 690–691 (1949).

1101. A. Roberts and W. F. Edgell, The microwave spectrum of $CF_2=CH_2$, *J. Chem. Phys.* **17**, 742–743 (1949).

1102. A. H. Sharbaugh, J. K. Bragg, T. C. Madison, and V. G. Thomas, The determination of the molecular structure of bromosilane by microwave measurements, *Phys. Rev.* **76**, 1412 (1949).

1103. A. H. Sharbaugh and J. Mattern, Microwave spectrum of methyl bromide, *Phys. Rev.* **75**, 1102 (1949).

1104. J. W. Simmons, The microwave spectra of CD_3Cl and CD_3I, *Phys. Rev.* **76**, 686 (1949).

1105. W. V. Smith and R. R. Unterberger, Microwave investigations of chloroform, *J. Chem. Phys.* **17**, 1348 (1949).

1106. M. W. P. Strandberg, Rotational absorption spectrum of HDO, *J. Chem. Phys.* **17**, 901–904 (1949).

1107. M. W. P. Strandberg, C. Y. Meng, and J. G. Ingersoll, The microwave absorption spectrum of oxygen, *Phys. Rev.* **75**, 1524–1528 (1949).

1108. M. W. P. Strandberg, C. S. Pearsall, and M. T. Weiss, On the electric dipole moment and vibration states of $H_3B^{10}CO$, *J. Chem. Phys.* **17**, 429 (1949).

1109. M. W. P. Strandberg, T. Wentink, Jr., and A. G. Hill, The microwave spectrum of carbonyl selenide, *Phys. Rev.* **75**, 827–832 (1949).

1110. M. W. P. Strandberg, T. Wentink, Jr., and R. L. Kyhl, Rotational absorption spectrum of OCS, *Phys. Rev.* **75**, 270–278 (1949).

1111. A. A. Westenberg, J. H. Goldstein, and E. B. Wilson, Jr., The microwave spectrum of chloroacetylene and deuterochloroacetylene, *J. Chem. Phys.* **17**, 1319–1321 (1949).

1112. E. Amble and B. P. Dailey, The structure and dipole moment of hydrazoic acid, *J. Chem. Phys.* **18**, 1422 (1950).

1113. B. Bak, E. S. Knudsen, E. Madsen, and J. Rastrup-Andersen, Preliminary analysis of the microwave spectrum of ketene, *Phys. Rev.* **79**, 190 (1950).

1114. B. Bak, R. Sloan, and D. Williams, Microwave investigation of SCSe, *Phys. Rev.* **80**, 101–102 (1950).

1115. C. I. Beard and B. P. Dailey, Structure and dipole moment of isothiocyanic acid, *J. Chem. Phys.* **18**, 1437–1441 (1950). Errata—*J. Chem. Phys.* **19**, 975 (1951).

1116. H. J. Bernstein, The structure of nitrosyl chloride from the microwave absorption spectrum, *J. Chem. Phys.* **18**, 1514 (1950).

1117. J. K. Bragg, T. C. Madison, and A. H. Sharbaugh, Microwave spectrum of CH_2CFCl, *Phys. Rev.* **77**, 148–149 (1950). Errata—*Phys. Rev.* **77**, 751 (1950).

1118. D. K. Coles, W. E. Good, and R. H. Hughes, Microwave spectrum of methyl cyanide and its isotopic modifications, *Phys. Rev.* **79**, 224 (1950).

1119. C. D. Cornwell, Microwave spectra of bromodiborane and vinyl bromide, *J. Chem. Phys.* **18**, 1118–1119 (1950).

1120. S. Geschwind, H. Minden, and C. H. Townes, Microwave measurements on the stable selenium isotopes in OCSe, *Phys. Rev.* **78**, 174–175 (1950).

1121. O. R. Gilliam, C. M. Johnson, and W. Gordy, Microwave spectroscopy in the region from two to three millimeters, *Phys. Rev.* **78**, 140–144 (1950).

1122. B. M. Girdwood, The microwave absorption spectrum of methanol, *Can. J. Res.* **28A**, 180–189 (1950).

1123. W. Gordy, H. Ring, and A. B. Burg, Microwave determination of the structure of borine carbonyl and of the nuclear moments of the stable boron isotopes, *Phys. Rev.* **78**, 512–517 (1950).

1124. W. Gordy and J. Sheridan, Microwave spectra of the methyl mercuric halides, *Phys. Rev.* **79**, 224 (1950).

1125. L. H. Jones, J. N. Shoolery, R. G. Shulman, and D. M. Yost, The molecular structure of isocyanic acid from microwave and infrared absorption spectra, *J. Chem. Phys.* **18**, 990–991 (1950).

1126. M. Kessler, H. Ring, R. Trambarulo, and W. Gordy, Microwave spectra and molecular structures of methyl cyanide and methyl isocyanide, *Phys. Rev.* **79**, 54–56 (1950).

1127. P. Kisliuk and C. H. Townes, The microwave spectra and molecular structure of phosphorus and arsenic trichloride, *J. Chem. Phys.* **18**, 1109–1111 (1950).

1128. J. H. N. Loubser and J. A. Klein, Absorption of millimeter waves in ND_3, *Phys. Rev.* **78**, 348 (1950).

1129. W. Low and C. H. Townes, Evidence from nuclear masses on proposed closed shells at 20 nucleons, *Phys. Rev.* **80**, 608–611 (1950).

1130. G. Matlack, G. Glocker, D. R. Bianco, and A. Roberts, The microwave spectra of isotopic methyl chloride, *J. Chem. Phys.* **18**, 332–334 (1950).

1131. H. T. Minden, J. M. Mays, and B. P. Dailey, The microwave spectrum of CH_3SiF_3, *Phys. Rev.* **78**, 347 (1950).

1132. W. J. Pietenpol, J. D. Rogers, and D. Williams, Microwave spectra of asymmetric top molecules, *Phys. Rev.* **78**, 480–481 (1950).

1133. S. J. Senatore, Microwave absorption spectra of POF_3, *Phys. Rev.* **78**, 293–294 (1950).

1134. A. H. Sharbaugh, B. S. Pritchard, and T. C. Madison, Microwave spectrum of CF_3Br, *Phys. Rev.* **77**, 302 (1950).

1135. A. H. Sharbaugh, B. S. Pritchard, V. G. Thomas, J. M. Mays, and B. P. Dailey, The microwave rotational spectrum and structure of bromogermane, *Phys. Rev.* **79**, 189 (1950).

1136. A. H. Sharbaugh, V. G. Thomas, and B. S. Pritchard, A determination of the dipole moment and molecular structure of fluorosilane, *Phys. Rev.* **78**, 64–65 (1950).

1137. J. Sheridan and W. Gordy, Interatomic distances in CF_3Br, CF_3I, and CF_3CN, *Phys. Rev.* **77**, 292–293 (1950).

1138. J. Sheridan and W. Gordy, Microwave spectra and molecular constants of trifluorosilane derivatives. SiF_3H, SiF_3CH, SiF_3Cl, and SiF_3Br, *Phys. Rev.* **77**, 719 (1950).

1139. J. Sheridan and W. Gordy, Microwave spectrum of methyl bromoacetylene, *Phys. Rev.* **79**, 224 (1950).

1140. J. Sheridan and W. Gordy, The nuclear quadrupole moment of N^{14} and the structure of nitrogen trifluoride from microwave spectra, *Phys. Rev.* **79**, 513–515 (1950).

1141. J. W. Simmons, W. E. Anderson, and W. Gordy, Microwave spectrum and molecular constants of hydrogen cyanide, *Phys. Rev.* **77**, 77–79 (1950). Errata—*Phys. Rev.* **86**, 1055 (1952).

1142. J. W. Simmons and W. O. Swan, The structure of methyl bromide from microwave spectra, *Phys. Rev.* **80**, 289–290 (1950).

1143. D. F. Smith, M. Tidwell, and D. V. P. Williams, The microwave spectrum of bromine monofluoride, *Phys. Rev.* **77**, 420–421 (1950).

1144. D. F. Smith, M. Tidwell, and D. V. P. Williams, The microwave spectrum of BrCl, *Phys. Rev.* **79**, 1007–1008 (1950).

1145. A. L. Southern, H. W. Morgan, G. W. Keilholtz, and W. V. Smith, The isotopic analysis of nitrogen by means of a microwave mass spectrograph, *Phys. Rev.* **78**, 639 (1950).

1146. R. Trambarulo and W. Gordy, Microwave spectra and molecular constants of CD_3NC and CD_3CN, *Phys. Rev.* **79**, 224–225 (1950).

1147. R. Trambarulo and W. Gordy, The microwave spectrum and structure of methyl acetylene, *J. Chem. Phys.* **18**, 1613–1616 (1950).

1148. R. R. Unterberger, R. Trambarulo, and W. V. Smith, Microwave determination of the structure of chloroform, *J. Chem. Phys.* **18**, 565–566 (1950).

1149. A. A. Westenberg and E. B. Wilson, Jr., The microwave spectrum and molecular structure of cyanoacetylene, *J. Am. Chem. Soc.* **72**, 199–200 (1950).

1150. J. Q. Williams and W. Gordy, Microwave spectra and molecular constants of tertiary butyl chloride, bromide, and iodide, *J. Chem. Phys.* **18**, 994–995 (1950).

1151. J. Q. Williams and W. Gordy, Microwave spectrum of bromoform and phosphorus tribromide, *Phys. Rev.* **79**, 225 (1950).

1152. E. Amble, The structure and dipole moment of trioxane, *Phys. Rev.* **83**, 210 (1951).

1153. W. E. Anderson, J. Sheridan, and W. Gordy, Microwave spectrum and molecular structure of GeF_3Cl, *Phys. Rev.* **81**, 819–821 (1951).

1154. W. E. Anderson, R. Trambarulo, J. Sheridan, and W. Gordy, The microwave spectrum and molecular constants of trifluoromethyl acetylene, *Phys. Rev.* **82**, 58–60 (1951).

1155. D. G. Burkhard and D. M. Dennison, The molecular structure of methyl alcohol, *Phys. Rev.* **84**, 408–417 (1951).

1156. R. O. Carlson, C. A. Lee, and B. P. Fabricand, The molecular beam electric resonance method study of thallium monochloride, *Phys. Rev.* **85**, 784–787 (1951).

1157. G. F. Crable and W. V. Smith, The structure and dipole moment of SO_2 from microwave spectra, *J. Chem. Phys.* **19**, 502 (1951).

1158. G. L. Cunningham, Jr., A. W. Boyd, R. J. Myers, W. D. Gwinn, and W. F. LeVan, The microwave spectra, structure, and dipole moments of ethylene oxide and ethylene sulfide, *J. Chem. Phys.* **19**, 676–685 (1951).

1159. S. Geschwind and R. Gunther-Mohr, Microwave Study of Ge, Si, and S masses, *Phys. Rev.* **81**, 882–883 (1951).

1160. R. H. Hughes, W. E. Good, and D. K. Coles, Microwave spectrum of methyl alcohol, *Phys. Rev.* **84**, 418–425 (1951).

1161. F. K. Hurd and W. D. Herschberger, Microwave spectrum of methyl mercaptan, *Phys. Rev.* **82**, 95–96 (1951).

1162. C. M. Johnson, R. Trambarulo, and W. Gordy, Microwave spectroscopy in the region from two to three millimeters. Pt. II, *Phys. Rev.* **84**, 1178–1180 (1951).

1163. P. Kisliuk and C. H. Townes, New microwave data on trichlorides of elements of the fifth column, *Phys. Rev.* **83**, 210 (1951).

1164. D. R. Lide, Jr., The microwave spectrum of methyl stannane, *J. Chem. Phys.* **19**, 1605–1606 (1951).

1165. C. C. Loomis and M. W. P. Strandberg, Microwave spectrum of phosphine, arsine, and stilbine, *Phys. Rev.* **81**, 798–807 (1951).

1166. R. G. Luce and J. W. Trischka, Molecular constants of $Cs^{133}Cl^{35}$, *Phys. Rev.* **83**, 851–852 (1951).

1167. N. W. Luft, General discussion, *Discussions Faraday Soc.* **10**, 117–118 (1951).

1168. H. Lyons, L. J. Rueger, R. G. Nuckolls, and M. Kessler, Microwave spectra of deutero-ammonias, *Phys. Rev.* **81**, 630–631 (1951).

1169. K. B. McAfee, Jr., Microwave spectrum of NO_2, *Phys. Rev.* **82**, 971 (1951).

1170. S. L. Miller, A. Javan, and C. H. Townes, The spin of O^{18}, *Phys. Rev.* **82**, 454–455 (1951).

1171. J. D. Rogers, W. J. Pietenpol, and D. Williams, The microwave absorption spectrum of nitrosyl chloride NOCl, *Phys. Rev.* **83**, 431–434 (1951).

1172. J. D. Rogers and D. Williams, Microwave absorption spectrum of hydrogen azide, *Phys. Rev.* **82**, 131 (1951).

1173. J. D. Rogers and D. Williams, Microwave absorption spectrum of formic acid vapor, *Phys. Rev.* **83**, 210 (1951).

1174. T. F. Rogers, Far wing absorption of atmospheric spectrum lines, *Phys. Rev.* **83**, 881 (1951).

1175. T. M. Shaw and J. J. Windle, Microwave spectrum and dipole moment of methyl mercaptan, *J. Chem. Phys.* **19**, 1063–1064 (1951).

1176. J. Sheridan and W. Gordy, The microwave spectra and molecular structures of trifluorosilane derivatives, *J. Chem. Phys.* **19**, 965–970 (1951).

1177. J. N. Shoolery, R. G. Shulman, and D. M. Yost, Dipole moment and electric quadrupole effects in HNCO and HNCS, *J. Chem. Phys.* **19**, 250–251 (1951).

1178. M. H. Sirvetz, The microwave spectrum of sulfur dioxide, *J. Chem. Phys.* **19**, 938–941 (1951).

1179. M. H. Sirvetz, The microwave spectrum of furan, *J. Chem. Phys.* **19**, 1609–1610 (1951).

1180. D. F. Smith, M. Tidwell, D. V. P. Williams, and S. J. Senatore, The microwave spectrum of carbonyl fluoride, *Phys. Rev.* **83**, 485 (1951).

1181. R. M. Talley and A. H. Nielsen, Vibration rotation transitions of C_2D_2 in the microwave region, *J. Chem. Phys.* **19**, 805–806 (1951).

1182. E. Amble, S. L. Miller, A. L. Schawlow, and C. H. Townes, Microwave spectrum and structure of ReO_3Cl, *J. Chem. Phys.* **20**, 192 (1952).

1183. R. O. Carlson, C. A. Lee, and B. P. Fabricand, The molecular beam electric resonance method study of thallium monochloride, *Phys. Rev.* **85**, 784–787 (1952).

1184. V. W. Cohen, Spectroscopy of radioactive molecules, *Ann. N.Y. Acad. Sci.* **55**, 904–914 (1952).

1185. R. M. Fristrom, The microwave spectrum of a slightly aspherical top—The structure and dipole moment of sulfuryl fluoride, *J. Chem. Phys.* **20**, 1–5 (1952).

1186. S. N. Ghosh, R. Trambarulo, and W. Gordy, Microwave spectra and molecular structures of fluoroform, chloroform, and methyl chloroform, *J. Chem. Phys.* **20**, 605–607 (1952).

1187. N. J. Hawkins, V. W. Cohen, and W. S. Koski, The microwave spectra of POF_3 and PSF_3, *J. Chem. Phys.* **20**, 528 (1952).

1188. H. J. Hrostowski, R. J. Myers, and G. C. Pimentel, The microwave spectra and dipole moment of stable pentaborane, *J. Chem. Phys.* **20**, 518 (1952).

1189. A. Javan and A. V. Grosse, Microwave spectrum of MnO_3F, *Phys. Rev.* **87**, 227 (1952).

1190. H. R. Johnson and M. W. P. Strandberg, The microwave spectrum of ketene, *J. Chem. Phys.* **20**, 687–695 (1952).

1191. P. Kisliuk and G. A. Silvey, The microwave spectrum of CF_3SF_5, *J. Chem. Phys.* **20**, 517 (1952).

1192. S. Kojima, K. Tsukada, S. Hagiwara, M. Mizushima, and T. Ito, Microwave spectra of $CHBr_3$ in the region from 11–12.5 centimeters, *J. Chem. Phys.* **20**, 804–808 (1952).

1193. D. R. Lide, Jr., Preliminary analysis of the pure rotational spectrum of methyl amine, *J. Chem. Phys.* **20**, 1812 (1952). Errata—*J. Chem. Phys.* **21**, 571 (1953).

1194. D. R. Lide, Jr., The microwave spectrum and structure of methylene fluoride, *J. Am. Chem. Soc.* **74**, 3548–3552 (1952).

1195. J. T. Massey and D. R. Bianco, Microwave absorption spectrum of H_2O_2, *Phys. Rev.* **85**, 717–718 (1952).

1196. J. M. Mays, Spectroscopic measurements on high-boiling, reactive, and unstable molecules, *Ann. N.Y. Acad. Sci.* **55**, 789–799 (1952).

1197. J. M. Mays and B. P. Dailey, Microwave spectra and structures of XYH_3 molecules, *J. Chem. Phys.* **20**, 1695–1703 (1952).

1198. S. L. Miller, L. C. Aamodt, G. Dousmanis, C. H. Townes, and J. Kraitchman, Structure of methyl halides, *J. Chem. Phys.* **20**, 1112–1114 (1952).

1199. R. Mockler, J. H. Bailey, and W. Gordy, Microwave investigations of $HSiCl_3$ and CH_3SiCl_3, *Phys. Rev.* **87**, 172 (1952).

1200. H. W. Morgan and J. H. Goldstein, The microwave spectrum of vinylacetate, *J. Chem. Phys.* **20**, 1981 (1952).

1201. A. H. Nethercot, J. A. Klein, and C. H. Townes, The microwave spectrum and molecular constants of hydrogen cyanide, *Phys. Rev.* **86**, 798–799 (1952).

1202. N. F. Ramsey, Vibrational and centrifugal effects on nuclear interactions and rotational moments in molecules, *Phys. Rev.* **87**, 1075–1079 (1952).

1203. A. L. Schawlow, Significance of the results of microwave spectroscopy for nuclear theory, *Ann. N.Y. Acad. Sci.* **55**, 955–965 (1952).

1204. J. Sheridan and W. Gordy, The microwave spectra and molecular structures of trifluoro-methyl bromide, iodide, and cyanide, *J. Chem. Phys.* **20**, 591–595 (1952).

1205. J. Sheridan and W. Gordy, The microwave spectra and molecular structures of methyl bromoacetylene and methyl iodoacetylene, *J. Chem. Phys.* **20**, 735–738 (1952).

1206. G. Silvey, W. A. Hardy, and C. H. Townes, Masses of the stable tellurium isotopes from the microwave spectrum of TeCS, *Phys. Rev.* **87**, 236 (1952).

1207. J. W. Simmons and J. H. Goldstein, The microwave spectra of the deuterated methyl halides, *J. Chem. Phys.* **20**, 122–124 (1952).

1208. D. F. Smith and D. W. Magnuson, The microwave spectrum of nitryl fluoride, *Phys. Rev.* **87**, 226–227 (1952).

1209. S. J. Tetenbaum, Microwave spectrum of BrCN at six millimeters, *Phys. Rev.* **86**, 440–446 (1952).

1210. S. J. Tetenbaum, Six-millimeter spectra of OCS and N_2O, *Phys. Rev.* **88**, 772–774 (1952).

1211. T. L. Weatherly and D. Williams, The microwave absorption spectrum of acetone vapor, *J. Chem. Phys.* **20**, 755 (1952).

1212. W. S. Wilcox and J. H. Goldstein, Evidence for a completely planar structure of pyrrole from its microwave spectrum, *J. Chem. Phys.* **20**, 1656–1657 (1952).

1213. W. S. Wilcox, J. H. Goldstein, and J. W. Simmons, The microwave spectrum of vinyl cyanide, *Phys. Rev.* **87**, 172 (1952).

1214. Q. Williams, J. T. Cox, and W. Gordy, Molecular structure of bromoform, *J. Chem. Phys.* **20**, 1524–1525 (1952).

1215. Q. Williams, J. Sheridan, and W. Gordy, Microwave spectra and molecular structures of POF_3, PSF_3, $POCl_3$, and $PSCl_3$, *J. Chem. Phys.* **20**, 164–167 (1952).

1216. F. Andersen, J. R. Andersen, B. Bak, O. Bastiansen, E. Risberg, and L. Smedvik, Electron diffraction and microwave investigation of tertiary butyl fluoride, *J. Chem. Phys.* **21**, 373 (1953).

1217. W. F. Arendale and W. H. Fletcher, The geometry of ketene, *J. Chem. Phys.* **21**, 1898 (1953).

1218. B. Bak, J. Bruhn, and J. Rastrup-Andersen, Microwave spectrum and structure of SiD_3F, *J. Chem. Phys.* **21**, 752–753 (1953).

1219. B. Bak, J. Bruhn, and J. Rastrup-Andersen, Microwave spectrum and structure of SiD_3Cl, *J. Chem. Phys.* **21**, 753–754 (1953).

1220. B. Bak and J. Rastrup-Andersen, Microwave investigation of pyridine, *J. Chem. Phys.* **21**, 1305–1306 (1953).

1221. Y. Beers and S. Weisbaum, An ultra-high frequency rotational line of HDO, *Phys. Rev.* **91**, 1014 (1953).

1222. R. Bird and R. C. Mockler, The microwave spectrum of the unstable molecule carbon monosulfide, *Phys. Rev.* **91**, 222 (1953).

1223. G. Birnbaum and A. A. Maryott, Change in the inversion spectrum of ND_3 from resonant to nonresonant absorption, *Phys. Rev.* **92**, 270–273 (1953).

1224. C. A. Burrus and W. Gordy, One-to-two millimeter wave spectroscopy II. H_2S, *Phys. Rev.* **92**, 274–277 (1953).

1225. C. A. Burrus and W. Gordy, One-to-two millimeter wave spectroscopy III. NO and DI, *Phys. Rev.* **92**, 1437–1439 (1953).

1226. H. D. Crawford, Two new lines in the microwave spectrum of heavy water, *J. Chem. Phys.* **21**, 2099 (1953).

1227. B. P. Dailey, The rotational spectrum and molecular structure of cyclopropyl chloride, *Phys. Rev.* **90**, 337–338 (1953).

1228. G. C. Dousmanis, T. M. Sanders, C. H. Townes, and H. J. Zeiger, Structure of HNCS from microwave spectra, *J. Chem. Phys.* **21**, 1416–1417 (1953).

1229. G. Erlandsson, Microwave spectrum of fluorobenzene, *Arkiv Fysik* **6**, 477–478 (1953).

1230. G. Erlandsson, Measurements of the microwave spectra of methyl alcohol and nitromethane, *Arkiv Fysik* **6**, 69–71 (1953).

1231. G. Erlandsson, Preliminary analysis of the microwave spectrum of formic acid, *Arkiv Fysik* **6**, 491–495 (1953).

1232. R. C. Ferguson and E. B. Wilson, Jr., The microwave spectrum and structure of thionyl fluoride, *Phys. Rev.* **90**, 338 (1953).

1233. A. Honig, M. L. Stitch, and M. Mandel, Microwave spectra of CsF, CsCl, and CsBr, *Phys. Rev.* **92**, 901–902 (1953).

1234. R. H. Hughes, The microwave spectrum and structure of ozone, *J. Chem. Phys.* **21**, 959–960 (1953).

1235. E. V. Ivash and D. M. Dennison, The methyl alcohol molecule and its microwave spectrum, *J. Chem. Phys.* **21**, 1804–1816 (1953).

1236. C. K. Jen, D. R. Bianco, and J. T. Massey, Some heavy water rotational absorption lines, *J. Chem. Phys.* **21**, 520–525 (1953).

1237. R. D. Johnson, R. J. Myers, and W. D. Gwinn, Microwave spectrum and dipole moment of ethylenimine, *J. Chem. Phys.* **21**, 1425 (1953).

1238. W. C. King and W. Gordy, One-to-two millimeter wave spectroscopy I, *Phys. Rev.* **90**, 319–320 (1953).

1239. P. Kisliuk and S. Geschwind, The microwave spectrum of arsenic trifluoride, *J. Chem. Phys.* **21**, 828–829 (1953).

1240. J. A. Klein and A. H. Nethercot, Microwave spectrum of DI at 1.5 mm wavelength, *Phys. Rev.* **91**, 1018 (1953).

1241. J. H. N. Loubser, Preliminary work on the microwave spectrum of acetic acid, *J. Chem. Phys.* **21**, 2231–2232 (1953).

1242. K. E. McCulloh and G. F. Pollnow, Microwave spectrum of pyridine, *J. Chem. Phys.* **21**, 2082 (1953).

1243. M. Mizushima, Theory of the rotational spectra of allene-type molecules, *J. Chem. Phys.* **21**, 1222–1224 (1953).

1244. M. Mizushima and P. Venkateswarlu, The possible microwave absorption in the molecules belonging to the point groups $D_{2d} = V_d$ and T_d, *J. Chem. Phys.* **21**, 705–709 (1953).

1245. R. C. Mockler, J. H. Bailey, and W. Gordy, Microwave spectra and molecular structures of $HSiCl_3$, CH_3SiCl_3, and $(CH_3)_3SiCl$, *J. Chem. Phys.* **21**, 1710–1713 (1953).

1246. R. C. Mockler and W. Gordy, Microwave spectrum of trimethyl chlorosilicane, *Phys. Rev.* **91**, 222 (1953).

1247. N. Muller, The microwave spectrum and structure of chlorofluoromethane, *J. Am. Chem. Soc.* **75**, 860–863 (1953).

1248. A. H. Nethercot and A. Javan, The microwave spectrum of $C_8H_{13}Br$ and $C_8H_{13}Cl$, *J. Chem. Phys.* **21**, 363–364 (1953).

1249. H. H. Nielsen, The infrared spectra and the molecular structure of pyramidal molecules, *J. Chem. Phys.* **21**, 142–144 (1953).

1250. R. G. Nuckolls, L. J. Rueger, and H. Lyons, Microwave absorption spectrum of ND_3, *Phys. Rev.* **89**, 1101 (1953).

1251. D. W. Posener and M. W. P. Strandberg, Microwave spectrum of HDO, *J. Chem. Phys.* **21**, 1401–1402 (1953).

1252. G. W. Robinson, The microwave spectrum of phosgene, *J. Chem. Phys.* **21**, 1741–1745 (1953).

1253. A. H. Sharbaugh, G. A. Heath, L. F. Thomas, and J. Sheridan, Microwave spectrum and structure of iodosilane, *Nature* **171**, 87 (1953).

1254. K. Shimoda and T. Nishikawa, Microwave spectrum of methylamine, *J. Phys. Soc. Japan* **8**, 133–134 (1953).

1255. K. Shimoda and T. Nishikawa, Microwave spectrum of methylamine, *J. Phys. Soc. Japan* **8**, 425–426 (1953).

1256. M. H. Sirvetz and R. E. Weston, The structure of phosphine, *J. Chem. Phys.* **21**, 898–902 (1953).

1257. D. F. Smith, The microwave spectrum and structure of chlorine trifluoride, *J. Chem. Phys.* **21**, 609–614 (1953).

1258. N. Solimene and B. P. Dailey, The rotational spectrum and molecular structure of methyl mercaptan, *Phys. Rev.* **91**, 464 (1953).

1259. T. E. Turner, V. C. Fiora, W. M. Kendrick, and B. L. Hicks, Preliminary analysis of the microwave spectrum of ethylenimine, *J. Chem. Phys.* **21**, 564–565 (1953).

1260. P. Venkateswarlu, R. C. Mockler, and W. Gordy, Microwave spectrum and molecular structure of trichlorogermane, *J. Chem. Phys.* **21**, 1713–1715 (1953).

1261. S. Weisbaum, Y. Beers, and G. Herrmann, S-band spectrum of HDO, *Phys. Rev.* **90**, 338 (1953).

1262. W. S. Wilcox, K. C. Brannock, W. Demore, and J. H. Goldstein, The microwave spectrum and general properties of ethylene imine, *J. Chem. Phys.* **21**, 563–564 (1953).

1263. B. Bak, L. Hansen, and J. Rastrup-Andersen, Microwave spectrum of pyridine, *J. Chem. Phys.* **22**, 565 (1954).

1264. B. Bak, L. Hansen, and J. Rastrup-Andersen, Microwave determination of the structure of pyridine, *J. Chem. Phys.* **22**, 2013–2017 (1954).

1265. C. A. Burrus and W. Gordy, Submillimeter wave spectroscopy, *Phys. Rev.* **93**, 897–898 (1954).

1266. C. A. Burrus, A. Jache, and W. Gordy, One-to-two millimeter wave spectroscopy V. PH_3 and PD_3, *Phys. Rev.* **95**, 706–708 (1954).

1267. C. D. Cornwell and R. L. Poynter, The microwave spectrum of vinyl iodide, *J. Chem. Phys.* **22**, 1257 (1954).

1268. B. B. Demore, W. S. Wilcox, and J. H. Goldstein, Microwave spectrum and dipole moment of pyridine, *J. Chem. Phys.* **22**, 876–880 (1954).

1269. G. Erlandsson, Microwave spectrum and molecular structure of fluorobenzene, *Arkiv Fysik* **7**, 189–192 (1954).

1270. G. Erlandsson, Microwave spectrum of cyclopentanone, *J. Chem. Phys.* **22**, 563–564 (1954).

1271. G. Erlandsson, Microwave spectrum of chlorobenzene, *Arkiv Fysik* **8**, 341–342 (1954).

1272. G. Erlandsson, Microwave spectrum of benzonitrile, *J. Chem. Phys.* **22**, 1152 (1954).

1273. R. C. Ferguson, The microwave spectrum, structure, and dipole moment of thionyl fluoride, *J. Am. Chem. Soc.* **76**, 850–853 (1954).

1274. W. Gordy, Spectroscopy from 1–5 mm wavelength, *J. Phys. Radium* **15**, 521–523 (1954).

1275. W. Gordy and C. A. Burrus, Spectrum of DBr in the one-millimeter wave region, *Phys. Rev.* **93**, 419–420 (1954).

1276. W. Gordy and J. Sheridan, Microwave spectra and structures of methyl mercury chloride and bromide, *J. Chem. Phys.* **22**, 92–95 (1954).

1277. G. R. Gunther-Mohr, R. L. White, A. L. Schawlow, W. E. Good, and D. K. Coles, Hyperfine structure in the spectrum of $N^{14}H_3$ I. Experimental results, *Phys. Rev.* **94**, 1184–1191 (1954).

1278. R. C. Gunton, J. F. Ollom, and H. N. Rexroad, The microwave spectrum and molecular structure of $(CH_3)_3SiF$, *J. Chem. Phys.* **22**, 1942 (1954).

1279. W. A. Hardy and G. Silvey, Microwave spectrum of TeCS and masses of the stable tellurium isotopes, *Phys. Rev.* **95**, 385–388 (1954).

1280. G. A. Heath, L. F. Thomas, and J. Sheridan, The structure of trifluorosilane from microwave spectra, *Trans. Faraday Soc.* **50**, 779–783 (1954).

1281. A. Honig, M. Mandel, M. L. Stitch, and C. H. Townes, Microwave spectra of the alkali halides, *Phys. Rev.* **96**, 629–642 (1954).

1282. H. J. Hrostowski and R. J. Myers, The microwave spectra, structure, and dipole moment of stable pentaborane, *J. Chem. Phys.* **22**, 262–265 (1954).

1283. A. Jache, G. Blevins, and W. Gordy, Millimeter wave spectrum of arsine, *Phys. Rev.* **95**, 299 (1954).

1284. A. Javan and A. Engelbrecht, Microwave absorption spectra of MnO_3F and ReO_3Cl, *Phys. Rev.* **96**, 649–658 (1954).

1285. P. Kisliuk, Dipole moments, nuclear quadrupole couplings, and the bonding orbitals in group *V*-trihalides, *J. Chem. Phys.* **22**, 86–92 (1954).

1286. S. Kojima and K. Tsukada, On the interpretation of the spectrum of bromoform, *J. Chem. Phys.* **22**, 2093–2094 (1954).

1287. J. A. Kraitchman and B. P. Dailey, The microwave spectrum of ethyl fluoride, *Phys. Rev.* **94**, 788 (1954).

1288. D. R. Lide, Jr., Microwave spectrum and structure of benzonitrile, *J. Chem. Phys.* **22**, 1577–1578 (1954).

1289. R. J. Lovell and E. A. Jones, Potential constants for carbonyl fluoride, *Phys. Rev.* **95**, 300 (1954).

1290. J. F. Lotspeich, A. Javan, and A. Engelbrecht, The microwave spectrum of ReO_3F, *Phys. Rev.* **94**, 789 (1954).

1291. J. T. Massey, C. I. Beard, and C. K. Jen, A microwave spectral series of deuterated hydrogen peroxide, *Phys. Rev.* **95**, 622 (1954).

1292. J. T. Massey and D. R. Bianco, The microwave spectrum of hydrogen peroxide, *J. Chem. Phys.* **22**, 442–448 (1954).

1293. M. Matricon and Bonnett, Spectrum of ethylamine, *J. Phys. Radium* **15**, 647–648 (1954).

1294. K. E. McCulloh and G. F. Pollnow, An investigation of the microwave spectrum of pyridine, *J. Chem. Phys.* **22**, 681–682 (1954).

1295. M. Peter and M. W. P. Strandberg, Microwave spectrum of OCS, *Phys. Rev.* **95**, 622 (1954).

1296. J. Sheridan and L. F. Thomas, Microwave spectrum of methylcyanoacetylene, *Nature* **174**, 798 (1954).

1297. K. Shimoda, T. Nishikawa, and T. Itoh, Microwave spectrum of methylamine, *J. Phys. Soc. Japan* **9**, 974–991 (1954).

1298. G. R. Slayton, J. W. Simmons, and J. Goldstein, Microwave spectrum and properties of vinylene carbonate, *J. Chem. Phys.* **22**, 1678–1679 (1954).

1299. N. Solimene and B. P. Dailey, Microwave spectrum of 1,1 difluoroethane, *J. Chem. Phys.* **22**, 2042–2044 (1954).

1300. F. Sterzer, $J = 0 \rightarrow 1$ rotational transition of trifluoroiodomethane, *J. Chem. Phys.* **22**, 2094 (1954). Erratum—*J. Chem. Phys.* **23**, 762 (1955).

1301. R. Trambarulo and P. M. Moser, Microwave spectrum of formic acid, *J. Chem. Phys.* **22**, 1622–1623 (1954).
1302. R. S. Wagner and B. P. Dailey, Microwave spectrum of ethyl chloride, *J. Chem. Phys.* **22**, 1459 (1954).
1303. W. S. Wilcox, J. H. Goldstein, and J. W. Simmons, The microwave spectrum of vinyl cyanide, *J. Chem. Phys.* **22**, 516–518 (1954).
1304. B. Bak, L. Hansen, and J. Rastrup-Andersen, Microwave spectra of deuterated furans—Structure of the furan molecule, *Discussions Faraday Soc.* **19**, 30–38 (1955).
1305. A. I. Barchukov, T. M. Minaeva, and A. M. Prokhorov, Microwave rotation spectrum of the ethyl chloride, C_2H_5Cl, *Zh. Eksperim. i Teor. Fiz.* **29**, 892 (1955).
1306. A. H. Barrett and M. Mandel, Microwave spectra of indium chloride and bromide, *Phys. Rev.* **99**, 666 (1955).
1307. N. G. Basov and A. M. Prokhorov, Possible method for obtaining active molecules for a molecular generator, *Zh. Eksperim i Teor. Fiz.* **28**, 249–250 (1955).
1308. G. S. Blevins, A. W. Jache, and W. Gordy, Millimeter wave spectra of AsH_3 and AsD_3, *Phys. Rev.* **97**, 684–686 (1955).
1309. J. H. Burkhalter, Microwave spectrum of cyclopentanone, *J. Chem. Phys.* **23**, 1172 (1955).
1310. C. A. Burrus, Jr., and W. Gordy, One-to-two millimeter wave spectra of TCl and TBr, *Phys. Rev.* **97**, 1661–1664 (1955).
1311. C. C. Costain, Microwave spectrum and molecular structure of methylchloroacetylene, *J. Chem. Phys.* **23**, 2037–2041 (1955).
1312. J. T. Cox, T. Gaumann, and W. J. O. Thomas, Millimeter wave spectrum of methyl mercury chloride, *Discussions Faraday Soc.* **19**, 52–55 (1955).
1313. G. Erlandsson, Microwave spectrum of cyclopentene oxide, *Arkiv Fysik* **9**, 341–343 (1955).
1314. J. Fine, J. H. Goldstein, and J. W. Simmons, Microwave spectrum of *s-trans*-acrolein, *J. Chem. Phys.* **23**, 601 (1955).
1315. J. P. Friend, R. F. Schneider, and B. P. Dailey, Microwave spectrum of cyclopropyl chloride, *J. Chem. Phys.* **23**, 1557 (1955).
1316. J. J. Gallagher, W. C. King, and C. M. Johnson, The microwave spectrum of $N^{15}O^{16}$, *Phys. Rev.* **98**, 1551 (1955).
1317. E. K. Gora, Microwave spectrum of the ozone molecule, *Phys. Rev.* **99**, 666 (1955).
1318. G. A. Heath, L. F. Thomas, E. I. Sherrard, and J. Sheridan, The microwave spectrum and structure of methyl diacetylene, *Discussions Faraday Soc.* **19**, 38–43 (1955).
1319. J. A. Howe and J. H. Goldstein, Microwave spectrum of propiolic aldehyde, *J. Chem. Phys.* **23**, 1223–1225 (1955).
1320. T. Ito, Microwave spectrum of $SPCl_3$, theoretical, *J. Phys. Soc. Japan* **10**, 56–59 (1955).
1321. A. W. Jache, G. S. Blevins, and W. Gordy, Millimeter wave spectra of SbH_3 and SbD_3, *Phys. Rev.* **97**, 680–683 (1955).
1322. T. Kojima and T. Nishikawa, Microwave spectrum of methyl mercaptan I, *J. Phys. Soc. Japan* **10**, 240–241 (1955).
1323. J. Kraitchman and B. P. Dailey, The microwave spectrum of ethyl fluoride, *J. Chem. Phys.* **23**, 184–190 (1955).
1324. R. J. Kurland, Microwave spectrum and planarity of formamide, *J. Chem. Phys.* **23**, 2202–2203 (1955).
1325. N. Kwak, J. W. Simmons, and J. H. Goldstein, Microwave spectrum of propiolactone, *J. Chem. Phys.* **23**, 2450 (1955).
1326. R. G. Lerner, J. P. Friend, and B. P. Dailey, Structure and barrier to internal rotation of formic acid from microwave data, *J. Chem. Phys.* **23**, 210 (1955).

1327. M. Mandel and A. H. Barrett, Pure rotation spectra of the thallium halides, *Phys. Rev.* **98**, 1159 (1955).

1328. A. A. Maryott and G. Birnbaum, Microwave absorption in compressed oxygen, *Phys. Rev.* **99**, 1886 (1955).

1329. D. J. Millen and K. M. Sinnott, The microwave spectrum and structure of nitryl chloride, *Chem. & Ind.* **1955**, 538 (1955).

1330. R. C. Mockler and G. R. Bird, Microwave spectrum of carbon monosulfide, *Phys. Rev.* **98**, 1837–1839 (1955).

1331. Y. Morino and E. Hirota, Mean amplitudes of thermal vibrations in polyatomic molecules III. The generalized mean amplitudes, *J. Chem. Phys.* **23**, 737–747 (1955).

1332. T. Nishikawa, T. Itoh, and K. Shimoda, Molecular structure of methylamine from its microwave spectrum, *J. Chem. Phys.* **23**, 1735–1736 (1955).

1333. D. W. Posener, Note on the X-band microwave spectrum of heavy water, *J. Chem. Phys.* **23**, 1728–1729 (1955).

1334. B. Rosenblum and A. H. Nethercot, Jr., Microwave spectra of tritium iodide and tritium bromide, *Phys. Rev.* **97**, 84–85 (1955).

1335. N. Solimene and B. P. Dailey, Structure and barrier height of methyl mercaptan from microwave data, *J. Chem. Phys.* **23**, 124–129 (1955).

1336. L. F. Thomas, E. I. Sherrard, and J. Sheridan, Microwave spectra of some partially deuteriated methyl derivatives I. Methyl cyanide and methyl acetylene, *Trans. Faraday Soc.* **51**, 619–625 (1955).

1337. K. Tsukada, Microwave spectra of $SPCl_3$, experimental, *J. Phys. Soc. Japan* **10**, 60–64 (1955).

1338. T. E. Turner, V. C. Fiora, and W. M. Kendrick, Microwave spectrum of imine-deuteriated ethylenimine, *J. Chem. Phys.* **23**, 1966 (1955).

1339. P. Venkateswarlu, H. D. Edwards, and W. Gordy, Methyl alcohol I. Microwave spectrum, *J. Chem. Phys.* **23**, 1195–1199 (1955).

1340. P. Venkateswarlu, H. D. Edwards, and W. Gordy, Methyl alcohol II. Molecular structure, *J. Chem. Phys.* **23**, 1200–1202 (1955).

1341. R. S. Wagner, N. Solimene, and B. P. Dailey, Microwave spectrum of ethyl bromide, *J. Chem. Phys.* **23**, 599 (1955).

1342. S. Weisbaum, Y. Beers, and G. Herrmann, Low frequency rotational spectrum of HDO, *J. Chem. Phys.* **23**, 1601–1605 (1955).

1343. Q. Williams and T. L. Weatherly, The microwave spectrum of nitrosyl bromide, *Phys. Rev.* **98**, 1159 (1955).

1344. F. A. Andersen, B. Bak, and S. Brodersen, Normal vibration frequencies of CD_3F, structure of CH_3F and CD_3F from infrared and microwave spectra, *J. Chem. Phys.* **24**, 989–992 (1956).

1345. B. Bak, D. Christensen, L. Hansen, and J. Rastrup-Andersen, Microwave determination of the structure of pyrrole, *J. Chem. Phys.* **24**, 720–725 (1956).

1346. B. Bak, D. Christensen, J. Rastrup-Andersen, and E. Tannenbaum, Microwave spectra of thiophene, 2- and 3-monodeutero, 3,3′-dideutero, and tetradeuterothiophene. Structure of the thiophene molecule, *J. Chem. Phys.* **25**, 892–896 (1956).

1347. A. I. Barchukov, T. Minaeva, and A. M. Prokhorov, Microwave rotation spectrum of the ethyl chloride molecule, *Soviet Phys. JETP (English Transl.)* **2**, 760 (1956).

1348. G. R. Bird, Microwave spectrum of NO_2—A rigid rotor analysis, *J. Chem. Phys.* **25**, 1040–1043 (1956).

1349. G. Erlandsson, Millimeter wave spectrum of formic acid, *J. Chem. Phys.* **25**, 379 (1956).

1350. G. Erlandsson, Millimeter wave spectrum of formaldehyde, *J. Chem. Phys.* **25**, 579–580 (1956).

1351. G. Erlandsson and J. Cox, Millimeter wave lines of heavy water, *J. Chem. Phys.* **25**, 778–779 (1956).

1352. H. G. Fitzky and H. Happ, The microwave spectrum of methyl alcohol, *Z. Naturforsch.* **11A**, 957–958 (1956).

1353. H. Hirakawa, A. Miyahara, and K. Shimoda, Microwave spectra of formaldehyde and methyl amine in the superhigh-frequency region, *J. Phys. Soc. Japan* **11**, 334–335 (1956).

1354. H. Hirakawa, T. Oka, and K. Shimoda, Microwave spectra of HCHO—d_1, d_2, *J. Phys. Soc. Japan* **11**, 1207 (1956).

1355. R. H. Hughes, Structure of ozone from the microwave spectrum between 9000 and 45000 Mc/sec, *J. Chem. Phys.* **24**, 131–138 (1956).

1356. A. W. Jache, P. M. Moser, and W. Gordy, Millimeter wave spectrum, molecular structure, and dipole moment of hydrogen selenide, *J. Chem. Phys.* **25**, 209–210 (1956).

1357. N. Kwak, J. H. Goldstein, and J. W. Simmons, Microwave spectrum of *beta*-propiolactone, *J. Chem. Phys.* **25**, 1203–1205 (1956).

1358. V. W. Laurie, Microwave spectrum and dipole moment of cyclopentadiene, *J. Chem. Phys.* **24**, 635–636 (1956).

1359. A. A. Maryott and G. Birnbaum, Microwave absorption in compressed gases-saturated hydrocarbons, *J. Chem. Phys.* **24**, 1022–1026 (1956).

1360. D. J. Millen and J. R. Morton, Microwave spectrum, structure, and dipole moment of nitric acid, *Chem. & Ind.* **1956**, 954 (1956).

1361. A. Okaya, Microwave hyperfine spectrum of formaldehyde, *J. Phys. Soc. Japan* **11**, 258–263 (1956).

1362. J. F. Ollom, A. A. Sinisgalli, H. N. Rexroad, and R. C. Gunton, Microwave spectrum and molecular structure of $(CH_3)_3SiBr$, *J. Chem. Phys.* **24**, 487–488 (1956).

1363. H. N. Rexroad, D. W. Howgate, R. C. Gunton, and J. F. Ollom, Microwave spectrum and molecular structure of $(CH_3)_3SiI$, *J. Chem. Phys.* **24**, 625 (1956).

1364. P. Swarup, Absorption and dispersion of microwaves in methyl bromide, *Z. Physik* **144**, 632–636 (1956).

1365. P. Swarup, Dispersion of microwaves in ND_3, *Phys. Rev.* **104**, 89–90 (1956).

1366. V. G. Veselago and A. M. Prokhorov, The HDSe microwave spectrum, *Zh. Eksperim. i Teor. Fiz.* **31**, 731 (1956).

1367. T. L. Weatherly and Q. Williams, Microwave spectrum and molecular constants of nitrosyl bromide, *J. Chem. Phys.* **25**, 717–721 (1956).

1368. R. Wertheimer, Absorption spectrum of formic acid vapor in the vicinity of 3 mm, *Compt. Rend.* **242**, 243–244 (1956).

1369. R. Wertheimer, Absorption spectrum of formic acid vapor between the wavelengths of 4.5 and 2.5 mm, *Arch. Sci.* (*Geneva*) **9**, 47–48 (1956).

1370. R. Wertheimer, The rotational spectrum and inertial constants of the formic acid molecule, *Compt. Rend.* **242**, 1591–1593 (1956).

1371. P. N. Wolfe, Microwave spectrum of chloroform, *J. Chem. Phys.* **25**, 976–981 (1956).

1372. L. Yarmus, Hyperfine structure in the *l*-type doubling spectrum of hydrogen cyanide, *Phys. Rev.* **104**, 365–367 (1956).

1373. W. Zeil, The microwave spectrum of trichloroacetonitrile and of 1,1,1-trichloroethane from 23,500 to 25,500 Mc, *Z. Electrochem.* **60**, 752–755 (1956). Errata—*Z. Elektrochem.* **60**, 1204 (1956).

1374. W. Zeil, The microwave spectrum of 1,1,1-trichloroethane, *Z. Naturforsch.* **11A**, 677–678 (1956).

1375. B. Bak, D. Christensen, L. Hansen-Nygaard, and E. Tannenbaum, Microwave determination of the structure of fluorobenzene, *J. Chem. Phys.* **26**, 134–137 (1957).

1376. B. Bak, D. Christensen, L. Hansen-Nygaard, and E. Tannenbaum, Microwave determination of the structure of trifluorobutyne, *J. Chem. Phys.* **26**, 241–243 (1957).

1377. J. G. Baker, D. R. Jenkins, C. N. Kenney, and T. M. Sugden, Microwave spectrum and structure of trichloroacetonitrile, *Trans. Faraday Soc.* **53**, 1397–1401 (1957).

1378. H. H. Blau, Jr. and H. H. Nielsen, Infrared absorption spectrum of formaldehyde vapor, *J. Mol. Spectry.* **1**, 124–132 (1957).

1379. C. A. Burrus and W. Gordy, Spectra of some symmetric top molecules in the one-to-four millimeter wave region, *J. Chem. Phys.* **26**, 391–394 (1957).

1380. W. F. Edgell, P. A. Kinsey, and J. W. Amy, The microwave spectra and structure of $CF_2=CH_2$, $CF_2=CHD$, and $CF_2=CD_2$, *J. Am. Chem. Soc.* **79**, 2691–2693 (1957).

1381. W. F. Edgell, G. B. Miller, and J. W. Amy, The microwave spectra and molecular structure of 1,1,1-trifluoroethane and its mono-, di-, and trideutero derivatives, *J. Am. Chem. Soc.* **79**, 2391–2393 (1957).

1382. P. Goedertier and K. L. Lee, Pure rotation spectra of light and heavy vinyl bromide by microwave method, *Ann. Soc. Sci. Bruxelles Ser. I* **71**, 128–133 (1957).

1383. P. Goedertier and K. L. Lee, Pure rotation spectra of vinyl bromide, *Ann. Soc. Sci. Bruxelles Ser. I* **71**, 184–188 (1957).

1384. H. Happ, Microwave spectrum of thallium (I) iodide and bismuth chloride in the 3 and 1.5 cm band, *Z. Physik* **147**, 567–572 (1957).

1385. A. Javan, Theory of a three-level maser, *Phys. Rev.* **107**, 1579–1589 (1957).

1386. T. Kojima and T. Nishikawa, Potential barrier and molecular structure of methyl mercaptan from its microwave spectra, *J. Phys. Soc. Japan* **12**, 680–686 (1957).

1387. Krishnaji and G. P. Srivastava, Microwave absorption in ethyl chloride, *Phys. Rev.* **106**, 1186–1189 (1957).

1388. R. J. Kurland and E. B. Wilson, Jr., Microwave spectrum, structure, dipole moment, and quadrupole coupling constants of formamide, *J. Chem. Phys.* **27**, 585–590 (1957).

1389. V. W. Laurie, Microwave spectrum, dipole moment, and structure of difluorosilane, *J. Chem. Phys.* **26**, 1359–1362 (1957).

1390. R. G. Lerner and B. P. Dailey, Microwave spectrum and structure of propionitrile, *J. Chem. Phys.* **26**, 678–680 (1957).

1391. R. G. Lerner, B. P. Dailey, and J. P. Friend, Microwave spectrum and structure of formic acid, *J. Chem. Phys.* **26**, 680–683 (1957).

1392. D. R. Lide, Jr., D. E. Mann, and R. M. Fristrom, Microwave spectrum and structure of sulfuryl fluoride, *J. Chem. Phys.* **26**, 734–739 (1957).

1393. D. W. Magnuson, Microwave spectrum and molecular structure of bromine trifluoride, *J. Chem. Phys.* **27**, 223–226 (1957).

1394. K. Matsuura, Y. Sugiura, and G. M. Hatoyama, Frequency of the ammonia (3,3) line, *Phys. Rev.* **106**, 607 (1957).

1395. I. A. Mukhtarov, Microwave spectra of 1,2-fluorochloroethane, *Soviet Phys. "Doklady" (English Transl.)* **2**, 357–358 (1957).

1396. B. D. Osipov, Hyperfine structure of rotational transition $J = 3 \to 4$ of the MeI^{127} molecule, *Opt. i Spektroskopiya* **3**, 94–95 (1957).

1397. E. D. Palik and E. E. Bell, Pure rotational spectra of the partially deuterated ammonias in the far infrared spectral region, *J. Chem. Phys.* **26**, 1093–1101 (1957).

1399. H. Selen, Microwave spectrum of chlorobenzene, *Arkiv Fysik* **13**, 81–83 (1957).

1400. K. Shimoda, Precise frequency of the 3,3 inversion line of NH_3, *J. Phys. Soc. Japan* **12**, 588 (1957).

1401. T. Sparstad and E. Amble, Microwave spectrum and structure of $(CH_3)_3CCN$, *J. Chem. Phys.* **27**, 317 (1957).

1402. L. F. Thomas, J. S. Heeks, and J. Sheridan, Microwave spectra of some molecules containing CF_3 and SiF_3 groups, Z. Elektrochem. **61**, 935–937 (1957).

1403. V. G. Veselago and A. M. Prokhorov, The HDSe microwave spectrum, Soviet Phys. JETP (English Transl.) **4**, 751 (1957).

1404. R. S. Wagner and B. P. Dailey, Microwave spectrum of ethyl chloride, J. Chem. Phys. **26**, 1588–1593 (1957).

1405. R. S. Wagner, B. P. Dailey, and N. Solimene, Microwave spectrum of ethyl bromide, J. Chem. Phys. **26**, 1593–1596 (1957).

1406. R. Wagner, J. Fine, J. W. Simmons, and J. H. Goldstein, Microwave spectrum, structure, and dipole moment of s-trans-acrolein, J. Chem. Phys. **26**, 634–637 (1957).

1407. R. Wertheimer, Molecular constants of formic acid from the rotational spectrum, Arch. Sci. (Geneva) **10**, 184–186 (1957).

1408. R. Wertheimer and M. Clouard, Absorption of sulfurous anhydride (SO_2) in the millimeter wave region, Compt. Rend. **245**, 1793–1794 (1957).

1409. B. Bak, D. Christensen, L. Hansen-Nygaard, and J. Rastrup-Andersen, The structure of vinyl fluoride, Spectrochim. Acta **13**, 120–124 (1958).

1410. B. Bak, L. Hansen-Nygaard, and J. Rastrup-Andersen, The structure of tertiary butyl isocyanide, J. Mol. Spectry. **2**, 54–57 (1958).

1411. B. Bak, L. Hansen-Nygaard, and J. Rastrup-Andersen, Complete determination of the structure of pyridine by microwave spectra, J. Mol. Spectry. **2**, 361–368 (1958).

1412. A. I. Barchukov and N. G. Basov, Frequencies and intensities of hyperfine structure lines of CH_3I (the transition $I = 0 \rightarrow 1$), Opt. i Spektroskopiya **4**, 532 (1958).

1413. A. I. Barchukov, T. M. Murine, and A. M. Prokhorov, Microwave spectrum and rotation constants of ethyl chloride molecule, Opt. i Spektroskopiya **4**, 521–523 (1958).

1414. A. I. Barchukov and A. M. Prokhorov, Quadrupole bond, dipole moment, and the internal rotation barrier in the CH_3GeH_3 molecule, determined from its rotational spectrum, Opt. i Spektroskopiya **5**, 530–534 (1958).

1415. A. I. Barchukov and A. M. Prokhorov, Microwave spectrum of CH_3GeH_3, Opt. i Spektroskopiya **4**, 799 (1958).

1416. A. H. Barrett and M. Mandel, Microwave spectra of thallium, indium, and gallium monohalides, Phys. Rev. **109**, 1572–1589 (1958).

1417. M. Cowan and W. Gordy, Precision measurements of millimeter and submillimeter wave spectra-deuterium chloride, deuterium bromide, and deuterium iodide, Phys. Rev. **111**, 209–211 (1958).

1418. A. P. Cox, L. F. Thomas, and J. Sheridan, Microwave spectra of diazomethane and its deutero derivatives, Nature **181**, 1000–1001 (1958).

1419. A. P. Cox, L. F. Thomas, and J. Sheridan, Microwave spectrum of nickel cyclopentadienyl nitrosyl and the configuration of the molecule, Nature **181**, 1157–1158 (1958).

1420. C. W. N. Cumper, Structure of some heterocyclic molecules, Trans. Faraday Soc. **54**, 1266–1270 (1958).

1421. G. Erlandsson, Millimeter wave spectrum of formic acid, J. Chem. Phys. **28**, 71–75 (1958).

1422. G. Erlandsson and H. Selen, Dipole moment of formic acid, Arkiv. Fysik **14**, 61–64 (1958).

1423. J. P. Friend and B. P. Dailey, Microwave studies of the structure of cyclopropyl derivatives, J. Chem. Phys. **29**, 577–582 (1958).

1424. H. G. Fitzky, The microwave rotation spectrum of thallium (I) halides, Z. Physik **151**, 351–364 (1958).

1425. E. Hirota, Rotational structure of the infrared absorption spectrum of hydrogen peroxide vapor, J. Chem. Phys. **28**, 839–846 (1958).

1426. E. Hirota, T. Oka, and Y. Morino, Microwave spectrum, structure, dipole moment, and quadrupole coupling constant of propargyl chloride, *J. Chem. Phys.* **29**, 444–445 (1958).

1427. N. A. Irisova, Determination of rotational constants of CH_3GeCl_3 from its super-high frequency absorption spectrum, *Izv. Akad. Nauk. SSSR Ser. Fiz.* **22**, 1307 (1958).

1428. T. Kojima, H. Hirakawa, and T. Oka, Microwave spectrum of hydrazine, *J. Phys. Soc. Japan* **13**, 321 (1958).

1429. Krishnaji and G. P. Strivastava, Microwave absorption in methyl halides, *Phys. Rev.* **109**, 1560–1563 (1958).

1430. J. Mattauch, Mass units for atomic weights and nucledic masses, *Z. Naturforsch.* **13A**, 572–596 (1958).

1431. D. J. Millen, and K. M. Sinnott, The microwave spectrum, structure, and dipole moment of nitryl chloride, *J. Chem. Soc.* **1958**, 350–355 (1958).

1432. I. A. Mukhtarov, Rotational constants of the molecule of $FH_2CCH_2Cl^{35}$, *Izv. Akad. Nauk. SSSR Ser. Fiz.* **22**, 1154–1156 (1958).

1433. L. Pierce, Microwave spectrum, internal barrier, structure, equilibrium conformation, and dipole moment of methyl monofluorosilane, *J. Chem. Phys.* **29**, 383–388 (1958).

1434. J. Sheridan, Microwave spectroscopy in analysis and process control, *Autom. Meas. Quality Process Plants, Proc. Conf. Swansea* **1957**, 185–194. Academic Press, New York, 1958.

1435. G. H. Steward and H. Eyring, The principle of minimum bending of orbitals, *J. Chem. Educ.* **35**, 550–557 (1958).

1436. J. D. Swalen and B. P. Stoicheff, Microwave spectrum of methyl difluorosilane, *J. Chem. Phys.* **28**, 671–674 (1958).

1437. R. Trambarulo, A. Clark, and C. Hearns, Planarity of the formic acid monomer, *J. Chem. Phys.* **28**, 736–737 (1958).

1438. V. G. Veselago, Determination of the structure of the HDSe molecule from the rotational microwave spectrum, *Izv. Akad. Nauk. SSSR Ser. Fiz.* **22**, 1150–1153 (1958).

1439. J. E. Boggs and H. C. Agnew, Nonresonant microwave absorption in certain halogen substituted methanes, *J. Phys. Chem.* **63**, 1127–1129 (1959).

1440. D. Christensen, Preliminary investigation of the microwave absorption of α-fluoronaphthalene, *Spectrochim. Acta* **15**, 767 (1959).

1441. L. Clayton, Q. Williams, and T. L. Weatherly, Nitryl chloride molecular constants from microwave spectrum analysis, *J. Chem. Phys.* **30**, 1328–1334 (1959). Errata— *J. Chem. Phys.* **31**, 554 (1959).

1442. C. C. Costain and J. R. Morton, Microwave spectrum and structure of propynal (HCCCHO), *J. Chem. Phys.* **31**, 389–393 (1959).

1443. A. P. Cox, L. F. Thomas, and J. Sheridan, Internuclear distances in ketene from spectroscopic measurements, *Spectrochim. Acta* **15**, 542–543 (1959).

1444. R. F. Curl, Jr., Microwave spectrum, barrier to internal rotation, and structure of methyl formate, *J. Chem. Phys.* **30**, 1529–1536 (1959).

1445. A. Danti and J. L. Wood, Far infrared spectrum and the barrier to internal rotation in 1,1,1,2-tetrafluoroethane, *J. Chem. Phys.* **30**, 582–584 (1959).

1446. A. DiGiacomo, On some phenomena related to the saturation of rotational resonances, *Nuovo Cimento* **14**, 1082–1092 (1959).

1447. V. E. Derr and J. J. Gallagher, Nitric oxide constants from microwave spectroscopy, *Bull. Am. Phys. Soc.* [2]**4**, 455 (1959).

1448. P. Favero, A. M. Mirri, and J. G. Baker, Millimeter wave spectrum and structure of formyl fluoride, *J. Chem. Phys.* **31**, 566–567 (1959).

1449. E. K. Gora, The rotational spectrum of ozone, *J. Mol. Spectry.* **3**, 78–99 (1959).

1450. D. R. Jenkins and T. M. Sugden, Microwave spectrum and structure of 1,1 difluorovinyl chloride, *Trans. Faraday Soc.* **55**, 1473–1479 (1959).

1451. P. H. Kasai, R. J. Myers, D. F. Eggers, Jr., and K. B. Wiberg, Microwave spectrum, structure, and dipole moment of cyclopropane, *J. Chem. Phys.* **30**, 512–516 (1959).

1452. T. Kasuya and T. Oka, Microwave spectrum of ethyl iodide, *J. Phys. Soc. Japan* **14**, 980–981 (1959).

1453. P. G. Kokeritz and H. Selen, Microwave spectrum and electric dipole moment of cyclopentanone, *Arkiv Fysik* **16**, 197–198 (1959).

1454. D. G. Kowalewski, P. Kokeritz, and H. Selen, Microwave spectrum and electric dipole moment of fluorobenzene, *J. Chem. Phys.* **31**, 1438 (1959).

1455. L. C. Krisher and E. B. Wilson, Jr., Microwave spectrum of acetyl cyanide, *J. Chem. Phys.* **31**, 882–889 (1959).

1456. V. W. Laurie, Microwave spectrum of methyl germane, *J. Chem. Phys.* **30**, 1210–1214 (1959).

1457. D. R. Lide, Jr., Microwave spectrum of trimethylarsine, *Spectrochim. Acta* **15**, 473–476 (1959).

1458. D. R. Lide, Jr. and D. E. Mann, Microwave spectrum and structure of N_2F_4, *J. Chem. Phys.* **31**, 1129–1130 (1959).

1459. D. R. Lide, Jr., R. W. Taft, Jr., and P. Love, Microwave absorption in the trimethylamine trimethylboron addition complex, *J. Chem. Phys.* **31**, 561–562 (1959).

1460. J. F. Lotspeich, A. Javan, and A. Engelbrecht, Microwave spectrum and structure of perrhenyl fluoride, *J. Chem. Phys.* **31**, 633–643 (1959).

1461. K. Matsuura, Frequency shift in ammonia absorption lines other than (3,3), *J. Phys. Soc. Japan* **14**, 1826 (1959).

1462. D. J. Meschi and R. J. Myers, The microwave spectrum, structure, and dipole moment of disulfur monoxide, *J. Mol. Spectry.* **3**, 405–416 (1959).

1463. H. W. Morgan and J. H. Goldstein, Microwave spectrum and molecular structure of vinyl fluoride, *J. Chem. Phys.* **30**, 1025–1028 (1959).

1464. I. A. Mukhtarov, Microwave spectrum of the $FH_2CCH_2Cl^{37}$ molecule, *Opt. i. Spektroskopiya* **6**, 260 (1959).

1465. L. Pekarek, Radiospectroscopy—A new branch of modern physics, *Pokroky Mat. Fys. Astron.* **4**, 42–53, 162–179 (1959).

1466. L. Pierce and L. C. Krisher, Microwave spectrum, internal barrier, structure, conformation, and dipole moment of acetyl fluoride, *J. Chem. Phys.* **31**, 875–882 (1959).

1467. L. Pierce and J. M. O'Reilly, Microwave spectrum, dipole moment, and internal barrier of 2-fluoropropene, *J. Mol. Spectry.* **3**, 536–547 (1959).

1468. W. E. Smith, The microwave spectra of isotopic molecules of sulfur dioxide, *Australian J. Phys.* **12**, 109–112 (1959).

1469. G. P. Srivastava, Microwave absorption in ethyl chloride, *Proc. Phys. Soc. (London)* **74**, 401–407 (1959).

1470. K. K. Svidzinskii, On the hyperfine structure of the rotational spectra of molecules of the symmetric rotor type, *Opt. Spectry. (USSR) (English Transl.)* **6**, 163–164 (1959).

1471. K. Takayanagi, Rotational transitions in hydrogen and deuterium, *J. Phys. Soc. Japan* **14**, 1458–1459 (1959).

1472. J. K. Tyler, A. P. Cox, and J. Sheridan, Molecular symmetry in cyclopentadienyl thallium and some related compounds from their microwave spectra, *Nature* **183**, 1182–1183 (1959).

1473. V. G. Veselago, Determination of the structure and dipole moment of HDSe from its microwave spectrum, *Opt. Spectry. (USSR) (English Transl.)* **6**, 286–289 (1959).

1474. R. Wertheimer, Absorption spectrum of sulfuric anhydride in the millimeter wave region, *Compt. Rend.* **248**, 1640–1641 (1959).

1475. B. Bak, S. Detoni, L. Hansen-Nygaard, J. T. Nielsen, and J. Rastrup-Andersen, Microwave determination of the structure of ethyl fluoride, *Spectrochim. Acta* **16**, 376–383 (1960).

1476. B. F. Burke, The radio-frequency spectrum of H_2^+, *Astrophys. J.* **132**, 514–515 (1960).

1477. J. D. Graybeal, Microwave spectrum and molecular structure of monochloroacetonitrile, *J. Chem. Phys.* **32**, 1258–1260 (1960).

1478. E. Hirota and Y. Morino, Microwave spectrum of malononitrile, $CH_2(CH)_2I$. The molecular structure in the ground vibrational state, *Bull. Chem. Soc. Japan* **33**, 158–162 (1960).

1479. N. A. Irisova and E. M. Dianov, Ultrahigh frequency absorption of CH_3GeF_3, *Opt. i Spektroskopiya* **9**, 261 (1960).

1480. T. S. Jaseja, Microwave spectrum of IBr and the determination of the molecular and nuclear parameters, *J. Mol. Spectry.* **5**, 445–457 (1960).

1481. D. R. Jenkins, R. Kewley, and T. M. Sugden, The microwave spectrum and structure of silyl isothiocyanate, *Proc. Chem. Soc.* **1960**, 220 (1960).

1482. L. G. Johnson, The microwave spectrum of quinuclidine, *J. Chem. Phys.* **33**, 949–950 (1960).

1483. T. Kasuya, Microwave spectrum of ethyl iodide II, *J. Phys. Soc. Japan* **15**, 1273–1277 (1960).

1484. T. Kasuya and T. Oka, Microwave spectrum of ethyl iodide I, *J. Phys. Soc. Japan* **15**, 296–303 (1960).

1485. R. Kewley, K. S. R. Murty, and T. M. Sugden, Microwave spectrum of sulfur chloride pentafluoride, *Trans. Faraday Soc.* **56**, 1732–1736 (1960).

1486. D. Kivelson, E. B. Wilson, Jr., and D. R. Lide, Jr., Microwave spectrum, structure, dipole moment, and nuclear quadrupole effects in vinyl chloride, *J. Chem. Phys.* **32**, 205–209 (1960).

1487. T. Kojima, Microwave spectrum of methyl mercaptan, *J. Phys. Soc. Japan* **15**, 1284–1291 (1960).

1488. L. C. Krisher, Microwave spectrum of acetyl cyanide, *J. Chem. Phys.* **33**, 304 (1960).

1489. L. C. Krisher, Microwave spectrum, barrier to internal rotation, and quadrupole coupling of acetyl bromide, *J. Chem. Phys.* **33**, 1237–1241 (1960).

1490. G. H. Kwei and R. F. Curl, Microwave spectrum of O^{18} formic acid and the structure of formic acid, *J. Chem. Phys.* **32**, 1592 (1960).

1491. V. W. Laurie, Microwave spectrum of *trans*-crotononitrile, *J. Chem. Phys.* **32**, 1588–1589 (1960).

1492. O. H. Leblanc, Jr., V. W. Laurie, and W. D. Gwinn, Microwave spectrum, structure, and dipole moment of formyl fluoride, *J. Chem. Phys.* **33**, 598–600 (1960).

1493. D. R. Lide, Jr., Microwave spectrum, structure, and dipole moment of propane, *J. Chem. Phys.* **33**, 1514–1518 (1960).

1494. C. C. Lin, Hyperfine structure of the microwave spectra of the NO molecule and the nuclear quadrupole moment of nitrogen, *Phys. Rev.* **119**, 1027–1028 (1960).

1495. M. W. Long, Q. Williams, and T. L. Weatherly, Microwave spectrum of $CFCl_3$, *J. Chem. Phys.* **33**, 508–516 (1960).

1496. A. A. Maryott and G. Birnbaum, Microwave absorption in compressed oxygen, *J. Chem. Phys.* **32**, 686–691 (1960).

1497. J. T. Massey, C. I. Beard, and C. K. Jen, Microwave spectral series of deuteriated hydrogen peroxide, *J. Mol. Spectry.* **5**, 405–415 (1960).

1498. D. J. Millen and J. R. Morton, The microwave spectrum of nitric acid, *J. Chem. Soc.* **1960**, 1523–1528 (1960).

1499. A. M. Mirri, Millimeter wave spectrum of deutero derivatives of formic acid, *Nuovo Cimento* **18**, 849–855 (1960).

1500. M. Mizushima, Theory of the radio-frequency spectra of the H_2^+ molecule-ion, *Astrophys. J.* **132**, 493–501 (1960).

1501. M. Mizushima, Theory of microwave absorption by compressed oxygen gas, *J. Chem. Phys.* **32**, 691–697 (1960).

1502. H. Moon, J. H. Goldstein, and J. W. Simmons, The microwave spectrum of chloroallene, *Spectrochim. Acta* **16**, 1267 (1960).

1503. N. Muller and R. C. Bracken, Microwave spectrum and structure of H_3SiCN and D_3SiCN, *J. Chem. Phys.* **32**, 1577–1578 (1960).

1504. T. Oka, Microwave spectrum of formaldehyde II. Molecular structure in the ground state, *J. Phys. Soc. Japan* **15**, 2274–2279 (1960).

1505. T. Oka, H. Hirakawa, and K. Shimoda, Microwave spectrum of formaldehyde I. K-type doubling spectra, *J. Phys. Soc. Japan* **15**, 2265–2273 (1960).

1506. L. Pierce and D. H. Petersen, Microwave spectrum, structure, dipole moment, and internal rotation of trimethylsilane, *J. Chem. Phys.* **33**, 907–913 (1960).

1507. A. M. Prokhorov and G. P. Shipulo, Microwave investigation of the molecules F_3BNH_3 and $F_3BN(CH_3)_3$, *Opt. Spectry. (USSR) (English Transl.)* **8**, 218–219 (1960).

1508. K. E. Reinert, Microwave spectrum and planar character of the nitrobenzene molecule, *Z. Naturforsch.* **15A**, 85–86 (1960).

1509. K. V. L. N. Sastry, Microwave spectrum of methyl amine I. Experimental details and spectrum of CD_3NH_2, *Proc. Indian Acad. Sci.* **51A**, 301–309 (1960).

1510. J. Sheridan, J. K. Tyler, E. E. Aynsley, R. E. Dodd, and R. Little, Microwave spectrum of fluorine cyanide, *Nature* **185**, 96 (1960).

1511. T. Shimizu and H. Takuma, Microwave spectrum of *cis* 1,2 dichloroethylene, *J. Phys. Soc. Japan* **15**, 646–650 (1960).

1512. J. K. Tyler and J. Sheridan, Microwave spectrum and structure of fluoroacetylene, *Proc. Chem. Soc.* **1960**, 119–120 (1960).

1513. W. Zeil, M. Winnewisser, H. K. Bodenseh, and H. Buchert, Microwave spectra of substituted acetylenes, *Z. Naturforsch.* **15A**, 1011–1013 (1960).

1514. B. Bak, Determination of the structure of α- and β-fluoronaphthalenes and other selected molecules by infrared and microwave techniques, *U.S. Dept. Com., Office Tech. Serv.*, AD 262, 113 (1961).

1515. B. Bak, D. Christensen, L. Hansen-Nygaard, and J. Rastrup-Andersen, The structure of thiophene, *J. Mol. Spectry.* **7**, 58–63 (1961).

1516. P. Cahill and S. Butcher, Microwave spectrum and barrier to internal rotation of methyl stannane, *J. Chem. Phys.* **35**, 2255–2256 (1961).

1517. C. C. Costain and G. P. Srivastava, Study of hydrogen bonding. The microwave rotational spectrum of CF_3COOH-$HCOOH$, *J. Chem. Phys.* **35**, 1903–1904 (1961).

1518. R. F. Curl, Jr., J. L. Kinsey, J. G. Baker, J. C. Baird, G. R. Bird, R. F. Heidelberg, T. M. Sugden, D. R. Jenkins, and C. N. Kenney, Microwave spectrum of chlorine dioxide I. Rotational assignment, *Phys. Rev.* **121**, 1119–1123 (1961).

1519. W. B. Dixon and E. B. Wilson, Jr., Microwave spectrum of methyl nitrate, *J. Chem. Phys.* **35**, 191–198 (1961).

1520. R. E. Goedertier, Rotational Spectrum of C^{13} enriched vinyl bromide. *Ann. Soc. Sci. Bruxelles Ser. I* **75**, 174–182 (1961).

1521. J. E. Griffiths and K. B. McAfee, Microwave spectrum of germanyl fluoride, *Proc. Chem. Soc.* **1961**, 456 (1961).

1522. S. de Hepcee, Rotational spectra of vinyl bromides in the ground state and a vibrationally excited state in the microwave region, *Ann. Soc. Sci. Bruxelles Ser. I* **75**, 194–211 (1961).

1523. A. R. Hilton, Jr., A. W. Jache, J. B. Beal, Jr., W. D. Henderson, and R. J. Robinson, Millimeter wave spectrum and molecular structure of oxygen difluoride, *J. Chem. Phys.* **34**, 1137–1141 (1961).

1524. E. Hirota, Microwave spectrum in the excited vibrational states of malononitrile, $CH_2(CN)_2$. A possible assignment of CCN bending modes, *J. Mol. Spectry.* **7**, 242–260 (1961).

1525. E. Hirota and Y. Morino, Microwave spectra of propargyl halides I. Molecular structure, dipole moment, and quadrupole coupling constant of propargyl chloride, *Bull. Chem Soc. Japan* **34**, 341–348 (1961).

1526. J. Hoeft, The microwave rotation spectrum of indium monochloride, *Z. Physik* **163**, 262–276 (1961).

1527. L. M. Imanov and Ch. O. Kadzhar, The Q branch in the microwave spectra of C_2H_5OH, *Dokl. Akad. Nauk Azerb. SSR* **17**, 861–863 (1961).

1528. B. E. Job and J. Sheridan, Microwave spectrum of fluoroacetonitrile, *Nature* **192**, 160–161 (1961).

1529. L. C. Krisher and E. B. Wilson, Jr., Microwave spectrum of acetyl cyanide, *U.S. Dept. Com. Office Tech. Serv. PB Rept.* 145,746 (1961).

1530. V. W. Laurie, Microwave spectrum of cis-difluoroethylene structures and dipole moments of fluoroethylenes, *J. Chem. Phys.* **34**, 391–394 (1961).

1531. V. W. Laurie, Microwave spectrum of isobutylene. Dipole moment, internal barrier, equilibrium conformation, and structure, *J. Chem. Phys.* **34**, 1516–1519 (1961).

1532. D. J. Millen and J. P. Annell, The microwave spectrum, structure, and nuclear quadrupole coupling coefficients of nitrosyl chloride, *J. Chem. Soc.* **1961**, 1322–1328 (1961).

1533. R. F. Miller and R. F. Curl, Jr., Microwave spectrum of O^{18} formyl fluoride and the structure of formyl fluoride, *J. Chem. Phys.* **34**, 1847–1848 (1961).

1534. A. M. Mirri, A. Guarnieri, and P. Favero, Millimeter wave spectrum and dipole moment of vinyl fluoride, *Nuovo Cimento* **19**, 1189–1194 (1961).

1535. J. M. O'Reilly and L. Pierce, Microwave spectrum, structure, dipole moment, and internal barrier of vinyl silane, *J. Chem. Phys.* **34**, 1176–1181 (1961).

1536. L. Pierce, R. Jackson, and N. DiCianni, Microwave spectrum, structure, and dipole moment of F_2O, *J. Chem. Phys.* **35**, 2240–2241 (1961).

1537. A. S. Rajan, Microwave spectrum of trichloroacetonitrile, *Proc. Indian Acad. Sci.* **53A**, 89–94 (1961).

1538. J. D. Rogers and D. Williams, Nitrosyl chloride structure, *J. Chem. Phys.* **34**, 2195–2196 (1961).

1539. K. M. Sinnott, Microwave spectrum of acetyl chloride, *J. Chem. Phys.* **34**, 851–861 (1961).

1539a. T. Yajima, Three-level maser action in gas II. Experimental study on formic acid, *J. Phys. Soc. Japan* **16**, 1709 (1961).

1540. K. Wada, Y. Kikuchi, C. Matsumura, E. Hirota, and Y. Morino, Microwave spectrum and molecular structure of CH_2ClCN, *Bull. Chem. Soc. Japan* **34**, 337–341 (1961).

1541. J. F. Westerkamp, Asymmetric top molecules in the microwave region II. Carbonyl cyanide and perfluorodimethyl ether, *Bol. Acad. Nacl. Cienc. (Cordoba, Rep. Arg.)* **42**, 191–200 (1961).

1542. W. Zeil, M. Winnewisser, and W. Huettner, The microwave spectrum of $(CH_3)_3CBr$ in the 20,000 Mc range, *Z. Naturforsch.* **16A**, 1248–1249 (1961).

1543. W. Zeil, M. Winnewisser, and K. Mueller, Microwave spectroscopic investigations of $(CH_3)_3CCl$ and $(CD_3)_3CCl$, *Z. Naturforsch.* **16A**, 1250 (1961).

1544. R. W. Zimmerer and M. Mizushima, Precise measurement of the microwave absorption frequencies of the oxygen molecule and the velocity of light, *Phys. Rev.* **121**, 152–155 (1961).

1545. B. Bak, D. Christensen, J. Christiansen, L. Hansen-Nygard, and J. Rastrup-Andersen, Microwave spectrum and internal barrier of rotation of methyl ketene, *Spectrochim. Acta* **18**, 1421–1424 (1962).

1546. B. Bak, D. Christensen, L. Hansen-Nygaard, and J. Rastrup-Andersen, Microwave spectrum and dipole moment of thiazole, *J. Mol. Spectry.* **9**, 222–224 (1962).

1547. B. Bak, D. Christensen, L. Hansen-Nygaard, L. Lipschitz, and J. Rastrup-Andersen, Microwave spectra of 1,3,4-thiadiazole and (S^{34}) 1,3,4-thiadiazole. Dipole moment of 1,3,4-thiadiazole, *J. Mol. Spectry.* **9**, 225–227 (1962).

1548. R. A. Beaudet, Microwave spectrum, barrier to internal rotation, and quadrupole coupling constants of *trans*-1-chloropropylene, *J. Chem. Phys.* **37**, 2398–2402 (1962).

1549. R. A. Beaudet and E. B. Wilson, Jr., Microwave spectrum and barrier to internal rotation of *cis*-1-fluoropropylene, *J. Chem. Phys.* **37**, 1133–1138 (1962).

1550. E. L. Beeson, T. L. Weatherly, and Q. Williams, Molecular constants of chlorodifluoromethane from microwave spectrum analysis, *J. Chem. Phys.* **37**, 2926–2929 (1962).

1551. J. C. Chauffoureaux, Microwave rotational spectra of vinylidene fluoride, *Bull. Classe Sci., Acad. Roy. Belg.* **48**, 1297–1307 (1962).

1552. C. C. Costain, Anomalies in the pure rotation spectrum of fluoroform in excited vibrational states, *J. Mol. Spectry.* **9**, 317–336 (1962).

1553. R. F. Curl, Jr., Microwave spectrum of chlorine dioxide III. Interpretation of the hyperfine coupling constants obtained in terms of the electronic structure, *J. Chem. Phys.* **37**, 779–784 (1962). Erratum—*J. Chem. Phys.* **38**, 1446 (1963).

1554. J. D. Graybeal and D. W. Roe, Microwave spectrum and dipole moment of monofluoroacetonitrile, *J. Chem. Phys.* **37**, 2503 (1962).

1555. M. L. Grenier-Besson and S. Maes, Interpretation of microwave spectra of pure rotation, *Publ. Group. Avan. Methodes Spectrog.* **1962**, 29 (1962).

1556. M. de Hemptinne, F. Greindl, and R. Riet, Rotation spectrum of SO_2, *Bull. Classe Sci., Acad. Roy. Belg.* **48**, 397–410 (1962).

1557. R. H. Jackson, The microwave spectrum, structure, and dipole moment of dioxygen difluoride, *J. Chem. Soc.* **1962**, 4585–4592 (1962).

1558. D. R. Jenkins, R. Kewley, and T. M. Sugden, Microwave spectrum and structure of silyl isothiocyanate, *Trans. Faraday Soc.* **58**, 1284–1290 (1962).

1559. B. E. Job and J. Sheridan, Propargyl fluoride and its microwave spectrum, *Nature* **193**, 677 (1962).

1560. W. H. Kirchoff and E. B. Wilson, Jr., The microwave spectrum and structure of NSF_3, *J. Am. Chem. Soc.* **84**, 334–336 (1962).

1561. V. W. Laurie, D. T. Pence, and R. H. Jackson, Microwave spectrum, structure, and dipole moment of carbonyl fluoride, *J. Chem. Phys.* **37**, 2995–2999 (1962).

1562. D. R. Lide, Jr., Microwave studies of butadiene derivatives I. Spectrum of fluoroprene, *J. Chem. Phys.* **37**, 2074–2079 (1962).

1563. J. H. N. Loubser, Microwave spectrum and structure of trichlorofluoromethane, *J. Chem. Phys.* **36**, 2808–2809 (1962).

1564. C. Matsumura, E. Hirota, T. Oka, and Y. Morino, Microwave spectrum of acetonitrile-d_3 CD_3CN, *J. Mol. Spectry.* **9**, 366–380 (1962).

1565. D. B. McLay and C. R. Mann, Microwave spectrum and molecular structure of CHF_2Cl, *Can. J. Phys.* **40**, 61–73 (1962).

1566. J. Michielsen-Effinger, Rotation spectrum of ethyl alcohol by microwaves, *Bull. Classe Sci., Acad. Roy. Belg.* **48**, 438–452 (1962).

1567. A. M. Mirri, P. Favero, A. Guarnieri, and G. Semerano, Millimeter spectrum of asymmetric triatomic nitrosyl chloride molecules, *Boll. Sci. Fac. Chim. Ind. Bologna* **20**, 110–114 (1962).

1568. A. Mozumder, The microwave spectrum of methyl alcohol I. General theory, *Proc. Natl. Inst. Sci. India Pt. A* **28**, 57–73 (1962).

1569. A. Mozumder, The microwave spectrum of methyl alcohol II. Numerical part, *Proc. Natl. Inst. Sci. India Pt. A* **28**, 74–88 (1962).

1570. I. A. Mukhtarov, Microwave spectrum of 1,1,2-trifluoroethane, *Izv. Akad. Nauk Azerb. SSR Ser. Fiz.-Mat. i Tekhn. Nauk* **18**, 59–63 (1962).

1571. L. J. Nugent and C. D. Cornwell, Microwave spectrum of methyldifluoroarsine, *J. Chem. Phys.* **37**, 523–534 (1962).

1572. L. J. Nugent, D. E. Mann, and D. R. Lide, Jr., Microwave structure determinations on tertiary butyl acetylenes and tertiary butyl cyanide, *J. Chem. Phys.* **36**, 965–971 (1962).

1573. T. Oka and Y. Morino, Analysis of the microwave spectrum of hydrogen selenide, *J. Mol. Spectry.* **8**, 300–314 (1962).

1574. L. Pierce and V. Dobyns, Molecular structure, dipole moment, and quadrupole coupling constants of diazirine, *J. Am. Chem. Soc.* **84**, 2651–2652 (1962).

1575. M. G. K. Pillai, Microwave spectrum of formaldoxime, *J. Phys. Chem.* **66**, 179–180 (1962).

1576. A. Rachman, Analysis of the microwave spectrum of m-fluorochlorobenzene, *Arkiv Fysik* **23**, 291–299 (1962).

1577. W. G. Rothschild and B. P. Dailey, Microwave spectrum of bromocyclobutane, *J. Chem. Phys.* **36**, 2931–2940 (1962).

1578. R. H. Schwendeman and G. D. Jacobs, Molecular structure of ethyl chloride, *J. Chem. Phys.* **36**, 1245–1250 (1962).

1579. R. H. Schwendeman and G. D. Jacobs, Microwave spectrum, structure, quadrupole coupling constants, and barrier to internal rotation of chloromethylsilane, *J. Chem. Phys.* **36**, 1251–1257 (1962).

1580. G. Semerano, The electronic and microwave spectrum of formyl fluoride, *U.S. Dept. Com., Office Tech. Serv. PB Rept.* 149,450 (1962).

1581. K. Shimoda, Maser spectry *in* Topics on Radiofrequency Spectroscopy, *Proc. Intern. School Phys. Enrico Fermi. 17th Course Varenna, August 1960*, Academic Press, New York, 1962.

1582. G. P. Shipulo, Microwave spectrum of the HDNCN and D_2NCN molecules, *Opt. i Spektroskopiya* **13**, 593–594 (1962).

1583. G. A. Sobolev, A. M. Shcherbakov, and P. A. Akishin, Rotational spectrum and the dipole moment of the vinyl acetylene molecule, *Opt. i Spektroskopiya* **12**, 147 (1962).

1584. W. M. Tolles and W. D. Gwinn, Structure and dipole moment of SF_4, *J. Chem. Phys.* **36**, 1119–1121 (1962).

1585. J. K. Tyler, L. F. Thomas, and J. Sheridan, Rotational spectrum of the cyanamide molecule, *J. Opt. Soc. Am.* **52**, 581 (1962).

1586. R. Van Riet, Rotational spectrum of the $S^{33}O_2$ molecule in the first excited state. *Bull. Classe Sci., Acad. Roy. Belg.* **48**, 659–667 (1962).

1587. R. Van Riet, Rotational spectrum of $S^{32}O_2$ and $S^{33}O_2$ molecules in the ground state and in the excited state of the v_2 vibration (interval 27,500–30,500 Mc), *Bull. Classe. Sci., Acad. Roy. Belg.* **48**, 1291–1296 (1962).

1588. V. F. Volkov, N. N. Vyshinskii, and N. K. Rudnevskii, Vibrational and rotational spectra of trimethylchlorosilane, triethylchlorosilane, and triethylchlorostannane, *Izv. Akad. Nauk SSR Ser. Fiz.* **26**, 1282–1285 (1962).

1589. W. Zeil, W. Huettner, and W. Plein, Microwave spectrum and quadrupole coupling constant of $(CH_3)_3CCl^{35}$, *Z. Naturforsch.* **17A**, 823–824 (1962).

1590. A. Bauder, F. Tank, and Hs. H. Guenthard, Microwave spectrum, dipole moment, and structure of cyclobutanone, *Helv. Chim. Acta* **46**, 1453–1463 (1963).

1591. S. S. Butcher, Microwave spectrum of propylene sulfide, *J. Chem. Phys.* **38**, 2310–2311 (1963).

1592. J. C. Chauffoureaux, Ground state of vinylidene fluoride. Data on the first excited state, *Ann. Soc. Sci. Bruxelles Ser. I* **77**, 171–176 (1963).

1593. A. P. Cox and A. S. Esbitt, Fundamental vibrational frequencies in ketene and the deuteroketenes, *J. Chem. Phys.* **38**, 1636–1643 (1963).

1594. R. F. Curl, Jr., V. M. Rao, K. V. L. N. Sastry, and J. A. Hodgeson, Microwave spectrum of methyl isocyanate, *J. Chem. Phys.* **39**, 3335–3340 (1963).

1595. E. A. V. Ebsworth, D. R. Jenkins, M. J. Mays, and T. M. Sugden, The preparation and structure of silyl azide, *J. Chem. Soc.* **1963**, 21 (1963).

1596. L. Esterowitz, Rotational transitions and centrifugal distortion in the UHF spectrum of formaldehyde, *J. Chem. Phys.* **39**, 247–248 (1963).

1597. C. Flanagan and L. Pierce, Microwave spectrum, structure, and quadrupole coupling tensor of ethyl bromide, *J. Chem. Phys.* **38**, 2963–2969 (1963).

1598. R. E. Goedertier, Rotation spectra, quadrupole coupling, and structure of vinyl bromide, *J. Phys. (Paris)* **24**, 633–637 (1963).

1599. L. M. Imanov and A. A. Abdurakhmanov, Microwave spectrum of CD_3CH_2OH, *Izv. Akad. Nauk Azerb. SSR Ser. Fiz-Mat. i Tekhn. Nauk* **19**, 79–82 (1963).

1600. L. M. Imanov and Ch. O. Kadzhar, The superhigh-frequency spectrum and dipole moment of the ethanol molecule, *Opt. i Spektroskopiya* **14**, 300–301 (1963).

1601. R. Kewley, K. V. L. N. Sastry, and M. Winnewisser, The millimeter wave spectra of isocyanic and isothiocyanic acids, *J. Mol. Spectry.* **10**, 418–441 (1963).

1602. R. Kewley, K. V. L. N. Sastry, M. Winnewisser, and W. Gordy, Millimeter wave spectroscopy of unstable molecular species I. Carbon monosulfide, *J. Chem. Phys.* **39**, 2856–2860 (1963).

1603. W. H. Kirchoff and E. B. Wilson, Jr., The microwave spectrum and structure of NSF, *J. Am. Chem. Soc.* **85**, 1726–1729 (1963).

1604. R. L. Kuczkowski, Sulfur monofluoride-microwave spectrum of a second isomer, *J. Am. Chem. Soc.* **85**, 3047–3048 (1963).

1605. R. L. Kuczkowski and E. B. Wilson, Jr., Microwave spectrum, structure, and dipole moment of cis-N_2F_2, *J. Chem. Phys.* **39**, 1030–1034 (1963).

1606. R. L. Kuczkowski and E. B. Wilson, Jr., Microwave and mass spectra of sulfur monofluoride, *J. Am. Chem. Soc.* **85**, 2028–2029 (1963).

1607. V. W. Laurie and D. T. Pence, Microwave spectra and structures of difluoroethylenes, *J. Chem. Phys.* **38**, 2693–2697 (1963).

1608. I. N. Levine, Structure of formaldoxime, *J. Chem. Phys.* **38**, 2326–2328 (1963).

1609. D. R. Lide, Jr., Microwave spectrum and structure of difluoroamine, *J. Chem. Phys.* **38**, 456–460 (1963).

1610. D. R. Lide, Jr., Microwave spectrum of aluminum monofluoride, *J. Chem. Phys.* **38**, 2027 (1963).

1611. J. S. Muenter and V. W. Laurie, Microwave spectrum, structure, and dipole moment of silyl acetylene, *J. Chem. Phys.* **39**, 1181–1182 (1963).

1612. I. A. Mukhtarov, Microwave spectrum of the $F_2HCCDHF$ molecule, *Dokl. Akad. Nauk SSSR* **148**, 566–568 (1963).

1613. I. A. Mukhtarov, Microwave spectrum of $CF_2=CHF$, *Opt. i Spektroskopiya* **15**, 563–564 (1963).

1614. I. A. Mukhtarov, Microwave spectrum of the F_2HC-CH_2F molecule, *Dokl. Akad. Nauk SSSR* **151**, 1076–1078 (1963).

1615. I. A. Mukhtarov, The microwave spectrum of trifluoroethane, *Fiz. Probl. Spektroskopii, Akad. Nauk SSSR, Materialy 13-Go (Trinadtsatogo) Soveshch., Leningrad, 1960* **2**, 85–87 (1963).

1616. R. Nelson, Microwave spectrum, molecular structure, and dipole moment of dimethyl-phosphine, *J. Chem. Phys.* **39**, 2382–2383 (1963).

1617. E. W. Neuvar and A. W. Jache, Microwave spectrum and structure of pentafluoro-sulfur bromide, *J. Chem. Phys.* **39**, 596–599 (1963).

1618. R. L. Poynter, Microwave spectrum, quadrupole coupling constants, and dipole moment of chlorobenzene, *J. Chem. Phys.* **39**, 1962–1966 (1963).

1619. T. N. Sarachman, Microwave spectrum of normal propyl chloride, *J. Chem. Phys.* **39**, 469–473 (1963).

1620. L. H. Scharpen and V. W. Laurie, Structure of isobutylene, *J. Chem. Phys.* **39**, 1732–1733 (1963).

1621. T. Shigenari, S. Kobayashi, and H. Takuma, (6.3) Rotational spectrum of formaldehyde by a radio-frequency beam-type maser, *J. Phys. Soc. Japan* **18**, 312–313 (1963).

1622. K. K. Svidzinskii, Calculation of the hyperfine structure of the inversion spectra of the ND_3 molecule, *Fiz. Probl. Spektroskopii, Akad. Nauk SSSR, Materialy 13-Go (Trinadtsatogo) Soveshch., Leningrad, 1960* **2**, 83–85 (1963).

1623. K. Takagi and T. Oka, Millimeter wave spectrum of formaldehyde, *J. Phys. Soc. Japan* **18**, 1174–1180 (1963).

1624. K. Takagi and S. Saito, Millimeter wave spectrum of SO_2, *J. Phys. Soc. Japan* **18**, 1840 (1963).

1625. J. K. Tyler, Microwave spectrum of nitramide, *J. Mol. Spectry.* **11**, 39–46 (1963).

1626. J. K. Tyler and J. Sheridan, Structural studies of linear molecules by microwave spectro-scopy, *Trans. Faraday Soc.* **59**, 2661–2670 (1963).

1627. R. Van Riet, Rotational spectrum of the $S^{34}O_2$ molecule in the first vibrational excited state (12,800–30,000 Mc) and complimentary study of the $S^{32}O_2$ and $S^{33}O_2$ molecules in the range 25,000–27,500 Mc, *Ann. Soc. Sci. Bruxelles Ser. I* **77**, 18–29 (1963).

1628. L. Wharton and W. Klemperer, Microwave spectrum of BaO, *J. Chem. Phys.* **38**, 2705–2708 (1963).

1629. L. Wharton, W. Klemperer, L. P. Gold, R. Strauch, J. J. Gallagher, and V. E. Derr, Microwave spectrum, spectroscopic constants, and electric dipole moment of Li^6F^{19}, *J. Chem. Phys.* **38**, 1203–1210 (1963).

1629a. A. Yariv and J. P. Gordon, The laser, *Proc. IEEE* **51**, 4–29 (1963).

1630. A. Bauer and J. Bellet, Rotation spectra of SO_2 in the millimeter region, *J. Phys. (Paris)* **25**, 805–808 (1964).

1631. A. Bauer and J. Bellet, Rotation spectrum of SO_2 in millimeter wavelengths (6 and 2.2 mm), *Compt. Rend.* **258**, 873–876 (1964).

1632. R. A. Beaudet, Microwave spectrum, barrier to internal rotation, and quadrupole coupling constants of *cis*-1-chloropropylene, *J. Chem. Phys.* **40**, 2705–2715 (1964).

1633. S. S. Butcher and E. B. Wilson, Jr., Microwave spectrum of propionaldehyde, *J. Chem. Phys.* **40**, 1671–1677 (1964).

1634. C. C. Costain and G. P. Srivastava, Microwave rotation spectra of hydrogen-bonded molecules, *J. Chem. Phys.* **41**, 1620–1627 (1964).

1635. P. A. Curnuck and J. Sheridan, Microwave spectrum of fluorobromoethane, *Nature* **202**, 591–592 (1964).

1636. L. Esterowitz and J. Rosenthal, Dipole moment of $N^{15}O_2^{16}$, *J. Chem. Phys.* **40**, 1986–1987 (1964).

1637. K. M. Evenson, J. L. Dunn, and H. P. Broida, Optical detection of microwave transi-tions between excited electronic states of CN and the identification of the transitions involved, *Phys. Rev.* **136**, 1566–1571 (1964).

1638. A. J. Herbert, F. W. Breivogel, Jr., and K. Street, Jr., Radio-frequency and microwave spectra of LiBr by the molecular-beam electric-resonance method, *J. Chem. Phys.* **41**, 2368–2376 (1964).

1639. C. D. Hollowell, A. J. Hebert, and K. Street, Jr., Radio-frequency and microwave spectra of NaF by the molecular beam electric-resonance method, *J. Chem. Phys.* **41**, 3540–3545 (1964).

1640. L. M. Imanov and A. A. Abdurakhmanov, Q branch of the microwave rotational spectra of the CD_3CH_2OH molecule, *Dokl. Akad. Nauk Azerb. SSR* **20**, 7–8 (1964).

1641. L. M. Imanov, A. A. Abdurakhmanov, and R. A. Ragimova, Microwave rotational spectrum of CH_3CD_2OH, *Izv. Akad. Nauk Azerb. SSR, Ser. Fiz.-Tekhn. i Mat. Nauk* **20**, 103–106 (1964).

1642. L. M. Imanov, A. A. Abdurakhmanov, and R. A. Ragimova, Microwave spectrum and effective rotational constants of the CD_3CH_2OH molecule, *Opt. i Spektroskopiya* **17**, 306–307 (1964).

1643. G. Jones and W. Gordy, Extension of submillimeter wave spectroscopy below a half millimeter wavelength, *Phys. Rev.* **135**, 295–296 (1964).

1644. G. Jones and W. Gordy, Submillimeter-wave spectra of HCl and HBr, *Phys. Rev.* **136**, 1229–1232 (1964).

1645. R. Kewley, K. V. L. N. Sastry, and M. Winnewisser, Microwave and millimeter wave spectra of hydrazoic acid, *J. Mol. Spectry.* **12**, 387–401 (1964).

1646. W. J. Lafferty and D. R. Lide, Jr., Rotational constants of excited vibrational states of $N_2^{14}O^{16}$, *J. Mol. Spectry* **14**, 407–408 (1964).

1647. D. R. Lide, Jr., Recent microwave spectral studies of high-temperature species, *Proc. 1st Meeting Interagency Chem. Rocket Propulsion Group Thermochem., New York, 1963* **1**, 1–2. Appl. Phys. Lab., Johns Hopkins University, Silver Spring, Maryland, 1964.

1648. D. R. Lide, Jr., P. Cahill, and L. P. Gold, Microwave spectrum of lithium chloride, *J. Chem. Phys.* **40**, 156–159 (1964).

1649. D. R. Lide, Jr. and M. Jen, Microwave studies of butadiene derivatives II. Isoprene, *J. Chem. Phys.* **40**, 252–253 (1964).

1650. J. Martins and E. B. Wilson, Jr., Microwave spectrum of xenon oxytetrafluoride, *J. Chem. Phys.* **41**, 570–571 (1964).

1651. D. B. McLay, Microwave spectrum of dichlorofluoroethane, *Can. J. Phys.* **42**, 720–730 (1964).

1652. Y. Morino, Y. Kikuchi, S. Saito, and E. Hirota, Equilibrium structure and potential function of sulfur dioxide from the microwave spectrum in the excited vibrational state, *J. Mol. Spectry.* **13**, 95–118 (1964).

1653. I. A. Mukhtarov, Microwave spectrum of the molecule F_2DCCD_2F, *Opt. i Spektroskopiya* **16**, 360 (1964).

1654. T. Oka, K. Takagi, and Y. Morino, Microwave spectrum of formaldehyde in vibrationally excited states, *J. Mol. Spectry.* **14**, 27–52 (1964).

1655. T. Oka, K. Tsuchiya, S. Iwata, and Y. Morino, Microwave spectrum of s-trioxane, *Bull. Chem. Soc. Japan* **37**, 4–7 (1964).

1656. M. G. Krishna Pillai, Microwave spectrum of $H_2C^{18}O$, *J. Annamalai Univ. Pt. B* **25**, 126–128 (1964).

1656a. N. M. Pozdeev and K. K. Kostein, Microwave spectrum of thiophene, *Tr. Komis. po Spektroskopii, Akad. Nauk SSSR* **3**, 231–239 (1964).

1657. H. E. Radford, 18-cm spectrum of OH, *Phys. Rev. Letters* **13**, 534–535 (1964).

1658. H. E. Radford, Synthesis of Diatomic molecules, *J. Chem. Phys.* **40**, 2732–2733 (1964).

1659. V. M. Rao and R. F. Curl, Jr., Microwave spectrum of vinyl formate, *J. Chem. Phys.* **40**, 3688–3690 (1964).

1660. J. S. Rigden and S. S. Butcher, Microwave spectrum of methyl hypochlorite, *J. Chem. Phys.* **40**, 2109–2114 (1964).

1661. K. V. L. N. Sastry and R. F. Curl, Jr., Microwave spectrum of N-methyl methylenimine, *J. Chem. Phys.* **41**, 77–80 (1964).

1662. R. H. Schwendeman, G. D. Jacobs, and T. M. Krigas, Molecular structure of cyclopropylchloride, *J. Chem. Phys.* **40**, 1022–1028 (1964).

1663. G. P. Srivastava, Microwave spectrum of monofluoro acetic acid, *Physica* **30**, 1913–1916 (1964).

1664. F. L. Tobiason and R. H. Schwendeman, Microwave spectrum, molecular structure, and quadrupole coupling constants of 2-chloropropane, *J. Chem. Phys.* **40**, 1014–1021 (1964).

1665. T. Toerring, The microwave rotation spectrum of lead monoxide, *Z. Naturforsch.* **19A**, 1426–1428 (1964).

1666. J. K. Tyler, Microwave spectrum of methinophosphide, HCP, *J. Chem. Phys.* **40**, 1170–1171 (1964).

1667. M. Winnewisser, K. V. L. N. Sastry, R. L. Cook, and W. Gordy, Millimeter wave spectroscopy of unstable molecular species II. Sulfur monoxide, *J. Chem. Phys.* **41**, 1687–1691 (1964).

1668. R. A. Beaudet, Microwave spectrum, isomeric form, and dipole moment of 1,1-difluorobutadiene, *J. Chem. Phys.* **42**, 3758–3760 (1965).

1669. R. A. Beaudet and R. L. Poynter, Microwave spectrum, structure, and dipole moment of 2,4-dicarbaheptaborane (7), *J. Chem. Phys.* **43**, 2166–2170 (1965).

1670. S. S. Butcher, Microwave spectrum of 1,3-cyclohexadiene, *J. Chem. Phys.* **42**, 1830–1832 (1965).

1671. S. S. Butcher, Microwave spectrum of 1,3,5-cycloheptatriene, *J. Chem. Phys.* **42**, 1833–1836 (1965).

1672. A. P. Cox and J. M. Riveros, Microwave spectrum and structure of nitric acid, *J. Chem. Phys.* **42**, 3106–3112 (1965).

1672a. D. Engelsen, H. A. Dijkerman, and J. Kerssen, Microwave absorption spectrum of methoxyethyne, *Rec. Trav. Chim.* **84**, 1357–1366 (1965).

1673. W. H. Flygare and J. T. Lowe, Nuclear quadrupole and spin-rotation interaction of O^{17} in formaldehyde, *Proc. Natl. Acad. Sci. U.S.* **53**, 576–579 (1965).

1674. W. H. Flygare and J. T. Lowe, Experimental study of the nuclear quadrupole and spin-rotation interaction of O^{17} in formaldehyde, *J. Chem. Phys.* **43**, 3645–3653 (1965).

1675. P. D. Foster, V. M. Rao, and R. F. Curl, Jr., Microwave spectrum of methyl vinyl ketone, *J. Chem. Phys.* **43**, 1064–1066 (1965).

1675a. M. C. L. Gerry and T. M. Sugden, Microwave spectrum and structure of silyl acetylene, *Trans. Faraday Soc.* **61**, 2091–2096 (1965).

1676. Y. Hanyu and J. E. Boggs, Microwave spectrum and molecular structure of nitrosobenzene, *J. Chem. Phys.* **43**, 3454–3456 (1965).

1677. J. Hoeft, The microwave rotational spectrum of SnS, *Z. Naturforsch.* **20A**, 313–316 (1965).

1678. J. Hoeft, Microwave rotation spectrum of SiSe, *Z. Naturforsch.* **20A**, 1122–1124 (1965).

1679. J. Hoeft, Microwave spectrum of SiS, *Z. Naturforsch.* **20A**, 1327–1329 (1965).

1680. L. M. Imanov, Ch. O. Kadzhar, and I. D. Isaev, Microwave rotational spectrum of the CH_3CH_2OH and CH_3CHDOH molecules, *Opt. i Spektroskopiya* **18**, 344–345 (1965).

1681. H. Kim and W. D. Gwinn, Microwave spectrum and dipole moment of cyclobutene, *J. Chem. Phys.* **42**, 3728–3729 (1965).

1682. W. J. Lafferty, D. R. Lide, Jr., and R. A. Toth, Infrared and microwave spectra of ClCN, *J. Chem. Phys.* **43**, 2063–2070 (1965).

1683. D. R. Lide, Jr., D. E. Mann, and J. J. Comeford, The vibrational assignment of sulfuryl fluoride, *Spectrochim. Acta* **21**, 497–501 (1965).

1684. G. Luss and M. D. Harmony, Pseudorigid-rotor behavior and centrifugal distortion in the microwave spectrum of 1,3-cyclohexadiene, *J. Chem. Phys.* **43**, 3768–3769 (1965).

1685. A. M. Mirri, F. Scappini, and P. G. Favero, Millimeter wave spectrum of PF_3 and PCl_3 and force constants determination, *Spectrochim. Acta* **21**, 965–971 (1965).

1686. Y. Morino and T. Tanaka, Microwave spectra of nitryl chloride in the excited vibrational states, *J. Mol. Spectry.* **16**, 179–190 (1965).

1687. R. Peter and H. Dreizler, Microwave spectrum of acetone in torsion ground state, *Z. Naturforsch.* **20A**, 301–312 (1965).

1688. L. Pierce, R. Nelson, and C. Thomas, Microwave and infrared spectra of sulfur dicyanide: Molecular structure, dipole moment, quadrupole coupling constants, centrifugal distortion constants and vibrational assignments, *J. Chem. Phys.* **43**, 3423–3431 (1965).

1689. V. M. Rao, R. F. Curl, Jr., P. L. Timms, and J. L. Margrave, Microwave spectrum of SiF_2, *J. Chem. Phys.* **43**, 2557–2558 (1965).

1690. V. M. Rao, J. T. Yardley, and R. F. Curl, Jr., Microwave spectrum of methyl thionylamine, *J. Chem. Phys.* **42**, 284–288 (1965).

1691. J. R. Rusk, Line-breadth study of the 1.64 mm absorption in water vapor, *J. Chem. Phys.* **42**, 493–500 (1965).

1692. J. R. Rusk, Temperature and Zeeman measurements on the 1.64 mm H_2O absorption line, *J. Chem. Phys.* **43**, 2919 (1965).

1693. E. Saegebarth and A. P. Cox, Microwave spectrum, structure, dipole moment, and quadrupole coupling constants of 1,2,5-oxadiazole, *J. Chem. Phys.* **43**, 166–173 (1965).

1694. G. A. Savariraj, Complement to the study of the microwave rotation spectra of the vinyl bromides, *Ann. Soc. Sci. Bruxelles, Ser. I* **78**, 200–222 (1964).

1695. R. H. Schwendeman and F. L. Tobiason, Microwave spectrum, quadrupole coupling constants, and heavy-atom geometry of 2-bromopropane, *J. Chem. Phys.* **43**, 201–205 (1965).

1696. H. J. Tobler, A. Bauder, and Hs. H. Guenthard, The microwave spectrum and dipole moment of azulene, *J. Mol. Spectry.* **18**, 239–246 (1965).

1697. M. L. Unland, V. Weiss, and W. H. Flygare, Barrier studies in the halopropenes I. The microwave spectrum, barrier to internal rotation, quadrupole coupling constants, and microwave double-resonance spectra of 2-chloropropene, *J. Chem. Phys.* **42**, 2138–2149 (1965).

1698. H. Weaver, D. R. W. Williams, N. H. Dieter, and W. T. Lum, Observations of a strong unidentified microwave line and of emission from the OH molecule, *Nature* **208**, 29–31 (1965).

1699. H. W. de Wijn, The microwave rotational spectra of thallium monochloride, *Physica* **31**, 1193–1214 (1965).

1699a. B. Bak, L. Nygaard, E. J. Pedersen, and J. Rastrup-Andersen, Microwave spectra of isotopic 1,3,4-thiadiazoles. Molecular structure of 1,3,4-thiadiazole, *J. Mol. Spectry.* **19**, 283–289 (1966).

1699b. A. P. Cox and R. Varma, Microwave spectrum, internal barrier, molecular structure and dipole moment of disilanyl fluoride, *J. Chem. Phys.* **44**, 2619–2625 (1966).

1699c. K. L. Dorris, C. O. Britt, and J. E. Boggs, Microwave spectrum, dipole moment, and ring-puckering vibration of vinylene carbonate, *J. Chem. Phys.* **44**, 1352–1355 (1966).

1699d. L. Frenkel and D. Woods, The microwave absorption by H_2O vapor and its mixtures with other gases between 100 and 300 Gc/s, *Proc. IEEE* **54**, 498–505 (1966).

1700. H. A. Gebbie, N. W. B. Stone, G. Topping, E. K. Gora, S. A. Clough, and F. X. Kneizys, Rotational absorption of some asymmetric rotor molecules. Pt. I. Ozone and sulfur dioxide, *J. Mol. Spectry.* **19**, 7–24 (1966).

1700a. G. E. Herberich, R. H. Jackson, and D. J. Millen, The microwave spectrum of dichlorine oxide. Molecular structure, centrifugal distortion coefficients, and force field, *J. Chem. Soc., A., Inorg., Phys., Theoret.* **1966**, 336–351 (1966).

1701. L. C. Krisher and W. G. Norris, Microwave spectrum of silver chloride, *J. Chem. Phys.* **44**, 391–394 (1966).

1702. L. C. Krisher and W. G. Norris, Microwave spectrum of silver bromide, *J. Chem. Phys.* **44**, 974–976 (1966).

1702a. R. L. Kuczkowski, D. R. Lide, Jr., and L. C. Krisher, Microwave spectra of alkali hydroxides: Evidence for linearity in CsOH and KOH, *J. Chem. Phys.* **44**, 3131–3132 (1966).

1703. W. M. Salathiel and R. F. Curl, Jr., Microwave spectrum of methylazide, *J. Chem. Phys.* **44**, 1288–1290 (1966).

1704. E. C. Thomas and V. W. Laurie, Microwave spectrum of germylacetylene, *J. Chem. Phys.* **44**, 2602–2604 (1966).

1705. T. Oka, Observations of $\Delta J = 3$ "forbidden" transition in ethyl iodide by the use of double resonance, *J. Chem. Phys.* **45**, 752–753 (1966).

1706. T. Oka, Observation of preferred collisional transitions in ethylene oxide by the use of microwave double resonance, *J. Chem. Phys.* **45**, 754–755 (1966).

1707. M. L. Unland and W. H. Flygare, Direct measurement of rotational relaxation, *J. Chem. Phys.* **45**, 2421–2432 (1966).

1708. R. C. Woods, A general program for the calculation of internal rotation splittings in microwave spectroscopy, *J. Mol. Spectry.* **21**, 4–24 (1966).

1709. L. H. Scharpen, J. S. Muenter, and V. W. Laurie, Determination of the polarizability anisotropy of OCS by microwave spectroscopy, *J. Chem. Phys.* **46**, 2431–2434 (1967).

1710. R. C. Woods, A general program for the calculation of internal rotation splittings in microwave spectroscopy. Part II. The *n*-top problem, *J. Mol. Spectry.* **22**, 49–59 (1967).

SHORT TABLE OF PHYSICAL CONSTANTS, CONVERSION FACTORS, AND WAVEGUIDE NOMENCLATURE

A. Physical Constants[†]

Velocity of light	c	2.997925×10^{10}	cm sec^{-1}
Electronic charge	e	4.80298×10^{-10}	esu
Electron rest mass	m	9.10908×10^{-28}	g
Boltzmann's constant	k	1.38054×10^{-16}	erg deg^{-1}
Planck's constant	h	6.62559×10^{-27}	erg sec
Bohr magneton	β	1.39960	MHz gauss^{-1}
Nuclear magneton	β_I	7.6227×10^{-4}	MHz gauss^{-1}

B. Conversion Factors[†]

Rotational constant B (MHz) and moment of inertia I_b (amu A^2)

$$I_b = \frac{5.05377 \times 10^5}{B}$$

Dipole moment (Debye) and electric field strength (volts cm^{-1}) to frequency

$\mu\varepsilon = 0.50344$ MHz cm Debye^{-1} volt^{-1}
1 Debye $= 10^{-18}$ esu

Energy units

1 electron-volt particle^{-1} $= 8065.73$ cm^{-1}
$= 2.3061 \times 10^4$ calories mole^{-1}
$= 1.60210 \times 10^{-12}$ erg

[†] Based on E. R. Cohen and J. W. M. DuMond, *Rev. Mod. Phys.* **37**, 537–594 (1965).

C. Rectangular Waveguide Data

Letter band designation	Frequency range (GHz)	Inside waveguide dimensions (inches)	TE$_{10}$ mode cutoff (GHz)
H	3.95–5.85	0.872 × 1.872	3.152
C	5.85–8.20	0.622 × 1.372	4.301
X	8.20–12.40	0.400 × 0.900	6.557
Ku	12.40–18.00	0.311 × 0.622	9.486
K	18.00–26.50	0.170 × 0.420	14.047
Ka	26.50–40.00	0.140 × 0.280	21.081
Q	33.00–50.00	0.112 × 0.244	24.186
E	60.00–90.00	0.061 × 0.122	48.350

APPENDIX 3 | EVALUATION OF $E(\kappa)$

The characteristic roots of the submatrices $\mathbf{0}^{\pm}, \mathbf{E}^{\pm}$ are the reduced energies $E(\kappa)$. Each submatrix is of the Jacobian or tridiagonal form and can be expressed as

$$\mathbf{H} = \begin{bmatrix} k_0 & b_1^{1/2} & 0 & \cdots \\ b_1^{1/2} & k_1 & b_2^{1/2} & \\ 0 & b_2^{1/2} & k_2 & \\ \cdot & \cdot & & \cdot \\ \cdot & \cdot & & \cdot \\ \cdot & \cdot & & \cdot \end{bmatrix} \tag{1}$$

Nonzero elements lie on the principal diagonal and the two contiguous diagonals. These matrices are easily diagonalized to a high degree of approximation by modern high-speed digital computer techniques [289, 318]. The original continued fraction approach which was first used to diagonalize these matrices is described here.

The matrices can be transformed to a form which allows the direct application of continued-fraction techniques.

$$D = L^{-1}HL = \begin{bmatrix} k_0 & 1 & 0 & \cdots \\ b_1 & k_1 & 1 & \cdots \\ 0 & b_2 & k_2 & \cdots \\ \cdot & & & \cdot \\ \cdot & & & \cdot \\ \cdot & & & \cdot \end{bmatrix} \tag{2}$$

L has the form

$$L = \begin{bmatrix} 1 & 0 & 0 & & \cdots \\ 0 & b_1^{-1/2} & 0 & \\ 0 & 0 & b_1^{-1/2}b_2^{-1/2} & \\ \cdot & & & \cdot \\ \cdot & & & \cdot \\ \cdot & & & \cdot \end{bmatrix} \tag{3}$$

The $E(\kappa)$ are eigenvalues of D and may be obtained by solving the secular determinant

$$|D - \lambda I| = 0 \tag{4}$$

The explicit forms for D are: for $\mathbf{E}^{\pm}$;

$$
D = \begin{bmatrix}
FJ(J+1) & 1 & 0 & \cdots \\
2H^2 f(J,1) & 4(G-F) + FJ(J+1) & 1 & \\
0 & H^2 f(J,3) & 16(G-F) + FJ(J+1) & \cdots \\
\vdots & \vdots & \vdots &
\end{bmatrix} \tag{5}
$$

for $\mathbf{0}^{\pm}$;

$$
D = \begin{bmatrix}
(G-F) + FJ(J+1) \pm Hf^{1/2}(J,0) & 1 & 0 \\
H^2 f(J,2) & 9(G-F) + FJ(J+1) & 1 \\
0 & H^2 f(J,4) & \\
\vdots & \vdots &
\end{bmatrix} \tag{6}
$$

For $\mathbf{E}^{-}$ the determinant D is obtained by removing the first row and column in (5) as indicated by the dashed line. The secular determinant can be written in continued-fraction form

$$(k_0 - \lambda) - \cfrac{b_1}{(k_1 - \lambda) - \cfrac{b_2}{(k_2 - \lambda) - b_3/(k_3 - \lambda) \cdots}} = 0 \tag{7}$$

where the actual values of the k's and b's may be obtained through inspection of the elements in (5) and (6). Except for low J values, the roots $E(\kappa)$ cannot be expressed in a closed mathematical form but must be calculated by an iterative process. To reduce the amount of computation, it is necessary to choose the representation which produces the fastest convergence of the solutions. Type I is used in the near-prolate case, type III in the near-oblate case, and type II for the most asymmetric case near $\kappa = 0$.

The mth root λ_m can be expanded in a continued fraction whose leading term is k_m.

$$\lambda_m = k_m - \cfrac{b_m}{(k_{m-1} - \lambda_m) - \cfrac{b_{m-1}}{(k_{m-2} - \lambda_m) - \cdots}}$$

$$- \cfrac{b_{m+1}}{(k_{m+1} - \lambda_m) - \cfrac{b_{m+2}}{(k_{m+2} - \lambda_m) - \cdots}} \tag{8}$$

An additional relation can be obtained from the trace equivalence of D and λI.

$$\sum k_m = \sum \lambda_m \tag{9}$$

This equation may be used to obtain the root for which convergence is poorest or as an accuracy check on the computations.

Tabulations of $E(\kappa)$ are available for various intervals of κ and up to $J = 40$. Linear interpolation between κ intervals of 0.01 or 0.001 is usually accurate enough to fit asymmetric rotor spectra. Second-difference interpolation for κ intervals of 0.01 will give $E(\kappa)$ values comparable to $E(\kappa)$ for κ intervals of 0.001 where linear interpolation is used.

The energy equations can be expressed in polynomial form by expanding the secular determinant in terms of the first principal minors which are of order $i + 1$. The recursion relations are

$$p_0 = k_0 - \lambda$$
$$p_1 = (k_1 - \lambda)p_0 - b_1$$
$$\cdot$$
$$\cdot \tag{10}$$
$$\cdot$$
$$p_i = (k_i - \lambda)p_{i-1} - b_i p_{i-2}$$

For D of order $n + 1$ the characteristic equation is

$$(-1)^{n+1} p_n = 0 \tag{11}$$

which gives the equations

$$\lambda - k_0 \qquad\qquad\qquad = 0$$
$$\lambda^2 - \lambda(k_1 + k_0) + k_1 k_0 - b_1 = 0$$
$$\lambda^3 - \lambda^2(k_2 + k_1 + k_0) + \lambda(k_2 k_1 + k_2 k_0 + k_1 k_0 - b_2 - b_1) \tag{12}$$
$$- k_2 k_1 k_0 + k_2 b_1 + k_0 b_2 = 0$$

Those values of $E(\kappa)$ listed in Table 1 are obtained from the linear and quadratic equations in this set. Table 2 gives the rigid rotor energies for these levels in terms of the rotational constants (h suppressed).

TABLE A3-1

VALUES OF REDUCED ENERGY PARAMETERS FOR SOME LOW J LEVELS
IN TERMS OF THE ASYMMETRY PARAMETER κ

$J_{K_{-1}K_1}$	$E(\kappa)$
0_{00}	0
1_{10}	$\kappa + 1$
1_{11}	0
1_{01}	$\kappa - 1$
2_{20}	$2[\kappa + (\kappa^2 + 3)^{1/2}]$
2_{21}	$\kappa + 3$
2_{11}	4κ
2_{12}	$\kappa - 3$
2_{02}	$2[\kappa - (\kappa^2 + 3)^{1/2}]$
3_{30}	$5\kappa + 3 + 2(4\kappa^2 - 6\kappa + 6)^{1/2}$
3_{31}	$2[\kappa + (\kappa^2 + 15)^{1/2}]$
3_{21}	$5\kappa - 3 + 2(4\kappa^2 + 6\kappa + 6)^{1/2}$
3_{22}	4κ
3_{12}	$5\kappa + 3 - 2(4\kappa^2 - 6\kappa + 6)^{1/2}$
3_{13}	$2[\kappa - (\kappa^2 + 15)^{1/2}]$
3_{03}	$5\kappa - 3 - 2(4\kappa^2 + 6\kappa + 6)^{1/2}$
4_{41}	$5\kappa + 5 + 2(4\kappa^2 - 10\kappa + 22)^{1/2}$
4_{31}	$10\kappa + 2(9\kappa^2 + 7)^{1/2}$
4_{32}	$5\kappa - 5 + 2(4\kappa^2 + 10\kappa + 22)^{1/2}$
4_{23}	$5\kappa + 5 - 2(4\kappa^2 - 10\kappa + 22)^{1/2}$
4_{13}	$10\kappa - 2(9\kappa^2 + 7)^{1/2}$
4_{14}	$5\kappa - 5 - 2(4\kappa^2 + 10\kappa + 22)^{1/2}$
5_{42}	$10\kappa + 6(\kappa^2 + 3)^{1/2}$
5_{24}	$10\kappa - 6(\kappa^2 + 3)^{1/2}$

The continued-fraction technique is not as limited as it may appear. Givens [294] has presented a method for transforming a general Hermitian matrix into tridiagonal form. This transformation facilitates the use of continued-fraction techniques on a large class of matrices. Modern computer methods make the diagonalization of these matrices for high J a relatively easy process.

For high J values where the $E(\kappa)$ must be obtained by iterative techniques, it is important from the standpoint of computational time that the continued-fraction expansion converge rapidly. Techniques aimed at improving the convergence rate [313, 315, 318] often employ the Newton–Raphson procedure. This is especially useful when the natural convergence of the continued fraction operation is slow.

Natural convergence [293] may be defined by the following operations. If $\lambda_m^{(0)}$ is the first approximation to the root λ_m and $\lambda_m^{(1)}$ is the result obtained by substituting $\lambda_m^{(0)}$ into the continued fraction, one has

$$\lambda_m^{(1)} = \alpha \lambda_m^{(0)} \tag{13}$$

TABLE A3-2

VALUES OF THE RIGID ROTOR ENERGY LEVELS IN TERMS OF THE ROTATIONAL
CONSTANTS

$J_{K_{-}K_1}$	$E(A, B, C)$
0_{00}	0
1_{10}	$A + B$
1_{11}	$A + C$
1_{01}	$B + C$
2_{20}	$2A + 2B + 2C + 2[(B - C)^2 + (A - C)(A - B)]^{1/2}$
2_{21}	$4A + B + C$
2_{11}	$A + 4B + C$
2_{12}	$A + B + 4C$
2_{02}	$2A + 2B + 2C - 2[(B - C)^2 + (A - C)(A - B)]^{1/2}$
3_{30}	$5A + 5B + 2C + 2[4(A - B)^2 + (A - C)(B - C)]^{1/2}$
3_{31}	$5A + 2B + 5C + 2[4(A - C)^2 - (A - B)(B - C)]^{1/2}$
3_{21}	$2A + 5B + 5C + 2[4(B - C)^2 + (A - B)(A - C)]^{1/2}$
3_{22}	$4A + 4B + 4C$
3_{12}	$5A + 5B + 2C - 2[4(A - B)^2 + (A - C)(B - C)]^{1/2}$
3_{13}	$5A + 2B + 5C - 2[4(A - C)^2 - (A - B)(B - C)]^{1/2}$
3_{03}	$2A + 5B + 5C - 2[4(B - C)^2 + (A - B)(A - C)]^{1/2}$
4_{41}	$10A + 5B + 5C + 2[4(B - C)^2 + 9(A - C)(A - B)]^{1/2}$
4_{31}	$5A + 10B + 5C + 2[4(A - C)^2 - 9(A - B)(B - C)]^{1/2}$
4_{32}	$5A + 5B + 10C + 2[4(A - B)^2 + 9(A - C)(B - C)]^{1/2}$
4_{23}	$10A + 5B + 5C - 2[4(B - C)^2 + 9(A - C)(A - B)]^{1/2}$
4_{13}	$5A + 10B + 5C - 2[4(A - C)^2 - 9(A - B)(B - C)]^{1/2}$
4_{14}	$5A + 5B + 10C - 2[4(A - B)^2 + 9(A - C)(B - C)]^{1/2}$
5_{42}	$10A + 10B + 10C + 6[(B - C)^2 + (A - B)(A - C)]^{1/2}$
5_{24}	$10A + 10B + 10C - 6[(B - C)^2 + (A - B)(A - C)]^{1/2}$

where α represents the continued fraction operation. $\lambda_m^{(I)}$ is then operated on
by α to give $\lambda_m^{(II)}$ and so on, until the iteration is terminated by a value of
$\lambda_m^{(i)}$ such that

$$\lambda_m^{(i)} - \lambda_m^{(i-1)} = \eta \tag{14}$$

$\eta \approx 0$ and is within the limits set for the iteration. Natural convergence is
the rate at which the successive approximations approach the correct root.

The Newton–Raphson technique is a second-order iteration procedure.
Let the secular equation be written in the general form

$$\begin{bmatrix} H_{11} - \lambda & H_{12} & & & 0 \\ H_{21} & H_{22} - \lambda & H_{23} & & \\ & \ddots & \ddots & \ddots & \\ & & H_{kk} - \lambda & & \\ & & & \ddots & \\ 0 & & & & H_{nn} - \lambda \end{bmatrix} = 0 \tag{15}$$

Define $f_k(\lambda)$ as

$$f_k(\lambda) = \lambda - H_{kk} - \frac{h_{k+1}^2}{R_{k+1}} - \frac{h_{k-1}^2}{R_{k-1}} \tag{16}$$

where

$$h_{k\pm\alpha}^2 = |H_{k\pm\alpha,k\pm\alpha\mp1}|^2 \tag{17}$$

$$R_{k\pm\alpha} = \lambda - H_{k\pm\alpha,k\pm\alpha} - \frac{h_{k\pm\alpha\pm1}^2}{R_{k\pm\alpha\pm1}}, \qquad \alpha = 1, 2, 3, \ldots \tag{18}$$

The roots of $f_k(\lambda)$ are the eigenvalues of $\mathbf{H}$ in (15). n different functions $f(\lambda)$ can be defined where n is the order of $\mathbf{H}$. If $\lambda^{(i)}$ is the ith approximation to an eigenvalue of $\mathbf{H}$, the expansion of $f_k(\lambda)$ about $\lambda^{(i)}$ gives

$$f_k(\lambda) = f_k(\lambda^{(i)}) + f_k'(\lambda^{(i)})[\lambda - \lambda^{(i)}] + \cdots \tag{19}$$

The higher terms are neglected. $f_k(\lambda)$ vanishes if $\lambda^{(i+1)}$ is taken as

$$\lambda^{(i+1)} = \lambda^{(i)} - \frac{f_k(\lambda^{(i)})}{f_k'(\lambda^{(i)})} \tag{20}$$

where

$$f_k'(\lambda) = \frac{df_k(\lambda)}{d\lambda} = 1 + \left(\frac{h_{k+1}}{R_{k+1}}\right)^2 \left[1 + \left(\frac{h_{k+2}}{R_{k+2}}\right)^2 (1 + \cdots)\right]$$

$$+ \left(\frac{h_{k-1}}{R_{k-1}}\right)^2 \left[1 + \left(\frac{h_{k-2}}{R_{k-2}}\right)^2 (1 + \cdots)\right] \tag{21}$$

Equation (20) offers an excellent improvement over the first-order iteration (14) which can be written as

$$\lambda^{(i)} - \lambda^{(i+1)} = f_k(\lambda^{(i)}) \tag{22}$$

Near degeneracies may become a problem for a near-symmetric top. A very good first approximation to a root is necessary to avoid convergence to the wrong root, and (20) must be used to avoid divergence. Note that from (21), $f_k'(\lambda) \geq 1$ and that (22) is convergent only for $1 \leq f_k'(\lambda) < 2$.

Although (20) should always be convergent, it is not necessarily convergent to the correct root. Two conditions which control this convergence are the initial choice $\lambda^{(0)}$ and the choice of $f(\lambda)$. A criterion [315] for the proper choice of $f(\lambda)$ is

$$f_k'(\lambda') \leq f_{k\pm\alpha}'(\lambda'), \qquad \alpha = 1, 2, 3, \ldots \tag{23}$$

where λ' is a given eigenvalue of $\mathbf{H}$.

The Newton–Raphson method can also be applied to the evaluation of the eigenvectors.

DERIVATION OF THE HAMILTONIAN FOR TREATING THE VIBRATION-ROTATION INTERACTION PROBLEM

APPENDIX 4

To derive the quantum-mechanical Hamiltonian used for the vibration-rotation interaction problem, the classical expression can be derived from a vector model and then transformed to quantum-mechanical form.[†] An appropriate model is shown in Fig. A4-1, where the atoms are treated as

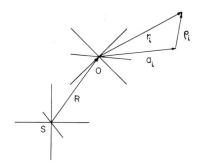

FIG. A4-1. Vector model for the derivation of the Hamiltonian for a nonrigid asymmetric rotor.

point masses vibrating about their equilibrium positions. Two reference coordinate systems are used in the derivation. One is fixed at the center of mass of the molecule and translates and rotates with the molecule. The second is a space-fixed axis system to which the molecular motions are referenced. The space-fixed axis system has its origin at S and the origin of the molecule-fixed system is at 0. 0 is the instantaneous center of mass of the molecule. The vectors $\mathbf{a}_i$, $\mathbf{r}_i$ and $\boldsymbol{\rho}_i$ describe the equilibrium position of the ith atom, the instantaneous position of that atom, and the displacement of the ith atom from its equilibrium position relative to the origin, respectively.

$$\mathbf{r}_i = r_i(x_i, y_i, z_i) = \mathbf{a}_i + \boldsymbol{\rho}_i \tag{1}$$

[†] The derivation given here was first developed by Wilson and Howard [335].

Let ω be the angular velocity of the molecule-fixed axis system and v_i be the velocity of the ith atom in the molecule-fixed system.

$$\mathbf{v}_i = (\dot{x}_i, \dot{y}_i, \dot{z}_i) \tag{2}$$

$$\omega = (\omega_x, \omega_y, \omega_z) \tag{3}$$

If $\mathbf{V}_i$ is the velocity of the ith atom in space and $\mathbf{R}$ is the vector connecting S and 0,

$$\mathbf{V}_i = \dot{\mathbf{R}} + \omega \times \mathbf{r}_i + \mathbf{v}_i \tag{4}$$

From this expression the kinetic energy of the molecule is

$$2T = \dot{R}^2 \sum_i m_i + \sum_i m_i(\omega \times \mathbf{r}_i) \cdot (\omega \times \mathbf{r}_i) + \sum_i m_i v_i^2$$
$$+ 2\dot{\mathbf{R}} \cdot \sum_i m_i \mathbf{v}_i + 2\dot{\mathbf{R}} \times \omega \cdot \sum_i m_i \mathbf{r}_i + 2\omega \cdot \sum_i m_i \mathbf{r}_i \times \mathbf{v}_i \tag{5}$$

Conditions defining the molecule-fixed system are

$$\sum_i m_i \mathbf{v}_i = \sum_i m_i \mathbf{r}_i = 0 \tag{6}$$

$$\sum_i m_i \mathbf{a}_i \times \mathbf{v}_i = 0 \tag{7}$$

Equation (7) implies that to a first approximation (small vibrational amplitudes[†]) no resultant angular momentum exists relative to the molecule-fixed system. After applying these conditions to (5), the kinetic energy can be written as a sum of translational, rotational, vibrational, and rotation-vibration contributions.

$$T = T_t + T_r + T_v + T_{rv} \tag{8}$$

$$T_t = \tfrac{1}{2}\dot{R}^2 \sum_i m_i \tag{9}$$

$$T_r = \tfrac{1}{2} \sum_i m_i(\omega \times \mathbf{r}_i) \cdot (\omega \times \mathbf{r}_i) \tag{10}$$

$$T_v = \tfrac{1}{2} \sum_i m_i v_i^2 \tag{11}$$

$$T_{rv} = \omega \cdot \sum_i m_i(\rho_i \times \mathbf{v}_i) \tag{12}$$

T_{rv} is usually called the Coriolis energy.

The translational terms may be dropped, and after expanding the remaining terms,

$$2T = \sum_\alpha I_{\alpha\alpha}\omega_\alpha^2 - 2\sum_{\alpha,\beta}{}' I_{\alpha\beta}\omega_\alpha\omega_\beta + \sum_i m_i v_i^2$$
$$+ 2\sum_\alpha \omega_\alpha \sum_i m_i(\rho_i \times \mathbf{v}_i)_\alpha \tag{13}$$

[†] $\mathbf{r}_i$ is replaced by $\mathbf{a}_i$. This is a good approximation for very small displacements.

for $\alpha = x, y, z$. In the second term, the factor 2 accounts for $I_{\alpha\beta} = I_{\beta\alpha}$ and the summation is for $\alpha \neq \beta$. i still represents a summation over the atoms.

The inertial constants are functions of the positions of the atoms and are not constants of the motion. They must be treated as instantaneous values. Equation (13) can be modified by the introduction of $3N - 6$ normal coordinates describing the molecular vibrations. The displacement coordinates $\Delta\alpha_i$ of ρ_i are related to the normal coordinates Q_k by the transformation matrix $\mathbf{l}$.

$$q_{\alpha i} = (m_i)^{1/2} \Delta\alpha_i = \sum_k l_{ik}^{(\alpha)} Q_k \tag{14}$$

The $q_{\alpha i}$ are mass-weighted Cartesian displacement coordinates. It follows that

$$\sum_k \dot{Q}_k^2 = \sum_i m_i v_i^2 = \sum_i (\dot{q}_{xi}^2 + \dot{q}_{yi}^2 + \dot{q}_{zi}^2) \tag{15}$$

To introduce the normal coordinates into the kinetic energy expression, the following quantities are defined.

$$X_k = \sum_{il} (l_{ik}^{(y)} l_{il}^{(z)} - l_{ik}^{(z)} l_{il}^{(y)}) Q_l \tag{16a}$$

$$Y_k = \sum_{il} (l_{ik}^{(z)} l_{il}^{(x)} - l_{ik}^{(x)} l_{il}^{(z)}) Q_l \tag{16b}$$

$$Z_k = \sum_{il} (l_{ik}^{(x)} l_{il}^{(y)} - l_{ik}^{(y)} l_{il}^{(x)}) Q_l \tag{16c}$$

These give

$$\sum_i m_i(\boldsymbol{\rho}_i \times \mathbf{v}_i)_x = \sum_i (q_{yi} q_{zi} - q_{zi} q_{yi}) = \sum_k X_k \dot{Q}_k \tag{17a}$$

$$\sum_i m_i(\boldsymbol{\rho}_i \times \mathbf{v}_i)_y = \sum_i (q_{zi} q_{xi} - q_{xi} q_{zi}) = \sum_k Y_k \dot{Q}_k \tag{17b}$$

$$\sum_i m_i(\boldsymbol{\rho}_i \times \mathbf{v}_i)_z = \sum_i (q_{xi} q_{yi} - q_{yi} q_{xi}) = \sum_k Z_k \dot{Q}_k \tag{17c}$$

The kinetic energy is now

$$2T = \sum_\alpha I_{\alpha\alpha} \omega_\alpha^2 - 2 \sum_{\alpha\beta}' I_{\alpha\beta} \omega_\alpha \omega_\beta + 2\omega_x \sum_k X_k \dot{Q}_k$$
$$+ 2\omega_y \sum_k Y_k \dot{Q}_k + 2\omega_z \sum_k Z_k \dot{Q}_k + \sum_k \dot{Q}_k^2 \tag{18}$$

For the proper quantum-mechanical treatment it is necessary to express the kinetic energy in terms of the angular momentum $\mathbf{P}$.

$$\mathbf{P} = \sum_i m_i \mathbf{r}_i \times \dot{\mathbf{r}}_i = \sum_i m_i[\mathbf{r}_i \times (\boldsymbol{\omega} \times \mathbf{r}_i)] + \sum_i m_i \mathbf{r}_i \times \mathbf{v}_i \tag{19}$$

The specific components are

$$P_x = \partial T/\partial \omega_x = I_{xx}\omega_x - I_{xy}\omega_y - I_{xz}\omega_z + \sum_k X_k \dot{Q}_k \tag{20}$$

$$P_y = \partial T/\partial \omega_y = -I_{xy}\omega_x + I_{yy}\omega_y - I_{yz}\omega_z + \sum_k Y_k \dot{Q}_k \tag{21}$$

$$P_z = \partial T/\partial \omega_z = -I_{xz}\omega_x - I_{yz}\omega_y + I_{zz}\omega_z + \sum_k Z_k \dot{Q}_k \tag{22}$$

and

$$p_k = \partial T/\partial \dot{Q}_k = \dot{Q}_k + X_k\omega_x + Y_k\omega_y + Z_k\omega_z \tag{23}$$

The P_i are rotational angular momenta about the molecule-fixed axes and the p_k are vibrational momenta associated with the kth normal mode of vibration. Making the appropriate substitutions, (18) becomes

$$2T = \sum_{\alpha,\beta} \mu_{\alpha\beta}(P_\alpha - p_\alpha)(P_\beta - p_\beta) + \sum_k p_k^2 \tag{24}$$

where

$$p_x = \sum_k X_k p_k \tag{25a}$$

$$p_y = \sum_k Y_k p_k \tag{25b}$$

$$p_z = \sum_k Z_k p_k \tag{25c}$$

and

$$\mu_{\alpha\alpha} = (I'_{\beta\beta}I'_{\gamma\gamma} - I'^2_{\beta\gamma})/\Delta \tag{26}$$

$$\mu_{\alpha\beta} = \mu_{\beta\alpha} = (I'_{\gamma\gamma}I'_{\alpha\beta} - I'_{\alpha\gamma}I'_{\beta\gamma})/\Delta \tag{27}$$

The subscripts α, β, and γ represent x, y, and z in any cyclic permutation. The μ's are functions of the Q_k only.

$$I'_{\alpha\alpha} = I_{\alpha\alpha} - \sum_k A_k^2 \tag{28}$$

$$I'_{\alpha\beta} = I_{\alpha\beta} + \sum_k A_k B_k \tag{29}$$

Here A_k, B_k, and C_k are identified with X_k, Y_k, and Z_k in the same permutation as α, β, and γ are related to x, y, and z.

$$\Delta = \begin{vmatrix} I'_{xx} & -I'_{xy} & -I'_{xz} \\ -I'_{xy} & I'_{yy} & -I'_{yz} \\ -I'_{xz} & -I'_{yz} & I'_{zz} \end{vmatrix} \tag{30}$$

Explicit expressions for the I' quantities have been given by Nielsen [336].

The transformation between angular velocities and angular momenta has the general form

$$2T = \boldsymbol{\omega}^+ \mathbf{I} \boldsymbol{\omega} = \mathbf{p}^+ \mathbf{I}^{-1} \mathbf{p} \tag{31}$$

Explicitly,

$$\omega_\alpha = \mu_{\alpha\alpha}(P_\alpha - p_\alpha) + \mu_{\alpha\beta}(P_\beta - p_\beta) + \mu_{\alpha\gamma}(P_\gamma - p_\gamma) \tag{32}$$

or

$$P_\alpha - p_\alpha = I'_{\alpha\alpha}\omega_\alpha - I'_{\alpha\beta}\omega_\beta - I'_{\alpha\gamma}\omega_\gamma \tag{33}$$

The process of converting the expression for kinetic energy into operational form is not straightforward, because the present form is expressed in terms of momenta which are not conjugate to any coordinates of the system. The noncommutative properties of momenta and coordinates p and q in operational form produce inequalities of the type $qpq^{-1}p \neq p^2$. This requires that a special approach be used in the formulation of the operational form of the Hamiltonian. For a conservative system, Podolsky [996] has derived the correct form for the Hamiltonian function in an arbitrary coordinate system.

Consider the transformation from a set of Cartesian coordinates $x_1, x_2, \ldots, x_n$ to the general coordinate system $u_1, u_2, \ldots, u_n$. A vector $\mathbf{r}$ in the general space can be expanded as

$$d\mathbf{r} = \frac{\partial \mathbf{r}}{\partial u_1} du_1 + \frac{\partial \mathbf{r}}{\partial u_2} du_2 + \cdots \tag{34}$$

The square of an element of length dl is then

$$dl^2 = d\mathbf{r} \cdot d\mathbf{r} = \sum_{ij} g_{ij} du_i du_j \tag{35}$$

g^{ij} is the inverse of the matrix g_{ij}. In terms of the generalized coordinates

$$2T = \sum_{ij} g_{ij}\dot{u}_i\dot{u}_j = \sum_{ij} g^{ij}p_i p_j \tag{36}$$

Let g represent the determinant of the matrix g^{ij}. $g^{-1/2}$ is the Jacobian of the Cartesian coordinates with respect to the generalized coordinates.

$$g_{ij} = \sum_k \frac{\partial x_k}{\partial u_i} \frac{\partial x_k}{\partial u_j} \tag{37}$$

The wave equation in the Cartesian system is

$$\nabla^2 \psi_x + K(E - V)\psi_x = 0 \tag{38}$$

Behavior of both the Laplacian and the wave function must be studied under the transformation to generalized coordinates.

$$\nabla^2 \psi_x = g^{1/2} \sum_i \frac{\partial}{\partial u_i} \left(g^{-1/2} \sum_j g^{ij} \frac{\partial \psi_x}{\partial u_j} \right) \tag{39}$$

The relation between ψ_x and ψ_u can be determined from the normalization condition. For ψ_x,

$$\int \psi_x^* \psi_x \, dx_1 \, dx_2 \cdots dx_n = 1 \tag{40}$$

From tensor analysis

$$dx_1 \, dx_2 \cdots dx_n = g^{-1/2} \, du_1 \, du_2 \cdots du_n \tag{41}$$

$g^{-1/2}$ is the density factor for the wave function ψ_x in the generalized space. To fulfill the normalization condition

$$\int \psi_u^* \psi_u \, du_1 \, du_2 \cdots du_n = 1 \tag{42}$$

$$\psi_x = g^{1/4} \psi_u \tag{43}$$

From (39) and (43), the proper wave equation is

$$g^{1/4} \sum_i \frac{\partial}{\partial u_i} \left(g^{-1/2} \sum_j g^{ij} \frac{\partial}{\partial u_j} g^{1/4} \psi_u \right) + K(E - V)\psi_u = 0 \tag{44}$$

In terms of the angular momenta, the Hamiltonian is written as

$$\mathbf{H} = \tfrac{1}{2} g^{1/4} \sum_{ij} \mathbf{p}_i g^{-1/2} g^{ij} \mathbf{p}_j g^{1/4} + \mathbf{V} \tag{45}$$

$$p_i = -i\hbar \frac{\partial}{\partial u_i} \tag{46}$$

Now let the momenta P_m not be conjugate to any set of coordinates but be related to the p_i by the transformation

$$p_i = \sum_m s_{im} P_m \tag{47}$$

With

$$G^{mn} = \sum_{ij} s_{im} g^{ij} s_{jn} \tag{48}$$

the kinetic energy is

$$2T = \sum_{m,n} G^{mn} P_m P_n \tag{49}$$

It is now necessary to find the conditions under which the Hamiltonian can be expressed in the form

$$\mathbf{H} = \tfrac{1}{2} G^{1/4} \sum_{m,n} \mathbf{P}_m G^{mn} G^{-1/2} \mathbf{P}_n G^{1/4} + \mathbf{V} \tag{50}$$

G is the determinant of G^{mn}. The inverse transformation

$$P_m = \sum_i s^{mi} p_i \tag{51}$$

is substituted into (50).

$$\mathbf{H} = \tfrac{1}{2}g^{1/4}s^{1/2} \sum_{ijkm} s^{mi}\mathbf{p}_i s_{km} g^{kj} g^{-1/2} s^{-1} \mathbf{p}_j g^{1/4} s^{1/2} + \mathbf{V} \tag{52}$$

s is the determinant of s_{im}. Also,

$$G = s^2 g \tag{53}$$

$$\sum_j s_{ij}s^{jl} = \delta_{il} \tag{54}$$

δ_{il} is the Kronecker delta. For (52) to reduce to (45) requires that

$$\sum_{im} s^{mi}\mathbf{p}_i s_{km} = s^{-1}\mathbf{p}_k s \tag{55}$$

A convenient set of coordinates and conjugate momenta are the Eulerian angles θ, ϕ, and χ and the normal coordinate Q_k associated with the momenta p_θ, p_ϕ, p_χ, and p_k. The transformation between these conjugate variables and the P_i is

$$P_x = \sin\chi p_\theta - \cos\chi \csc\theta\, p_\phi + \cos\chi \cot\theta\, p_\chi \tag{56}$$

$$P_y = \cos\chi\, p_\theta + \sin\chi \csc\theta p_\phi - \sin\chi \cot\theta p_\chi \tag{57}$$

$$P_z = p_\chi \tag{58}$$

$$P_k = p_k \tag{59}$$

Use has been made of the vector relationships between the components of $\boldsymbol{\omega}$ and $\dot{\theta}$, $\dot{\phi}$ and $\dot{\chi}$, in terms of which the $\mathbf{P}_i$ are first written. The other necessary transformation satisfying the condition (55) is

$$(P_x - p_x) = P_x - \sum_k X_k p_k \tag{60}$$

$$(P_y - p_y) = P_y - \sum_k Y_k p_k \tag{61}$$

$$(P_z - p_z) = P_z - \sum_k Z_k p_k \tag{62}$$

$$P_k = p_k \tag{63}$$

Thus the Hamiltonian can be expressed as

$$\mathbf{H} = \tfrac{1}{2}\mu^{1/4} \sum_{\alpha\beta} (\mathbf{P}_\alpha - \mathbf{p}_\alpha)\mu_{\alpha\beta}\mu^{-1/2}(\mathbf{P}_\beta - \mathbf{p}_\beta)\mu^{1/4}$$
$$+ \tfrac{1}{2}\mu^{1/4} \sum_k \mathbf{p}_k \mu^{-1/2}\mathbf{p}_k \mu^{1/4} + \mathbf{V} \tag{64}$$

which is identical with Equation (3-84).

DERIVATION OF THE INERTIAL DEFECT

As indicated by Eq. (4-111), the inertial defect can be written as a sum of three contributions originating from vibrational, centrifugal, and electronic effects.

$$\Delta = \Delta(\text{vib}) + \Delta(\text{cent}) + \Delta(\text{elect}) \tag{1}$$

The vibrational contribution is usually the dominant term.

Taking vibration-rotation interactions into consideration, Oka and Morino have derived a general expression for the inertial defect in order to obtain explicit expressions for $\Delta(\text{vib})$, $\Delta(\text{cent})$, and $\Delta(\text{elect})$ [471]. The vibration-rotation Hamiltonian in Eq. (3-98) can be expressed as

$$H = H^{(0)} + H^{(2)} \tag{2}$$

$$H^{(0)} = \tfrac{1}{2}\sum_\alpha \frac{P_\alpha^2}{I_{\alpha\alpha}^e} \tag{3}$$

$$
\begin{aligned}
H^{(2)} =& \sum_{\alpha\beta}\frac{P_\alpha P_\beta}{I_{\alpha\alpha}^e I_{\beta\beta}^e}\sum_k (v_k + 1)\left[\frac{1}{4\pi}\sqrt{\frac{h}{c}}\left\{\frac{3k_{kkk}a_k^{\alpha\beta}}{\omega_k^{3/2}} + \sum_{k'}\frac{k_{kkk'}a_{k'}^{\alpha\beta}}{\omega_{k'}^{3/2}}\right\}\right.\\
&+ \left.\sum_{k'}\frac{h}{\pi c}\frac{\omega_k}{\omega_k^2 - \omega_{k'}^2}\zeta_{kk'}^{(\alpha)}\zeta_{kk'}^{(\beta)} - \frac{h}{8\pi^2 c\omega_k}\left\{A_{kk}^{\alpha\beta} - \sum_\xi \frac{a_k^{\alpha\xi}a_k^{\beta\xi}}{I_{\xi\xi}^e}\right\}\right]\\
&- \sum_{\alpha\beta\gamma\delta}\frac{P_\alpha P_\beta P_\gamma P_\delta}{I_{\alpha\alpha}^e I_{\beta\beta}^e I_{\gamma\gamma}^e I_{\delta\delta}^e}\sum_k \frac{a_k^{\alpha\beta}a_k^{\gamma\delta}}{32\pi^2 c^2\omega_k^2}
\end{aligned}
\tag{4}
$$

$a_k^{\alpha\beta}$ and $A_{kk}^{\alpha\beta}$ are coefficients of Q_k and Q_k^2 in the expansion of $I_{\alpha\beta}$ in Eq. (4-3). $\zeta_{kk'}^{(\alpha)}$ is the Coriolis coupling coefficient. The first and second-order coefficients $a_k^{\alpha\beta}$ and $A_{kk}^{\alpha\beta}$ can be expressed explicitly in terms of the moments of inertia and the coefficients of the **l** matrix of Eq. (3-21). Oka and Morino have given the necessary relationships as

$$a_k^{\alpha\alpha} = 2\sum_i (m_i)^{1/2}[\beta_i l_{ik}^{(\beta)} + \gamma_i l_{ik}^{(\gamma)}] \tag{5}$$

$$a_k^{\alpha\beta} = -\sum_i (m_i)^{1/2} [\alpha_i l_{ik}^{(\beta)} + \beta_i l_{ik}^{(\alpha)}]$$

$$= -2\sum_i (m_i)^{1/2} \alpha_i l_{ik}^{(\beta)} = -2\sum_i (m_i)^{1/2} \beta_i l_{ik}^{(\alpha)} \qquad (\alpha \neq \beta) \qquad (6)$$

$$A_{kk}^{\alpha\alpha} = \sum_i [(l_{ik}^{(\beta)})^2 + (l_{ik}^{(\gamma)})^2] = 1 - \sum_i (l_{ik}^{(\alpha)})^2 \qquad (7)$$

$$A_{kk}^{\alpha\beta} = -\sum_i l_{ik}^{(\alpha)} l_{ik}^{(\beta)} \qquad (\alpha \neq \beta) \qquad (8)$$

$$\zeta_{kk'}^{(\alpha)} = \sum_i (l_{ik}^{(\beta)} l_{ik'}^{(\gamma)} - l_{ik'}^{(\beta)} l_{ik}^{(\gamma)}) \qquad (9)$$

$$\sum_\alpha A_{kk}^{\alpha\alpha} = 2 \qquad (10)$$

$$\sum_k \zeta_{kk'}^{(\alpha)} \zeta_{kk'}^{(\beta)} = A_{k'k'}^{\alpha\beta} - \frac{1}{4}\sum_\xi \frac{a_k^{\alpha\xi} a_{k'}^{\beta\xi}}{I_{\xi\xi}^e} \qquad (11)$$

$$\sum_k (a_k^{\alpha\alpha})^2 = 4I_{\alpha\alpha}^e \qquad (12)$$

$$\sum_k (a_k^{\alpha\beta})^2 = \frac{(I_{\alpha\alpha}^e)^2 - (I_{\alpha\alpha}^e - I_{\beta\beta}^e)^2}{I_{\gamma\gamma}^e} \qquad (\alpha \neq \beta) \qquad (13)$$

$$\sum_k a_k^{\alpha\alpha} a_k^{\beta\beta} = 2(I_{\alpha\alpha}^e + I_{\beta\beta}^e - I_{\gamma\gamma}^e) \qquad (\alpha \neq \beta) \qquad (14)$$

$$\sum_k A_{kk}^{\alpha\alpha} = 2N - 4 + \frac{I_{\alpha\alpha}^e - I_{\gamma\gamma}^e}{2I_{\beta\beta}^e} + \frac{I_{\alpha\alpha}^e - I_{\beta\beta}^e}{2I_{\gamma\gamma}^e} \qquad (15)$$

$$\sum_k \sum_\alpha A_{kk}^{\alpha\alpha} = 3(2N - 4) \qquad (16)$$

$$\sum_k A_{kk}^{\alpha\beta} = 0 \qquad (\alpha \neq \beta) \qquad (17)$$

It is now possible to introduce the planar property of the molecule. The y axis is chosen perpendicular to the molecular plane which contains the x and z axes. Cross terms in $P_x P_y$ and $P_y P_z$ vanish due to symmetry. In C_{2v} and V_h molecules, the coefficient of the $P_x P_z$ term vanishes, although it exists for C_s and C_{2h} symmetries.

The planar symmetry of a molecule forces a separation of the out-of-plane and in-plane vibrations, and $l_{ik}^{(x)} = l_{ik}^{(z)} = 0$ when k refers to an out-of-plane mode, while $l_{ik}^{(y)} = 0$ when k refers to an in-plane vibration. Therefore, for in-plane vibrations

$$A_{kk}^{zz} + A_{kk}^{xx} = A_{kk}^{yy} = 1 \qquad (18)$$

$$a_k^{zz} + a_k^{xx} = a_k^{yy} \qquad (19)$$

and for out-of-plane vibrations

$$A_{kk}^{xx} = A_{kk}^{zz} = 1 \qquad (20)$$

$$A_{kk}^{yy} = 0 \tag{21}$$

$$a_k^{xx} = a_k^{yy} = a_k^{zz} = 0 \tag{22}$$

Neglecting crossterms between the in-plane momenta P_x and P_z and using the explicit definition of the centrifugal distortion coefficient $\tau_{\alpha\beta\gamma\delta}$ obtained from (3-133)

$$\tau_{\alpha\beta\gamma\delta} = -\sum_k \frac{1}{I_{\alpha\alpha}^e I_{\beta\beta}^e I_{\gamma\gamma}^e I_{\delta\delta}^e} \frac{a_k^{\alpha\beta} a_k^{\gamma\delta}}{8\pi^2 hc^2 \omega_k^2} \tag{23}$$

the effective moments of inertia are

$$I_{\alpha\alpha}^0 = I_{\alpha\alpha}^e - \sum_k (v_k + \tfrac{1}{2}) \left[\frac{1}{2\pi} \left(\frac{h}{c}\right)^{1/2} \left\{ \frac{3k_{kkk}}{\omega_k^{3/2}} a_k^{\alpha\alpha} + \sum_{k'}' \frac{k_{kkk'}}{\omega_{k'}^{3/2}} a_{k'}^{\alpha\alpha} \right\} \right.$$
$$\left. + \frac{h}{\pi^2 c} \left\{ \sum_{k'}' \frac{\omega_{k'}^2}{\omega_k(\omega_k^2 - \omega_{k'}^2)} (\zeta_{kk'}^{\gamma(\alpha)})^2 + \frac{3}{4} \frac{A_{kk}^{\alpha\alpha}}{\omega_k} \right\} \right] - \frac{h^3}{8\pi^2} C_\alpha (I_{\alpha\alpha}^e)^2 \tau_{zxzx} \tag{24}$$

$$C_x = C_z = -2; \qquad C_y = 3 \tag{25}$$

The inertial defect can now be calculated by using (24), (4-109), and the simplifications introduced by planar symmetry. Vibrational and centrifugal contributions are

$$\Delta(\text{vib}) = \sum_k \frac{h}{\pi^2 c} \left(v_k + \frac{1}{2}\right) \sum_{k'}' \frac{\omega_{k'}^2}{\omega_k(\omega_k^2 - \omega_{k'}^2)} [(\zeta_{kk'}^{\gamma(x)})^2$$
$$+ (\zeta_{kk'}^{\gamma(z)})^2 - (\zeta_{kk'}^{\gamma(y)})^2] + \sum_t \frac{3h}{2\pi^2 c\omega_t} \left(v_t + \frac{1}{2}\right) \tag{26}$$

$$\Delta(\text{cent}) = -\hbar^4 \tau_{zxzx} \left(\frac{3}{4}\frac{I_{yy}}{C} + \frac{I_{xx}}{2B} + \frac{I_{zz}}{2A}\right) \tag{27}$$

t refers to out-of-plane vibrations only. A, B, and C are obtained from the rotational part of the total Hamiltonian (2)

$$H_r = AP_z^2 + BP_x^2 + CP_y^2 + D(P_xP_z + P_zP_x) \tag{28}$$

and contain contributions from $H^{(2)}$ as well as $H^{(0)}$.

$\Delta(\text{elect})$ reflects the contributions to the inertial defect of the out-of-plane bonding electrons.

$$\Delta(\text{elect}) = -\frac{m}{M} [I_{yy}g_{yy} - I_{zz}g_{zz} - I_{xx}g_{xx}] \tag{29}$$

m and M are the electron and proton masses, respectively, and the $g_{\alpha\alpha}$ are the components of the g tensor related to the rotational magnetic moment of the molecule.

APPENDIX 6 COUPLING OF ANGULAR MOMENTUM VECTORS

A. The Clebsch–Gordan and Racah Coefficients

Let two angular momentum vectors $\mathbf{J}_1$ and $\mathbf{J}_2$ couple to form a resultant $\mathbf{J}$. In the uncoupled representation, $\mathbf{J}_1^2$, $\mathbf{J}_2^2$, J_{1Z}, and J_{2Z} are diagonal. If $\psi_{J_1M_1}$ and $\psi_{J_2M_2}$ are the eigenfunctions, the eigenvalues are given by

$$\mathbf{J}_1^2\psi_{J_1M_1} = J_1(J_1 + 1)\psi_{J_1M_1}$$

$$\mathbf{J}_2^2\psi_{J_2M_2} = J_2(J_2 + 1)\psi_{J_2M_2}$$

$$J_{1Z}\psi_{J_1M_1} = M_1\psi_{J_1M_1}$$

$$J_{2Z}\psi_{J_2M_2} = M_2\psi_{J_2M_2}$$

M_1 and M_2 are the respective projection quantum numbers. There are also four commuting operators which are diagonal in the coupled representation. These may be $\mathbf{J}^2$, J_Z, $\mathbf{J}_1^2$, and $\mathbf{J}_2^2$, where

$$\mathbf{J} = \mathbf{J}_1 + \mathbf{J}_2$$

and

$$J_Z\psi_{JM} = M\psi_{JM}$$

ψ_{JM} is the eigenfunction of the coupled representation. The two representations are connected by a unitary transformation.

$$\psi_{JM} = \sum_{M_1}\sum_{M_2} C(J_1J_2J; M_1M_2M)\psi_{J_1M_1}\psi_{J_2M_2}$$

The coefficients are the Clebsch–Gordan coefficients which vanish unless $M = M_1 + M_2$. Their properties are thoroughly discussed by Rose [583]. The V coefficients defined by Racah can be related to the Clebsch–Gordan coefficients by

$$C(J_1J_2J; M_1M_2M) = (-1)^{J+M}(2J + 1)^{1/2}V(J_1J_2J; M_1M_2 - M)$$

Desirable symmetry characteristics make the V coefficients very convenient in some situations [496].

409

The Racah coefficients [497] appear where the coupling of three angular momenta is considered.

$$\mathbf{J} = \mathbf{J}_1 + \mathbf{J}_2 + \mathbf{J}_3$$

Coupling three angular momenta leads to six operators which may be diagonalized simultaneously. $\mathbf{J}_1$ may be coupled with $\mathbf{J}_2$ to form a resultant $\mathbf{J}'$, which then is coupled with $\mathbf{J}_3$ to give $\mathbf{J}$. In this representation, the diagonal operators are $\mathbf{J}_1^2$, $\mathbf{J}_2^2$, $\mathbf{J}_3^2$, $\mathbf{J}'^2$, $\mathbf{J}^2$, and J_Z. In another representation, $\mathbf{J}_2$ can couple with $\mathbf{J}_3$ to form $\mathbf{J}''$, which then forms $\mathbf{J}$ with $\mathbf{J}_1$. The unitary transformation connecting these two representations may be expressed as

$$\psi_{JM}(J') = \sum_{J''} C(J', J'')\psi_{JM}(J'')$$

leading to the Racah coefficients $W(J_1J_2JJ_3;J'J'')$.

$$C(J', J'') = [(2J'' + 1)(2J' + 1)]^{1/2} W(J_1J_2JJ_3;J'J'')$$

The properties of these coefficients are thoroughly discussed by Biedenharn *et al.* [538]. If the Racah coefficients are expressed as $W(abcd;ef)$, $C(J', J'')$ may be written as [583, 538]

$$C(e, f) = \langle ab(e)dc|abd(f)c \rangle = [(2e + 1)(2f + 1)]^{1/2} W(abcd;ef)$$

where the coupling representations are

$$\mathbf{a} + \mathbf{b} = \mathbf{e}; \qquad \mathbf{e} + \mathbf{d} = \mathbf{c}$$

$$\mathbf{b} + \mathbf{d} = \mathbf{f}; \qquad \mathbf{f} + \mathbf{a} = \mathbf{c}$$

B. The Wigner–Eckart Theorem

The Wigner–Eckart theorem provides a means of factoring the matrix elements of an irreducible tensor. For such a tensor T_{jm}

$$\langle J'M'|T_{jm}|JM \rangle = C(JjJ';MmM')\langle J'\|T_j\|J \rangle$$

The coefficient clearly expresses the conservation of angular momentum, since it vanishes unless $M + m = M'$ and $\mathbf{J} + \mathbf{j} = \mathbf{J}'$. The double bar notation signifies a reduced matrix element. This notation is used whenever projection quantum number dependence is removed from a matrix element.

Racah [496] has given an expression for the matrix element of the scalar product of two tensors which is used to evaluate the off-diagonal matrix elements of H_Q in Chapter 5.

$$\langle \gamma J_1 J_2 JM|(\mathbf{T}^{(k)} \cdot \mathbf{U}^{(k)})|\gamma' J'_1 J'_2 JM \rangle$$

$$= (-1)^{J_1 + J_2 - J} \sum_{\gamma''} \langle \gamma J_1\|\mathbf{T}^{(k)}\|\gamma'' J'_1 \rangle \langle \gamma'' J_2\|\mathbf{U}^{(k)}\|\gamma' J'_2 \rangle W(J_1 J_2 J'_1 J'_2;Jk)$$

THE VAN VLECK TRANSFORMATION

The Van Vleck transformation is an approximate diagonalization procedure which facilitates the factoring of an infinite energy matrix into small submatrices which may be treated individually. Its primary purpose is to separate, to a suitable degree of approximation, nearly degenerate energy levels from the remainder of the energy matrix.

The energy matrix can be expanded as

$$\mathbf{H} = \mathbf{H}_0 + \lambda\mathbf{H}_1 + \lambda^2\mathbf{H}_2 + \cdots$$

Elements of $\mathbf{H}_0$ lie entirely in diagonal blocks, while the perturbation terms may have elements inside and outside these blocks. If a transformation is applied to $\mathbf{H}$ to remove the off-diagonal elements of $\mathbf{H}_1$, i.e., those matrix elements of $\mathbf{H}_1$ which connect separate blocks of $\mathbf{H}_0$, the most important off-diagonal terms which remain are second-order elements. These connecting terms first contribute to the energy in the fourth order, and the energy matrix is essentially diagonal up through third order.

Van Vleck (see Jordahl [1012] and Kemble [1028]) formulated a canonical transformation $\mathbf{T}$ to remove the first-order terms in λ. $\mathbf{T}$ may be expanded in terms of a Hermitian matrix $\mathbf{S}$.

$$\mathbf{T} = e^{i\lambda\mathbf{S}} = \mathbf{I} + i\lambda\mathbf{S} - \tfrac{1}{2}\lambda^2\mathbf{S}^2 + \cdots$$

$\mathbf{I}$ is a unit matrix. The transformed matrix $\mathbf{G}$ has the form

$$\mathbf{G} = \mathbf{T}^{-1}\mathbf{H}\mathbf{T} = \mathbf{G}_0 + \lambda\mathbf{G}_1 + \lambda^2\mathbf{G}_2 + \cdots$$

$\mathbf{T}$ is unitary to the second order in λ. Using Herschbach's notation,[†] the effect of the transformation is

$$\mathbf{T}^{-1}\begin{bmatrix} \langle m|\mathbf{H}|m'\rangle & \langle m|\mathbf{H}|n\rangle \\ \langle n|\mathbf{H}|m\rangle & \langle n|\mathbf{H}|n'\rangle \end{bmatrix}\mathbf{T} = \begin{bmatrix} \langle m|\mathbf{H}|m'\rangle & 0 \\ 0 & \langle n|\mathbf{H}|n'\rangle \end{bmatrix}$$

[†] D. R. Herschbach, unpublished work, Harvard University, Cambridge, Massachusetts. Also see [670].

where the new $\langle m|\mathbf{H}|m'\rangle$ contain correction terms from the off-diagonal elements. Through first-order in λ, m and m' label the submatrix to be separated from $\mathbf{H}$, and n and n' label states outside this submatrix. Expanding the transformed Hamiltonian and equating equal powers of λ

$$\mathbf{G}_0 = \mathbf{H}_0$$

$$\mathbf{G}_1 = \mathbf{H}_1 + i(\mathbf{H}_0\mathbf{S} - \mathbf{S}\mathbf{H}_0)$$

$$\mathbf{G}_2 = \mathbf{H}_2 + i(\mathbf{H}_1\mathbf{S} - \mathbf{S}\mathbf{H}_1) + \mathbf{S}\mathbf{H}_0\mathbf{S} - \tfrac{1}{2}(\mathbf{H}_0\mathbf{S}^2 + \mathbf{S}^2\mathbf{H}_0)$$

$$\mathbf{G}_3 = \mathbf{H}_3 + i(\mathbf{H}_2\mathbf{S} - \mathbf{S}\mathbf{H}_2) + \mathbf{S}\mathbf{H}_1\mathbf{S} - \tfrac{1}{2}(\mathbf{H}_1\mathbf{S}^2 + \mathbf{S}^2\mathbf{H}_1)$$

$$\qquad + \tfrac{1}{2}i(\mathbf{S}\mathbf{H}_0\mathbf{S}^2 - \mathbf{S}^2\mathbf{H}_0\mathbf{S}) - \tfrac{1}{6}i(\mathbf{H}_0\mathbf{S}^3 - \mathbf{S}^3\mathbf{H}_0)$$

The transformation matrix $\mathbf{S}$ can now be constructed from its required characteristics. Terms which would alter the diagonal submatrices labeled by m or n are set equal to zero.

$$\langle m|\mathbf{S}|m'\rangle = \langle n|\mathbf{S}|n'\rangle = 0$$

In order to force $\langle m|\mathbf{G}_1|n\rangle$ to vanish, it follows that

$$\langle m|\mathbf{S}|n\rangle = i\langle m|\mathbf{H}_1|n\rangle/(E_m - E_n)$$

This definition of $\mathbf{S}$ leads to the following expression for the submatrix $\langle m|\mathbf{G}|m'\rangle$, good to third order. In most cases only the second-order terms are needed.

$$\langle m|\mathbf{G}|m'\rangle = E_m\delta_{mm'} + \lambda\langle m|\mathbf{H}_1|m'\rangle + \lambda^2\langle m|\mathbf{H}_2|m'\rangle + \lambda^3\langle m|\mathbf{H}_3|m'\rangle$$

$$+ \frac{\lambda^2}{2}\sum_n{}' \left[\frac{\langle m|\mathbf{H}_1|n\rangle\langle n|\mathbf{H}_1|m'\rangle}{E_m - E_n} + \frac{\langle m|\mathbf{H}_1|n\rangle\langle n|\mathbf{H}_1|m'\rangle}{E_{m'} - E_n} \right]$$

$$+ \frac{\lambda^3}{2}\sum_n{}' \left[\frac{\langle m|\mathbf{H}_1|n\rangle\langle n|\mathbf{H}_2|m'\rangle}{E_m - E_n} + \frac{\langle m|\mathbf{H}_2|n\rangle\langle n|\mathbf{H}_1|m'\rangle}{E_{m'} - E_n} \right]$$

$$- \frac{\lambda^3}{2}\sum_n{}'\sum_{m''}{}' \left[\frac{\langle m|\mathbf{H}_1|m''\rangle\langle m''|\mathbf{H}_1|n\rangle\langle n|\mathbf{H}_1|m'\rangle}{(E_{m''} - E_n)(E_{m'} - E_n)} \right.$$

$$+ \frac{\langle m|\mathbf{H}_1|n\rangle\langle n|\mathbf{H}_1|m''\rangle\langle m''|\mathbf{H}_1|m'\rangle}{(E_m - E_n)(E_{m''} - E_n)} \Bigg]$$

$$+ \lambda^3\sum_n{}'\sum_{n'}{}' \left[\frac{\langle m|\mathbf{H}_1|n\rangle\langle n|\mathbf{H}_1|m'\rangle\langle n'|\mathbf{H}_1|m'\rangle}{(E_m - E_n)(E_{m'} - E_{n'})} \right]$$

The λ's are retained to identify the perturbation order. The same general approach can be used to extend the correction to fourth and higher orders, although this would rarely be necessary.

In the internal rotation problem, the Van Vleck treatment is used to produce an approximate factoring of the torsional states by effectively diagonalizing the energy matrix in the torsional quantum number v. The transformation also finds application for general vibration-rotation interactions and for the Stark effect whenever near degeneracies must be considered [335, 655, 840].

INTERNAL ROTATION SPLITTINGS FOR THE IAM

The following explicit expressions have been given by Hecht and Dennison [668] for the hindered internal rotation splittings between the A and E components of a level $J_{K_{-1}K_1}$ in terms of the IAM parameters Δ_K and β. The rotational constants a, b, and c are expressed in energy units where $a < b < c$. Using the rotational constant notation of Chapter 2, $c \to hA$, $b \to hB$, and $a \to hC$.

$J = 0$:

$$E(0_{00}) = \Delta_0$$

$J = 1$:

$$E(1_{01}) = \Delta_0 + \beta^2(\Delta_1 - \Delta_0)$$

$$E(1_{11}) = \Delta_1 - \beta^2(\Delta_1 - \Delta_0)$$

$$E(1_{10}) = \Delta_1$$

$J = 2$:

$$\left.\begin{matrix} E(2_{02}) \\ E(2_{20}) \end{matrix}\right\} = \frac{1}{2}(\Delta_0 + \Delta_2) \pm \frac{a + b - 2c}{4[(b-a)^2 + (c-b)(c-a)]^{1/2}}(\Delta_2 - \Delta_0)$$

$$\pm \frac{3\beta^2(c-b)(\Delta_2 - \Delta_0)}{4[(b-a)^2 + (c-b)(c-a)]^{1/2}} - \frac{\beta^2}{2}(1 - \beta^2)$$

$$\times (\Delta_2 + 3\Delta_0 - 4\Delta_1)\left[1 \mp \frac{2a - b - c}{2[(b-a)^2 + (c-b)(c-a)]^{1/2}}\right]$$

$$E(2_{12}) = \Delta_1 + \beta^2(1 - \beta^2)(\Delta_2 + 3\Delta_0 - 4\Delta_1)$$

$$E(2_{11}) = \Delta_1 + \beta^2(\Delta_2 - \Delta_1)$$

$$E(2_{21}) = \Delta_2 - \beta^2(\Delta_2 - \Delta_1)$$

$J = 3$:

$$\begin{Bmatrix} E(3_{12}) \\ E(3_{30}) \end{Bmatrix} = \frac{1}{2}(\Delta_1 + \Delta_3) \pm \frac{[(8c - 7b - a) + 15\beta^2(b - c)]}{8[4(b - c)^2 + (a - b)(a - c)]^{1/2}}$$

$$\times (\Delta_1 - \Delta_3) - \frac{\beta^2}{4}(1 - \beta^2)(5\Delta_1 - 8\Delta_2 + 3\Delta_3)$$

$$\times \left[1 \mp \frac{b + c - 2a}{2[4(b - c)^2 + (a - b)(a - c)]^{1/2}} \right]$$

$$E(3_{22}) = \Delta_2 + \frac{\beta^2}{2}(1 - \beta^2)(5\Delta_1 - 8\Delta_2 + 3\Delta_3)$$

$$\begin{Bmatrix} E(3_{31}) \\ E(3_{13}) \end{Bmatrix} = \frac{1}{2}(\Delta_1 + \Delta_3) - \frac{\beta^2}{4}(17\Delta_1 - 8\Delta_2 + 3\Delta_3 - 12\Delta_0)$$

$$+ \frac{\beta^4}{4}(3 - 2\beta^2)(15\Delta_1 - 6\Delta_2 + \Delta_3 - 10\Delta_0)$$

$$\pm \left\{ \frac{(7a + b - 8c)(\Delta_3 - \Delta_1) - 2\beta^2(17\Delta_1 - 8\Delta_2 + 3\Delta_3 - 12\Delta_0)}{8[4(a - c)^2 + (b - a)(b - c)]^{1/2}} \right\}$$

$$\pm \left\{ \frac{5\beta^2(c - b)(\Delta_3 - 2\Delta_2 - \Delta_1 + 2\Delta_0)(2 - 3\beta^2)}{16[4(a - c)^2 + (b - a)(b - c)]^{1/2}} \right\}$$

$$\pm \left\{ \frac{[2\beta^2(9a + 2b - 11c) + \beta^4(3 - 2\beta^2)(7c + b - 8a)]}{16[4(a - c)^2 + (b - a)(b - c)]^{1/2}} \right\}$$

$$\begin{Bmatrix} E(3_{03}) \\ E(3_{21}) \end{Bmatrix} = \frac{1}{2}(\Delta_0 + \Delta_2) + \frac{\beta^2}{4}(17\Delta_1 - 8\Delta_2 + 3\Delta_3 - 12\Delta_0)$$

$$- \frac{\beta^4}{4}(3 - 2\beta^2)(15\Delta_1 - 6\Delta_2 + \Delta_3 - 10\Delta_0)$$

$$\pm \left\{ \frac{4(a + b - 2c)(\Delta_2 - \Delta_0) + \beta^2(3a - 7b + 4c)}{16[4(b - a)^2 + (c - a)(c - b)]^{1/2}} \right\}$$

$$\pm \left\{ \frac{5\beta^2(4 - 3\beta^2)(a + 3b - 4c)(\Delta_3 - 2\Delta_2 - \Delta_1 + 2\Delta_0)}{64[4(b - a)^2 + (c - a)(c - b)]^{1/2}} \right\}$$

$$\pm \left\{ \frac{[4\beta^2(12b - 8a - 4c) + \beta^4(3 - 2\beta^2)(17a - 13b - 4c)]}{64[4(b - a)^2 + (c - a)(c - b)]^{1/2}} \right\}$$

BARRIERS TO INTERNAL ROTATION DETERMINED BY MICROWAVE

APPENDIX 9 SPECTROSCOPY

Tables A9-1–6 compare internal barrier heights, conformations, and methyl group tilt angles for a number of molecules which have been studied by microwave spectroscopy. A more detailed compilation through 1962 has been given by Herschbach [737].

The effects of group substitutions in related series of molecules such as CH_3CH_2X, CH_3COX, and $CH_3CH=CHX$, where X may be hydrogen, a halogen, an alkyl group, etc., are determined by comparing barrier values given in the tables. For example, a general decrease in V_3 might usually be expected from CH_3CH_2X to $CH_3CX=CH_2$ to $CH_3CH=CHX$ to CH_3COX; however, exceptions can be expected.

It is difficult to make correct empirical predictions of barrier heights because many factors can affect $V(\alpha)$. These include the bond length associated with the torsional motion, molecular symmetry, electronegativity of the substituents, and the type of bonding. The following comparisons provide examples.

Substitution of silicon for carbon in ethane-type compounds results in a reduction of V_3 which may be related to the increase in bond length. Extension through germanium and tin does not alter this reasoning. The reduction in barrier height from carbon to silicon is approximately a factor of two for ethane-type molecules and is even greater through *t*-butane-type molecules.

In the C—V group, the barrier increases as methyl groups are added to molecules like NH_3, PH_3, and AsH_3. The rate of increase is greatest for the amines, on the order of one kilocalorie per methyl group. The phosphines show an analogous trend and limited data about the arsenes is in agreement. This trend is absent in the methyl-substituted silanes where the barriers for methylsilane and dimethylsilane are nearly identical; the barrier in trimethylsilane is slightly larger. However, the C—VI compounds show a factor of two increase upon addition of a second methyl group to methyl alcohol or methyl mercaptan.

Some very important reversals of this tendency come in the acetaldehyde-acetone and propylene oxide-*cis*-2,3-epoxybutane series. Addition of a second methyl group forces approximately a twofold barrier reduction. When an ethyl group is added, the barrier is reduced even more. It is interesting to note that both of these exceptions occur when the carbon atom to which the methyl group is attached is also bonded to an oxygen atom.

A valuable by-product of the study of internal barriers is a determination of the minimum energy or equilibrium configuration of the top and frame. For the most fundamental case of ethane, the staggered form has a lower energy than the eclipsed form. It is evident that the forces which provide the hindering potential will dictate the favored configuration. One important conclusion is the general preference for the staggered form over the eclipsed form. The eclipsed form is the orientation of maximum torsional energy. If a complete quantum-mechanical calculation for the total energy of the molecule were done for the staggered and eclipsed forms, a simple difference would yield the barrier height directly; however, this difference of two relatively large quantities would be subject to large percentage errors.

The last few entries in Table A9-5 represent rotational isomers which have been studied by microwave spectroscopy. The *gauche* and *cis* forms are generally favored over the *trans* structure.

In the close study of methyl group structure inherent in the investigation of internal rotation, it has been observed that in some molecules the axis of the methyl group is not colinear with the $C-X$ bond about which the hindered rotation is executed. For $C-O$, $C-N$, and $C-S$ bonds where the atom X has one or more sets of lone pair electrons, the axis of the methyl group appears to be tilted up toward the unshared electrons. This effect also has been observed for methyl groups bonded to unsaturated carbon atoms, e.g., $(CH_3)_2C=O$.

The presence of a tilted methyl group is usually detected either from the internal rotation splittings, provided they are sensitive to the orientation of the top axis through the direction cosines, or from a study of species with partially deuterated methyl groups (CH_2D and CHD_2) [722, 755].

A nonequivalent hybridization scheme has been applied to dimethyl ether; by assuming the experimentally determined HCH angles to be orbital angles, $sp^{3.11}$ and $sp^{2.87}$ hybridizations were calculated for the CH_a and CH_s bonds. a and s refer to positions in and out of the COC plane, respectively. It has been proposed that this hybridization and the apparent "bent bonds" in CH_3XCH_3 molecules might be the result of a nonbonded repulsion between the two methyl groups [480], although the presence of lone pair or π electrons seems to be prerequisite. The existence of a "bent bond" would appear to have a relatively strong effect on the barrier.

In the following tables error limits are not listed and may be obtained from the appropriate references.

TABLE A9-1

BARRIERS TO INTERNAL ROTATION ABOUT $CH_3—C$ BONDS

Molecule	Formula	V(cal/mole)	References
Ethyl fluoride	CH_3CH_2F	3310	[659]
1,1-Difluoroethane	CH_3CHF_2	3180	[659]
Methyl fluoroform	CH_3CF_3	3500	[621]
Ethyl chloride	CH_3CH_2Cl	3685	[1578]
Ethyl bromide	CH_3CH_2Br	3567	[702]
Ethyl iodide	CH_3CH_2I	3220	[1483]
Ethyl cyanide	CH_3CH_2CN	3050	[700]
Ethyl alcohol	CH_3CH_2OH	772	[743a]
Propane	$CH_3CH_2CH_3$	3555	[755b]
Ethyl silane	$CH_3CH_2SiH_3$	2650	[737]
cis-Propionaldehyde	CH_3CH_2CHO	2280	[1633]
trans-Propyl fluoride	$CH_3CH_2CH_2F$	2690	[725]
gauche-Propyl fluoride	$CH_3CH_2CH_2F$	2670	[725]
Isobutane	$(CH_3)_3CH$	3900	[691]
t-Butyl fluoride	$(CH_3)_3CF$	4300	[691]
Acetaldehyde	CH_3CHO	1167	[673, 698]
Acetyl fluoride	CH_3COF	1041	[1466]
Acetyl chloride	CH_3COCl	1296	[1539]
Acetyl bromide	CH_3COBr	1305	[1489]
Acetyl cyanide	CH_3COCN	1270	[1455]
Acetic acid	CH_3COOH	497	[683]
Acetone	$(CH_3)_2CO$	778	[705, 755]
Methyl vinyl ketone	$CH_3COCHCH_2$	1250	[1675]
cis-Butanone	$CH_3COC_2H_5$	500	[737]
Propylene	$CH_3CH=CH_2$	1978	[676]
trans-Fluoropropene	$CH_3CH=CHF$	2200	[681]
cis-Fluoropropene	$CH_3CH=CHF$	1057	[1549]
2-Chloropropene	$CH_3CCl=CH_2$	2671	[758]
cis-Chloropropene	$CH_3CH=CHCl$	622	[1632]
2-Fluoropropene	$CH_3CF=CH_2$	2432	[1467]
trans-Crotononitrile	$CH_3CH=CHCN$	>2100	[1491]
cis-Crotononitrile	$CH_3CH=CHCN$	1400	[733]
Methyl ketene	$CH_3CH=C=O$	1200	[1545]
Methyl allene	$CH_3CH=C=CH_2$	1589	[677]
Isobutylene	$(CH_3)_2C=CH_2$	2210	[1531]
Propylene oxide	$CH_3CH—CH_2$ $\diagdown O \diagup$	2560	[682]
cis-2,3-Epoxybutane	$CH_3CH—CHCH_3$ $\diagdown O \diagup$	1607	[723]
1-Chloro-2-butyne	$CH_3C\equiv CCH_2Cl$	<100	[701]
Methylsilylacetylene	$CH_3C\equiv CSiH_3$	<3	[752]
1-Trifluorobutyne-2	$CH_3C\equiv CCF_3$	<300	[737]

Table A9-1 (*continued*)

Molecule	Formula	V(cal/mole)	References
Propylene sulfide	$CH_3CH—CH_2$ $\diagdown S \diagup$	3240	[1591]
t-Butyl acetylene	$(CH_3)_3CC{\equiv}CH$	~4000	[1572]
t-Butyl cyanide	$(CH_3)_3CCN$	~4000	[1572]
p-Fluorotoluene	$CH_3C_6H_4F$	13.82	[755a]

TABLE A9-2
BARRIERS TO INTERNAL ROTATION ABOUT IV—IV BONDS OTHER THAN CARBON—CARBON

Molecule	Formula	V(cal/mole)	References
Methylsilane	CH_3SiH_3	1670	[674,698]
Methylfluorosilane	CH_3SiFH_2	1559	[1433]
Methyldifluorosilane	CH_3SiF_2H	1255	[1436]
Methyltrifluorosilane	CH_3SiF_3	1200	[1176]
Dimethylsilane	$(CH_3)_2SiH_2$	1647	[721]
Trimethylsilane	$(CH_3)_3SiH$	1830	[1506]
Ethylsilane	$C_2H_5SiH_3$	1980	[737]
Chloromethylsilane	CH_2ClSiH_3	2550	[1579]
Vinylsilane	$CH_2{=}CHSiH_3$	1500	[1535]
Methylgermane	CH_3GeH_3	1239	[1456]
Methylstannane	CH_3SnH_3	650	[1516]
Disilanyl fluoride	SiH_3SiH_2F	1048	[1699b]

TABLE A9-3
BARRIERS TO INTERNAL ROTATION ABOUT IV—III AND IV—V BONDS

Molecule	Formula	V(cal/mole)	References
Methylamine	CH_3NH_2	1980	[786]
Dimethylamine	$(CH_3)_2NH$	3300	[816]
Trimethylamine	$(CH_3)_3N$	4400	[690]
Methylphosphine	CH_3PH_2	1960	[719]
Dimethylphosphine	$(CH_3)_2PH$	2200	[616]
Trimethylphosphine	$(CH_3)_3P$	2600	[1691]
Methyldifluoroarsine	CH_3AsF_2	1332	[1571]
Trimethylarsine	$(CH_3)_3As$	1500–2500	[1457]
Nitromethane	CH_3NO_2	6.03	[665]
Methylisocyanate	CH_3NCO	49	[1594]
Trifluoronitromethane	CF_3NO_2	74.4	[757]
Methylazide	CH_3N_3	714	[1703]
Methylborondifluoride	CH_3BF_2	13.77	[679]

TABLE A9-4
BARRIERS TO INTERNAL ROTATION ABOUT IV—VI BONDS

Molecule	Formula	V(cal/mole)	References
Methyl alcohol	CH_3OH	1070	[1235]
Methyl hypochlorite	CH_3OCl	3060	[1660]
Methyl formate	CH_3OOCH	1190	[1444]
Methyl nitrate	CH_3ONO_2	2321	[1519]
Dimethyl ether	$(CH_3)_2O$	2720	[699]
Ethylmethyl ether	$C_2H_5OCH_3$	2530	[737]
Methyl mercaptan	CH_3SH	1268	[1487]
Dimethylsulfide	$(CH_3)_2S$	2118	[722]
Dimethyldisulfide	$(CH_3)_2S_2$	1600	[756a]
Methyl thiocyanate	CH_3SCN	1590	[754]

TABLE A9-5
MINIMUM ENERGY CONFIGURATIONS

Molecule	Configuration	References
CH_3CH_2F	Staggered	[1475]
CH_3CH_2Cl	Staggered	[654]
CH_3SiH_3	Staggered	[674]
CH_3SiH_2F	Staggered	[1433]
CH_3SiHF_2	Staggered	[1436]
CH_2ClSiH_3	Staggered	[1579]
CH_3GeH_3	Staggered	[1456]
CH_3CHO	Methyl group eclipses oxygen and staggers hydrogen	[673]
CH_3COF	Methyl group eclipses oxygen and staggers fluorine	[1466]
CH_3COCl	Methyl group eclipses oxygen and staggers chlorine	[1539]
CH_3COCN	Methyl group eclipses oxygen and staggers cyanide group	[1455]
$(CH_3)_3CH$	Each methyl group staggered with respect to methine group	[881]
$(CH_3)_3N$	Each methyl group staggered with respect to lone pair	
$(CH_3)_3SiH$	Each methyl group staggered with respect to Siline group	[1506]
$(CH_3)_2O$	Each methyl group staggered with respect to opposite C=O bond	[699]
$(CH_3)_2S$	Each methyl group staggered with respect to opposite C=S bond	[722]
$(CH_3)_2CH_2$	Each methyl group staggered with respect to methylene group	[1493]
$(CH_3)_2C=CH_2$	Methyl groups staggered with respect to the line colinear with the double bond	[1531]
$(CH_3)_2NH$	Methyl groups stagger the C—N—C plane opposite from the N—H group	[816]
$CH_3CH=CH_2$	Methyl group eclipses double bond and staggers methine H	[687]
$SiH_3CH=CH_2$	Silyl group staggered with respect to methine group	[1535]

Table A9-5 (*continued*)

Molecule	Configuration	References
CH_3OOCH	Methyl group staggered with respect to formyl group	[1444]
C_6H_5OH	Planar	[711]
NH_2NH_2	Dihedral angle of 90°	[805]
NF_2NF_2	Dihedral angle of 65°	[1458]
H_2O_2	Dihedral angle of 120°	[732]
$CH_3CH_2CH_2F$	*Gauche* configuration of CH_3 and F slightly more stable than *trans*	[725]
$CH_3CH_2CH_2CN$	*Gauche* configuration of F and CN slightly more stable than *trans*	[726]
$CH_2FCH=CH_2$	*Cis* configuration of F and $C=CH_2$ slightly more stable than *trans*	[750]

TABLE A9-6

SOME APPROXIMATE METHYL GROUP TILT ANGLES

Molecule	Bond	Angle	References
CH_3OH	C—O	~5°	[668]
$(CH_3)_2O$	C—O	~5°	[480,699]
CH_3OOCH	C—O	~6°	[1444]
CH_3SH	C—S	2.5°	[1487]
$(CH_3)_2S$	C—S	2.5°	[722]
CH_3NH_2	C—N	~3°	[793]
$(CH_3)_2CO$	C—C	1.3°	[755]
CH_3COCl	C—C	1.6°	[755]
CH_3COCN	C—C	2.0°	[755]
$SiH_3CH=CH_2$	Si—C	1.8°	[1535]

VANISHING OF ODD-ORDER NONDEGENERATE STARK CORRECTIONS

In linear and symmetric-top molecules where $K = 0$ and asymmetric rotors in the absence of any degeneracies or near-degeneracies, perturbation theory gives Stark effect corrections dependent on only even powers of the electric field; all odd-order terms vanish. Golden and Wilson [840] have illustrated this for the third-order correction $E^{(3)}$, and it applies to all higher odd-order terms. The correction $E^{(3)}$ which is proportional to the third power of the electric field is given by nondegenerate perturbation theory as

$$E^{(3)} = - \sum_{j \neq i} \frac{\langle i|H_\varepsilon|i\rangle \langle i|H_\varepsilon|j\rangle \langle j|H_\varepsilon|i\rangle}{(E_i^{(0)} - E_j^{(0)})^2}$$

$$+ \sum_{j \neq i} \sum_{k \neq i} \frac{\langle i|H_\varepsilon|j\rangle \langle j|H_\varepsilon|k\rangle \langle k|H_\varepsilon|i\rangle}{(E_i^{(0)} - E_j^{(0)})(E_i^{(0)} - E_k^{(0)})} \tag{1}$$

Because the first-order correction vanishes in the nondegenerate case, all diagonal elements $\langle i|H_\varepsilon|i\rangle = 0$, eliminating the first term in (1). All terms vanish except those for which i, j, and k are different, and $\langle i|H_\varepsilon|j\rangle$, $\langle j|H_\varepsilon|k\rangle$, and $\langle k|H_\varepsilon|i\rangle$ must correspond to different direction-cosine terms in the perturbation matrix of Fig. 8-2. One of these must be imaginary according to Table 2-11, and therefore, $E^{(3)} = 0$.

A. Periodic Solutions of Mathieu's Equation

Mathieu's equation is given in Eq. (6-47) as

$$\left(\frac{d^2}{dx^2} - s\cos^2 x \right) y(x) = -by(x) \tag{1}$$

where b is an eigenvalue and s is a parameter chosen to be nonnegative. For integral values of N, $\cos^2 x$ is invariant under the transformation $x \rightarrow x + N\pi$; consequently, there exist periodic solutions of (1) with period $N\pi$ in x. If σ is integral, a periodic solution of (1) may be represented by a Fourier expansion of the following form:

$$y(x) = \exp(i2\sigma x/N) \sum_{k=-\infty}^{\infty} B_k \exp(i2kx) \tag{2}$$

Because the summation in (2) runs from $k = -\infty$ to $k = +\infty$, it is clear that values for σ which differ by N lead to the same solution of (1). Thus, if solutions invariant under $x \rightarrow x + N\pi$ are required, it is necessary to consider only N values of σ, and these are conveniently chosen such that $0 \le |\sigma| \le N/2$.

Substitution of the expansion (2) into (1) yields the algebraic conditions

$$B_{k-1} + (M_k - \lambda)B_k + B_{k+1} = 0 \tag{3}$$

where

$$k = 0, \pm 1, \pm 2, \cdots$$

$$M_k = (16/N^2 s)(Nk + \sigma)^2$$

and

$$\lambda = \frac{4}{s}\left(b - \frac{s}{2} \right)$$

[†] Based on Part I of "Tables for the Internal Rotation Problem" by Michiro Hayashi and Louis Pierce, Dept. of Chemistry, Univ. of Notre Dame, Notre Dame, Indiana, pp. 3–9 (1961) (also see [718]).

From (2) it is evident that the two solutions corresponding to $\pm\sigma$ have the same periodicity; from (3) it is further seen that they belong to the same eigenvalue. Thus the periodic solutions of (1) are associated with doubly degenerate eigenvalues except when $\sigma = 0$ or $\sigma = N/2$. The $\sigma = 0$ solutions exist for all values of N and have the period π in x. The $\sigma = N/2$ solutions apply only to even values of N and have period 2π in x. The number of distinct eigenvalues corresponding to a given N is then $(N + 1)/2$ if N is odd and $(N + 2)/2$ if N is even.

When necessary, particular eigenfunctions and eigenvalues will be specified using the following notation: $y_{v\sigma N}$ is a solution of (1) which is invariant under $x \rightarrow x + N\pi$ and belongs to the eigenvalue $b_{v\sigma}(N\pi)$ where $v = 0, 1, 2, \ldots$, and $b_{v'\sigma}(N\pi) > b_{v\sigma}(N\pi)$ when $v' > v$. Note from (2) that $y_{v\sigma'N'} = y_{v\sigma N}$ and therefore $b_{v\sigma'}(N'\pi) = b_{v\sigma}(N\pi)$ if $(\sigma'/N') = (\sigma/N)$. While $y_{v\sigma N}$ is invariant under $x \rightarrow x + N\pi$, the periodicity is $N\pi$ only if N and σ do not have any common integral factors.

Since $\cos^2 x$ is invariant under $x \rightarrow -x$, the nondegenerate solutions of (1) have the property

$$y(-x) = \pm y(x)$$

If $y(x)$ has the period π in x, (2) may be replaced by the orthonormal expansions

$$y_v(x) = \frac{D_0}{\sqrt{2}} + \sum_{k=1} D_k^v \cos 2kx \qquad (v \text{ even}) \qquad (4a)$$

or

$$y_v(x) = \sum_{k=1} D_k^v \sin 2kx \qquad (v \text{ odd}) \qquad (4b)$$

If $y(x)$ has the period 2π, it may be expanded as

$$y_v(x) = \sum_{k=0} D_k^v \cos[(2k + 1)x] \qquad (v \text{ odd}) \qquad (5a)$$

or

$$y_v(x) = \sum_{k=0} D_k^v \sin[(2k + 1)x] \qquad (v \text{ even}) \qquad (5b)$$

If the period of $y(x)$ is $N\pi$ and N is greater than 2, then expansion (2) is appropriate and

$$y_{v\sigma N}(-x) = y_{v\sigma N}^*(x) = y_{v-\sigma N}(x) \qquad (6)$$

B. Determination of b and $y(x)$

Two limiting cases are of interest:
(a) As $s \rightarrow 0$

$$y_{v\sigma N} \rightarrow \left(\frac{1}{\sqrt{2\pi}}\right) \exp[i2(k + \sigma/N)x]$$

$$b_{v\sigma}(N\pi) \rightarrow 4(Nk + \sigma)^2/N^2$$

$$y_{v\sigma N} \to \left(\frac{1}{\sqrt{2\pi}}\right) \exp[i2mx/N]$$

$$b_{v\sigma}(N\pi) \to 4m^2/N^2$$

where $m = \sigma$ modulo N.

(b) As $s \to \infty$ for $b \ll s$, Mathieu's equation is closely related to Hermite's equation, and this relationship may be used to show that

$$b_{v\sigma}(N\pi) \to b_v = 2\sqrt{s}(v + \tfrac{1}{2}), \qquad v = 0, 1, 2, \ldots$$

In this limit the eigenvalues b are independent of the boundary conditions imposed on the solutions $y(x)$.

General solutions of (1) must be obtained by numerical procedures. For solutions of (3) to exist, the determinant of the coefficients of the B_k must vanish; this condition specifies the eigenvalues b. Degenerate eigenvalues corresponding to periodic solutions must satisfy the determinantal equation

$$\begin{vmatrix} \ddots & & & & & \\ & 1 & & & 0 & \\ \ddots & & & & & \\ & (M_{k-1} - \lambda) & 1 & & & \\ \ddots & & & & & \\ & 1 & (M_k - \lambda) & 1 & & \\ & & 1 & (M_{k+1} - \lambda) & & \ddots \\ 0 & & & 1 & & \ddots \\ & & & & & \ddots \end{vmatrix} = 0 \qquad (7)$$

The determinant is of Jacobian form similar to the determinants encountered in the solution for the reduced energies of a rigid rotor in Appendix 3. A continued fraction expansion using the Newton-Raphson procedure can also be employed here. The Fourier coefficients B_k may be obtained from the recursion formula

$$\frac{B_{k \pm m}}{B_{k \pm m \pm 1}} = G_{k \pm m} \qquad (8)$$

where

$$G_{k \pm 1} = (\lambda - M_{k \pm 1} - G_{k \pm 2})^{-1}$$

The nondegenerate solutions of (1) may also be handled by the continued fraction technique; however, the trigonometric expansions are used in place of the exponential expansions. In particular, the secular determinants are of the following forms:

(a) $\sigma = 0$, $N = 1, 2, 3, \ldots$. The periodicity of x is π. If v is even (cosine expansion), λ must satisfy

$$
\begin{vmatrix}
(M_0 - \lambda) & 2^{1/2} & 0 & \\
2^{1/2} & (M_1 - \lambda) & 1 & \\
& 1 & (M_2 - \lambda) & \ddots \\
0 & & 1 & \ddots
\end{vmatrix} = 0 \tag{9}
$$

If v is odd (sine expansion), λ must satisfy a determinantal equation related to (9) by omitting the first row and column.

(b) $\sigma = N/2$, N even. The periodicity of x is 2π, and λ must satisfy

$$
\begin{vmatrix}
(M_0' - \lambda) & 1 & 0 & \\
1 & (M_1 - \lambda) & 1 & \\
& 1 & (M_2 - \lambda) & \ddots \\
0 & & 1 & \ddots
\end{vmatrix} = 0 \tag{10}
$$

where $M_0' = M_0 - 1$ if v is even (sine expansion), and $M_0' = M_0 + 1$ if v is odd (cosine expansion).

C. Fourier Expansion of Mathieu Eigenvalues and Nonperiodic Mathieu Functions

Use of the expansion (2) yields periodic solutions of Mathieu's equation. If in (2) σ is replaced by σ' where σ' is nonintegral, but real, nonperiodic solutions of (1) are obtained. It is possible to relate the periodic and nonperiodic solutions in a very useful way. The relationship depends on the fact that the transformation $\sigma' \to \sigma' + N$ does not lead to a new solution. Thus if an angle γ is defined as

$$
\gamma = \frac{2\pi}{N} \sigma' \tag{11}
$$

and σ' is regarded as a continuous variable, the eigenvalues b are periodic in γ with period 2π. Moreover, the eigenvalues are even functions of γ since the solutions corresponding to $\pm\sigma'$ belong to the same eigenvalue. Consequently, the eigenvalues may be expanded in a Fourier series

$$b_{v\gamma} = \sum_{l=0}^{\infty} w_l \cos l\gamma \tag{12}$$

If $\sigma' - \sigma$ is an integer, then $b_{v\gamma} = b_{v\sigma}(N\pi)$ which is an eigenvalue corresponding to a periodic solution of (1). The Fourier coefficients w_l in (12) depend on v and s but not on N or σ. For $b \ll s$, (12) converges very rapidly and only the first few w_l are important. For a given v and s, if enough eigenvalues corresponding to either periodic or nonperiodic solutions of (1) are available, they may be used to compute the necessary number of w_l's, and they serve as the basis for the computation of any Mathieu eigenvalue (as specified by γ) for the same v and s.

APPENDIX 12

PERTURBATION COEFFICIENTS FOR THE INTERNAL ROTATION PROBLEM

The perturbation coefficients $W_{v\sigma}^{(n)}$ tabulated by M. Hayashi and L. Pierce in Part IV of "Tables for the Internal Rotation Problem" are reproduced here. This tabulation extends the earlier work of Herschbach [670] to $n = 0$, $d, 1, 2, 3, 4, 5, 6$ for the torsional states $v = 0, 1, 2$ in intervals of 2 in s for $s < 100$ and intervals of 4 in s for $s > 100$. A range of s values from 4 to 200 is covered.

The bootstrap method introduced by Herschbach was used in the calculation with the Fourier coefficients w_l computed in Part III of the original tables.

A sublevel, $v = 0$

s	n = 0	n = d	n = 2	n = 4	n = 6
4	3.4759381408	.0353714444	.6519395656	-.0960211375	-.0190128093
6	4.6421583882	.0528377328	.4348452594	-.1002004984	-.0071108385
8	5.5935970086	.0615959587	.2806305542	-.0798508348	.0012911261
10	6.4055737303	.0644272649	.1807155904	-.0572482724	.0038946124
12	7.1226182477	.0640909813	.1175864104	-.0394715002	.0038827310
14	7.7714548606	.0622723401	.0776406904	-.0269306024	.0031320209
16	8.3688326587	.0598625603	.0520677713	-.0184115077	.0023402327
18	8.9257779981	.0573035035	.0354468248	-.0126815894	.0016963738
20	9.4498964530	.0548029850	.0244726811	-.0088194803	.0012167118
22	9.9466559632	.0524507771	.0171157153	-.0061969294	.0008715826
24	10.4201306279	.0502782900	.0121127700	-.0043988600	.0006264174
26	10.8734497031	.0482888515	.0086654191	-.0031532475	.0004527186
28	11.3090793622	.0464729948	.0062609480	-.0022813700	.0003293383
30	11.7290059654	.0448161271	.0045650467	-.0016649533	.0002412502
32	12.1348592200	.0433023107	.0033565633	-.0012249790	.0001779536
34	12.5279974179	.0419160566	.0024872211	-.0009081178	.0001321598
36	12.9095680092	.0406431029	.0018563512	-.0006779933	.0000987950
38	13.2805516771	.0394706816	.0013948104	-.0005095405	.0000743161
40	13.6417950974	.0383875346	.0010545949	-.0003853186	.0000562351
42	13.9940357525	.0373838144	.0008020438	-.0002930783	.0000427934
44	14.3379210474	.0364509405	.0006133328	-.0002241400	.0000327388
46	14.6740232644	.0355814448	.0004714537	-.0001723018	.0000251736
48	15.0028514213	.0347688245	.0003641657	-.0001330977	.0000194495
50	15.3248607902	.0340074061	.0002825919	-.0001032872	.0000150954
52	15.6404606258	.0332922383	.0002202500	-.0000805036	.0000117670
54	15.9500205005	.0326189702	.0001723731	-.0000630053	.0000092100
56	16.2538755454	.0319837845	.0001354355	-.0000495046	.0000072368
58	16.5523308338	.0313833131	.0001068128	-.0000390429	.0000057078
60	16.8456650380	.0308145771	.0000845408	-.0000309022	.0000045179
62	17.1341335619	.0302749330	.0000671414	-.0000245422	.0000035881
64	17.4179711821	.0297620275	.0000534978	-.0000195556	.0000028593
66	17.6973943227	.0292737596	.0000427598	-.0000156304	.0000022854
68	17.9726030125	.0288082477	.0000342797	-.0000125306	.0000018321
70	18.2437825808	.0283638017	.0000275605	-.0000100745	.0000014730
72	18.5111051321	.0279388993	.0000222197	-.0000081222	.0000011876
74	18.7747308354	.0275321660	.0000179616	-.0000065657	.0000009600
76	19.0348090552	.0271423567	.0000145568	-.0000053211	.0000007780
78	19.2914793477	.0267683416	.0000118265	-.0000043230	.0000006321
80	19.5448723417	.0264090923	.0000096313	-.0000035206	.0000005147
82	19.7951105197	.0260636712	.0000078615	-.0000028737	.0000004201
84	20.0423089130	.0257312209	.0000064313	-.0000023509	.0000003437
86	20.2865757228	.0254109564	.0000052725	-.0000019273	.0000002818
88	20.5280128750	.0251021567	.0000043315	-.0000015833	.0000002315
90	20.7667165189	.0248041591	.0000035656	-.0000013034	.0000001905
92	21.0027774764	.0245163528	.0000029410	-.0000010750	.0000001571
94	21.2362816461	.0242381741	.0000024303	-.0000008883	.0000001298
96	21.4673103698	.0239691016	.0000020119	-.0000007354	.0000001075
98	21.6959407637	.0237086525	.0000016686	-.0000006099	.0000000891
100	21.9222460201	.0234563789	.0000013864	-.0000005067	.0000000741
104	22.3681558904	.0229747224	.0000009616	-.0000003515	.0000000514
108	22.8055568708	.0225211352	.0000006713	-.0000002454	.0000000358
112	23.2349183118	.0220930084	.0000004715	-.0000001723	.0000000252
116	23.6566679296	.0216880592	.0000003330	-.0000001217	.0000000178
120	24.0711968036	.0213042806	.0000002366	-.0000000864	.0000000126
124	24.4788636246	.0209398998	.0000001687	-.0000000616	.0000000090
128	24.8799983310	.0205933445	.0000001213	-.0000000443	.0000000064

INTERNAL ROTATION PROBLEM

A sublevel, $v = 0$ (continued)

s	$n = 0$	$n = d$	$n = 2$	$n = 4$	$n = 6$
132	25.2749052371	.0202632147	.0000000873	-.0000000319	.0000000046
136	25.6638657348	.0199482593	.0000000631	-.0000000230	.0000000033
140	26.0471406408		.0000000461	-.0000000168	.0000000024
144	26.4249722450	.0193594957	.0000000335	-.0000000122	.0000000017
148	26.7975860998		.0000000244	-.0000000089	.0000000013
152	27.1651925976	.0188193445	.0000000182	-.0000000066	.0000000009
156	27.5279883601		.0000000133	-.0000000048	.0000000007
160	27.8861574667	.0183214939	.0000000098	-.0000000036	.0000000005
164	28.2398725480		.0000000074	-.0000000027	.0000000003
168	28.5892957590	.0178607202	.0000000054	-.0000000019	.0000000002
172	28.9345796466		.0000000041	-.0000000015	.0000000002
176	29.2758679300	.0174326580	.0000000032	-.0000000011	.0000000001
180	29.6132961984		.0000000022	-.0000000008	.0000000001
184	29.9469925415	.0170336280	.0000000014	-.0000000005	.0000000000
188	30.2770781167		.0000000014	-.0000000005	.0000000000
192	30.6036676653	.0166605035	.0000000009	-.0000000003	.0000000000
196	30.9268699762		.0000000007	-.0000000002	.0000000000
200	31.2467883104	.0163106092	.0000000007	-.0000000002	.0000000000

A sublevel, $v = 1$

s	$n = 0$	$n = d$	$n = 2$	$n = 4$	$n = 6$
10	19.1080673250	1.3279993638	-4.2449269458	6.7750631488	-15.0980770103
12	20.8730744318	.7975418675	-2.7287394688	2.8396796423	-3.6875967543
14	22.5622447029	.5433701761	-1.8351413697	1.4104878829	-1.1603621013
16	24.1804823108	.4051620367	-1.2738151136	.7914173575	-.4502885703
18	25.7327207458	.3225123956	-.9048326374	.4840034887	-.2048348006
20	27.2237860020	.2693858862	-.6541210883	.3147750477	-.1051379213
22	28.6582981987	.2332223582	-.4794784203	.2140421915	-.0592637531
24	30.0406075982	.2074238375	-.3554586852	.1503946901	-.0359326429
26	31.3747588966	.1882812755	-.2660282108	.1083026910	-.0230702931
28	32.6644771647	.1735919905	-.2007278063	.0794731165	-.0154952340
30	33.9131693227	.1619874823	-.1525444289	.0591837956	-.0107828833
32	35.1239360169	.1525846547	-.1166707717	.0445979200	-.0077152782
34	36.2995898851	.1447959855	-.0897519175	.0339341809	-.0056436385
36	37.4426772360	.1382181454	-.0694114445	.0260311505	-.0042014668
38	38.5555010597	.1325667954	-.0539450054	.0201084514	-.0031725051
40	39.6401439689	.1276453673	-.0421171292	.0156281234	-.0024231814
42	40.6984902000	.1232998469	-.0330239943	.0122119280	-.0018685987
44	41.7322461644	.1194219724	-.0259989530	.0095890906	-.0014524851
46	42.7429593022	.1159263566	-.0205467156	.0075630944	-.0011367239
48	43.7320351615	.1127548985	-.0162968871	.0059896253	-.0008948605
50	44.7007527247	.1098516044	-.0129707861	.0047615872	-.0007081075
52	45.6502780801	.1071789450	-.0103575726	.0037988185	-.0005628992
54	46.5816765583	.1047052581	-.0082969171	.0030408993	-.0004493419
56	47.4959234769	.1024048719	-.0066662899	.0024419232	-.0003600550
58	48.3939136363	.1002567313	-.0053716314	.0019668259	-.0002894994
60	49.2764697024	.0982433814	-.0043404350	.0015887149	-.0002335292
62	50.1443496060	.0963502053	-.0035165664	.0012868154	-.0001889527
64	50.9982530775	.0945648476	-.0028564023	.0010450222	-.0001533200
66	51.8388274181	.0928767728	-.0023259177	.0008508021	-.0001247427
68	52.6666726079	.0912769246	-.0018984763	.0006943552	-.0001017509
70	53.4823458286	.0897574599	-.0015531602	.0005679986	-.0000831998
72	54.2863654744	.0883115388	-.0012734829	.0004656789	-.0000681886
74	55.0792147178	.0869331590	-.0010464163	.0003826207	-.0000560113
76	55.8613446804	.0856170219	-.0008616278	.0003150359	-.0000461077
78	56.6331772634	.0843584248	-.0007109030	.0002599156	-.0000380340

A sublevel, $v = 1$ (continued)

s	$n = 0$	$n = d$	$n = 2$	$n = 4$	$n = 6$
80	57.3951076740	.0831531736	-.0005876905	.0002148595	-.0000314362
82	58.1475066862	.0819975104	-.0004867533	.0001779511	-.0000260327
84	58.8907226713	.0808880540	-.0004038937	.0001476550	-.0000215985
86	59.6250834185	.0798217507	-.0003357377	.0001227367	-.0000179524
88	60.3508977771	.0787958323	-.0002795659	.0001021992	-.0000149470
90	61.0684571348	.0778077814	-.0002331846	.0000852430	-.0000124665
92	61.7780367569	.0768553015	-.0001948167	.0000712162	-.0000104146
94	62.4798969950	.0759362921	-.0001630216	.0000595932	-.0000087147
96	63.1742843862	.0750488262	-.0001366266	.0000499437	-.0000073032
98	63.8614326507	.0741911321	-.0001146790	.0000419211	-.0000061303
100	64.5415635998	.0733615771	-.0000963974	.0000352371	-.0000051522
104	65.8816061465	.0717809653	-.0000684049	.0000250048	-.0000036561
108	67.1959780591	.0702962127	-.0000488066	.0000178408	-.0000026086
112	68.4861009579	.0688980233	-.0000350047	.0000127956	-.0000018709
116	69.7532699808	.0675783260	-.0000252306	.0000092228	-.0000013485
120	70.9986689644	.0663300711	-.0000182720	.0000066791	-.0000009766
124	72.2233833702	.0651470681	-.0000132926	.0000048590	-.0000007104
128	73.4284113484	.0640238539	-.0000097121	.0000035502	-.0000005190
132	74.6146732567	.0629555558	-.0000071258	.0000026047	-.0000003808
136	75.7830198874	.0619379532	-.0000052491	.0000019187	-.0000002805
140	76.9342396103		-.0000038817	.0000014189	-.0000002074
144	78.0690646012	.0600395843	-.0000028811	.0000010531	-.0000001539
148	79.1881762936		-.0000021458	.0000007844	-.0000001146
152	80.2922101699	.0583024026	-.0000016038	.0000005862	-.0000000857
156	81.3817599858		-.0000012028	.0000004396	-.0000000642
160	82.4573815085	.0567049604	-.0000009047	.0000003307	-.0000000483
164	83.5195958354		-.0000006829	.0000002496	-.0000000365
168	84.5688923491	.0552295944	-.0000005169	.0000001889	-.0000000276
172	85.6057317560		-.0000003925	.0000001434	-.0000000209
176	86.6305464493	.0538616085	-.0000002988	.0000001092	-.0000000159
180	87.6437456313		-.0000002282	.0000000834	-.0000000121
184	88.6457182223	.0525886627	-.0000001746	.0000000638	-.0000000093
188	89.6363265844		-.0000001339	.0000000489	-.0000000071
192	90.6174176802	.0514003091	-.0000001028	.0000000376	-.0000000055
196	91.5578194848		-.0000000794	.0000000290	-.0000000042
200	92.5483432691	.0502876350	-.0000000614	.0000000224	-.0000000032

A sublevel, $v = 2$

s	$n = 0$	$n = d$	$n = 2$	$n = 4$	$n = 6$
20	39.2604969139	.2420756706	2.9753691 98	-1.2458339389	11.0610615999
22	42.0422239114	.2179151856	2.6042149066	-.4741497748	1.4685361295
24	44.7076450681	.2048911646	2.2850871824	-.3509364919	.1447852417
26	47.2573078821	.1987121112	1.9929847297	-.3273801500	-.0115953526
28	49.6949020751	.1965794287	1.7237138694	-.3162558809	-.0269029032
30	52.0264211112	.1966099954	1.4778723364	-.3030802352	-.0234234718
32	54.2592873679	.1975518952	1.2567853201	-.2850729758	-.0161061814
34	56.4015731728	.1986143142	1.0611561338	-.2625711115	-.0082270641
36	58.4613971171	.1993422334	.8906650526	-.2370676365	-.0014099349
38	60.4465149294	.1995149482	.7440378284	-.2103219662	.0037145592
40	62.3640821618	.1990647822	.6193151163	-.1838794366	.0071444282
42	64.2205473833	.1980156036	.5141565029	-.1588588290	.0090867123
44	66.0216332578	.1964394679	.4260998509	-.1359546502	.0098927947
46	67.7723703083	.1944282046	.3527458059	-.1155054267	.0099128986
48	69.4771579244	.1920762299	.2918714949	-.0975885107	.0094331423
50	71.1398359880	.1894711487	.2414886546	-.0821119685	.0086719263
52	72.7637571922	.1866893992	.1998626734	-.0688851492	.0077807121

INTERNAL ROTATION PROBLEM (*continued*)

A sublevel, $v = 2$ (continued)

s	$n = 0$	$n = d$	$n = 2$	$n = 4$	$n = 6$
54	74.3518547095	.1837949413	.1655074922	-.0576710511	.0068604994
56	75.9067027872	.1808396394	.1371666029	-.0482194378	.0059728350
58	77.4305695444	.1778644803	.1137878143	-.0402875987	.0051519679
60	78.9254621943	.1749011114	.0944961347	-.0336513823	.0044135135
62	80.3931653652	.1719734094	.0785676449	-.0281108102	.0037621054
64	81.8352733632	.1690989316	.0654054896	-.0234911063	.0031952354
66	83.2532172477	.1662901867	.0545187724	-.0196420476	.0027067680
68	84.6482875254	.1635557083	.0455043950	-.0164360885	.0022891091
70	86.0216531784	.1609009403	.0380315690	-.0137654843	.0019336760
72	87.3743776490	.1583289545	.0318290039	-.0115400936	.0016324329
74	88.7074322960	.1558410246	.0266741572	-.0096846537	.0013778233
76	90.0217077610	.1534370798	.0223843968	-.0081365031	.0011630002
78	91.3180236021	.1511160617	.0188097653	-.0068436314	.0009819655
80	92.5971364917	.1488762012	.0158270292	-.0057629051	.0008295101
82	93.8597472211	.1467152332	.0133348163	-.0048585783	.0007011654
84	95.1065067118	.1446305608	.0112496478	-.0041010320	.0005931175
86	96.3380211943	.1426193808	.0095027021	-.0034657259	.0005021355
88	97.5548566932	.1406787780	.0080371690	-.0029323131	.0004254829
90	98.7575429256	.1388057961	.0068060936	-.0024839220	.0003608639
92	99.9465767032	.1369974895	.0057706230	-.0021065559	.0003063502
94	101.1224249176	.1352509611	.0048985594	-.0017885923	.0002603333
96	102.2855271668	.1335633891	.0041631853	-.0015203597	.0002214505
98	103.4362980774	.1319320449	.0035423020	-.0012938118	.0001885656
100	104.5751293637	.1303543058	.0030174404	-.0011022455	.0001607262
104	106.8184361747	.1273497154	.0021967924	-.0008026235	.0001171262
108	109.0181881113	.1245309248	.0016062261	-.0005869344	.0000856983
112	111.1768583105	.1218810743	.0011792975	-.0004309722	.0000629512
116	113.2966891289	.1193850444	.0008693066	-.0003177076	.0000464192
120	115.3797222489	.1170293172	.0006432720	-.0002351106	.0000343585
124	117.4278237048	.1148018219	.0004777796	-.0001746306	.0000255237
128	119.4427048796	.1126917804	.0003561356	-.0001301721	.0000190274
132	121.4259402696	.1106895608	.0002663831	-.0000973693	.0000142343
136	123.3789826274	.1087865439	.0001999150	-.0000730736	.0000106825
140	125.3031759589		.0001505181	-.0000550192	.0000080439
144	127.1997667437	.1052479982	.0001136816	-.0000415550	.0000060759
148	129.0699136827		.0000861192	-.0000314800	.0000046029
152	130.9146961997	.1020232167	.0000654307	-.0000239176	.0000034971
156	132.7351219002		.0000498535	-.0000182235	.0000026645
160	134.5321331370	.0990691319	.0000380892	-.0000139231	.0000020357
164	136.3066128144		.0000291784	-.0000106659	.0000015595
168	138.0593895392	.0963503782	.0000224104	-.0000081919	.0000011977
172	139.7912422056		.0000172557	-.0000063076	.0000009222
176	141.5029040916	.0938376524	.0000133190	-.0000048686	.0000007118
180	143.1950665259		.0000103048	-.0000037668	.0000005507
184	144.8683821846	.0915064645	.0000079914	-.0000029211	.0000004271
188	146.5234680593		.0000062111	-.0000022704	.0000003319
192	148.1609081367	.0893361811	.0000048380	-.0000017685	.0000002585
196	149.7812558253		.0000037766	-.0000013805	.0000002018
200	151.3850361547	.0873092859	.0000029542	-.0000010798	.0000001578

Appendix 12

E sublevel,

s	n = 0	n = d	n = 2	n = 4
4	4.0109426155	.2250306600	-.2319489044	.2479084519
6	4.9719532858	.1632235494	-.2021790763	.0002496948
8	5.7971998007	.1235869383	-.1375442863	.0308179555
10	6.5335207992	.0999567152	-.0897909617	.0267596292
12	7.2047348824	.0850668907	-.0586646542	.0193128248
14	7.8252470033	.0750231065	-.0387885203	.0133605955
16	8.4047371676	.0678218632	-.0260253963	.0091778211
18	8.9501507473	.0623902805	-.0177209984	.0063328501
20	9.4666931572	.0581222697	-.0122356150	.0044073514
22	9.9583896746	.0546569524	-.0085576282	.0030977087
24	10.4284282993	.0517688226	-.0060563100	.0021991824
26	10.8793828476	.0493107210	-.0043326844	.0015765405
28	11.3133647382	.0471626373	-.0031304655	.0011406566
30	11.7321298423	.0453151209	-.0022825201	.0008324657
32	12.1371557615	.0436569007	-.0016782811	.0006124873
34	12.5296989706	.0421705356	-.0012436106	.0004540589
36	12.9108378721	.0408274008	-.0009281756	.0003389966
38	13.2815057626	.0396052755	-.0006974052	.0002547703
40	13.6425164377	.0384865942	-.0005272975	.0001926593
42	13.9945843321	.0374572483	-.0004010219	.0001465391
44	14.3383405439	.0365057446	-.0003066664	.0001120700
46	14.6743457159	.0356226030	-.0002357268	.0000861509
48	15.0031004900	.0347999172	-.0001820828	.0000665488
50	15.3250540654	.0340310273	-.0001412959	.0000516436
52	15.6406112619	.0333102743	-.0001101250	.0000402518
54	15.9501383915	.0326328109	-.0000861865	.0000315026
56	16.2539681754	.0319944553	-.0000677177	.0000247523
58	16.5524038857	.0313915766	-.0000534064	.0000195214
60	16.8457228574	.0308210033	-.0000422704	.0000154511
62	17.1341794814	.0302799504	-.0000335707	.0000122711
64	17.4180077702	.0297659600	-.0000267489	.0000097778
66	17.6974235669	.0292768531	-.0000213799	.0000078152
68	17.9726264571	.0288106096	-.0000171398	.0000062653
70	18.2438014300	.0283657357	-.0000137802	.0000050372
72	18.5111203286	.0279404360	-.0000111098	.0000040611
74	18.7747431197	.0275333907	-.0000089808	.0000032828
76	19.0348190109	.0271433357	-.0000072784	.0000026605
78	19.2914874361	.0267691263	-.0000059132	.0000021615
80	19.5448769288	.0264097231	-.0000048156	.0000017603
82	19.7951158963	.0260641795	-.0000039307	.0000014368
84	20.0423133115	.0257316317	-.0000032156	.0000011754
86	20.2865793288	.0254112890	-.0000026362	.0000009636
88	20.5280158374	.0251024268	-.0000021657	.0000007916
90	20.7667189576	.0248043789	-.0000017828	.0000006517
92	21.0027794878	.0245165320	-.0000014705	.0000005375
94	21.2362833083	.0242383205	-.0000012151	.0000004441
96	21.4673117458	.0239692215	-.0000010059	.0000003677
98	21.6959419049	.0237087509	-.0000008343	.0000003049
100	21.9222469684	.0234564598	-.0000006932	.0000002533
104	22.3681565481	.0229747775	-.0000004808	.0000001757
108	22.8055573299	.0225211729	-.0000003356	.0000001227
112	23.2349186342	.0220930344	-.0000002357	.0000000861
116	23.6566681574	.0216880773	-.0000001665	.0000000608
120	24.0711969654	.0213042932	-.0000001183	.0000000432
124	24.4788637401	.0209399086	-.0000000843	.0000000308

INTERNAL ROTATION PROBLEM (*continued*)

$v = 0$

$n = 6$	$n = 1$	$n = 3$	$n = 5$
.3316720500	-.7941803579	.7542620418	-.1822695365
.0675938362	-.4452443108	.3903387194	-.1325675666
.0112932810	-.2617257106	.2137620704	-.0656622729
.0005046280	-.1602752886	.1252741551	-.0344835716
-.0013848166	-.1014166293	.0772411648	-.0196453706
-.0014282223	-.0658998003	.0494267259	-.0119339626
-.0011333577	-.0437763658	.0325313282	-.0075971394
-.0008377318	-.0296300702	.0218938166	-.0050051621
-.0006052122	-.0203827894	.0150070846	-.0033840532
-.0004347963	-.0142223415	.0104473257	-.0023348955
-.0003128828	-.0100499426	.0073713130	-.0016377498
-.0002262497	-.0071824815	.0052628631	-.0011646986
-.0001646316	-.0051859919	.0037974045	-.0008381454
-.0001206106	-.0037795197	.0027662514	-.0006094380
-.0000889739	-.0027780987	.0020326578	-.0004472508
-.0000660799	-.0020581180	.0015055320	-.0003309715
-.0000493975	-.0015358451	.0011233073	-.0002467889
-.0000371580	-.0011538606	.0008438309	-.0001853047
-.0000281175	-.0008723455	.0006379039	-.0001400378
-.0000213967	-.0006633997	.0004850834	-.0001064643
-.0000163694	-.0005072880	.0003709171	-.0000813934
-.0000125868	-.0003899272	.0002850966	-.0000625532
-.0000097247	-.0003011848	.0002202070	-.0000483111
-.0000075477	-.0002337148	.0001708743	-.0000374854
-.0000058835	-.0001821529	.0001331742	-.0000292132
-.0000046050	-.0001425561	.0001042235	-.0000228617
-.0000036184	-.0001120071	.0000818885	-.0000179620
-.0000028539	-.0000883352	.0000645815	-.0000141654
-.0000022589	-.0000699156	.0000511147	-.0000112113
-.0000017940	-.0000555262	.0000405947	-.0000089039
-.0000014296	-.0000442423	.0000323447	-.0000070940
-.0000011427	-.0000353621	.0000258526	-.0000056701
-.0000009160	-.0000283491	.0000207255	-.0000045456
-.0000007365	-.0000227924	.0000166631	-.0000036546
-.0000005938	-.0000183756	.0000134340	-.0000029464
-.0000004800	-.0000148541	.0000108596	-.0000023817
-.0000003890	-.0000120384	.0000088010	-.0000019302
-.0000003160	-.0000097804	.0000071503	-.0000015682
-.0000002573	-.0000079650	.0000058230	-.0000012771
-.0000002100	-.0000065014	.0000047530	-.0000010424
-.0000001718	-.0000053186	.0000038883	-.0000008528
-.0000001409	-.0000043603	.0000031877	-.0000006991
-.0000001157	-.0000035821	.0000026188	-.0000005743
-.0000000952	-.0000029488	.0000021558	-.0000004728
-.0000000785	-.0000024322	.0000017781	-.0000003899
-.0000000649	-.0000020098	.0000014693	-.0000003222
-.0000000537	-.0000016638	.0000012164	-.0000002667
-.0000000445	-.0000013799	.0000010088	-.0000002212
-.0000000370	-.0000011465	.0000008382	-.0000001838
-.0000000257	-.0000007953	.0000005814	-.0000001275
-.0000000179	-.0000005552	.0000004059	-.0000000890
-.0000000126	-.0000003899	.0000002850	-.0000000625
-.0000000089	-.0000002754	.0000002013	-.0000000441
-.0000000063	-.0000001956	.0000001430	-.0000000313
-.0000000045	-.0000001395	.0000001020	-.0000000223

PERTURBATION COEFFICIENTS FOR THE

E sublevel,

s	n = 0	n = d	n = 2	n = 4
128	24.8799984140	.0205933507	-.0000000606	.0000000221
132	25.2749052968	.0202632191	-.0000000436	.0000000159
136	25.6638657780	.0199482625	-.0000000315	.0000000115
140	26.0471406724		-.0000000230	.0000000084
144	26.4249722679	.0193594973	-.0000000167	.0000000061
148	26.7975861165		-.0000000122	.0000000044
152	27.1651926101	.0188193454	-.0000000091	.0000000033
156	27.5279883692		-.0000000066	.0000000024
160	27.8861574735	.0183214944	-.0000000049	.0000000018
164	28.2398725531		-.0000000037	.0000000013
168	28.5892957627	.0178607204	-.0000000027	.0000000009
172	28.9345796495		-.0000000020	.0000000007
176	29.2758679322	.0174326582	-.0000000016	.0000000005
180	29.6132961999		-.0000000011	.0000000004
184	29.9469925425	.0170336280	-.0000000007	.0000000002
188	30.2770781177		-.0000000007	.0000000002
192	30.6036676660	.0166605036	-.0000000004	.0000000001
196	30.9268699767		-.0000000003	.0000000001
200	31.2467883109	.0163106093	-.0000000003	.0000000001

E sublevel,

s	n = 0	n = d	n = 2	n = 4
10	17.2758687401	.1562665692	1.3703893657	-.3231260785
12	19.5040791392	.1627925600	1.0627067751	-.3394172092
14	21.5462135763	.1686697414	.7988150888	-.3019609744
16	23.4276852303	.1712426925	.5906260726	-.2416678810
18	25.1740595476	.1706180331	.4343863343	-.1824314114
20	26.8077142062	.1677590513	.3199852029	-.1340738019
22	28.3469876710	.1635955152	.2369281938	-.0977676155
24	29.8064872879	.1587915831	.1765953650	-.0714658427
26	31.1977576947	.1537654953	.1325489539	-.0526210135
28	32.5299538941	.1487625656	.1001697771	-.0390978948
30	33.8104027906	.1439185838	.0761897921	-.0293207281
32	35.0450380257	.1393029052	.0582998004	-.0221818801
34	36.2387263629	.1349458203	.0448603426	-.0169157088
36	37.3955102478	.1308549384	.0346987629	-.0129926747
38	38.5187877542	.1270250887	.0269693523	-.0100438572
40	39.6114474401	.1234442210	.0210571200	-.0078093061
42	40.6759698189	.1200969186	.0165113284	-.0061037616
44	41.7145048187	.1169664751	.0129991614	-.0047935067
46	42.7289314895	.1140361024	.0102732098	-.0037810586
48	43.7209045711	.1112896109	.0081483720	-.0029945761
50	44.6918912188	.1087117676	.0064853574	-.0023806754
52	45.6432002845	.1062884612	.0051787719	-.0018993611
54	46.5760059026	.1040067489	.0041484501	-.0015204212
56	47.4913666736	.1018548372	.0033331378	-.0012209375
58	48.3902414121	.0998220235	.0026858145	-.0009834086
60	49.2735021870	.0978986198	.0021702176	-.0007943575
62	50.1419452022	.0960758674	.0017582832	-.0006434077
64	50.9962999490	.0943458524	.0014282012	-.0005225111
66	51.8372369542	.0927014225	.0011629589	-.0004254010
68	52.6653743856	.0911361101	.0009492382	-.0003471776
70	53.4812837136	.0896440615	.0007765801	-.0002839993
72	54.2854945955	.0882199721	.0006367415	-.0002328395
74	55.0784991075	.0868590288	.0005232082	-.0001913104

INTERNAL ROTATION PROBLEM (*continued*)

$v = 0$ (continued)

$n = 6$	$n = 1$	$n = 3$	$n = 5$
-.0000000032	-.0000001003	.0000000733	-.0000000160
-.0000000023	-.0000000722	.0000000528	-.0000000115
-.0000000016	-.0000000522	.0000000381	-.0000000083
-.0000000012	-.0000000381	.0000000278	-.0000000061
-.0000000008	-.0000000277	.0000000202	-.0000000044
-.0000000006	-.0000000202	.0000000147	-.0000000032
-.0000000004	-.0000000150	.0000000110	-.0000000024
-.0000000003	-.0000000110	.0000000080	-.0000000017
-.0000000002	-.0000000081	.0000000059	-.0000000013
-.0000000001	-.0000000061	.0000000044	-.0000000009
-.0000000001	-.0000000044	.0000000032	-.0000000007
-.0000000001	-.0000000034	.0000000025	-.0000000005
.0000000000	-.0000000026	.0000000019	-.0000000004
.0000000000	-.0000000018	.0000000013	-.0000000002
.0000000000	-.0000000012	.0000000009	-.0000000001
.0000000000	-.0000000012	.0000000008	-.0000000001
.0000000000	-.0000000008	.0000000005	-.0000000001
.0000000000	-.0000000006	.0000000004	.0000000000
.0000000000	-.0000000006	.0000000004	.0000000000

$v = 1$

-.1171940000	1.5874487808	-.4640230031	-.1520632368
-.0763065967	1.2901485818	-.4895946466	-.1345236681
-.0187944926	1.0238383798	-.4755048423	-.0767206022
.0129656913	.7977205741	-.4267366972	-.0239592831
.0226858102	.6140968008	-.3615488504	.0088576649
.0216959272	.4695573887	-.2949358310	.0241879182
.0174254317	.3580060020	-.2349956300	.0286692818
.0130514281	.2728911796	-.1846452833	.0276388892
.0095211696	.2083218808	-.1439739573	.0243275506
.0069071676	.1594403224	-.1118542982	.0204180600
.0050345952	.1224236292	-.0868108682	.0166845755
.0037035669	.0943407965	-.0674177426	.0134256297
.0027542029	.0729767088	-.0524464736	.0107090379
.0020705968	.0566696653	-.0408970637	.0085022130
.0015726076	.0441770147	-.0319801891	.0067361625
.0012053321	.0345698622	-.0250833661	.0053346988
.0009314008	.0271530159	-.0197361230	.0042277678
.0007248755	.0214048681	-.0155785860	.0033552466
.0005677188	.0169329347	-.0123362417	.0026678123
.0004471187	.0134408327	-.0097996316	.0021258611
.0003538980	.0107039241	-.0078087688	.0016980252
.0002813861	.0085512992	-.0062412187	.0013596577
.0002246335	.0068524183	-.0050030462	.0010914723
.0001799957	.0055071958	-.0040219871	.0008784150
.0001447439	.0044386009	-.0032422743	.0007087362
.0001167646	.0035871257	-.0026207388	.0005732627
.0000944763	.0029066310	-.0021238550	.0004648220
.0000766600	.0023612185	-.0017255076	.0003778002
.0000623713	.0019228578	-.0014052834	.0003077894
.0000508754	.0015695924	-.0011471825	.0002513263
.0000415999	.0012841647	-.0009386186	.0002056771
.0000340943	.0010529709	-.0007696682	.0001686846
.0000280056	.0008652517	-.0006324765	.0001386358

PERTURBATION COEFFICIENTS FOR THE

E sublevel,

s	$n = 0$	$n = d$	$n = 2$	$n = 4$
76	55.8607554330	.0855568575	.0004308139	-.0001575180
78	56.6326910882	.0843094773	.0003554515	-.0001299578
80	57.3947057580	.0831132589	.0002938452	-.0001074297
82	58.1471737976	.0819648883	.0002433766	-.0000889756
84	58.8904464482	.0808613341	.0002019469	-.0000738275
86	59.6248538064	.0797998190	.0001678689	-.0000613683
88	60.3507065800	.0787777941	.0001397829	-.0000510996
90	61.0682976578	.0777929161	.0001165923	-.0000426215
92	61.7779035195	.0768430277	.0000974083	-.0000356081
94	62.4797855025	.0759261390	.0000815108	-.0000297966
96	63.1741909452	.0750404122	.0000683133	-.0000249718
98	63.8613542202	.0741841472	.0000573395	-.0000209605
100	64.5414976718	.0733557687	.0000481987	-.0000176186
104	65.8815593631	.0717769288	.0000342024	-.0000125024
108	67.1959446793	.0702933900	.0000244033	-.0000089204
112	68.4860770175	.0688960377	.0000175023	-.0000063978
116	69.7532527250	.0675769212	.0000126153	-.0000046114
120	70.9986564678	.0663290719	.0000091360	-.0000033395
124	72.2233742792	.0651463536	.0000066463	-.0000024295
128	73.4284047061	.0640233406	.0000048560	-.0000017751
132	74.6146683832	.0629552153	.0000035629	-.0000013023
136	75.7830162974	.0619376846	.0000026245	-.0000009593
140	76.9342369556		.0000019408	-.0000007094
144	78.0690626307	.0600394412	.0000014405	-.0000005265
148	79.1881748260		.0000010729	-.0000003922
152	80.2922090730	.0583023252	.0000008019	-.0000002931
156	81.3817591631		.0000006014	-.0000002198
160	82.4573808897	.0567049178	.0000004523	-.0000001653
164	83.5195953683		.0000003414	-.0000001248
168	84.5688919956	.0552295707	.0000002584	-.0000000944
172	85.6057310875		.0000001962	-.0000000717
176	86.6305462449	.0538615952	.0000001494	-.0000000546
180	87.6437464752		.0000001141	-.0000000417
184	88.6457181028	.0525886551	.0000000873	-.0000000319
188	89.6368264928		.0000000669	-.0000000244
192	90.6174176099	.0514003047	.0000000514	-.0000000188
196	91.5878194304		.0000000397	-.0000000145
200	92.5483432271	.0502876324	.0000000307	-.0000000112

E sublevel,

s	$n = 0$	$n = d$	$n = 2$	$n = 4$
20	41.8017921168	.3765096002	.0777849741	-3.1084512613
22	44.2583124298	.4093793001	-.2884999726	-2.3955255609
24	46.6178485787	.4176146967	-.5229967134	-1.5948894398
26	48.8858288778	.4078265306	-.6355146291	-.9349059912
28	51.0699881395	.3879205592	-.6588960558	-.4824125184
30	53.1783595205	.3640175463	-.6276272222	-.2067770447
32	55.2183265442	.3398524619	-.5683481236	-.0527920759
34	57.1963196343	.3173068215	-.4985182268	.0264210760
36	59.1178237788	.2971146746	-.4283115614	.0627021155
38	60.9875023545	.2793960053	-.3630035601	.0755469299
40	62.8093436051	.2639842468	-.3048821916	.0762415402
42	64.5867928278	.2506049146	-.2545442812	.0710961772
44	66.3228600443	.2389643784	-.2117012729	.0635413206
46	68.0202037812	.2287894256	-.1756523217	.0553823826

INTERNAL ROTATION PROBLEM (*continued*)

v = I (continued)

n = 6	*n* = I	*n* = 3	*n* = 5
.0000230538	.0007124747	−.0005208146	.0001141724
.0000190170	.0005878537	−.0004297266	.0000942122
.0000157181	.0004859769	−.0003552602	.0000778921
.0000130163	.0004025157	−.0002942529	.0000645202
.0000107992	.0003340000	−.0002441686	.0000535410
.0000089762	.0002776406	−.0002029690	.0000445082
.0000074735	.0002311918	−.0001690147	.0000370643
.0000062332	.0001928370	−.0001409758	.0000309161
.0000052073	.0001611089	−.0001177814	.0000258303
.0000043573	.0001348153	−.0000985592	.0000216149
.0000036516	.0001129881	−.0000826026	.0000181160
.0000030651	.0000948373	−.0000693328	.0000152054
.0000025761	.0000797200	−.0000582818	.0000127826
.0000018280	.0000565704	−.0000413576	.0000090707
.0000013043	.0000403627	−.0000295085	.0000064719
.0000009354	.0000289487	−.0000211638	.0000046417
.0000006742	.0000208655	−.0000152544	.0000033456
.0000004883	.0000151108	−.0000110473	.0000024229
.0000003552	.0000109929	−.0000080367	.0000017626
.0000002595	.0000080319	−.0000058719	.0000012878
.0000001904	.0000058930	−.0000043082	.0000009449
.0000001402	.0000043410	−.0000031736	.0000006960
.0000001037	.0000032101	−.0000023648	.0000005147
.0000000769	.0000023827	−.0000017419	.0000003820
.0000000573	.0000017746	−.0000012974	.0000002845
.0000000428	.0000013263	−.0000009696	.0000002126
.0000000321	.0000009947	−.0000007272	.0000001595
.0000000241	.0000007482	−.0000005470	.0000001199
.0000000182	.0000005648	−.0000004129	.0000000905
.0000000138	.0000004274	−.0000003125	.0000000685
.0000000104	.0000003246	−.0000002373	.0000000520
.0000000079	.0000002471	−.0000001806	.0000000396
.0000000060	.0000001887	−.0000001379	.0000000302
.0000000046	.0000001444	−.0000001056	.0000000231
.0000000035	.0000001108	−.0000000810	.0000000177
.0000000027	.0000000850	−.0000000622	.0000000136
.0000000021	.0000000657	−.0000000480	.0000000105
.0000000016	.0000000508	−.0000000371	.0000000081

v = 2

−.9316068465	−4.2159716911	3.0446080916	3.7439424618
.4462575537	−3.5626941463	2.9920949094	1.5029975288
1.0969182739	−2.9619891530	2.6793377805	.2925505778
1.0238345881	−2.4342424609	2.259037129	−.2764593683
.7195703773	−1.9857394868	1.8365063786	−.4555089296
.4427039408	−1.6130543552	1.4640309091	−.4498608117
.2535858685	−1.3077616817	1.1571206726	−.3800015931
.1389254943	−1.0597904669	.9128087572	−.3007376312
.0733136665	−.8593041352	.7214133889	−.2315850969
.0368745961	−.6975463999	.5722964928	−.1767636052
.0170215346	−.5670973739	.4560808234	−.1350073626
.0064057245	−.4618409439	.3651984799	−.1036820732
.0008863114	−.3768140626	.2937809912	−.0802400608
−.0018388755	−.3080242494	.2373567241	−.0626266884

Appendix 12

E sublevel,

s	n = 0	n = d	n = 2	n = 4
48	69.6811950607	.2198416749	-.1455490062	.0475220094
50	71.3079661244	.2119199788	-.1205357313	.0403697117
52	72.9024477765	.2048576251	-.0998182450	.0340705021
54	74.4663983770	.1985177045	-.0826921013	.0286327092
56	76.0014267235	.1927882172	-.0685495195	.0239985702
58	77.5090104453	.1875775853	-.0568752913	.0200825467
60	78.9905110673	.1828107983	-.0472377537	.0167917535
62	80.4471865632	.1784262164	-.0392780766	.0140364958
64	81.8802019830	.1743729704	-.0326995241	.0117349525
66	83.2906385756	.1706088705	-.0272575749	.0098150607
68	84.6795017100	.1670987349	-.0227511668	.0082146497
70	86.0477278182	.1638130569	-.0190151992	.0068808138
72	87.3961905288	.1607269434	-.0159141697	.0057689512
74	88.7257061177	.1578192669	-.0133368848	.0048416871
76	90.0370383781	.1550719891	-.0111920857	.0040678791
78	91.3309029866	.1524696175	-.0094048178	.0034216011
80	92.6079714323	.1499987689	-.0079134790	.0028813343
82	93.8688745609	.1476478165	-.0066673892	.0024292257
84	95.1142057800	.1454066041	-.0056248135	.0020504810
86	96.3445239620	.1432662135	-.0047513440	.0017328389
88	97.5603560796	.1412187734	-.0040185800	.0014661412
90	98.7621995999	.1392573033	-.0034030443	.0012419523
92	99.9505246658	.1373755841	-.0028853116	.0010532780
94	101.1257760807	.1355680515	-.0024492798	.0008942962
96	102.2883751246	.1338297043	-.0020815927	.0007601798
98	103.4387212099	.1321560340	-.0017711511	.0006469059
100	104.5771933975	.1305429574	-.0015087203	.0005511227
104	106.8199387848	.1274840797	-.0010983962	.0004013117
108	109.0192867350	.1246271218	-.0008031131	.0002934672
112	111.1776649044	.1219502886	-.0005896488	.0002154861
116	113.2972836912	.1194350818	-.0004346533	.0001588538
120	115.3801622090	.1170656561	-.0003216360	.0001175553
124	117.4281504750	.1148263281	-.0002388898	.0000873153
128	119.4429484518	.1127111957	-.0001780678	.0000650860
132	121.4261224560	.1107038396	-.0001331915	.0000486846
136	123.3791193546	.1087970059	-.0000999575	.0000365368
140	125.3032789016		-.0000752590	.0000275096
144	127.1998444927	.1052538084	-.0000568408	.0000207775
148	129.0699725811		-.0000430596	.0000157400
152	130.9147409490	.1020264637	-.0000327153	.0000119588
156	132.7351559959		-.0000249267	.0000091117
160	134.5321591869	.0990709701	-.0000190446	.0000069615
164	136.3066327701		-.0000145892	.0000053329
168	138.0594048661	.0963514316	-.0000112052	.0000040959
172	139.7912540072		-.0000086278	.0000031538
176	141.5029132008	.0938382629	-.0000066595	.0000024343
180	143.1950735736		-.0000051524	.0000018834
184	144.8683876500	.0915068221	-.0000039957	.0000014605
188	146.5234723072		-.0000031055	.0000011352
192	148.1609114455	.0893363927	-.0000024190	.0000008842
196	149.7812584082		-.0000018883	.0000006902
200	151.3850381751	.0873094123	-.0000014771	.0000005399

Internal Rotation Problem (*continued*)

$v = 2$ (continued)

$n = 6$	$n = 1$	$n = 3$	$n = 5$
−.0030429124	−.2522742164	.1925370179	−.0492930499
−.0034328616	−.2070084625	.1567518251	−.0391078806
−.0034007257	−.1701852112	.1280435588	−.0312541855
−.0031633520	−.1401721568	.1049120504	−.0251420888
−.0028401501	−.1156627973	.0861999221	−.0203437290
−.0024953774	−.0956097965	.0710082618	−.0165466611
−.0021620955	−.0791720974	.0586342197	−.0135201262
−.0018561682	−.0656730457	.0485250095	−.0110923172
−.0015836671	−.0545671987	.0402433029	−.0091335311
−.0013455362	−.0454140381	.0334414292	−.0075450804
−.0011400870	−.0378570943	.0278417359	−.0062512199
−.0009643000	−.0316073553	.0232214840	−.0051929841
−.0008147744	−.0264300591	.0194013971	−.0043243874
−.0006880695	−.0221341515	.0162366405	−.0036091387
−.0005810098	−.0185638666	.0136098552	−.0030184439
−.0004907001	−.0155919777	.0114256694	−.0025293166
−.0004145993	−.0131143831	.0096063704	−.0021233036
−.0003504990	−.0110457570	.0080884851	−.0017855248
−.0002965126	−.0093160417	.0068200473	−.0015039262
−.0002510360	−.0078676203	.0057584197	−.0012687051
−.0002127213	−.0066530286	.0048685478	−.0010718623
−.0001804204	−.0056331045	.0041215590	−.0009068530
−.0001531751	−.0047754824	.0034936194	−.0007682990
−.0001301666	−.0040533739	.0029650280	−.0006517773
−.0001107252	−.0034445721	.0025194672	−.0005536365
−.0000942828	−.0029306415	.0021434025	−.0004708585
−.0000803631	−.0024962542	.0018255883	−.0004009422
−.0000585631	−.0018171782	.0013288318	−.0002917312
−.0000428491	−.0013285723	.0009714662	−.0002132165
−.0000314756	−.0009753048	.0007131838	−.0001564980
−.0000232096	−.0007189781	.0005256810	−.0001153379
−.0000171792	−.0005320174	.0003889743	−.0000853345
−.0000127618	−.0003951401	.0002888941	−.0000633741
−.0000095137	−.0002945330	.0002153359	−.0000472356
−.0000071171	−.0002203022	.0001610627	−.0000353283
−.0000053412	−.0001653323	.0001208743	−.0000265132
−.0000040219	−.0001244790	.0000910054	−.0000199606
−.0000030379	−.0000940141	.0000687322	−.0000150748
−.0000023014	−.0000712200	.0000520676	−.0000114197
−.0000017485	−.0000541108	.0000395594	−.0000086763
−.0000013322	−.0000412285	.0000301414	−.0000066107
−.0000010178	−.0000314995	.0000230287	−.0000050507
−.0000007797	−.0000241304	.0000176413	−.0000038691
−.0000005988	−.0000185332	.0000135493	−.0000029717
−.0000004611	−.0000142704	.0000104328	−.0000022881
−.0000003559	−.0000110147	.0000080526	−.0000017661
−.0000002753	−.0000085220	.0000062303	−.0000013664
−.0000002135	−.0000066088	.0000048316	−.0000010596
−.0000001659	−.0000051366	.0000037552	−.0000008236
−.0000001292	−.0000040010	.0000029251	−.0000006415
−.0000001009	−.0000031232	.0000022833	−.0000005007
−.0000000789	−.0000024431	.0000017861	−.0000003917

The Zeeman effect[†] is a perturbation of atomic or molecular energy levels by an external magnetic field which results in a lifting of the spatial M degeneracy. In some ways it is very similar to the Stark effect; just as the Stark effect depends on the electric dipole moment, the Zeeman interaction originates from the resultant magnetic moment of a molecule. The interaction energy according to classical electromagnetic theory takes a form similar to (8-3)

$$H_{\mathcal{H}} = -\boldsymbol{\mu} \cdot \mathcal{H} \tag{1}$$

where $\boldsymbol{\mu}$ is the resultant magnetic moment and $\mathcal{H}$ is the magnetic field strength. For a system of particles, the magnetic moment can be defined in terms of the velocity $\mathbf{v}_i$ of the ith particle and its radius vector $\mathbf{r}_i$.

$$\boldsymbol{\mu} = \frac{1}{2c} \sum_i q_i(\mathbf{r}_i \times \mathbf{v}_i) \tag{2}$$

q_i is the charge. The charged particles possessing magnetic moments may be either electrons or nuclei. If $J\hbar$ is the total angular momentum of a particle, its magnetic moment is given by

$$\boldsymbol{\mu} = \frac{gq\hbar}{2mc}\mathbf{J} \tag{3}$$

m is the mass of the particle. g is referred to as the splitting or g factor. The quantity $\beta = |e|\hbar/2mc$ for an electron is called the Bohr magneton. Because g may have some rotational dependence, it is often written as g_J. For the magnetic moments of nuclei, β can be replaced by the nuclear magneton β_I by using the proton mass in place of the electron mass.

The magnitude of the Zeeman interaction generally falls into one of two categories: small splittings for molecules in $^1\Sigma$ electronic states and relatively large splittings for molecules with resultant electronic orbital angular

---

[†] For more detailed discussions see Strandberg [19], Townes and Schawlow [20], Jen [907], Eshbach and Strandberg [930], and Burke and Strandberg [935].

momentum (Π, ... states) or molecules with resultant electron spin angular momentum ($^2\Sigma$, $^3\Sigma$, ...). In almost all cases, the ground electronic state is $^1\Sigma$ and very small Zeeman splittings are produced. Exceptions include NO [950], O_2 [947] and OH [940].

Vector definitions used to describe the various forms of Zeeman interaction are listed in Table A13-1.

TABLE A13-1

DEFINITIONS OF ANGULAR MOMENTUM VECTORS USED IN APPENDIX 13[a]

S	Electron spin angular momentum
I	Nuclear spin angular momentum
L	Total electronic orbital angular momentum
N	Angular momentum of the nuclear frame
P = N + L	Total angular momentum (neglecting I)

[a] Different notations are often used in the literature; one complete set of vector definitions is given in Table 7-1 by Townes and Schawlow [20].

First-Order Zeeman Effect

The existence of a first-order Zeeman energy correction does not depend on the presence of an internal energy level degeneracy. From (1), the first-order energy for the general case of an asymmetric rotor is

$$E^{(1)} = -\langle J\tau M|\mu_Z|J\tau M\rangle \mathscr{H} \tag{4}$$

where the magnetic field strength $\mathscr{H}$ is constant and directed along the space-fixed Z axis. Evaluation of the matrix elements depends on the molecular model; however, to determine the effect of the Zeeman splitting, the energy correction can be written as

$$E^{(1)} = -g_J\beta_I M\mathscr{H} \tag{5}$$

where β_I is the nuclear magneton and g_J absorbs the rotational dependence. Neglecting higher-order Zeeman corrections, each rotational level labeled by J will be split into $2J + 1$ Zeeman levels; the splitting is symmetric about the zero-field level. For a symmetric-top molecule, the magnetic moment can be resolved into components along the figure axis μ_K and normal to the figure axis $\mu_\perp$.

$$\mu_K = g_K\beta_I K \tag{6}$$

$$\mu_\perp = g_\perp\beta_I[J(J + 1) - K^2]^{1/2} \tag{7}$$

Then

$$E^{(1)} = -\left[g_\perp + (g_K - g_\perp)\frac{K^2}{J(J + 1)}\right]\beta_I M\mathscr{H} \tag{8}$$

$g_\perp$ can be measured from $K = 0$ transitions and used to determine g_K in $K \neq 0$ transitions.

The selection rules $\Delta M = 0, \pm 1$ apply for dipole radiation. For π transitions ($\Delta M = 0$) the Zeeman shift is

$$\Delta v_\pi = (g_J - g'_J)\frac{M\beta_I\mathcal{H}}{h} \tag{9}$$

where the prime identifies the upper state. If $g_J - g'_J \approx 0$, the Zeeman splitting produces no change in the rotational spectrum. For σ transitions ($\Delta M = \pm 1$),

$$\Delta v_\sigma = [(g_J - g'_J)M \pm g'_J]\frac{\beta_I\mathcal{H}}{h} \tag{10}$$

when M is the lower state value. If $g_J - g'_J \approx 0$, only two Zeeman components will appear symmetrically spaced about the zero-field line.

When g_J changes significantly with rotational state, the π spectrum will exhibit $2J + 1$ Zeeman components while the σ spectrum will have $2(2J + 1)$ components. Here J labels the lower state. When higher-order contributions to the Zeeman perturbation are important, the splitting will no longer be completely symmetrical.

Zeeman Effect in $^1\Sigma$ States

In a pure $^1\Sigma$ electronic state, the net orbital and net spin angular momenta are both zero. Most molecules have $^1\Sigma$ ground electronic states, because stable bonding usually involves the pairing of even numbers of electrons; the resultant **L** and **S** both vanish. However, Zeeman effects in $^1\Sigma$ states are made possible by rotation-induced magnetic moments and the relatively strong coupling of nuclear magnetic moments with molecular rotation. Molecular rotation causes a slight mixing of excited states with the $^1\Sigma$ ground state to produce an electronic orbital angular momentum which is no longer zero. Because the electron mass is so small relative to the nuclear masses, the rotational energy of a molecule can be treated in terms of the nuclei alone. However, electronic contributions to the resultant magnetic moment can be large due to the relative magnitude of the electron charge. The nuclear contribution to the magnetic moment can be obtained by expanding (2), while the electronic contribution can be calculated from a perturbation treatment.

Treating the molecule as a rigid rotor, the Hamiltonian can be expressed as

$$H = \frac{1}{2}\sum_g \frac{N_g^2}{I_g} + \frac{1}{2m}\sum_g\sum_k (p_g)_k^2 + V \tag{11}$$

$(p_g)_k$ is the linear momentum of the kth electron along the gth principal axis, and V is the electronic potential function. The unperturbed electronic problem is

$$H_e^{(0)} = \frac{1}{2m} \sum_g \sum_k (p_g)_k^2 + V \tag{12}$$

Substituting the relation $\mathbf{P} = \mathbf{L} + \mathbf{N}$ into (11), the Hamiltonian becomes

$$H = \frac{1}{2} \sum_g \frac{P_g^2}{I_g} - \sum_g \frac{P_g L_g}{I_g} + \frac{1}{2} \sum_g \frac{L_g^2}{I_g} + H_e^{(0)} \tag{13}$$

$\mathbf{L} = 0$ in a "nonrotating" $^1\Sigma$ state, and $\mathbf{L} \ll \mathbf{P}$ in a "rotating" state. The resulting perturbation H' consists of two terms.

$$H' = -\sum_g \frac{P_g L_g}{I_g} + \frac{1}{2} \sum_g \frac{L_g^2}{I_g} \tag{14}$$

where the second term can usually be neglected. The first term in (13) describes the molecular rotation.

Using perturbation theory involving the first-order corrected electronic wave functions

$$\psi^{(1)} = \psi_0^{(0)} + \sum_n{}' \sum_g \frac{P_g}{I_g} \frac{\langle n|L_g|0\rangle}{E_n - E_0} \psi_n^{(0)} \tag{15}$$

the electronic contribution to the rotational magnetic moment is

$$\mu_g^e = \frac{1}{2} \sum_{g'} [G_{gg'}^e + (G_{gg'}^e)^*] P_{g'} \tag{16}$$

where

$$G_{gg'}^e = -\frac{e}{mcI_{g'}} \sum_n{}' \frac{\langle 0|L_g|n\rangle \langle n|L_{g'}|0\rangle}{E_n - E_0} \tag{17}$$

$$(G_{gg'}^e)^* = -\frac{e}{mcI_{g'}} \sum_n{}' \frac{\langle 0|L_{g'}|n\rangle \langle n|L_g|0\rangle}{E_n - E_0} \tag{18}$$

The matrix elements $\langle 0|L_g|n\rangle$ connect the ground ($^1\Sigma$) and nth electronic states of energies E_0 and E_n. Expanding (2) leads to a nuclear contribution of

$$\mu_g^n = \sum_{g'} G_{gg'}^n P_{g'} \tag{19}$$

where

$$G_{gg'}^n = (G_{gg'}^n)^* = \frac{1}{2cI_{g'}} \sum_k e_k(|r_k|^2 \delta_{gg'} - x_{kg}x_{kg'}) \tag{20}$$

$\delta_{gg'}$ is the Kronecker delta. Equations (17), (18) and (20) can be combined by defining

$$G_{gg'} = G_{gg'}^n + G_{gg'}^e \tag{21}$$

It follows that

$$\mu_g = \frac{1}{2} \sum_{g'} (G_{gg'} + G_{gg'}^*) P_{g'} \tag{22}$$

Through the direction cosines ϕ_{Zg}, μ_g can be related to μ_Z

$$\mu_Z = \sum_g \phi_{Zg}\mu_g \tag{23}$$

Before the matrix elements of μ_Z can be evaluated, μ_g^n must be written in a symmetrized Hermitian form since μ_g^n does not commute with the direction-cosine transformation [930].

$$\mu_Z^n = \tfrac{1}{2}\sum_g \sum_{g'} G_{gg'}^n (P_{g'}\phi_{Zg} + \phi_{Zg}P_{g'}) \tag{24}$$

Because there exist matrix elements of ϕ_{Zg} off-diagonal in n, μ_g^e commutes with ϕ. Finally,

$$\mu_Z = \tfrac{1}{2}\sum_g \sum_{g'} (G_{gg'}P_{g'}\phi_{Zg} + G_{gg'}^*\phi_{Zg}P_{g'}) \tag{25}$$

Table A13-2 shows the important matrix elements of μ_Z in a symmetric rotor basis as given by Eshbach and Strandberg [930]. β_I is the nuclear magneton $|e|\hbar/2M_p c$ where M_p is the proton mass and the $g_{gg'}$ are dimensionless gyromagnetic tensor elements

$$g_{gg'} = \frac{\hbar}{\beta_I}G_{gg'} \tag{26}$$

Zeeman Effect in the Presence of Hyperfine Splittings

For an external magnetic field in the presence of a nuclear quadrupole moment, a treatment similar to that described for an external electric field in Chapter 8 is appropriate. In the weak field case where J and F are still good quantum numbers

$$E^{(1)} = -(\alpha_J g_J + \alpha_I g_I)\beta_I M_F \mathcal{H} \tag{27}$$

$$\alpha_J = \frac{F(F+1) + J(J+1) - I(I+1)}{2F(F+1)} \tag{28}$$

$$\alpha_I = \frac{F(F+1) + I(I+1) - J(J+1)}{2F(F+1)} \tag{29}$$

In the strong-field case, the nuclear coupling is broken and quadrupole hyperfine structure appears only as a perturbation on the Zeeman components. From (5) the energy becomes

$$E^{(1)} = -g_J \beta M \mathcal{H} - g_I \beta_I I \mathcal{H} \tag{30}$$

where g_I is the g factor for the nuclear magnetic moment, β is the Bohr magneton, and β_I is the nuclear magneton.

TABLE A13-2
MATRIX ELEMENTS OF μ_Z IN A SYMMETRIC ROTOR BASIS[a]

$\langle JKM|\mu_Z|JKM\rangle$

$$= \beta_I M\left\{\frac{g_{xx} + g_{yy}}{2} + \frac{K^2}{J(J+1)}\left[g_{zz} - \frac{g_{xx} + g_{yy}}{2}\right]\right.$$

$$\left. + \frac{iK}{J(J+1)}\left[\frac{g_{yx} - g_{yx}^*}{2} - \frac{g_{xy} - g_{xy}^*}{2}\right]\right\}$$

$\langle JKM|\mu_Z|J, K+1, M\rangle$

$$= \beta_I M\frac{[J(J+1) - K(K+1)]^{1/2}}{4J(J+1)}\{i[K(g_{zx} + g_{xz}^*)$$

$$+ (K+1)(g_{xz} + g_{zx}^*)] + K(g_{zy} + g_{yz}^*) + (K+1)(g_{yz} + g_{zy}^*)\}$$

$\langle JKM|\mu_Z|J, K+2, M\rangle$

$$= \beta_I M\frac{\{[J(J+1) - K(K+1)][J(J+1) - (K+1)(K+2)]\}^{1/2}}{8J(J+1)}$$

$$\times \{2(g_{yy} - g_{xx}) + i[g_{xy} + g_{xy}^* + g_{yx} + g_{yx}^*]\}$$

$\langle JKM|\mu_Z|J+1, KM\rangle$

$$= \frac{1}{2(J+1)}\left\{\frac{[(J+1)^2 - K^2][(J+1)^2 - M^2]}{(2J+1)(2J+3)}\right\}^{1/2}\{K(2g_{zz} - g_{xx} - g_{yy})$$

$$- i[J(g_{xy} - g_{yx}) + (J+2)(g_{xy}^* - g_{yx}^*)]\}$$

$\langle JKM|\mu_Z|J+1, K\pm 1, M\rangle$

$$= \frac{1}{2(J+1)}\left\{\frac{(J\pm K+1)(J\pm K+2)[(J+1)^2 - M^2]}{(2J+1)(2J+3)}\right\}^{1/2}$$

$$\times \{-K(ig_{xz} \pm g_{yz}) - (K\pm 1)(ig_{xz}^* \pm g_{yz}^*)$$

$$+ (J\pm K)(g_{zy} + g_{zx}) + (J\pm K+1)(g_{zy}^* \pm ig_{zx}^*)\}$$

$\langle JKM|\mu_Z|J+1, K\pm 2, M\rangle$

$$= \frac{1}{4(J+1)}\left\{\frac{(J\pm K)(J\pm K+1)(J\pm K+2)(J\pm K+3)[(J+1)^2 - M^2]}{(2J+1)(2J+3)}\right\}^{1/2}$$

$$\times \left\{\pm(g_{xx} - g_{yy}) - \frac{i}{2}(g_{xy} + g_{xy}^* + g_{yx} + g_{yx}^*)\right\}$$

[a] From Ref. [930].

Zeeman Effects in Paramagnetic Molecules

In a $^1\Sigma$ electronic state, the rotational magnetic moment is of the order of a nuclear magneton; when a resultant electronic orbital or spin magnetic moment is present, the effective magnetic moment is of the order of a Bohr magneton, i.e., approximately 2000 times larger. It follows that in the latter case the perturbation produced by an external magnetic field can be very large, leading to significant Zeeman splittings. Interpretation of the Zeeman effect can be accomplished with a vector model representing the important angular momenta.

Five vector models discussed by Hund are usually used to treat linear paramagnetic molecules [7]. In nonlinear molecules, the electronic orbital angular momentum is usually quenched since no component of L is quantized. Once an appropriate vector model has been specified, the Zeeman energy can be calculated. Hund's models and molecules with resultant electronic angular momentum are discussed in detail by Herzberg [7] and Townes and Schawlow [20].

STARK CORRECTIONS FOR A LINEAR MOLECULE[†]

Equation (8-20) expresses the Stark correction through the fourth power in the external field resulting from the dipole moment μ. If the polarizability interaction is included, corrections proportional to ε^4 arise from terms in α_A^2 and $\alpha_A\mu^2$ as well as μ^4. The appropriate perturbation results are

$$E^{(2)}(\alpha_A) = \frac{1}{8}\left\{\frac{[(J-1)^2 - M^2][J^2 - M^2]}{(2J-3)(2J+1)(2J-1)^3}\right.$$
$$\left. - \frac{[(J+1)^2 - M^2][(J+2)^2 - M^2]}{(2J+1)(2J+5)(2J+3)^3}\right\}\frac{\alpha_A^2\varepsilon^4}{hB}$$

$$E^{(3)}(\alpha_A, \mu) = \frac{1}{8}\left\{\frac{(J^2 - M^2)[(J+1)^2 - M^2]}{(2J-1)(2J+3)J^2(J+1)^2}\right.$$
$$- \frac{[(J+1)^2 - M^2][(J+2)^2 - M^2](4J+5)}{(2J+1)(2J+5)(J+1)^2(2J+3)^3}$$
$$\left. - \frac{[(J-1)^2 - M^2][J^2 - M^2](4J-1)}{(2J-3)(2J+1)J^2(2J-1)^3}\right\}\frac{\alpha_A\mu^2\varepsilon^4}{h^2B^2}$$

$$E^{(4)}(\mu) = K(J, M)\frac{\mu^4\varepsilon^4}{h^3B^3}$$

$$= \frac{1}{8}\left\{\frac{[(J-1)^2 - M^2][J^2 - M^2]}{(2J-3)(2J+1)J^2(2J-1)^3}\right.$$
$$- \frac{[(J+1)^2 - M^2][(J+2)^2 - M^2]}{(2J+1)(2J+5)(J+1)^2(2J+3)^3}$$
$$\times \frac{[J^2 - M^2][(J+1)^2 - M^2]}{(2J-1)(2J+3)(2J+1)^2J^2(J+1)^2}$$
$$+ \frac{[(J+1)^2 - M^2]^2}{(2J+3)^2(2J+1)^2(J+1)^3}$$
$$\left. - \frac{[J^2 - M^2]^2}{(2J+1)^2(2J-1)^2J^3}\right\}\frac{\mu^4\varepsilon^4}{h^3B^3}$$

[†] From L. H. Scharpen, J. S. Muenter, and V. W. Laurie [1709].

AUTHOR INDEX

Numbers in parentheses are reference numbers and indicate that an author's work is referred to although his name is not cited in the text. Numbers in italic show the page on which the complete reference is listed.

Stoicheff, B. P., *338, 379,* 419(1436), 420 (1436)

Stone, N. W. B., 302(184a), *326, 391*

Strandberg, M. W. P., 56(1109), 124(929, 942), 229, 232, 251, 268(1110), 269(1109), 281(1109), 291, 294, 316, *319, 321, 322, 323, 328, 329, 334, 335, 340, 341, 342, 346, 352, 355, 356, 359, 364, 365, 366, 368, 369, 372, 373,* 440, 444, 445(930)

Strauch, R. G., 4(189), 291(170), 295(184), 303(184), 309(189), 311(191d), 312(191c), 315(191d), 317, *325, 326, 327, 387*

Strauss, H. L., 237(822), 243(822), *354*

Street, K., Jr., *326, 387, 388*

Strine, G. L., *325*

Stuckelberg, E. C. G., 209(760), *352*

Suarez, V., *322*

Sugden, T. M., *320, 323, 377, 379, 381, 382, 384, 386, 389*

Sugiura, Y., *329, 377*

Sutherland, G. B. B. M., 216(779), *352*

Sutter, D., *351, 352,* 420(756a)

Sverdlov, L. M., *338*

Svidzinskii, K. K., *380, 387*

Swalen, J. D., 151, 153(703), 155(705), 158(705), 164, 166(703), 168(703), 171(682, 688), 183, 186(688), 191(688), 198(705), 220, 221(810), 229, *332, 346, 347, 348, 349, 354, 379,* 396(315), 398(315), 418(682, 705)

Swan, P. R., Jr., *334, 346*

Swan, W. O., *367*

Swarup, P., *376*

Szasz, G. J., *345*

T

Tabor, W. J., 33, *348,* 418(683)

Taft, R. W., Jr., *380*

Takagi, K., *387, 388*

Takahashi, I., *321, 329*

Takahashi, S., *350, 351,* 420(754)

Takayanagi, K., *380*

Takuma, H., *324, 360, 361, 382, 387*

Talley, R. M., *369*

Tanabe, Y., *342*

Tanaka, T., *390*

Tang, A.-C., *346*

Tank, F., *385*

Tannenbaum, E., 187(665), 191(665), *346, 347, 375, 376, 377,* 419(665)

Tate, P. A., *322*

Tatevskii, V. M., *350*

Teller, E., *362*

ter Haar, D., *363*

Tetenbaum, S. J., 56(1210), *370*

Thaddeus, P., *324, 325, 360, 361*

Thomas, C., *390*

Thomas, E. C., *391*

Thomas, L. F., 58(1318, 1336), 237(796), *338, 353, 372, 373, 374, 375, 378, 379, 385*

Thomas, L. H., 216, *352*

Thomas, V. G., *366, 367*

Thomas, W. J. O., 58(390, 1312), *335, 374*

Thompson, H. B., *357*

Thompson, L. E., 222(816a), *354*

Thompson, M. C., *323*

Tidwell, M., 124(1143), *367, 369*

Timms, P. L., *390*

Tinkham, M., *329, 359*

Tobiason, F. L., *389, 390*

Tobler, H. J., 277, 294, 295(195), *326, 327, 390*

Toerring, T., *389*

Tolles, W. M., 191(757), *351, 354, 357, 385,* 419(757)

Tomassini, M., *352*

Tomita, K., *329*

Topping, G., 238(807), *353, 391*

Torizuka, Y., *360*

Torkington, P., *345*

Torring, T., *337*

Toth, R. A., *389*

Townes, C. H., 48(20), 56(1281), 74(349), 123(20), 124(1281), 128, 131(508), 134, 136(507), 139(20), 143(507), 235(20), 256, 257(848), 260(848), 261, 263, 270(852), 271(852), 277(852), 279(20, 836), 280, 281(852), 288(20), 302(84), 314(101), 316(17), *319, 321, 322, 327, 333, 337, 340, 341, 342, 343, 355, 356, 358, 359, 360, 364, 365, 366, 367, 368, 369, 370, 371, 373,* 440, 441(940), 446

Toyama, M., *339*

Trambarulo, R. F., 58(1162), 316(17), *319, 356, 367, 368, 369, 374, 379*

Treacy, E. B., *361*

Trifonov, E. D., *332*

Trischka, J. W., *341, 368*

Tsuchuja, T., *388*

Tsukada, K., *369, 373, 375*

Tuller, W. G., *321*

Turkevich, J., *364*

SUBJECT INDEX

A

Absorption cells, 294–295, 298–299, 304–305, 309–317
  balanced bridge, 298–299, 313
  beam maser, 313–314
  Fabry–Perot interferometer, 304–305
  free space, 314
  high temperature, 310
  molecular beam, 310–312
  parallel plate, 278, 309–310
  for reactive species, 314–315
  Stark effect, 294–295
  Zeeman effect, 315–317
Absorption coefficient, 35
Absorption intensity, *see* Intensity of absorption
Anharmonic potential constants, 73–74, 89
Asymmetric rotor, 19–35, 40–41, 48, 75–87, 98–100, 103–108, 121, 126–137, 148, 167–184, 188–199, 226–243, 273
  centrifugal distortion, 81–87
  energy levels, 19–32, 393–398
  intensity of absorption, 33–36, 40–42
  internal rotation, 148, 167–184, 188–199
  inversion, 226–243
  matrix elements, 20
  near axis coordinates, 103–105
  nonplanar, 99–100
  nonrigid effects, 75–80
  nuclear quadrupole coupling, 121, 126–137
  nuclear spin statistics, 40–41
  planar, 98–99, 105–108
  reduced mass for inversion, 229–232
  selection rules, 27–31
  Stark effect, 273
  wave functions, 24–27, 41, 48
  Zeeman effect, 443–447

Asymmetric rotor group, 28–29
Asymmetry parameters, 20–22
Attenuator, 288
Average structure, 112–113

B

Backward-wave oscillator, 289
Barriers to internal rotation, 416–421
Beam-maser spectrometers, 312–314
Bent bond, 417
Bohr magneton, *see* Magneton
Bolometers, 304
Born–Oppenheimer principle, 3
Bridge spectrometer, 298–299, 307

C

Casimir's function, 123
Center of mass, 7
Centrifugal distortion, 51–60, 65, 70–71, 81–87
  asymmetric rotor, 81–87
  linear molecules, 54–57
  symmetric rotor, 57–60
Centrifugal force, 52
Clebsch–Gordan coefficients, 409
Conversion factors, 392
Coriolis coupling, 51–54, 60–64, 66–72, 79–81, 186–190
  degenerate splitting, 66
  internal rotation, 186–190
Coriolis coupling constant, 60–61, 66
Coriolis force, 52–53, 62
Crystal detectors, 283, 297–298, 313
Crystal harmonic generators, 302–303
Crystal noise, 296–299